D0555192

SYSTEMATIC BIOLOGY

PROCEEDINGS OF AN INTERNATIONAL CONFERENCE

Conducted at
THE UNIVERSITY OF MICHIGAN
Ann Arbor, Michigan
June 14–16, 1967
Sponsored by the
NATIONAL RESEARCH COUNCIL

PUBLICATION 1692
NATIONAL ACADEMY OF SCIENCES
WASHINGTON, D.C. 1969

Supported by NSF Contract No. C310, Task Order 122, and by the University of Michigan.

Available from

PRINTING AND PUBLISHING OFFICE
NATIONAL ACADEMY OF SCIENCES
2101 CONSTITUTION AVENUE
WASHINGTON, D.C. 20418

Library of Congress Catalog Card Number: 68-61878

Foreword

Before beginning the program, I want to express our thanks to those who have been responsible, in one way or another, for bringing you here today. Also, I want you to know the names of the persons who have been working in your behalf. It also is appropriate that I tell you something of the history of this conference, as many of you might not know how it came about.

The conference does not have a long history. The first occurrence that could be considered part of the ontogeny of this conference was the calling together of nine systematists to discuss what the Division of Biology and Agriculture of the National Research Council might do to further the interests of systematic biology. This two-day meeting, under the chairmanship of Lincoln Constance, was held in June 1965 at the National Academy of Sciences. It was supported by the National Science Foundation and the Smithsonian Institution. One of the many proposals discussed by this group was that there be an international conference on systematic biology. Later, in February 1966, the Division of Biology and Agriculture prepared and submitted to the National Science Foundation a formal proposal outlining such a conference. In early fall, the following persons were appointed to serve as the Organizing Committee, which held its first meeting last October:

Charles G. Sibley, *Chairman*

Richard D. Alexander	Richard S. Cowan
Lincoln Constance	William R. Lockhart
John O. Corliss	Ernst Mayr

Usually, in organizing conferences of this type, certain speakers are invited, and if they accept they are allowed to choose their own topics. This committee reversed the procedure; it selected the topics and then searched for appropriate speakers and discussants. Early in the organizational phase, some of our colleagues expressed their fears that this meeting would turn out to be another case of the same old people talking to one another. Such remarks constituted a challenge, and we set out to prove them wrong. We feel sure that the speakers and discussants will leave no doubt as to our success.

You may wonder at times why a particular scientist is a discussant on a certain paper instead of on another one. It is not because the committee could not tell a botanist from a zoologist but because it wanted you to hear the individual in a context which, while not at all removed from his competence, was somewhat new for him. Another element in the conference that you may find somewhat different is that the speakers and discussants include both young turks and members of the old guard. This was done purposely, because the committee thinks the combination is good.

The Local Committee, comprised of Arnold Kluge, chairman, Thomas E. Moore, Edward Voss, and Warren Wagner, has worked hard to provide the necessities that keep body and soul together. We owe its members a large vote of thanks. As Dr. Norman pointed out, we must thank the National Science Foundation for its support, and also the University of Michigan, which has been generous in many ways.

The speakers and discussants, of course, deserve our special thanks. For myself and for the other members of the Organizing Committee I thank these busy persons who have given so generously to this conference. We know that many of them had to prepare lengthy papers on short notice, and all of them had to spend considerable time in preparing special papers or in participating as discussants. They all responded nobly to our invitations, and we are grateful.

We look forward to a successful International Conference on Systematic Biology and to the publication of its proceedings. We trust that many benefits will result.

Charles G. Sibley
Chairman

Preface

The evolution of international conferences is an adaptive response to the age of rapid air travel and the availability of increased financial support for scientific research. This greater mobility and the better nourishment available to modern science offers improved opportunities for personal contacts among scientists with common interests. Such contacts can be expected to result in better understanding and more rapid progress. This, then, is the justification, if needed, for organizing this or any other international conference. It is hardly necessary to note that understanding of all kinds between persons from different parts of the world was never needed more.

Our hope was to bring together botanists and zoologists from many parts of the world, representing various approaches to systematic biology. We decided very early in the planning to involve some of the younger generation of taxonomists and to press well-known persons into new roles. Instead of issuing invitations to speakers to present papers on topics they themselves chose, we assumed dictatorial powers by choosing the topics first and matching the speakers and discussants to them.

This volume of formal papers is the visible record of the conference, but we all know that the debates and discussions outside the auditorium also form part of the enduring, if invisible, record. Perhaps one day we will have the courage to organize the ultimate in conferences with no formal papers and all discussions held in hallways and beer parlors. The cycle would start again, no doubt, when somebody tired of drawing diagrams on envelopes and tablecloths and said, "Do you suppose we could find a projector? I just happen to have a slide in my pocket."

This conference and this volume do not pretend to cover all aspects of systematic biology, nor are they more than summaries of the state of the art of those aspects that are included. There is always need for such summarizing discussions and publications, and we who brought this one to reality hope that its shortcomings will stimulate others to fill the gaps.

Charles G. Sibley
Chairman

PLANNING COMMITTEE

CHARLES G. SIBLEY, *CHAIRMAN*
RICHARD D. ALEXANDER
LINCOLN CONSTANCE
JOHN O. CORLISS
RICHARD S. COWAN
W. R. LOCKHART
ERNST MAYR
WARREN H. WAGNER, JR.

LOCAL COMMITTEE

ARNOLD G. KLUGE
THOMAS E. MOORE
EDWARD G. VOSS
WARREN H. WAGNER, JR.

Contents

A. GEOFFREY NORMAN

Welcoming Remarks

The University of Michigan is privileged to be host to many professional groups. Some of their programs deal with wholly new fields of science and technology; others are concerned with a review of the evolutionary changes in older fields that are being stimulated by the development of new procedures, instruments, and perspectives. This meeting falls in the latter group.

We have a sharpened sense of history around the campus this year. We are celebrating the sesquicentennial of the founding of the University of Detroit in 1817. That was 20 years before the State of Michigan was admitted to the Union, and when Detroit was on the northwest frontier of the country. In 1842, when the population of the state was less than that of Ann Arbor today, the University was moved to Ann Arbor, where it occupied a 40-acre site just south of this building. This is an old university, by New World standards, and the one that became the archetype for subsequent universities that were established as the new nation continued to develop westward. Initially, this was not a state-supported institution, as we understand that term today, but it became one as its role and its relationship to the state emerged; consequently, there is good reason for the University of Michigan having been called the mother of state universities.

Our sense of history today causes us to examine the beginnings, on this campus, of various activities in the natural sciences, a branch of which you came here to discuss. In 1838 the Board of Regents selected one Asa Gray as professor of botany and induced him to accept what appears to have been a sabbatical year in Europe, charging him with the task of purchasing there those books that he might think appropriate and necessary for the University's library. The Regents allocated to Gray a sum of money for this purpose. In due course the books arrived, but the professor did not. Apparently, institutional recruiting was as intense then as it seems to be now. Just what happened next with Gray is not quite clear. His leave was extended, but he never took up formal residence in Ann Arbor; instead, he joined the faculty of that prestigious rival—now graced by Professor Ernst Mayr—which, in our lighter moments here, we refer to as the "Michigan of the East." We mean Harvard, of course, where Asa Gray spent the rest of his distinguished career.

This abortive start did not deter the Regents, who in 1842 appointed Abraham Sager as professor of botany and zoology. This started a long, branching line of appointments in biology that has brought to the University those colleagues of mine who have helped organize this conference. Along the way, we find such names as Alexander Winchell, Volney M. Spalding, J. B. Steere, Charles Adams, Calvin H. Kauffman, H. A. Gleason, and H. H. Bartlett—to mention only a few who are well known to systematists and taxonomists the world over.

A development that had particular importance in shaping systematic biology on the Michigan campus was the establishment of a complex of museums as research units supported by state funds. The mission entrusted to Asa Gray was only a part of a regential action authorizing "the purchase of philosophical and other apparatus . . . a library and a cabinet of natural history." The establishment of this "cabinet of natural history" led to the assembly of sizable collections by 1864 and to the construction of a museum building in 1880. Incidentally, the original museum building was demolished not long ago, although it long since had been replaced as a home for the University's collections. The real architect of the museum system was Alexander Ruthven, who came to the presidency of the University from his position as director of the Museum.

Through the years the staffs, never large, of the museums and the herbarium, and the staffs of the various departments have taken a prominent part in the development of the evolving structure of systematic and taxonomic biology. We would like to think that this is the reason you were willing to come to Ann Arbor for this meeting.

As Dr. Sibley has remarked, perhaps I am in somewhat of a conflict-of-interest situation at this conference, but I prefer to be regarded as one who represents a coalescence of interest, which spares you the necessity of having still another speaker at this time.

The conference program lists an impressive array of talented speakers, thanks to the effective work of the committee under the chairmanship of Dr. Sibley, who has related to you the circumstances that led to the organization of this meeting. I pay tribute to Dr. Sibley for his leadership and untiring efforts. I am sure he is as gratified as I am at the sight of this large group, whose members have chosen to come here from near and far. I also thank the representatives of the National Science Foundation which provided the funds necessary for organizing the conference.

I am confident that this meeting will stand as a landmark, and that it will exert a catalytic effect on the further evolution of this important field of biology. But I must not impede further the progress of your work. May your stay in Ann Arbor be both pleasant and rewarding.

ERNST MAYR

Introduction: The Role of Systematics in Biology

There are many ways of dealing with the topic assigned to me. One might give a history of the role taxonomy has played in the development of biology; one might concentrate on the present status of systematics in biology; or one might attempt, in a timeless and somewhat philosophical way, to delineate the niche that systematics occupies within the total conceptual framework of biology. Further thought makes it evident that the three approaches are interdependent to such a degree that all must receive due consideration.

Let me start with the question, what do we mean by "systematics," the role of which I am to describe? To answer this question meaningfully requires an excursion into the history as well as the philosophy of biology. The ancient Greeks saw a natural order in the world which, they thought, could be demonstrated and classified by certain logical procedures. They tried to discover the true nature (essence) of things and approached classification through the methods of logic. Indeed, Aristotle, the first great classifier, was also the father of logic. The underlying philosophy, now usually referred to as essentialism (from essence), dominated the thinking of taxonomists up to and including Linnaeus. Taxonomic nomenclature and the so-called typological thinking of taxonomists right up to our day have been permanently affected by the Aristotelian legacy.

HISTORY OF TAXONOMY

During the early history of biology, the Aristotelian influence was no great handicap. Botany and zoology, to state it in a highly oversimplified manner, arose during the sixteenth century as applied sciences, attached to medicine. Botany began as a broadened study of medicinal herbs, and early botanical gardens were herb gardens. With but one or two exceptions, all the great botanists and herbalists from the sixteenth to the eighteenth century (Linnaeus included) were professors of medicine or practicing physicians. Zoology arose in connection with human anatomy and physiology. When botany and zoology became independent sciences, the first concern of the two fields was to bring order into the diversity of nature. Taxonomy was therefore their dominant concern and, indeed, in the eighteenth and early nineteenth centuries botany and zoology were virtually coextensive with taxonomy. Moreover, by sheer necessity, taxonomy at that period was essentially the technique of identification.

The middle third of the nineteenth century was a period of decisive change to which many separate streams of development contributed. Increasing professionalism was one. Increasing specialization was another, to mention just two. Taxonomy itself accelerated the change by introducing several new concepts into biology. The greatest unifying theory in biology, the theory of evolution, was largely a contribution made by the students of diversity, as we might call the taxonomists. It is no coincidence that Darwin wrote his *Origin of Species* after encountering taxonomic problems during the voyage of *The Beagle* and after eight years of concentrated work on barnacle taxonomy. Comparison of different kinds of organisms is the core of the taxonomic method and leads at the same time to the question of how these differences originated. The findings of explorer taxonomists, paleotaxonomists, and comparative anatomists inexorably led to the establishment and eventual acceptance of the theory of evolution.

One might have expected that the acceptance of evolution would result in a great flowering of taxonomy and enhancement of its prestige during the last third of the nineteenth century. This was not the case—in part for almost purely administrative reasons. The most exciting consequences of the findings of systematics were studied in university departments, while the very necessary but less exciting descriptive taxonomy, based on collections, was assigned to the museums. Furthermore, most taxonomists were satisfied to use evolutionary concepts for rather practical purposes, such as a source of evidence on which to base inferences on classification. As a consequence, evolutionary biology did not contribute as much to strengthening the bridge between taxonomy and other branches of biology as might have been expected. The great contributions to biology made by taxonomists during this period, such as population thinking, the theory of geographic speciation, the biological species concept, and several others that will be dealt with separately, were incorporated into biology anonymously and in such a way that taxonomy did not receive due credit.

Biology is no exception to the well-known phenomenon that there is a continuous change of fashions and frontiers in science. Since the 1870's there has been one breakthrough after another, beginning with the improvements of the microscope and the exciting discoveries of cytology. Perhaps the dominant trend during this period was an increasing interest in biological mechanisms and in the chemical-physical explanation of biological functions. This led to the flourishing of various branches of physiology, of endocrinology, of genetics, of embryology, of immunology, of neurophysiology, of biochemistry, and of biophysics. Taxonomy, the oldest, the most classical branch of biology, inevitably suffered in competition with all these brilliant developments. Whenever there was an interesting new growing point in taxonomy, it quickly became independent and left behind a rather descriptive, static and sometimes almost clerical residue. The older persons among us remember the days when taxonomy was regarded by most biologists as an identification service. Some of the best universities in this country refused to accept PhD theses in taxonomy. The Guggenheim Foundation was the only granting agency that considered taxonomy worthy of support. Under these circumstances it was not surprising that only the most dedicated naturalists would choose taxonomy as their life's work, and we must pay tribute here to some inspired teachers who attracted gifted youngsters into our field.

Even today, systematists feel that they are not getting their full share of recognition, of financial support, and of superior graduate students, yet one must recognize that circumstances have changed dramatically for the better in the last 20 or 30 years. This change has had many causes, but for some aspects it is not easy to say what is cause and what is effect. Taxonomists played a decisive role in the development of the synthetic theory of evolution, and this fact is being increasingly recognized by the leaders of biology. Julian Huxley and others have emphasized that taxonomy is a vital branch of biology. Simultaneously we have witnessed a steady improvement in the scientific training of taxonomists. In order to obtain a position it is no longer sufficient that the young taxonomist know how to describe new species, he is now expected to have acquired an adequate training in, and understanding of, genetics, statistics, animal behavior, biochemistry, and other branches of experimental-functional biology. The bridge between museums and universities is being broadened and strengthened in many places, and the strong barriers between a narrowly defined taxonomy and the adjacent branches of biology are being obliterated. This new generation of taxonomists is no longer satisfied to work on preserved specimens. This new breed of naturalist-taxonomists insists on studying taxa as living organisms and pursues its investigations in the field and in the experimental laboratory, wherever effort will be most productive.

The ultimate result of these developments has been general recognition that the universe of the taxonomist is far greater than was previously envisioned. Taxonomists now take an ever-increasing interest in evolutionary, ecological, and behavioral research and, indeed, have assumed leading roles in these fields. Until very recently the terms taxonomy and systematics were generally considered to be synonymous. In view of current developments, it seems advantageous to restrict the term taxonomy to the theory and practice of classifying, more narrowly defined, and to use the term systematics for the study of organic diversity, more broadly defined. This new viewpoint is represented by Simpson's definition (1961), "Systematics is the scientific study of the kinds and diversity of organisms and of any and all relationships among them." In short, *systematics is the study of the diversity of organisms.*

When I undertook my assignment to prepare this presentation, I assumed that I should adopt this broad definition. The lectures and discussions during this conference confirm that this is, indeed, the definition of systematics that is adopted by the current leaders in the field. But there is an additional reason why we should define systematics so broadly.

THE POSITION OF SYSTEMATICS IN BIOLOGY

When we look at biology as a whole we see that systematics occupies a unique position. Some years ago (Mayr, 1961) I pointed out that there are basically two biologies. One deals with functional phenomena and investigates the causality of biological functions and processes; the other, evolutionary biology, deals with the historical causality of the existing organic world. Functional biology takes much of its technique and *Fragestellung* from physics and chemistry, and is happiest when it can reduce observed biological phenomena to physical-chemical processes. Evolutionary biology, dealing with highly complex systems, operated by historically evolved genetic programs, must pursue a very different strategy of research in order to provide explanations. Its most productive method is the comparative method for which the taxonomists have laid the foundation. Indeed, I can hardly think of an evolutionary problem that has not developed out of some finding of taxonomy.

One can express these basic concerns also in a somewhat different manner. At one extreme, biology is preoccupied with the ultimate building stones and ultimate unit processes that are the common denominators throughout. This has largely been the concern of molecular biology, from the structure of macromolecules to such functional unit processes as the Krebs cycle. As legitimate as the reductionist methodology is when applied to functional problems, it quickly carries us down to a level where we leave behind most of what is most typically biological, and we are left with a subject matter that is essentially physical-chemical. This is surely true for the chemistry and physics of the ultimate building stones and unit processes of living organisms. If this were the only level of integration in biology, it would be quite legitimate to combine biology with chemistry or physics.

At the other extreme is preoccupation with the level of biology that deals with whole organisms, with uniqueness, and with systems. It is a matter of historical record that taxonomists are among those biologists who have been most consistently concerned with whole organisms and who have most consistently stressed the organismic, the systems, approach to biology.

No one will question the immense importance of molecular phenomena, but they are not the only aspect of biology. As Michael Ghiselin has stated so perceptively, just as architecture is more than the study of building materials, so is biology more than the study of macromolecules. In systematics, in evolutionary biology, and in much of organismic biology, one normally deals with hierarchical levels of biological integration that are many orders of magnitude above the molecular. Each level has its specific problems and its appropriate methods and techniques. That there is such a difference in levels of integration is taken completely for granted in the physical sciences. No one would expect the aeronautical engineer to base the design of airplane wings on the study of elementary particles. But a unique role for each level is even more evident at the different levels of biological integration.

Lest I be misunderstood, I see no conflict between molecular biology and organismic biology (including systematics), but it must be emphasized that each level of integration poses its own specific problems, requires its own methods and techniques, and develops its own theoretical framework and generalizations. This has been clearly recognized and frequently stated by the foremost leaders of molecular biology. Consistent with this is the fact that faculty and curricula in the areas of systematics, ecology, and evolutionary biology have recently been strengthened in several of the leading American universities. As a result, systematics has now become better integrated into biology than at any time since the days of Darwin.

The role of systematics should now be quite clear: It is one of the cornerstones of all biology. It is the branch of biology that produces most of our information on the levels of integration designated as natural populations and higher taxa. It supplies urgently needed facts, but more importantly, it cultivates a way of thinking—a way of approaching biological problems—that is alien to the reductionist but tremendously important for the balance and well-being of biology as a whole.

THE CONTRIBUTIONS OF SYSTEMATICS TO BIOLOGY

Many biologists do not appreciate the magnitude of the contributions made by systematics. And yet these achievements are extraordinary, even if we adopt the narrowest definition of taxonomy. They include the description of about one million species of animals and a half million species of higher and lower plants, as well as their arrangement in a system. This classification, though we continue to modify it in detail, is, on the whole, amazingly logical, internally consistent, and stable. It is an immensely useful system of information storage and retrieval. All the comparative work of morphologists, physiologists, and phylogenetically inclined molecular biologists would be meaningless if it were not for the classification.

Taxonomists supply a desperately needed identification service for taxa of ecological significance and for the current determination of fossil species needed for work in stratigraphy and geological chronology. In all areas of applied biology good taxonomy is indispensable: in public health, in the study of vector-borne diseases and of parasites; in the study of the relatives of cultivated plants and of domestic animals; and in the study of insect pests and of their biological control. Much work in conservation, wildlife management, and the study of renewable natural resources depends for its effectiveness on the soundness of taxonomic research. The faunas, floras, handbooks, and manuals prepared by taxonomists are indispensable in many branches of biology and are widely used by the general public.

As important as these descriptive and service functions of taxonomy are, they are only part of the contribution of systematics, to many of us the least important part. I have already pointed out that evolutionary biology was founded upon the work of taxonomists. They also supplied the solutions of many individual evolutionary problems, including the role of isolation, the mechanism of speciation, the nature of isolating mechanisms, rates of evolution, trends of evolution, and the problem of the emergence of evolutionary novelties. More than have any other kind of biologists, taxonomists (including paleontologists) have made significant contributions to all these subjects.

There is hardly a taxonomic operation during which the systematist does not have to face basic biological questions. In order to assign specimens to species he must study variability, particularly polymorphism, and quite often, he has to undertake a rather complete population analysis, including the study of life cycles. In the study of polytypic species he concerns himself with geographic variation and its meaning, he studies the adaptation of local populations, and he tests the validity of climatic rules. When studying the population structure of species, he examines isolates and belts of hybridization. Indeed, taxonomists have developed in the last two generations a veritable "science of the species," in the same sense in which cytology is the science of the cell and histology is the science of tissues. At every step the systematist must think about the adaptation of populations, their past histories, and the magnitude of dispersal (gene exchange between populations).

Many new concepts that arose out of the work of taxonomists have since diffused broadly into genetics, ecology, physiology, and other areas of biology. By far, the most important of these, as I have often stressed in the past, is population thinking. Biology, as all other sciences, was permeated by typological thinking until late in the nineteenth century, and still is to a certain extent. When the learning psychologist speaks of "The Rat" or "The Monkey," or when the racist speaks of "The Negro," these are instances of typological thinking. The early Mendelians were pure typologists. A mutation changed "The Wildtype," and the result was a new type of organism–according to De Vries, a new species. I have pointed out elsewhere (Mayr, 1963) that taxonomists began as early as the 1840's and 1850's to collect large series of individuals–population samples as we would now say–and to describe the variation of these samples. From this purely pragmatic operation eventually emerged a wholly new way of thinking that replaced typological essentialism. From taxonomy, population thinking spread into adjacent fields and was in part instrumental for the development of population genetics and population cytology. Population thinking now has spread into the behavior field–into physiology and ecology. This one conceptual contribution has been of such great benefit to vast areas of biology that it alone justifies support for systematics.

As the interests of the systematists broaden, it is becoming more and more true that systematics has become, as stated by Julian Huxley (1940), "one of the focal points of biology." Although he may not be able to solve these problems himself, it is the systematist who frequently poses the problems that are of concern to the population geneticist, the physiologist, the embryologist, and the ecologist. For instance, systematics poses the problems in the area of ecology that deals with the phenomena of diversity, the differences in the richness of faunas and floras in different climatic zones and habitats, etc. A succession of prominent taxonomists have led the study of species competition, niche utilization, and structure of ecosystems.

Environmental physiology owes much to systematics. Zoological systematists like C. L. Gloger, J. A. Allen, and Bernhard Rensch have made major contributions to the discovery of adaptive geographic variation and the establishment of climatic rules. Up to the 1920's it was almost universally believed that geographic differences among populations of a species were nongenetic modifications of the phenotype and were of no evolutionary interest. As it was then stated, "the type of the species is not affected." It was zoologists with taxonomic competence who demonstrated the genetic basis for adaptive differences between geographic races. The stress on unique characteristics of individuals, the recognition of differences between populations, and the emphasis on the phenotype as a compromise between multiple selection pressures all represent thinking that came directly from evolutionary systematics, but that has exercised and is continuing to exercise a profound influence on environmental physiology.

Taxonomic principles as applied to the interpretation of man's evolution by Simpson, LeGros Clark, Mayr, and Simons have decisively added to our understanding of man's evolution and of hominid classification. The chaos of 29 generic names and more than 100 specific names caused by the earlier typological approach was replaced by a biologically oriented classification in which three genera, *Paranthropus, Australopithecus,* and *Homo* (the latter with two species) are recognized.

Whole branches of biology could not exist without systematics. Biological oceanography is one example, biogeography another. The latter field has been so traditionally the domain of the taxonomists that it is unnecessary to stress the contribution of systematics. Cytogenetics and bioacoustics are other areas of biology that derive much of their inspiration from systematics. Systematists have contributed enormously to ethology through their studies of comparative behavior, particularly of insects.

These contributions must be stressed for two reasons. One is that those persons who have come into biology from the outside (e.g., physics or chemistry) simply do not know this aspect of history. The other is that there has been a tendency, even among those who know the situation, to give credit to the neighboring fields—population genetics, ecology, or ethology—even when the advances were made by practicing taxonomists and were made possible only by the experience they had gained as taxonomists. It is totally misleading to limit the labels taxonomy or systematics to purely clerical, descriptive operations and to give a different label to the broader findings and concepts that are the direct result of the more elementary operations. Regrettably, even some taxonomists have supported the myth that all the more biologically interesting activities and findings of the taxonomist are not a part of taxonomy. In this connection it will be of some importance, in order to clarify the situation, to add a few words on the structure of systematics.

THE STRUCTURE OF SYSTEMATICS

In the earlier part of this presentation I described how systematics, as we now understand it, emerged from essentialism and nominalism (by rejecting these concepts) and came to be based on the fact of evolution. Systematists began to study organic diversity as the product of evolution and to recognize that every classification is a scientific theory with the properties of any scientific theory: i.e., it is explanatory, because it explains the existence of natural groups as the products of common descent; it is predictive because it can make highly accurate predictions as to the pattern of variation of unstudied features of organisms and the placing of newly discovered species. Finally, systematics established many new contacts with other areas of biology by adopting the thesis that the characteristics of the living organism are as important (or more so) for classification as those of preserved specimens.

How did these profound changes in the science of systematics affect its working procedure? In some ways not at all, because the needs for sound classification have not changed. There is still the same need to order the diversity of nature into its elementary units—the biological species. Sorting variable individuals and populations into species (and naming and describing them) is sometimes referred to as alpha taxonomy. There is still need for some alpha taxonomy, even in as mature a branch of systematics as bird taxonomy. New species, new subspecies, and all sorts of new taxa of birds are still being found. We still discover occasionally that a species given in the literature is nothing but a variant of another species. In ornithology we still are in need of compilations, checklists, and descriptive works of various sorts that fall under the designation of alpha or beta taxonomy. Yet even in these relatively elementary procedures of taxonomy there is a drastic difference between doing them in a typological (essentialist) fashion or in a biological-evolutionary fashion.

The typologist acts as if he is dealing with the "essential natures" of created types. He stresses morphotypes and discontinuities; variation is treated as a necessary evil to be ignored as much as possible. The biological systematist knows that he is dealing with samples of variable natural populations, and he is interested in the biological meaning of this variation. He knows that he is dealing with living organisms and wants to study all their attributes, whether they concern morphology, behavior, ecology, or biochemistry.

An understanding of the biological meaning of variation and of the evolutionary origin of groups of related species is even more important for the second stage of taxonomic activity—the sorting of species into groups of relatives (taxa) and their arrangement in a hierarchy of higher categories. This activity is what the term classification denotes; it is also referred to as beta taxonomy. No matter how interested a taxonomist is in the evolutionary and ecological aspects of the taxa he studies, he must also devote a major share of his time to alpha and beta taxonomy, not only because so much work still remains to be done, but also because the more interesting biological problems are found only through research in alpha and beta taxonomy.

THE FUTURE OF SYSTEMATICS

I would be rather pessimistic about the future of taxonomy if it were only an identification service for other branches of biology, as some of our less imaginative colleagues think. But anyone who realizes that systematics opens one of the most important doors toward understanding life in all its diversity cannot help but feel optimistic.

Environmental biology, behavioral biology, and even molecular biology are all moving in our direction. The most exciting aspect of biology is that, by contrast with physics and chemistry, it is not possible to reduce all phenomena to a few general laws. Nothing is as typically biological as the never-ending variety of solutions found by organisms to cope with similar challenges of the environment. Nothing is more intriguing than the study of differences between related organisms and the challenge to explain these differences as the result of natural selection. Even in cases where the ultimate solution may come from genetics or biochemistry, it is the systematist who usually poses the challenging questions. The opportunities for exciting research are virtually unlimited. This is becoming clearer and more widely appreciated every year.

These opportunities are not without obligations. Let us remember at all times that every taxonomist is a spokesman for systematics. He must carry out his activities in such a way as to reflect favorably on his field. Let us remember that taxonomy is not a kind of stamp collecting but a branch of biology. Let us desist from all practices that are injurious to the prestige of systematics, as for instance by indulging in nomenclatural practices that lower the value of scientific nomenclature as an information storage and retrieval system. Finally, let us remember that in virtually every taxonomic finding certain generalizations that are of value and broad interest to biology as a whole are implicit. It will help our relationships with other branches of biology if we make these findings known. They are bound to have impact well beyond the limits of systematics.

It is my sincere belief that systematics is one of the most important and indispensable, one of the most active and exciting, and one of the most rewarding branches of biological science. I know of no other subject that teaches us more about the world we live in.

REFERENCES

Huxley, J. A. 1940. The new systematics, Clarendon Press, Oxford.

Mayr, E. 1961. Cause and effect in biology. Science 134:1501–1506.

Mayr, E. 1963. Animal species and evolution, The Belknap Press of Harvard University Press, Cambridge, Massachusetts.

Simpson, G. G. 1961. Principles of animal taxonomy, Columbia University Press, New York. p. 7.

FRANS A. STAFLEU

A Historical Review of Systematic Biology

TWENTY CENTURIES OF GREEKS: PLATO, ARISTOTLE, AND THEOPHRASTUS

The safest general characterization of the European philosophical tradition is that it consists in a series of footnotes to Plato.

—ALFRED NORTH WHITEHEAD

It would be futile to attempt to cover in this brief space the 24 centuries of human effort to cope with the multiplicity of living beings. At most, I can sketch only the development of some guiding ideas and can mention the work of some of the most outstanding biological systematists.

The first attempts at systematizing biological knowledge and, more specifically, the knowledge of forms took place in the golden age of Greece, during the fourth century B.C. One may even argue that systematics started with human speech because the naming of abstract concepts, not of individual items, was equivalent to classification. Still, biological systematics as we know it today—presenting a comprehensive and interpretative picture of the world of living beings—actually has its roots in seventeenth and eighteenth century thought. The various attempts at biological systematics made between the lifetimes of Aristotle and Ray are extremely interesting from the cultural point of view, illustrating, as they do, the gradual growth of independent research and accompanying and often nicely illustrating the great adventures of the human spirit. For an understanding of systematics today, however, the history of the attempts made in the past three centuries is much more important. I shall review only briefly, therefore, that long first era in which systematics was characterized so much more by what Francis Bacon in his *Novum Organum* of 1620 called "anticipation of nature" (human reasoning that is "rash and premature" when applied to nature) than by "interpretation of nature" (human reasoning "properly deduced from things"). (For a quotation see Osborn, 1929, p. 3.)

For zoological systematics, we go back to Aristotle to find the first application of scientific induction to living beings. For botany, Aristotle's pupil, friend, and successor at the Lyceum, Theophrastos of Eresos, undoubtedly stands at the cradle of systematics. Neither with Aristotle nor with Theophrastos, however, do we find anything like a clearly worked out classification of living beings. There are some main divisions: Aristotle distinguished between several groups of invertebrate animals (e.g., the Malacostraca [Crustacea] are separated from the Entoma [insects], and the Malakia [Cephalopoda] are separated from the other mollusks), and he distinguished classes like reptiles, fishes, birds, and mammals; Theophrastos divided the plant world into trees, shrubs, undershrubs, and herbs. Both philosophers described or mentioned many genera, arranging several of them in groups that we now recognize as families or orders, but their treatment does not amount to a comprehensive classification. In a very general sense, the use of the categories "genus" and "species" is very old and corresponds to the need for both a comprehensive and a diagnostic category in dealing with one's environment.

The term "genus" (Greek, *genos*) had a general and relative meaning and could be applied to any group whose unity had to be expressed. The term "species" (Greek, *eidos*) was used for the members of that group. Aristotle would call birds or fishes "genera" and speak of many "species of fishes and birds." In classificatory logic, the categories "genus" and "species" are both "classes." The word "taxon" for a taxonomic group of any rank is a twentieth-century term. The philosophical background of human knowledge in general cannot be treated here.

Although Plato and Aristotle worked out the principles of logical classification and division, they did not use these principles for setting up a strictly dichotomous system based on the aphorism *tertium non datur,* containing classes in a hierarchical order. The relatively limited number of living beings with which they were dealing did not make this necessary. They encountered in nature what they called "genera"—groups having an essential unity that everyone realized. When the genera were described in more detail, it became apparent that they could be arranged in different ways, depending upon the choice of characteristics. In botany, the number of genera remained rather limited for some time, mainly because of the tremendous importance attached to the differences between cultivated plants and those growing in the wild. The latter hardly counted, and they were greatly neglected even though Theophrastos, an exceptionally astute observer, tried to break through this barrier.

In the long period between the golden age of Greece and the sixteenth century, scientists dealing with systematics limited themselves to the making of an inventory of the "natural genera." Vague though this notion may seem to be now, the natural genera were very real to the biologists of ancient and medieval times. The distinction between genera and species reflects a very general process by which the human mind arranges objects in classes and expresses this arrangement by the giving of names. Most biologists felt there was no need for a further classification.

In many ways Aristotle was much more advanced in his incomplete and sketchy classification of the animal world than most of his followers well into the seventeenth century. His basic division of the invertebrates is superior even to that of Linnaeus. Theophrastos clearly describes groups of genera that we recognize now as monocots and dicots, and also smaller groups like grasses—Liliaceae, Amaryllidaceae, Umbelliferae, etc.—cases of "natural families." The main criteria consciously advanced by Aristotle and Theophrastos for their simple classification, however, were based far less on an inductive evaluation of observation and experience than the above would lead us to believe. Both worked with typical aprioristic criteria as a basis for their classifications. By deductive reasoning it was concluded that logical division should be based on those features that were of greatest importance for life in general—growth and reproduction in plants, and the circulatory system in animals (both those with red blood and those without).

The Platonic principle of plenitude—of a world filled with all possible phenomena without room for new ones, a timeless structure—was at the basis of what looks most like a system with Aristotle—his ladder of nature. This principle, according to which there are no distinct lines of separation between living beings and which describes nature as a series of easy gradations having, in principle, no gaps and no jumps, continued to play an important role in biology in general, and particularly in systematics, until well into the nineteenth century. However, since Aristotle and Theophrastos gave no concrete systems based on inductively obtained information on structural affinities, this principle of plenitude plays a much lesser role with them than with some later authors.

In medieval times, little of importance was added to the knowledge that the great Greeks had brought forward. On the contrary, there was a definite decrease in inductive research and a gradual increase of uncritical imitation of the ancients:

> ... the reverence for antiquity and the authority of men who have been esteemed great in philosophy, and general unanimity, have retarded men from advancing in science and almost enchanted them.
>
> —Francis Bacon, *Novum Organum,* 1620 (as quoted in Osborn, 1929, p. 25).

The inventories of "natural genera" (taxonomic groups, or taxa, of specific, generic or even higher rank, but sometimes also unrecognizable) often were simple alphabetic enumerations. In the sixteenth century the German botanists Otto Brunfels (1530–1536) and Leonhard Fuchs (1542) arranged the genera essentially in alphabetic order, as did Conrad Gesner in his four-volume *Historia Animalium* of 1551-1587. These authors, however, were responsible for a certain increase in scientific research and for a certain measure of dissociation from the texts of the ancients. The Renaissance opened the human mind for a renewed, unbiased study of nature. In botany, the first intimation of this independent observation came through illustrations. Brunfels (1530-1536) based his text on the ancients, but his figures, by Hans Weiditz, were taken from nature, as were those of Fuchs (1542).

Hieronymus Bock (1498 to 1554) acquired a superior knowledge of floral morphology, although this knowledge had little influence on his classification, which was based upon combinations of vegetative characteristics. The first to abandon fully the almost blind trust in ancient botany and to rely upon his own observations was Valerius Cordus (1515 to 1544), with whom Renaissance botany reached maturity. This astute observer and independent thinker, however, met death at the age of 29 while on a trip to Italy. Had he lived longer, Cordus no doubt would have produced a comprehensive classification.

Man started reconnoitering the world. The Spanish and Portuguese empires grew rapidly, and the increase in travel and trade, combined with nature research in the Old World, resulted in an explosion of knowledge of forms, both of plants and animals. The sheer bulk of this new information finally stimulated biologists to set up a system of information storage and retrieval that was more efficient than arrangements by alphabet, by enumeration, or by benefits to man. Systematics was born out of sheer necessity; and it grew rapidly in the sixteenth and seventeenth centuries because of the efforts to keep pace with the great increase in knowledge.

OF RENAISSANCE AND REASON: CESALPINO TO MAGNOL

Per inductionem et experimentum omnia.
Non igitur auctoritas destituta rationibus valeat: neque vetustas quidquam praescribat.

–J. JUNG

It was during the Renaissance, and as a result of it, that biologists, all thoroughly acquainted with the teachings of Plato and Aristotle, started using consistently the principles of classification and logical division developed by the ancients. The tendency to classify living beings rigorously in a hierarchy of collective units gained ground rapidly.

When considering the historical development of systematics it should be realized that certain contingent principles have almost continuously interfered with, and sometimes even governed, the attitude of biologists with respect to classification.

The first set of contingent attitudes that has greatly influenced systematics through the ages is the conflict between independent personal observation and induction, or experience, and *a priori* or deductive reasoning. Theophrastos might have observed extremely interesting phenomena in the wild, but attention remained centered upon cultivated plants, or at any rate on plants useful to man; and his observation might have revealed to him that the young plants of all the species he knew could be divided clearly into those having two first-leaves and those having only one, but since "growth" was considered a primary characteristic of life, the division between woody plants and herbs was deemed more important.

Another fundamental contingency in human thought has already been mentioned. The Platonic principle of plenitude, the ladder of nature, the great chain of being (Lovejoy, 1960), or whatever other term is used for this vision of the universe, sets forth that there are infinite gradations but no discrete barriers between living beings. "Tout es plein dans la nature . . . et à cause de la plénitude du monde, tout est lié" (Leibniz, 1714:31); the principle of continuity is thus derived from that of plenitude (see also Lovejoy, 1960:144). This principle is clearly antisystematic, and it makes any system arbitrary. On the other hand, there is the other philosophical approach to the world—the approach of logical classification and division, an *entweder oder,* a "this-or-that," a *tertium non datur.* These philosophical principles logically contradict each other, but each plays its role in the history of systematic thought. The clash is between the abstract logical structure of species, genera, and classes and the overwhelming profusion of nature. In the seventeenth century an attempt was made to master this profusion of nature by systematizing and, if possible, by applying mathematics and a mechanistic approach. In biological systematics this attempt is reflected by the quest for rational and precise definitions rather than for comprehensive descriptions. The early natural systems developed in the eighteenth century represented a partial victory for the Platonian principle; the modern biological species concept, a partial victory for the realization that discrete entities do occur in nature.

However, I am running too far ahead. Let us look at the first botanical systematist in the strict sense, Andrea Cesalpino (1519 to 1603).

The development of plant classification forged ahead of that of animals. After all, it took a long time before botanists started to work seriously on cryptograms. Until the end of the eighteenth century, botany was phanerogamy; and with this restriction it is clear that it was much simpler to know plants than to know animals, to record plants' life phases, and to know plants in their entirety. General resemblances in habit were easily noticed, and this led to the recognition of natural families such as grasses and Umbelliferae. Further resemblances in flower and fruit structure soon led to a better description of what are now called genera.

The notion of natural families appears in the earliest writings and is based on simple experience. This spontaneous recognition was followed by similar arrangements, by analogy, and by other genera. The result was a steady increase in knowledge of the natural families of higher plants, and this knowledge, in turn, resulted in a remarkably stable system.

These generalities, however, were not enough. Practice demanded a more precise knowledge and mode of distinction of genera and species. For each plant it was necessary to know its specific identity, if only because of its benefits for man. It should also be realized that in the sixteenth century (with Cesalpino, for example) the categories of genus and species were still relatively undefined.

When trying to recognize a logical order in the facts presented to him, Cesalpino (1583) realized that one could classify in many different ways. The system that resulted from one's classification, he found, depended upon one's choice of characters. A logical question was: Which characters are the most important? Anatomy, the guiding line in zoology, was almost unknown in plants. The notions of Aristotelian and Theophrastean physiology presented themselves almost automatically: Certain parts have a fundamental significance, namely those which contribute most to "nutrition" and to "generation," the two vital operative aspects of plants. The nutritive aspect (growth) was considered all-important, and this was why woody and herbaceous (duration of life!) was such an important split. A further important criterion was the seed, and especially the embryo and the seedling, in analogy with the importance of the animal embryo.

Cesalpino's work shows the first consistent application of this Aristotelian aprioristic principle to plant classification. It also shows from the beginning, and once and for all, the impossibility of obtaining a satisfactory picture of main affinities on the basis of speculative physiology (cf. Daudin, 1926). Bremekamp (1953a), however, in a recent re-examination of Cesalpino's classification, has demonstrated that even with Cesalpino this emphasis on deductively chosen characteristics is only half-hearted.

The need for a logical justification of any scientific activity was felt very heavily at that time, but, in addition to being an Aristotelian philosopher, Cesalpino was, like Aristotle himself, a born observer and an inductive natural scientist. The choice of characters for Cesalpino's higher divisions was dogmatic and arbitrary, but his ultimate system, with 32 groups of related genera, is far too natural to have been reached on the basis of preconceived notions. The "literary embellishment of somewhat doubtful taste," of which Bremekamp (1953a, p. 584) speaks, played a minor role. Cesalpino started out with certain natural groups known to him intuitively or by tradition, and he added a rather irrelevant and certainly unimportant superstructure. In reality, he first observed, then drew conclusions and looked for significant combinations of characteristics, and ended up with the first truly scientific attempt at classification. The work of this first real systematist shows again the struggle between preconceived notions and direct, unbiased observation. A careful analysis of Cesalpino's 32 groups reveals that his unbiased observation was victorious, as most of these groups are easily recognizable now as families or orders of phanerogams.

Cesalpino was the first in a series of systematists who struggled between speculative, preconceived notions and direct observation of nature, or, stated in other terms, between the "artificial" and the "natural," between logical division and natural affinity, between thinking about facts and the facts themselves, between theory and practice. Again and again we see in the course of later centuries this clash between the desire for a practical and pragmatic or idealistic—but at any rate simple and logical—system and the invincible obstacle of long-recognized natural entities. I shall not enter into the question of what is "natural." The term has had a special meaning in every phase of our culture, and often it had several meanings at the same time. As used here, the term simply reflects the general recognition in nature of certain units (taxonomic groups) by a widespread group of observers—units based upon general habit or an intuitive evaluation of combinations of characters.

I now mention, very briefly, some of many systematists who made further steps in the slow progress of inductive reasoning and independent observation in natural history during the sixteenth and seventeenth centuries. Charles de l'Escluse (1526 to 1609) and Rembert Dodoens (1517 to 1585) produced impressive pieces of original work that are sometimes hidden in great compilations (Clusius 1601,

1605; Dodoens 1583); and Caspar Bauhin (1560 to 1624) embodied nomenclatural reform and comprehensiveness in his *Pinax* (Bauhin, 1623). We find remarkably independent theoretical clearness in Joachim Jung, who, in his *Isagoge Phytoscopia* of 1678, laid a foundation for objective botanical terminology. Robert Hooke (1635 to 1702), Marcellus Malpighi (1623 to 1694), Nehemiah Grew (1628 to 1711), and Antonie van Leeuwenhoek (1630 to 1723) were great observers who disclosed the rich world of plant anatomy and of microscopic life in general, and Rudolf Jakob Camerarius (1665 to 1721) carried out experiments on sexuality in plants. All these men added impressively to the number of facts with which the systematists would have to deal.

One of the most important steps in the emancipation from preconceived notions toward unbiased inductive research was taken by the Frenchman Pierre Magnol (1638 to 1715), who, more than a century after Cesalpino, made the first clear plea for a classification based upon a combination of characters. Also, Magnol (1689) was the first to use the term "family" in exactly the way we use it now. He found that each family has a combination of characters of its own and, very significantly, that a character that was important for one family did not necessarily have the same importance in another family (cf. Stafleu, 1963:153-154):

> In the same way therefore as one recognizes families among the animals, in the same way we propose them for the plants . . . .
>
> This relation between the animals and the plants has given me occasion to reduce the plants to certain families, in comparison with the families of man; and since it has appeared to me impossible to draw the characters of those families only from the fructification, I have chosen the parts of plants where we find combined the most characteristic items, such as the roots, the branches, the flowers and the seeds. There is even in numerous plants a certain likeness, an affinity that does not consist of the parts as considered separately, but as a whole; an important affinity, but which cannot be expressed . . . .
>
> We think that all parts which do not serve the fruit are no more accidental than the arms and legs are accidental parts of the animals.

Magnol's ideas reflect a continuous interplay between constructive, pragmatic reasoning and the resistance, based upon a deeper analysis of nature in combination with traditional notions on affinity, against it. This struggle between the "artificial" and the "natural," which I mentioned earlier, had a very happy outcome in botany, namely, the natural system. Facts and viewpoints in constant interaction are characteristic of modern science; in systematic biology this process led first to the natural systems and, later of course, to the theory of evolution.

FACING THE FACTS: RAY TO LINNAEUS

All depends on keeping the eye steadily fixed upon the facts of nature. . . .

–FRANCIS BACON

A contemporary of Magnol who had an even greater influence on systematics than that French botanist was the great English philosopher and naturalist John Ray (1628 to 1695), whose first major systematic treatise, *Methodus Plantarum Nova,* appeared in 1682, a few years before Magnol's *Prodromus.* For Ray, a method was indispensable for the memorization of facts, but he made it quite clear that no method is exhaustive: "nature objects against being enclosed within the limits of whatever method."

Above all, Ray was a pragmatist. He rejected all arrangements based on anything other than morphological criteria (ecology, medical properties), yet he retained, though it was "neither exact nor philosophical," the old Theophrastean subdivision into woody plants and herbs. (For a detailed analysis of this system, see, for example, Vines, 1913 and Raven, 1950). However, Ray (1703) used the actual terms Monocotyledones and Dicotyledones; he based his higher categories upon relatively few characters, and, except for the lower groups (equivalent to families and genera), he used combinations of characters. Also, he attempted to assign to the category "genus" taxonomic groups of comparable importance; in other words, he tried to stabilize and to give a factual rather than a relative meaning to the categories "genus" and "species."

Like Cesalpino, Ray shows a dualism in procedure. He bases the higher groups, which are not grasped at once by the human mind as collective units, on an arbitrary choice of characters with a strict priority scheme. For the lower categories his method is more relaxed, free of methodology, and with a more liberal choice of criteria.

Ray's dichotomous tables of the higher categories are actually based on practical experience (monocots versus dicots for instance) and resemble only superficially the Aristotelian logical division. The naturalist uses the practice of logical division but is not its slave.

Adanson, the greatest proponent of the natural system, recognized this very clearly. He said that the idea of Ray's system was excellent and that Ray would have succeeded even more had he been as great a botanist as he was a learned writer and judicious compiler (Adanson, 1763, 1:xxi).

Another key figure in the development of systematics was the botanist Joseph Pitton de Tournefort (1656 to 1708), who was even more pragmatic than Ray. It is not surprising that he was more pragmatic, because the increase in the number of known plant species was such that the first demand became more and more one for order, for a method that would enable the user to find as quickly as possible the species to which a specimen belonged. Tournefort admitted that he did not offer a universal or natural method. His aim was to provide a key, to make it possible to have *une connaissance plus facile,* and he did not worry when some of his higher groups were manifestly at variance with some of the traditionally recognized natural entities.

"Connaître les plantes, c'est précisément savoir les noms qu'on leur a donnés par rapport à la structure de quelques-unes de leurs parties." (Tournefort, 1694, I:1.) This is a characteristic and important statement: The knowledge of names is the indispensable requirement for a knowledge of the medicinal properties of the plant.

Tournefort concentrated his efforts upon a clear delimitation of the genera by means of easily recognizable, plainly visible characters. For this reason, and for no other, he chose characters of the fruits and the flowers. For higher categories one should use, arbitrarily, only one set of characteristics, for which he chose that of the flower for its didactical advantages:

> . . . il semble que les fleurs soient encore plus propres que les semences pour établir les classes des plantes, à cause que ces parties attachent la vue plus agréablement, et qu'elles frappent plus vivement l'imagination. (Tournefort, 1694, 1:45–46.)

The next part of the story is more familiar. The eighteenth century witnessed an unprecedented increase in the number of new animals and plants that came to the attention of the naturalists. The nomenclatural and taxonomic systems proliferated, but the gap widened between their coverage and effectiveness on the one hand and the information explosion on the other. More and more systems were developed, all based upon simple characters, but these systems simply could not cope with the needs. The clumsy way of naming species, by means of elaborate, diagnostic phrases, was certainly one of the major obstacles. The phrase names grew longer and longer. Nobody used the same names for species, and the orderly genius of Linnaeus found a great task to accomplish. It is impossible to do justice here to the importance of Linnaeus to systematic biology. His practical and orderly mind grasped the first need of biology:

Filum ariadneum Botanices est Systema, sine quo chaos est Res herbaria. . . . Systematicis, qui filum hoc duxere, omni aevo honos permanebit, quum eo destituo Maeandros Botanices errantes intrarent omnes. (Linnaeus 1751, No. 156.)

The implication is clear: The system is the "thread of Ariadne," without which botany would be chaos. The systematist aims at an internationally acceptable system by which botanists reach the same conclusions and by which their work becomes comparable. One should be careful not to lose the thread of Ariadne in imitating nature, as was the case with Morison and Ray ("cavendum ne imitando naturam filum ariadneum (156) amittamus, uti Morisonus & Rajus," Linnaeus 1751, No. 160).

Linnaeus' training and background were scholastic, and his whole approach is Aristotelian (see, e.g., Cain, 1958; Bremekamp, 1953 b and c; Lindroth, 1966). It has often been said, correctly, that, as far as ideas are concerned, Linnaeus stood at the end of an era. His absolute criterion of the constancy of species—the dogma of special creation—was conspicuous and already somewhat old-fashioned in its original form. Later in life Linnaeus put forward an entirely different theory, one that involved some 6,000 specially created prototypes and speciation by means of hybridization. The original dogma of the constancy of species, however, played only a minor role in this method. Really primary in Linnaeus' method was his principle that biology is based on fixed genera (cf. Daudin, 1926:35–36). The botanist and the zoologist could in principle know all the genera; the master would know most of the species (Linnaeus, 1751, No. 256). Knowledge was possible through definition of the taxa by means of their "essential" characters.

The Tournefortian theme of the definition of genera is further elaborated by Linnaeus (1751: No. 159): All species with the same geometrical disposition of the parts of the flower belong to one genus. The criteria are number, shape, size, and proportion, and these determine the "essence" of the genus. The essence lies, therefore, in the structure of the flower—a scholastic and an *a priori* concept which, however, found support in the high information content of the involved flower structure. As usual, it is difficult to say whether theory preceded or followed practical experience, although Linnaeus was so outspoken in his scholastic philosophy that one is inclined to accept his reasoning at face value. Five obligatory ranks are recognized—class, order, genus, species, and variety—in close parallel to the five categories of scholastic philosophy as applied in other sciences: *genus summum, genus intermedium, genus proximum, species, individuum* (Linnaeus, 1751: No. 155).

The great merit of the sexual system was that it provided a simple, easy-to-comprehend structure for storage and retrieval of information. It standardized usage. In combination with the code designations for species of the binomial system (Linnaeus, 1753), it provided a simple and highly useful framework that was internationally acceptable and that led different people to the same result. It is clear that in the beginning the Linnaean nomenclatural revolution created some confusion, but the intrinsic merits of the system soon overcame its disadvantages (see, e.g., Stearn 1957, 1959).

Although he admitted that it was provisional and not "natural," Linnaeus nevertheless was convinced that the sexual system had high taxonomic value because it kept the natural genera intact (this was round-about reasoning, because the natural genera were defined by means of the structure of the flowers, just as the system) and especially because he considered the flower characters as expressing the "essence." And what, after all, in scholastic thinking, was the difference between essence and nature? For Linnaeus the essential characteristics were the diagnostic features derived from the fructification; the natural character, according to his *Philosophia Botanica,* would show *all* differences and single characteristics of the fructification insofar as they are useful for the delimitation of the species.

For Linnaeus, species and genera were realities, created as such and existing in nature. In scholastic language, Linnaeus' attitude here was that of a realist. With respect to classes and orders, however, his attitude was typically that of a nominalist; they are the works of "nature and art." The more plants we know the more the gaps will be filled, and the boundaries between the orders and classes eventually will disappear. These taxa have no objective reality, but are ideas of our own making. The Platonic principle of plenitude made its appearance here in the higher echelons, but Linnaeus drew the line with the genera and species. The famous aphorism of the *Philosophia Bo-*

tanica, "nature makes no jumps," and the statement that all plants touch each other as the countries on a map of the world (Linnaeus, 1751; No. 77) are applicable here. Linnaeus' attitude toward the natural families is well known—he had an outline, he recognized their existence, but he was not convinced that their full recognition was within reach. Perhaps he was not even convinced of the desirability of elaborating a natural system.

Toward the middle of the eighteenth century, therefore, we see the victory of the ingenious and simple method of classification of plants developed by Linnaeus. However, classification is not yet systematics; a key is not a monograph. What about the multiple affinities? What about the major task of systematics to present a picture of the structure of the animal and vegetable world? Practical need temporarily had drowned the voices of those who were more philosophical, who were happy to know the names but who expected more of systematics than pure diagnostic classification, who wanted to describe instead of to define. In this respect, the second half of the century saw a strong reaction, coming mainly from France.

Before we leave Linnaeus, however, there should be a few words on the situation in zoology, which was radically different from that in botany. From the beginning, the higher units in zoology stood out much more clearly than did the genera and species—a situation that was exactly the opposite in botany.

The urge for classification in zoology, as embodied also in the work of Linnaeus, was even more directly the result of the pressure of facts. The general delimitation of the higher units was determined, of old, mainly by anatomy, especially the circulatory system, but, again, mainly for the higher animals. The anatomy of the lower animals remained almost as obscure as the morphology of the fungi in botany, but there was a difference. Many of the invertebrates had hard parts—cockles, shells, etc.—that reached the many natural history cabinets. The cabinet-taxonomists had to work with these incomplete vestiges of living animals. A science such as conchology could arise, but a man like Adanson, who pleaded that the systematics of mollusks should be based on the entire living animals (Adanson, 1757, "Coquillages"), remained an exception.

The notion of natural genera was difficult to apply in zoology, and, as a result, Linnaeus did not really introduce an artificial method for the classification of animals. The pressure of the facts was such that

Linnaeus, an excellent observer, gave in almost completely; clearly, his higher taxa often were based on combinations of characters. On the other hand, it must be admitted that Linnaeus' zoological classification was, in several respects, behind that of Aristotle. Linnaeus included the whales in Mammalia only in the twelfth edition, in 1766, of his *Systema Naturae;* they were among the fishes in all previous editions. Linnaeus' *Insecta* are, in fact, the Arthropoda because they include crustaceous groups and spiders; his Vermes were highly mixed. Aristotle's classification was much superior in this respect. Agassiz (1857) said ". . . it was left for Cuvier to introduce order in this chaos"; but perhaps it might be said that it was left to Lamarck and Cuvier.

In the work of Linnaeus we again find embodied the two characteristic contingencies of early biological systematics. First, there was the struggle between the pressure of facts and the pressure of ideas, in which Linnaeus, purely pragmatically, gives preponderance to the ideas in botany and to the facts in zoology; second, there was the perpetual contingency in the human mind of wanting to have a hierarchy of living beings arranged in discrete classes, even though one was convinced of the existence of a gradual series from the imperfect to the more complex, with almost unnoticeable transitions. There are no empty spaces, "nullus hiatus est, nulla fractio, nulla dispersio formarum: invicem connexae sunt, velut anulus anulo" (T. E. Nieremberg, as quoted by Daudin, 1926: 93). Linnaeus, that archsystematist and convinced believer in specially created species and genera, also could not dissociate himself fully from this age-old biological paradox.

FROM CLASSIFICATION TO SYSTEMATICS: BUFFON AND ADANSON

C'est renoncer volontairement au plus grand nombre des avantages que la Nature nous offre pour la connoître, que de refuser de se servir de toutes les parties des objets que nous considérons. . . .

—BUFFON

The road from classification to systematics, from diagnostic keys to an interpretative representation of the world of living beings, was shown by two French biologists of exceptional accomplishment:

Buffon and Adanson. In second line there were Daubenton, Lamarck, de Jussieu, and Cuvier.

So far, classification of living beings had been a timeless affair, as had been the study of the natural sciences as a whole. Time was never taken into account; it was silently assumed that species did not change; the Aristotelian classificatory logic knew no time element. The Greek and Renaissance view of nature was timeless. Relatively few authors had ever tried to define a species concept at all, let alone one that included the role of time. Aristotle considered fecundity in animals as a specific character (Agassiz, 1857: 209). Linnaeus (1751, No. 157) stated that we count as many species as there were created in the beginning. He mentioned the law of generation, which accounts for the production of identical unchanging forms, but that is as far as time goes. In George-Louis Leclerq, Comte de Buffon (1707 to 1788) we encounter, however, a biologist who had exceptional insight; who was almost free from traditional thought, and especially religious overtones; who had a highly intelligent though somewhat speculative mind; and who was highly original and in many ways far ahead of his time.

Diametrically opposed to Linnaeus, often completely misinterpreting his merits and intentions, and seldom taking the trouble to describe carefully and sort precisely the great multitude of facts, Buffon managed to formulate strikingly original thoughts that foreshadowed the great developments of the future.

For Buffon, a species has a physical identity because it is the total sum of all individuals forming a reproductive community (Buffon, 1753, 4:384–386). This physical identity is the only fixed point in systematics; it gives the species a natural existence, which, in principle, cannot be attained by any of the higher taxa—". . . les espèces sont les seuls êtres de la Nature." (Buffon, 1749–1769, 13:i.)

Comparative anatomy reveals a common plan in the organization of groups of animals. The species may now be too far apart to hybridize, but we may ask whether this was always the case. Could presently allied but independent species not have arisen from common ancestors? If systematics has a meaning at all, what can it be other than the expression of community of origin, true genealogical relationship? (Buffon used the word "genealogy"; the word "phylogeny" did not exist at the time.) "On pourra dire également . . . que l'homme et le singe ont eu une origine commune comme le cheval et l'âne. . . .

(Buffon, 1753, 4:382.) We can know what a species is only by comparing its present situation in nature with its situation in the past, by comparing present specimens with past ones.

Lines of separation exist in nature only between the species because of their biological reality (interfertility); all other dividing lines, such as those between genera, families, and orders, are unreal, not constant, uncertain.

I have paraphrased Buffon's opinions as we find them expressed mainly in the fourth volume of his *Histoire Naturelle.* Elsewhere Buffon partially withdraws some of his most daring statements, or rephrases them more cautiously. He did this because of outside pressure, however, and it does not detract from their intrinsic value. The chapter on monkeys and apes contains some of Buffon's most daring statements, but there is no "monkey business" here. With all his shortcomings, his pomposity, his well-known disdain for the opinions of others, and especially for those of a mere *nomenclateur,* such as Linnaeus, who works with an abstract aprioristic system, Buffon formulates here some fundamental biological concepts. He is modern because: (1) he formulates the biological species concept *avant-la-lettre,* and with only a vague notion of populations; (2) he radically points at the nominalist character of genera and of taxa of higher categories (Linnaeus considers genera as "natural," that is, "real," but shares Buffon's opinion on the higher groups); (3) he explicitly introduces the time element in systematics; and (4) he formulates the idea of phylogenetic relationship (though using the word "degeneration") mainly by recognizing that the present fertility barriers between species may not always have existed and that common structure can be understood only in the light of common ancestry.

Buffon's introduction of the historical element was of the greatest importance for the evolution of biology as an independent science. In the first place, this introduction heralded the modern view of nature. As mentioned before, nature had so far been timeless; if there was change, this change was cyclical, never directed to a different ultimate result. "Progress" and "development" became new elements in the picture of nature, elements that would later be called evolution (see, e.g., Collingwood, 1945, and Stafleu, 1966a).

A further consequence of Buffon's views was that, for the first time, biological knowledge became dissociated from physics. Biology evolved from natural history. Scientific method in natural history as part of pre-nineteenth-century physics was dominated exclusively by mathematics; historical knowledge in combination with mathematical analysis *in sensu lato* is characteristic of modern biology. Definition of timeless "essentials" was no longer sufficient—life should be described in all its phenomena. In Cassirer's words, ". . . there is in the making a transition to a conception of nature which no longer seeks to devise and explain becoming from being, but being from becoming." (Cassirer, 1951:80.) We might also say that biology moved from "definition" to "description."

Buffon was the outspoken enemy of all "systems" because they are based only on definitions. Accepting the principle of continuity, he furthermore denied the existence of all barriers, except those between species in certain phases of their existence. Here again we meet the duality between discrete entities and continuity, but this time on a purely biological basis. This was an enormous step forward, but a step that was almost unnoticed. Buffon's great disadvantage was the absence of empirical proof, and this was the main reason why his attack upon the dogma of the constancy of species remained unsuccessful. However, his far-flung imagination fertilized the minds of his compatriots Adanson, Daubenton, and Lamarck.

Zoologists such as Daubenton, who wanted to work with all animals of a certain group, and industrious botanists such as Adanson soon discovered—with all their professed admiration for Buffon's ideas—that a practical systematist cannot work with the principle of continuity. Buffon, modern as he might be, was too old-fashioned in this respect.

Adanson (1727 to 1806) remarked that Buffon's picture of the living world would indicate that the only reality is a constant stream of individuals, changing and merging with each other without any definite divisions between them. In the last instance there would then be only one universal being (cf. Stafleu, 1963:183). This, however, went too far for Adanson. It may well be that nature is one and undivided with respect to the supreme being, but it is certainly divided for us *et cela sufit.* These three words ("and this is sufficient") show Adanson's modern approach. It is good and well that there is divine unity, but what matters is the picture presented to the human mind, to human reason. This essentially nominalist attitude enabled Adanson to search for the discontinuities in nature, or at any rate for the various situations in nature in which changes are abrupt rather than gradual.

On this basis, but fully in agreement with the ideas expressed by Buffon on the artificiality of the various "systems," Adanson started his search for what he called "the natural method."

In the first volume of his *Familles des Plantes,* Adanson (1763) gave a detailed and critical account of methods and principles of plant classification. This theoretical work, the first of its kind, was of great importance for the understanding of eighteenth-century systematics. (For a detailed treatment of Adanson's book, see Stafleu, 1963.) Adanson accepted Magnol's concept of the natural families, and he elaborated this theme for families as well as for genera. He did not single out any characters *a priori,* but made an inventory of as many characters and affinities as possible. The inventory was a series of 65 artificial arrangements of the genera, with each arrangement based on a single character or on a few characters. From it Adanson derived his "natural method," which was the prototype of all subsequent natural systems in botany. We would now describe it as a system based on a great many characters and character complexes, with a high degree of information. Adanson refused to admit *a priori* weighting of characters; he evaluated them *a posteriori,* after careful comparison and consideration. Recently, Burtt (1966) proposed calling this process "intrinsic" weighting of characters, as opposed to "extrinsic" weighting on the basis of extraneous *a priori* arguments as to "essence" and "naturalness," etc.

Adanson, who made himself as free as possible from traditional thought, was flatly opposed to the Aristotelian-scholastic systematics of Linnaeus. However, it would be wrong to see Adanson only in his reaction to Linnaeus. His importance, like that of Buffon and Daubenton, went much further and, in a way, was autonomous. He made classification into systematics.

The step was still only a first one. Adanson was deeply interested in the fossil record but he could do very little with it–understandably so, when we take into account that he was mainly concerned with phanerogams. He shared Buffon's ideas on the origin of species by hybridization, and he was the first to speak of the role of hereditary mutations for the process of speciation. It would lead me too far from my present subject to provide further details here (see Stafleu, 1963:167–170), but these features show how modern and daring were the new views of these eighteenth-century biologists who were truly children of the Enlightenment, of the *siècle des lumières.*

In England, Erasmus Darwin (1731 to 1802) set forth pre-evolutionary ideas that might well be compared with those of his French contemporaries. Erasmus Darwin's influence on systematics, however, cannot be compared with that of Buffon and Adanson. With some regret, therefore, I must leave this interesting figure out of account here. The same holds for the Genevese philosopher and zoologist Charles Bonnet (1720 to 1793), follower of Leibniz and defender of a "gradation ascendante."

Louis Jean Marie Daubenton (1716 to 1799) was Buffon's collaborator for the systematic treatment of most of the mammals. As early as 1751, in the *Grande Encyclopédie,* and in 1753, in the fourth volume of the *Histoire Naturelle* (Buffon, 1749–1769), which was a joint effort with Buffon, Daubenton argued that the *nomenclateur* (the diagnostic biologist, the one who classifies) caused a hindrance to independent progress. He believed that the picture of nature must consist of complete descriptions—not solely of the so-called important characters, but of all of them, external as well as internal. Anatomy is of capital importance to zoological taxonomy, not just the gross morphology of the outer parts. Daubenton (in Buffon, 1749–1769, 4:118–119) stressed that behavior and anatomy be used in systematics:

> The naturalists have too much neglected this part; most of them seem to have restricted themselves to knowing the products of nature only by looking at the bark, just like travelers who would only look at the walls of the cities, of the facades of the palaces instead of entering them and inspecting closely all artistic masterpieces which are kept inside. Let us not imitate those superficial observers . . . (Translated from Daudin, 1926:133.)

Daubenton's aim was to give full descriptions by means of uniform designations so as to obtain a better notion (*a posteriori*) of what are really essential characteristics. In this way one would obtain a general knowledge of all animals, "a type of knowledge which is among the most important that we can derive of natural history." Again, the ultimate aim of the taxonomist is systematics, not classification.

TIME WILL HAVE NO STOP: THE PRE-DARWINIAN NINETEENTH CENTURY

> *But thought's the slave of life, and life's time's fool,*
> *And time, that takes survey of all the world,*
> *Must have a stop.*
> —SHAKESPEARE

As a result of the efforts of Buffon, Daubenton, and Adanson, France remained a country where the Linnaean system never reached the same supremacy as, for instance, it did in England; nevertheless, the Linnaean school was a strong one. The struggle that developed between the proponents of the two schools became at one time—early in the French Revolution—a political issue. On this, as well as on many other causes, the Paris biologists were deeply divided for many years. This, however, was incidental and not characteristic of the real trends in biology. Both movements did much to promote systematics. The Linnaean sexual system had a great appeal for reformers like Jean-Jacques Rousseau, and it was more easily comprehensible for the layman than the more esoteric natural system. The almost undisputed reign of the natural history cabinets in zoology, with their emphasis on partial remains only, also stimulated the use of the Linnaean method.

The natural system in biology played a role that can be compared with that of the natural system of elements in chemistry. The search for connecting links was a powerful stimulus for research. Comparable stimulus later was to be added by the theory of evolution.

In zoology, it was not before 1790, in France as well as elsewhere, that the study of the internal structure of invertebrate animals received sufficient impetus to be used as a basis for classification and, ultimately, for a natural system.

Botany, as has been said, was ahead of zoology in the development of a natural system, but only as it pertained to phanerogamy. Adanson was followed by remarkable figures like J. B. P. A. M. de Lamarck (1744 to 1829), with his *Flore Françoise* (1778) and by Antoine-Laurent de Jussieu (1748 to 1836), with his highly polished and successful *Genera Plantarum* of 1789 (see Stafleu, 1964).

In zoology, Georges Cuvier (1769 to 1832) and Lamarck (in his later days) provided the great impetus (see, e.g., Coleman, 1964). Around the turn of the century, therefore, the natural system came of age. In 1812 Cuvier proposed a classification of the animal kingdom based on what he considered the four essentially different plans of anatomical structure ("quatre plans généraux . . . d'après lesquels tous les animaux semblent avoir été modelés. . . ."): mollusks, radiates, articulates, and vertebrates (Cuvier, 1812). This was unquestionably the greatest step forward in animal classification since Aristotle. Cuvier was a convinced believer in divine intervention and also a steadfast defender of the Neoplatonic idealism in biology. In this respect, as well as in others, he was a typical eighteenth-century thinker, although his main work was done in the early decades of the nineteenth century. In assembling facts and in developing the natural system for zoology, however, Cuvier undoubtedly led the field for many years, even though, as Cain (1959) has shown, his approach contained many *a priori* elements and was, in that respect, theoretically behind that of Adanson. Cuvier (1817, 1:vi) describes the mutual influence of comparative anatomy and zoological systematics as follows:

> Je dus donc, et cette obligation me prit un temps considérable, je dus faire marcher de front l'anatomie et la zoologie, les dissections et le classement; chercher dans mes premieres remarques sur l'organisation, des distributions meilleures; m'en servir pour arriver à des remarques nouvelles; employer encore ces remarques à perfectionner les distributions; faire sortir enfin de cette fécondation mutuelle des deux sciences l'une par l'autre, un système zoologique propre à servir d'introducteur et de guide dans le champ de l'anatomie, et un corps de doctrine anatomique propre à servir de développement et d'explication au système zoologique.*

Buffon's challenging but vague ideas about speciation and evolution were further elaborated upon by Lamarck. After having had to abandon botany at the time of the reorganization of the Paris *Muséum d'Histoire Naturelle* because of his appointment to the chair of invertebrate zoology in 1793, Lamarck subjected the methods and classification used in zoology to an even more profound analysis than he had those of botany in 1778. Excellent observer, unbiased thinker, and hard worker, Lamarck produced an impressive series of studies that supplemented Cuvier's work in zoology. His *Système des Animaux sans Vertèbres* of 1801 was followed by his greater *Histoire Naturelle des Animaux sans Vertèbres* of 1815–1822. In addition, Lamarck developed a theory of evolution that he set forth in his *Philosophie Zoologique* of 1809. Even though highly controversial and in several respects erroneous, Lamarckism stimulated biological research and profoundly influenced systematic thinking. Lamarck's two basic laws were the rule of use and nonuse (lack of use of an organ causes it to disappear) and the inheritance of acquired changes, variations, or adaptations (Lamarck, 1809, 1:235).

Lamarck was one of the two originators of the word "biology," which was coined early in the century by Lamarck (1809, 1:xviii) and by the German L. C. Treviranus at about the same time. This change of terminology reflects change from natural history in the old, timeless view of nature, to the new dynamic view which recog-

*For an English translation see Agassiz (1857:213–214).

nizes the processes of change and evolution as characteristic of life. The change of name also reflects a limitation of the subject—natural history included the earth sciences (cf. Linnaeus, 1753); biology restricted itself to the life sciences. Whereas eighteenth-century natural history was still very much part of *la physique,* nineteenth-century biology constituted itself as an independent discipline.

In the first half of the nineteenth century the domination of aprioristic thinking—whether in terms of Aristotelian classificatory logic or of Platonic "plenitude"—gradually ebbed in face of the continuing stream of new information taken directly from nature. Travel increased, with the world wide open after the Napoleonic times, and better instruments (for instance, microscopical) became available for more detailed research. Biologists started to make great comprehensive inventories (see Stafleu, 1966c). In botany, I can refer to the great *Prodromus* of Augustin Pyrame and Alphonse de Candolle (1824–1873) and to the *Flora Brasiliensis* project of Carl F. P. von Martius; and in zoology there is the so-called "Disciples Edition" of Cuvier's *Le Règne Animal* (1836–1849). These undertakings were the first great cooperative international enterprises in biology. Then there came a great increase in teamwork, international contacts, the number of biologists, the exchange of museum specimens, and communications in general. The first half of the nineteenth century was one of feverish activity, of stocktaking, and of growth of knowledge. The great natural systems in botany and zoology took their ultimate shape.

However, the restive human mind could not be satisfied with stocktaking and with extension only of an essentially eighteenth-century natural system. The seeds of time consciousness sown by Buffon and Adanson and later by Lamarck had begun to germinate. Circumstances became more favorable for this germination through the explosive growth of knowledge of fossil remains. The growth of time consciousness was greatly stimulated by the rapid development of paleontology (e.g., Cuvier, 1821–1824) and of paleobotany (Brongniart, 1828, 1828–1837; Sternberg, 1820–1838; see also Stafleu, 1966d). As soon as the biologist becomes time conscious, his search for a time-based interpretation of the living world can start. This growing time consciousness put an end, at last, to the 23-century-old domination of the timeless Platonian principle of plenitude, of the fullness of the present world, which had been the basis of so much biological thinking.

The definitive introduction of the time dimension in biological thought, after some hesitant beginnings in the eighteenth century, gave a great impetus to even more purely inductive research and to a still less biased approach to nature. There were many early speculations and theories; and while most of these were incompletely based on fact, they often were extremely powerful in keeping minds on the move. I have already mentioned Lamarck and Lamarckism, but we can think also of the German nature-philosophy of the Oken type, and of the now perhaps somewhat antiquated ideas of men like Goethe. The Germans developed their *Entwicklungs-Geschichte,* in which it was often unclear whether *Verwandtschaft* was genetical relationship or formal affinity. Sometimes it was both, and sometimes only the latter. All these feverish movements played their parts. As a reaction against the purely speculative elements there arose a renewed emphasis on facts and on inductive research as embodied in Schleiden's *Grundzüge der Wissenschaftlichen Botanik* of 1842, which, in the second edition, carried an extra title as a slogan: *Die Botanik als inductive Wissenschaft Behandelt.* After the efforts of Cuvier, Brongniart, and Lamarck, France temporarily lost its supremacy in producing new ideas, and German science took the lead for the first time. Soon afterwards, England's scientists also assumed decisive roles.

In systematics, the first half of the century witnessed, therefore, a steady growth of the still timeless natural system; on the other hand, it witnessed an explosive eruption of speculative ideas and theories that had only a limited effect on systematics. Even so, this aftermath of the romantic movement was of great indirect importance. Physiology, phytochemistry, anatomy, and morphology developed rapidly, partly with the help of a new technology. Microscopic plants and animals came into the picture. For the first time, fungi and algae, as well as many groups of invertebrate animals, could be treated with success, thanks to the rapidly improving optical devices.

DARWIN AND AFTER

"Before and after Darwin" will always be the ante et post urbem conditam *of biological history. Before Darwin, the theory; after Darwin, the causes.*

—OSBORN

Our review comes now to the momentous year 1859, the year of the publication of Charles Darwin's *Origin of Species,* the year of the

Umwertung aller Werte in biology and, certainly, also in systematics. I have come on familiar ground now, so there is no need to explain how human thought was affected and how the face of biology was changed by this supreme crisis in biological thinking. Eighteenth-century "progress" had matured to nineteenth-century "evolution." In systematics, the natural systems based on formal affinities obtained overnight, as it were, real historical significance. In the enthusiasm of the first decades—an enthusiasm of which the traces are still recognizable in much modern writing—it was assumed that the natural system gave a true picture of phylogenetic reality.

By adding the time dimension so decisively to biological research, Darwin, and of course Wallace, had shown the intrinsic significance of what so far had been looked upon as only a blueprint of creation. Classification and its logical outcome, systematics, no longer needed to be purely formal. The first task now was the representation of the descent of recent living beings. The reproductive communities that we study now have emerged from former communities with different delimitations and other characteristics. Biologists soon became convinced that they had found in the natural system the system that was inherent in nature, that is, the system showing the phylogenetic relationships.

We now know that the simple transformation of formal affinities into historical relationship was not always correct. This transformation must take place with much feeling for gradual differences and shades of meaning and with a better knowledge of the mechanics of evolution. Darwinism, however, with its revolutionary élan and its daring statement of the problems, opened the way for modern genetics and experimental systematics.

I cannot pursue the development of the last century in any detail. It merits a paper of its own. When asked to give a historical account of systematics I hesitated between giving a more detailed review of the stormy developments of the century since Darwin, or one that would show how systematics grew until the beginning of what we can call modern systematics. Because I chose the latter course, I refer to a previous publication (Stafleu, 1966b) for a detailed account of developments since 1859. The so-called evolutionary systems of the first 50 or 60 years after Darwin, and even many of today, are based on an assessment of formal affinities, without experimental or fossil evidence, but seen in the light of this essential theory. It was only through the more refined methods of genetics developed after Mendel and de Vries in the 1920's that the third great step in the evolution of systematics was made—the step from description to experiment. The "new systematics" presented itself in the 1930's (Huxley, 1940), again with a great *Schwung* and with a somewhat overenthusiastic evaluation of the initial results. Yet, experimental cytological work and population analysis turned systematics into biosystematics (see, e.g., Mayr 1942, 1963; Stebbins 1950).

The development of the biological species concept played an essential role, more or less to be compared on the specific level to that of Darwin's theory of evolution for the whole of biology. Even if one cannot apply this biological species concept in particular cases (and there are many—think of the tropical floras and faunas), it provides a background for the biologist in the evaluation of his more "old-fashioned" characteristics and combinations of formal affinities. Formal systematics and biosystematics are logically contingent; one cannot merely translate the results from the one language into the other. However, we live in a contingent world (Lovejoy, 1960), and logical contingencies have often been extremely productive for the progress of science. We encountered such contingencies between classification in discrete units and the principle of plenitude, between pragmatic artificiality and idealistic natural systems, between formal affinities and phylogenetic views. All these conflicts of methods and approach fertilized the science of systematics. In the immediate past we have seen the birth of a new contingency—between the numerical approach and the biological approach. This is so much a feature of the present that I shall not include it in my review.

Present-day systematics is a fascinating science that derives its support from many new sources. A completely new dimension is given to it by molecular systematics, a revolutionary development that, later on, may well be seen to match the Darwinian revolution.

Systematics as a synthetic science is more than ever a science of the future.

REFERENCES

Adanson, M. 1757. Histoire naturelle du Sénégal. Paris. [Includes "Coquillages."]

Adanson, M. 1763. Familles des plantes. 2 vol. Paris.
Agassiz, L. 1857. An essay on classification. [Edward Lurie, ed. 1962. Cambridge, Massachusetts.]
Bauhin, C. 1623. Pinax theatri botanici. Basel.
Bremekamp, C. E. B. 1953a. A re-examination of Cesalpino's classification. Acta Bot. Neer. 1(4):580–593.
Bremekamp, C. E. B. 1953b. Linné's significance for the development of phytography. Taxon 2:47–54.
Bremekamp, C. E. B. 1953c. Linné's views on the hierarchy of the taxonomic groups. Acta Bot. Neer. 2(2):242–253.
Brongniart, A. T. 1828. Prodrome d'une histoire des végétaux fossiles. Paris.
Brongniart, A. T. 1828–1837. Histoire des végétaux fossiles. 2 vol. Paris.
Brunfels, O. 1530–1536. Herbarum vivae eicones. 3 vol. Strasbourg.
Buffon, G.-L. L., Comte de. 1749–1769. Histoire naturelle, générale et particulière, avec la description du Cabinet du Roi. 15 vol. Paris.
Cain, A. J. 1958. Logic and memory in Linnaeus's system of taxonomy. Proc. Linn. Soc. London 169:144–163.
Cain, A. J. 1959. Deductive and inductive methods in post-Linnaean taxonomy. Proc. Linn. Soc. London 170:185–217.
Candolle, A. P. de, and Alph. de Candolle. 1824–1873. Prodromus systematis naturalis regni vegetabilis. 17 vol. Paris.
Cassirer, E. 1951. The philosophy of the enlightenment. Princeton, Princeton University Press.
Cesalpino, A. 1583. De plantis libri XVI. Florence.
Clusius, C. (Charles de L'Escluse). 1601. Rariorum plantarum historia. Antwerpen.
Clusius, C. 1605. Exoticorum libri decem. Leiden.
Coleman, W. 1964. Georges Cuvier, zoologist. Cambridge, Mass., Harvard University Press.
Collingwood, R. G. 1945. The idea of nature. New York, Oxford University Press. [Reprinted 1961.]
Cuvier, G. L. C. F. D. 1812. Sur un nouveau rapprochement à établir entre les classes qui composent le règne animal. Ann. Mus. Hist. Nat. 19:73.
Cuvier, G. L. C. F. D. 1817. Le règne animal. 4 vol. Paris.
Cuvier, G. L. C. F. D. 1821–1824. Recherches sur les ossements fossiles. 4 vol. Paris.
Cuvier, G. L. C. F. D. 1836–1849. Le règne animal. 3rd ["Disciples"] ed. 17 vol. Paris.
Darwin, C. 1859. The origin of species by means of natural selection or the preservation of favoured races in the struggle for life. John Murray, London. [Facsimile ed. with introduction by E. Mayr. 1964. Cambridge, Massachusetts, Harvard University Press.]
Daubenton, L. M. M. 1753. *In* Buffon. 1749–1769. Histoire naturelle, générale et particulière, avec la description du Cabinet du Roi. Vol. 4.
Daudin, H. 1926. De Linné à Jussieu. Méthodes de la classification et idée de série en botanique et zoologie (1740–1790). Paris, Felix Alcan.

Dodoens, R. 1583. Stirpium historiae pemptades sex, sive libri XXX. Antwerpen.
Fuchs, L. 1542. De historia stirpium commentarii. Basel.
Huxley, J. [ed.]. 1940. The new systematics. London, Oxford University Press.
Jung. J. 1678. Isagoge phytoscopia, ut ab ipso privatis in collegiis auditoribus solita fuit tradi. Hamburg.
Jussieu, A. L. de. 1789. Genera plantarum. Paris.
Lamarck, J. B. P. A. M. de. 1778. Flore françois. 3 vol. Paris.
Lamarck, J. B. P. A. M. de. 1801. Système des animaux sans vertèbres. Paris.
Lamarck, J. B. P. A. M. de. 1809. Philosophie zoologique. 2 vol. Paris.
Lamarck, J. B. P. A. M. de. 1815–1822. Histoire naturelle des animaux sans vertèbres. 7 vol. Paris.
Leibniz, G. W. 1714. Principes de la nature et de la grâce.
Lindroth, S. 1966. Two centuries of Linnaean studies. *In* T. R. Buckram [ed] Bibliography and natural history. Lawrence, Kansas, University of Kansas Libraries.
Linnaeus, C. 1751. Philosophia botanica. Stockholm.
Linnaeus, C. 1753. Species plantarum. Stockholm.
Lovejoy, A. O. 1960. The great chain of being. New York and London (reprint). [First published 1936; Cambridge, Massachusetts, Harvard University Press.]
Magnol, P. 1689. Prodromus historiae generalis plantarum in quo familiae plantarum per tabulas disponuntur. Montpellier, France.
Mayr, E. 1942. Systematics and the origin of species from the viewpoint of a zoologist. New York; reprinted New York 1964, Columbia University Press.
Mayr, E. 1963. Animal species and evolution. Cambridge, Massachusetts, Harvard University Press.
Osborn, H. 1929. From the Greeks to Darwin. 2nd ed. New York, London.
Raven, C. E. 1950. John Ray, naturalist. 2nd ed. Cambridge, Cambridge University Press.
Ray, J. 1682. Methodus plantarum nova. London.
Ray, J. 1703. Methodus plantarum emendata et aucta. London.
Stafleu, F. A. 1963. Adanson and the "Familles des plantes," p. 123–264. *In* G. H. M. Lawrence [ed.] Adanson 1:123–264. Pittsburgh, Hunt Botanical Library.
Stafleu, F. A. 1964. Introduction to Jussieu's Genera plantarum. *In* A. L. Jussieu, Genera plantarum, Paris 1789; facsimile reprint Weinheim.
Stafleu, F. A. 1966a. F. A. W. Miquel, Netherlands botanist. Amsterdam [Wentia 16:1–95], North Holland Publishing Company.
Stafleu, F. A. 1966b. Tasten of tellen. Een eeuw theorie en praktijk in de plantensystematiek. Amsterdam.
Stafleu, F. A. 1966c. The great Prodromus. *In* A. P. et Alph. de Candolle, Prodromus, facsimile edition. Lehre J. Cramer.
Stafleu, F. A. 1966d. Brongniart's Histoire des végétaux fossiles. Taxon 15:320–324.
Stearn, W. T. 1957. An introduction to the Species Plantarum and cognate

botanical works of Carl Linnaeus. *In* C. Linnaeus, Species plantarum, Ray Society facsimile edition, Vol. 1. London, Ray Society.
Stearn, W. T. 1959. The background of Linnaeus's contributions to the nomenclature and methods of systematic biology. Syst. Zool. 8:1–22.
Stebbins, G. L., Jr. 1950. Variation and evolution in plants, New York, Columbia University Press.
Sternberg, K. M. von. 1820–1838. Versuch einer geognostisch-botanischen Darstellung der Flora der Vorwelt. Leipzig, Praha, Regensburg.
Tournefort, J. Pitton de. 1694. Élements de botanique, ou méthode pour connoître les plantes. 3 vol. Paris.
Vines, S. H. 1913. Robert Morison and John Ray, p. 8–43. *In* F. W. Oliver. Makers of British botany. Cambridge, Cambridge University Press.

MICHAEL T. GHISELIN

The Principles and Concepts of Systematic Biology

Authors who have written whole volumes on the topic assigned to me include Hennig (1950); Mayr *et al.* (1968); Remane (1952); and Simpson (1961). In order to do some justice to the title, I will treat some principles and concepts that sorely need to be clarified but that are so fundamental that their analysis should be applicable to a wide variety of important problems in systematic theory. The present discussion, therefore, will be limited to two basic concepts: the natural system and the character.

The expression "natural system" had a very special meaning to such Aristotelians as Linnaeus (Cain, 1956, 1962). It had to do with the so-called essential natures of the things classified. But such older views are not particularly relevant to the present analysis, because their metaphysical basis, the doctrine of essences, has gradually lost support (Hull, 1965). With the growth of nineteenth-century empiricism, different attitudes toward the structure of the universe brought about a change in usage. This conception is clearly expressed by John Stuart Mill (1874:466–467):

> The ends of scientific classification are best answered when the objects are formed into groups respecting which a greater number of general propositions can be made, and those propositions more important, than could be made respecting any other groups into which the same things could be distributed.

A substantial proportion of contemporary systematists probably would support this position, at least as a general statement of aims. But the statement is vague. It may be interpreted in several ways, and many qualifications are needed.

One difficulty with Mill's view is the problem of how to decide whether a proposition is "important" or not. A widely accepted interpretation is that the propositions must be empirical. This is not quite the same as to say that they should be "general." The term "empirical" would exclude propositions about the classifier or his opinions. Classification should relate to something we discover, not something we read into the data. As Darwin (1859:411) puts it, "This classification is not arbitrary, like the groupings of the stars in constellations." But this stricture is not always observed. Thus, Gilmour (1940:472) says:

A natural classification is that grouping which endeavors to utilize *all* the attributes of the individuals under consideration, and is hence useful for a very wide range of purposes.

One might object that a system is natural not if it *endeavors* to utilize all attributes (whatever that means) but if it *succeeds.* A rich man is not one who *tries* to accumulate wealth. This distinction underlies a basic difference in metaphysical outlook. In biological research, we generally are able to sidestep questions concerning ultimate reality. It is easy, therefore, to overlook the effect of metaphysical ideas on scientific thinking. Nonetheless, it is easy to find basic metaphysical disagreements underlying ostensibly scientific controversies over taxonomic principles. It is impossible to avoid metaphysics altogether—to deny metaphysics is itself a metaphysical position. The scientist's best defense is to know and be aware of the problems, avoid the pitfalls, and adopt a critical point of view.

Many of us would be inclined to reject Gilmour's basic metaphysical premise. Gilmour is a *phenomenalist:* he identifies things (*noumena*) with sense impressions (*phenomena*). This is why he says (Gilmour, 1940:464):

For example, the object which we call a chair consists partly of a number of experienced sense-data such as colours, shapes, and other qualities, and partly of the concept *chair* which reason has constructed to "clip" these data together.

And again, two pages later:

It should never be forgotten, however, that the individual is a concept, a rational construction from sense-data, and that the latter are the real objective material of classification.

Many biologists doubtless would prefer to maintain that the objective material of classification is not sense impressions but organisms and populations. In adhering to a philosophical idea, one ought to be consistent and carry the idea to its logical conclusion.

Few biologists are likely to accept all the consequences of phenomenalism, yet many do tend to confuse statements about the data of classification with statements about matters of fact. There is clearly an ambiguity when Sneath (1962:292) says that natural taxa are those that "are based on as many features as possible." He seems to maintain that a natural system is a system having the inductive support of as many characters as the taxonomist can accumulate. "Natural," therefore is predicated of the nature of the sample and has nothing to do with the objectively real relationships. Such a statement does not necessarily assert that a natural system corresponds to any set of propositions–about the organisms themselves–that are materially true or false.

The importance of drawing a distinction between the data and the facts is seen readily when it is realized that, in attacking phylogenetic taxonomy, Sokal (1962) and others have asserted that it is difficult, if not impossible, to know whether a system is based on phylogeny. But the issue they raise is not one of the system's being *supported by* phylogeny but rather of its *corresponding to* phylogeny. Opponents of evolutionary taxonomy have presupposed two contradictory metaphysical theories in defending their own views, on the one hand, and in attacking those of their colleagues, on the other. In defense, they use a coherence theory of truth (i.e., if it is consistent, it is true); in offense, they use a correspondence theory (it is true if it mirrors objective reality). Likewise, an equally incompatible element of pragmatic metaphysics (if it works, it is true) is embraced wherever it seems expedient (as in Gilmour's definition of "natural"). Such maneuvers are unfair, to say the least, and the resulting philosophies may be dismissed as self-contradictory.

Being logically consistent has distinct advantages. If a correspondence criterion is consistently adhered to, the issue of whether a system is phylogenetic resolves to a very simple distinction. When a phylogeneticist says that a system is phylogenetic, he usually means that the hierarchy, or system of classes, is so arranged as to emphasize branching sequences (clades) rather than evolutionary levels (grades). Or he may mean, unless he is mistaken, that he has succeeded in handling the data so as to distinguish between clades and convergent or parallel groups. Thus, analytical philosophy is of considerable utility to the working biologist, as it provides a tool for dealing with the effects of verbal confusion. Misunderstandings about language underlie most of the controversies in systematic theory.

I hope I am not being unfair when I say that those who reject, as a defining property of "natural," some kind of correspondence to an order independent of the sample of data have ulterior motives. They want so to define their terms that whatever they say is true by definition. But to say that "natural system" means "the system that I have devised" is to lose sight of the goals of science—to generalize beyond what is obviously implicit in the data.

When a correspondence theory is presupposed, at least two interpretations of "natural" are likely to be put forth. The system would correspond to either phylogeny or over-all similarity. The first major use of "natural," the phylogenetic criterion, is frequently modified to mean "evolutionary" in a broad sense, not just "genealogical" (Mayr, 1965; Gisin, 1964). Some version of an evolutionary system is widely accepted, at least as an ideal, but any variety of evolutionary properties may be included. It is only for reasons of theoretical importance, however, that nonevolutionary relationships are not made part of our natural classifications. An arrangement of organisms on a purely ecological basis would fit the definition of "natural," and the notion of natural classification is applicable to nonbiological systems, as in the periodic table of the elements, which correspond to chemical laws. There is no contradiction. A system is natural if it corresponds to some empirical relationships. One might add that "natural" does not admit of degrees of naturalness, although a system may contain both natural and artificial elements.

The second main use of "natural system" would have to be a correspondence with "over-all similarity." It has as its basic rationale the notion of a proportion of logically possible "general propositions" (Mill, 1874) or of attributes. In an earlier work (Ghiselin, 1966) I argued that this is a nonsensical idea. There is no "over-all similarity" because things are not similar "over all" but only "over some." And if it is true, as Mayr (1965:75-76) says, that both pheneticists and evolutionary taxonomists "agree that natural taxa are those that share the greatest number of attributes," then both groups are seriously deluded. When we say that two things are similar, we mean that they share certain attributes or characters. But the relation of similarity must have all its terms supplied, and words such as "over-all" and "the greatest number" simply do not suffice. "John is similar to" obviously means nothing. "John is similar to Mary" also is nonsense, although we tend to read some meaning into it. Only statements like "John is similar to Mary in that both are English" have meaning. Only if there were a finite number of characters or attributes could we refer to a similarity in any but an explicitly designated sample of them. There is no objectively real number of attributes (cf. Wittgenstein, 1961:57). That is a figment of the imagination.

Evidently the notion that a finite number of attributes exists results from an equivocation: the word "character" is used in a variety of ways (for another, cf. Michener and Sokal, 1957). Usually, "character" designates attributes–for example, "white." On the other hand, it may mean a thing, such as a leg or other tangible object of which the attribute is predicated. Sometimes this ambiguity gives no trouble, as in Whitten's paper entitled "The Tracheal System as a Systematic Character in Larval Diptera" (1959). Here, it is obvious what is meant. The mere possibility of a logical error is no evidence that the error has been, or must be, committed. This point frequently has been overlooked, as in Sokal's (1962:246) assertion that phylogenetic systematics involves circular reasoning.*

Yet there are instances where the equivocation has had adverse effects. Plate (1914), for instance, argued that the number of characters used in a study is unimportant, on the grounds that Pilsbry's excellent classification of chitons used only one character, the shell. But Pilsbry actually used many attributes of the single organ. Another example is the numerous arguments over the relative significance of so-called adaptive and nonadaptive characters, which are largely verbal disputes. Parts, such as the nervous system, generally are thought to have adaptive significance. But attributes predicated of those parts–for example, that the nervous system is dorsal or ventral–may reasonably be thought irrelevant to the function of the adaptive part.

*It is clearly an erroneous conception of circularity that led Sokal (1962:246) to assert that circular reasoning is involved when phylogenetic hypotheses are used to support relationships "which in turn yield judgments concerning the phylogenetic relationships of other structures and forms." The word "other" vitiates the argument.

Sibley (1962:115) clearly saw that there is a problem with respect to the word "character," for he says:

Usually it means an item in a given list of measured or otherwise characterized units but one person may treat a structure as one character while another applies calipers to a dozen different dimensions of the same structure and emerges with 12 characters.

This basically correct analysis may be carried further, and to do so casts doubt on one of Sibley's other views—namely, his apparent identification of the characters of systematics (which are attributes) with the mutons, and the like, of molecular biology (which are particular things). At least the following quotations (Sibley, 1962:108–109) seem to presuppose something more than a correspondence between some entities of both types: "The *sequence* of the amino acid links in a protein chain is the only genetically determined property of a protein." And: "The ultimate method would be the determination of the complete sequences for all the proteins produced by each species, for this would be a complete genetic description of the species." Clearly, a protein has a percentage composition in the whole organism, position effects exist, and a complete description of a species would have to include its biogeography.

Evidently the numerical pheneticists' notion of "over-all similarity" derives from the same false premise. Sneath (1957:186), for example, says:

The use of "number of features" may also be justified on the grounds that quantitative differences depend ultimately on qualitative differences in genes or in nucleotides to which the concept of number is applicable.

The conclusion does not follow; the argument is an instance of the fallacy of accident. Every man is the progeny of a parent to whom the attribute of being female applies. But this does not imply that all men are female. We can refer, meaningfully, to a number of parts of a given kind, but not to an abstract number of parts, or of attributes that might be predicated of such parts.

Actually, the confusion runs even deeper. Many students of taxonomic theory have failed to distinguish between *intrinsic* and *relational* properties, or without good reason they have preferred the former. A tooth's whiteness is an intrinsic property; its being homologous to other ectodermal structures is a relational property. There seems to be a natural prejudice for intrinsic properties in classification; this preference amounts to a metaphysical position. Some of the resistance to phylogenetic classification is due to the fact that an organism's genealogy is a relational, not an intrinsic, property. Much the same may be said of some (but not all) objections to the biological species definition. A "morphological species" is a set of things, each with a given set of intrinsic properties. A biological species is a group of things-in-relation.

Again, we may note how little this symposium deals with paleontology and biogeography—that is, with temporal and spatial relations, which are, in fact, a very important aspect of systematics. It is revealing, too, to note that some of the so-called "cladists" (Hennig, 1950; Kiriakoff, 1952; Crowson, 1965) are deeply concerned with biogeography. As a clade is more predictive of geographical distribution patterns than a grade, we can understand their attitude. Again, the arguments over how to delineate the class Mammalia (Bigelow, 1961; Olson, 1959; Reed, 1960; Simpson, 1959, 1960; Van Valen, 1960) reflect little more than different metaphysical attitudes toward relational properties. There is no logical reason why classification systems should not correspond to both kinds of attributes. It is true, as Hull (1964), especially, has pointed out, that the Linnaean hierarchy is not well suited to express cladistic relationships. But auxiliary devices, such as the "numericlature" of Hull (1966) may be used, and systematics is more inclusive than the formal hierarchy that epitomizes some of its generalizations. We may see a further inclination toward relational properties in the use of evolutionary trends in determining categorical rank (Edmunds, 1962; Gisin, 1966; Inger, 1958).

The metaphysical prejudice against relational properties does far more than affect our classification systems. It generates a fundamentally erroneous picture of the logic of inference in systematics. To avoid misunderstandings, it seems reasonable to express my great optimism for the future of molecular systematics. However, its value derives largely from its wealth of detail, not from its exhausting the full scope of biologically significant attributes. A whole spectrum of relational properties is scarcely affected by it. Historical nexes may be abstracted from biogeography, from the temporal succession of fossils, and from synecological relations, such as parasitology. DNA is not ultimate reality, and biology is not just a branch of chemistry, any more than architecture is merely the study of building materials. Likewise, Sokal and Sneath (1963) contradict themselve when in one place (p. 56–57) they say that phylogenetic classifications are based on phenetic evidence, which they identify with the genome (p. 64), and elsewhere (p. 94) affirm the relevance of distribution to phylogeny and admit that biogeography need not "represent any character in the genotype." Again, it is clearly incorrect that ". . .both phylogenists and classical taxonomists base their classifications on those similarities that are expressed in shared, constantly correlated character complexes. . . ." (Mayr, 1965:75). Although Mayr informs me that he did not intend to support this view, it has been widely advocated (Danser, 1950:135; Sneath, 1961:124–126; Remane, 1952:12). Let us put the argument for this notion into the form of a syllogism:

All systems of phylogenists and classical taxonomists are classifications.
Some systems of phylogenists and classical taxonomists are based on phenetic data alone.
All classifications are based on phenetic data alone.

But consider this counterexample:

All coins are money.
Some coins are made of copper.
All money is made of copper.

Just as the existence of silver or paper money refutes the counterexample, the existence of *even one* biogeographical or other nonphenetic premise in an argument for a phylogeny refutes the notion that all classification is necessarily phenetic. As the inductive support for a classification may be derived from a single logical system, it is clear that the biogeographical and paleontological support for our placement of one form may have an effect on the way we treat any other. The main objection to biogeography and paleontology has been that it is more convenient to begin with morphology (Borgmeier, 1957: 62). But this argument is based on a confusion between logical priority and temporal succession (Ghiselin, 1966).

Far more important, we lose sight of the fact that not all the inductive support for a phylogenetic inference need consist of attributes. Laws of nature occur as premises in arguments for phylogenies. This fact flatly refutes the widely expressed (Sokal and Sneath, 1963;

Danser, 1950; Remane, 1952) notion that "Darwin did not bring any new methodological ideas into taxonomy" (Lubischew, 1963:423). This view is contradicted so obviously by the changed manner of dealing with rudimentary structures (Darwin, 1859:486; 1851; 1854; 1877) that one wonders why it was ever taken seriously. With the concept of descent through modification by natural selection, it became possible (but not inevitable) to abandon the notion of systematics as merely "putting together those things that resemble each other most, all their characters being taken into consideration" (Cain, 1962:9). Rather, the systematist constructs a hypothetical model of evolutionary processes and events and tests it by its predictive capacity, by its coherence, and by its consistency with laws of nature (Mayr, 1965:75, 77). This process, the modern, hypothetico-deductive scientific method, is the basis of inference in all sciences, whether historical or not (Popper, 1965; Cohen and Nagel, 1934).

In spite of assertions that systematists work by intuition, there are now—and have long existed—sound, objective canons of evidence. Much unfortunate controversy has resulted because, in distinction to such other historical sciences as geology and comparative linguistics, little effort has been made to render these principles explicit. The present symposium, as may be particularly well seen in the contribution by Bock (see page 411), has provided an admirable opportunity to help fill this need.

ACKNOWLEDGMENTS

Support for this research was provided by the Ford Foundation through a grant to the Systematics-Ecology Program, of which this is Contribution No. 116. The criticisms of M. R. Carriker, D. L. Hull, Ernst Mayr, and T. J. M. Schopf are gratefully acknowledged.

REFERENCES

Bigelow, R. S. 1961. Higher categories and phylogeny. Syst. Zool. 10:86–91.
Borgmeier, T. 1957. Basic questions of systematics. Syst. Zool. 6:53–69.
Cain, A. J. 1956. The genus in evolutionary taxonomy. Syst. Zool. 5:97–109.
Cain, A. J. 1962. The evolution of taxonomic principles, p. 1–13.
In G. C. Ainsworth and P. H. A. Sneath, Microbial classification: Twelfth

symposium of the Society for General Microbiology held at the Royal Institution, London, April 1962. Cambridge University Press, Cambridge.

Cohen, M. R., and E. Nagel. 1934. An introduction to logic and scientific method. Harcourt, Brace and Co., New York. 467 p.

Crowson, R. A. 1965. Classification, statistics and phylogeny. Syst. Zool. 14:144–148.

Danser, B. H. 1950. A theory of systematics. Bibl. Biotheor. 4:117–180.

Darwin, C. 1851. A monograph on the sub-class Cirripedia, with figures of all the species. The Lepadidae; or pedunculated cirripedes. Ray Society, London. 400 p.

Darwin, C. 1854. A monograph on the sub-class Cirripedia, with figures of all the species. The Balanidae (or sessile cirripedes); the Verrucidae, etc., etc. Ray Society, London. 684 p.

Darwin, C. 1859. On the origin of species by means of natural selection, or the preservation of favoured races in the struggle for life. John Murray, London. 490 p.

Darwin, C. 1877. The various contrivances by which orchids are fertilised by insects. 2nd ed. D. Appleton, New York. 300 p.

Edmunds, G. F., Jr. 1962. The principles applied in determining the hierarchic level of the higher categories of Ephemeroptera. Syst. Zool. 11:22–31.

Ghiselin, H. T. 1966. On psychologism in the logic of taxonomic controversies. Syst. Zool. 15:207–215.

Gilmour, J. S. L. 1940. Taxonomy and philosophy, p. 461–474. *In* J. Huxley, The new systematics. Clarendon, Oxford.

Gisin, H. 1964. Synthetische theorie der Systematik. Z. Zool. Syst. Evolutionsforsch. 2:1–17.

Gisin, H. 1966. Signification des modalités d' évolution pour la theorie de la systematique. Z. Zool. Syst. Evolutionsforsch. 4:1–12.

Hennig, W. 1950. Grundzüge einer theorie der phylogenetischen Systematik. Deutscher Zentralverlag, Berlin. 370 p.

Hull, D. L. 1964. Consistency and monophyly. Syst. Zool. 13:1–11.

Hull, D. L. 1965. The effect of essentialism on taxonomy—two thousand years of stasis. I, II. Brit. J. Phil. Sci. 15:314–326, 16:1–18.

Hull, D. L. 1966. Phylogenetic numericlature. Syst. Zool. 15:14–17.

Inger, R. F. 1958. Comments on the definition of genera. Evolution 12:370–384.

Kiriakoff, S. G. 1952. L'usage des catégories taxonomiques intermédiaires dans la classification. Ann. Soc. Roy. Zool. Belgique 83:87–106.

Lubischew, A. A. 1963. On some contradictions in general taxonomy and evolution. Evolution 17:414–430.

Mayr, E. 1965. Numerical phenetics and taxonomic theory. Syst. Zool. 14:73–91.

Mayr, E., E. G. Linsley, and R. L. Usinger. 1968. Methods and principles of systematic zoology. 2nd ed. McGraw-Hill, New York.

Michener, C. D., and R. R. Sokal. 1957. A quantitative approach to a problem in classification. Evolution 11:130–162.

Mill, J. S. 1874. A system of logic, ratiocinative and inductive, being a connected view of the principles of evidence and the methods of scientific investigation. 8th ed. Longmans Green and Co., London. 622 p.

Olson, E. C. 1959. The evolution of mammalian characters. Evolution 13:344–353.

Plate, L. 1914. Prinzipien der Systematik mit besonderer Berücksichtigung der Systems der Tiere, p. 92–164. *In* P. Hinneberg, Die Kultur der Gegenwart, 3 Teil, 4 Abt., Vol. 4. Teubner, Leipzig.

Popper, K. R. 1965. The logic of scientific discovery. 3rd ed. Harper & Row, New York. 480 p.

Reed, C. A. 1960. Polyphyletic or monophyletic ancestry of mammals, or, What is a class? Evolution 14:314–322.

Remane, A. 1952. Die Grundlagen des naturlichen Systems, der vergleichenden Anatomie und der Phylogenetik. 2nd ed. Geest and Portig, Leipzig. 364 p.

Sibley, C. G. 1962. The comparative morphology of protein molecules as data for classification. Syst. Zool. 11:108–118.

Simpson, G. G. 1959. Mesozoic mammals and the polyphyletic origin of mammals. Evolution 13:405–414.

Simpson, G. G. 1960. Diagnoses of the classes Reptilia and Mammalia. Evolution 14:388–392.

Simpson, G. G. 1961. Principles of animal taxonomy. Columbia University Press, New York. 247 p.

Sneath, P. H. A. 1957. Some thoughts on bacterial classification. J. Gen. Microbiol. 17:184–200.

Sneath, P. H. A. 1961. Recent developments in theoretical and quantitative taxonomy. Syst. Zool. 10:118–139.

Sneath, P. H. A. 1962. The construction of taxonomic groups, p. 289–332. *In* G. C. Ainsworth and P. H. A. Sneath, Microbial classification: Twelfth symposium of the Society for General Microbiology held at the Royal Institution, London, April 1962. Cambridge University Press, Cambridge.

Sokal, R. R. 1962. Typology and empiricism in taxonomy. J. Theoret. Biol. 3:230-267.

Sokal, R. R., and P. H. A. Sneath. 1963. Principles of numerical taxonomy. W. H. Freeman and Co., San Francisco. 359 p.

Van Valen, L. 1960. Therapsids as mammals. Evolution 14:304–313.

Whitten, J. H. 1959. The tracheal system as a systematic character in larval Diptera. Syst. Zool. 8:130–139.

Wittgenstein, L. 1961. Tractatus logico-philosophicus. Routledge and Kegan Paul, London. 166 p.

Discussion

David L. Hull

THE NATURAL SYSTEM AND THE SPECIES PROBLEM

In 1940 J. S. L. Gilmour ("Taxonomy and Philosophy," in *The New Systematics,* p. 468) characterized a natural classification as follows:

> To sum up, starting from basic epistemological considerations, we are led to the view that a natural classification of living things is one which groups together individuals having a large number of attributes in common, whereas an artificial classification is composed of groups having only a small number of common attributes; further, that a natural classification can be used for a wide range of purposes, whereas an artificial classification is useful only for the limited purpose for which it was constructed; and lastly that both types are created by the classifier for the purpose of making inductive generalizations regarding living things.

The basic epistemological considerations of which Gilmour speaks are those of sense-data phenomenalism. One of the consequences of phenomenalism that biologists are unlikely to accept is that it makes intersubjectivity and, hence, objectivity of scientific knowledge impossible. But much of what Gilmour says about taxonomy is independent of his epistemology.

An important element in Gilmour's characterization of natural classification and one that is often ignored by his followers is that the purpose of constructing a classification is to permit the formation of inductive generalizations. As Ghiselin has pointed out, J. S. Mill (*Logic,* 1843:466–467) expressed a similar view almost a hundred years earlier. He too emphasized that the properties "according to which objects are classified should, if possible, be those which are causes of many other properties." Of the many properties that could be used to construct a classification, those causally connected to many others are the most fruitful because they group the elements of the classification into classes whose names function not only in the most inductive generalizations but in the most theoretically significant generalizations (Carl G. Hempel, 1965, *Aspects of Scientific Explanation,* 139, 156). In biology these generalizations are biological laws. There are many possible natural classifications—classifications that reflect empirical relations. The preferred classification is the one that provides concepts that function in the most pervasive biological theories. A contemporary logician, Irving M.

Copi (1954, "Essences and Accidents," *The Journal of Philosophy,* 706–719) stated the preference as follows:

The scientist's sorting or classifying of objects is relative to this interest, which is not well served by classifying things on the basis of properties which are either most obvious or most immediately practical. It is better served by classifying things in terms of properties which are relevant to the framing of a maximum number of causal laws and the formation of explanatory theories.

Thus, I think the proposal to classify according to something called "over-all phenetic similarity" at this stage in the history of biology is misdirected (Sokal and Sneath, 1963, *Principles of Numerical Taxonomy,* 11; Donald H. Colless, 1967, "An Examination of Certain Concepts in Phenetic Taxonomy," *Systematic Zoology,* 16:15). Of course, in the absence of any biological theories, a taxonomist can only classify as neutrally as possible, hoping that his classification will be useful. But when highly confirmed and powerful biological theories (like the evolutionary and genetic theories) are available, taxonomists cannot ignore them without frustrating the purpose of science. Perhaps an analogous example might help. When physicians were largely ignorant of the etiology of diseases, their classifications were largely descriptive and symptomatological. As the etiology of various diseases became better known, medical classifications became increasingly more theoretical and, hence, scientifically more significant (Hempel, 1965:140; R. R. Sokal, 1963, "Numerical Taxonomy and Disease Classification," *The Diagnostic Process*). Similarly, with the development of evolutionary and genetic theories, the scientifically neutral (but metaphysically committed) morphological definition of species has given way to a scientifically committed definition—a definition that is expressed in terms of reproductive isolation, gene pools, and evolutionary unity.

Scientists have a strong desire to get their work *done*—a desire for a degree of stability and closure that is incompatible with the growth, and occasional abandonment, of scientific theories (A. J. Cain, 1958, "Logic and Memory in Linnaeus's System of Taxonomy," *Proc. Linn. Soc. London,* 169:147). If scientific classifications and, hence, scientific concepts could be made theoretically neutral, they would remain stable and unchanging in the midst of all these fluctuations; but they would also become, thereby, scientifically useless. The meaning of words like "species," "gene," and "electron" have fluctuated widely as the theories in which they are embedded have continued to grow. This is the price of scientific significance. It would be a blatant case of premature closure to legislate operational definitions of such theoretically significant terms as "species" and "gene" now that evolutionary and genetic theories are in the midst of a great synthesis.

UNIT CHARACTERS AND GENETIC THEORY

Since the adherents of the various schools of taxonomy have begun to make use of the increased precision permitted by numerical techniques, the problem of just what is to be regarded as a unit character can no longer be ignored. It is beginning to vie with the species problem for attention. Sokal, Sneath, and other numerically minded taxonomists have realized that if character determination is not made precise and objective, much of the precision and objectivity of numerical methods of evaluation is lost. For this reason, they have addressed themselves to the problem of defining "unit character." These efforts are interesting in two respects: first, Sokal and Sneath seem to presuppose a metaphysics called logical atomism; second, they have sought recourse to a scientific theory.

Sokal and Sneath (1963) provide two definitions of unit character: one is theoretical, and the other is a working definition. The theoretical definition is that a unit character is "an attribute possessed by an organism about which one statement can be made, thus yielding a single piece of information." According to logical atomists, the world of our senses is analyzable into atomic facts and discourse into atomic sentences. Each atomic sentence is to express a single atomic fact. Atomic facts in turn are analyzable only into objects and atomic sentences into names. These objects and names are held to be absolutely simple. Each name simply denotes an object (Ludwig Wittgenstein, 1928, *Tractatus Logico-Philosophicus*). The logical atomists could never give any examples of these atomic facts or objects; but, from purely metaphysical considerations, there *must* be such facts and objects. Similarly, Sokal and Sneath (1963:72) say:

It is somewhat embarassing to find that within the concept of natural taxonomic groups there are similar concepts of natural organ groups, and we may question whether there are not yet other concepts (such as natural gene groups) concealed within these, like a nest of Chinese boxes. There must, however, be some limit to this process, even if the limit lies at the fine structure of the genes.

The "must" in the preceding quotation sounds very much like a metaphysical must. The important issue is, however, whether the units that must exist are to be absolutely simple, as the logical atomists maintained, or whether something less will do. If the history of philosophy during the last 50 years has anything to teach, it is that the quest for absolute simples is futile. All that can be hoped for are temporary units–units that are treated as simple only for the purposes of a particular study. Perhaps this is what Sokal and Sneath intend; if so, then we may leave off talking of such abtruse matters and return to issues more directly relevant to taxonomy.

Sokal and Sneath tentatively identify unit characters with the units of the genetic code. I think this is a promising move. If evolutionists are justified in making "species" a theoretical term in evolutionary theory, then the pheneticists are justified in making "unit character" a theoretical term in genetic theory. As Ghiselin has pointed out, however, the interactions of these genetic units with each other and with the environment are likely to present formidable difficulties. In addition, it should be noticed that in making "unit character" a theoretical term all the same kinds of instability and openness that the pheneticists deplore in evolutionary classification will be introduced into their classifications. For example, evolutionists divide a single morphological species into two separate sibling species if these two groups have had different evolutionary developments. Similarly, if the pheneticists are serious in what they say concerning DNA, then the same chemical structure would have to be treated as two separate unit characters if it results in some specimens from one biochemical pathway and in others from a different pathway.

Convergence and its associated problems are not confined to biology or even to empirical science. It presents analogous problems in game theory. For example, R. Duncan Luce and Howard Raiffa (1967, *Games and Decisions,* p. 41) say:

A connected graph consists of a collection of points (called nodes or vertices) and branches between certain pairs of nodes such that a path can be traced out from each point to every other point. A graph may have closed loops of branches. . . . A connected graph with no such loops of branches is called a *tree.* The graph of a game is a tree, which is called a *game tree.* It may not seem reasonable to assume the graph of a game is a tree, for in such games as chess the same arrangements of pieces on the board can be arrived at by several different routes which appears to mean that closed loops of branches can exist. However, in game theory we choose to consider two moves as different moves if they have different past histories, even if they have exactly the same possible future moves and outcomes.

Game theorists, evolutionists, and pheneticists have all made the same decision concerning convergence. In game theory if two moves have different past histories, then they are different moves, even if they have exactly the same possible future moves and outcomes. In evolutionary theory if two taxa have different evolutionary histories, then they are different taxa, even if they might be similar overall. In phenetic theory if two characters have different biochemical histories, then they are different characters, even if they are otherwise observationally identical. Like it or not, pheneticists have become theoretical scientists! Sokal and Sneath certainly have not said the final word on the subject of unit characters, but they have made an important first step in solving the problem. They have provided a theoretically significant definition of an important term in taxonomy.

OPERATIONAL DEFINITIONS

Numerical taxonomists have placed considerable emphasis on operational definitions. In fact, one of their main criticisms of traditional taxonomy is that it is not "operational," a term that is fast becoming an honorific title to be brandished in contemporary biology as was the phrase "inductive method" in Darwin's day. Exactly what operationists mean by "operational" is hard to pin down. There is both a strong and a weak thesis of operationism. If operationism is merely the thesis that scientific terms must have *some* empirical content or that scientific statements must be at least *partially* confirmable, then it is unobjectionable (Sokal and Camin, 1965, "The Two Taxonomies: Areas of Agreement and Conflict," *Systematic Zoology* 14:179). But on this weak thesis there is no reason to reject such terms as "blood relationship," "subspecies," and "homology" as being non-operational. The rejection of these and other terms follows only from the strong operationist thesis that scientific terms must have *nothing but* completely specifiable empirical content or that scientific statements must be *totally* confirmable or verifiable.

There are many objections to this strong thesis, but the principal one is that no theoretical term or theoretical statement can meet such stringent standards—including those in physics. Strong operationism is incompatible with theoretical science. Operationists are correct in emphasizing the empirical content of scientific terms, but they are mistaken in ignoring their systematic or theoretical import. As C. G. Hempel (1965:146) has observed:

> . . . clear and objective criteria of application [which operational definitions are formulated to provide] are not enough: to be scientifically useful a concept must lend itself to the formulation of general laws or theoretical principles which reflect uniformities in the subject matter under study, and which thus provide a basis for explanation, prediction, or generally scientific understanding.

The importance of empirical laws in the formulation of natural classifications is again forced upon us. Strict operationism is incompatible with the construction of a classification that can offer any hope of being natural. To conclude these brief and obviously unenthusiastic remarks on operationism, I can find no better statement than that made by P. W. Bridgman (1954, "The Present State of Operationalism," in *The Validation of Scientific Theories,* p. 74) as he looked back over the history of his brainchild and admitted:

> . . . I feel that I have created a Frankenstein, which has certainly got away from me. I abhor the word *operationalism* or *operationism,* which seems to imply a dogma, or at least a thesis of some kind. The thing that I have envisaged is too simple to be dignified by so pretentious a name.

Discussion

Hermann Gisin

As I have no training in philosophy, I do not feel competent to discuss philosophical arguments. I agree with Dr. Ghiselin, however, that misunderstandings underlie a major portion of controversies in systematic theory. As a biologist, I feel obliged to clarify the situation on the basis of biological facts.

Dr. Ghiselin stresses the importance of cladistics, which is one of the two basic kinds of evolutionary events. Indeed, synthetic theory of evolution distinguishes (a) splitting by reproductive isolation or cladogenesis and (b) progression by natural selection or anagenesis. The former process predominates in some lineages (the clades), the latter in others (the grades). Dr. Ghiselin says "the phylogenetic criterion is frequently modified to mean 'evolutionary' in a broad sense." I shall not try to specify who modified what in this respect.

In fact, the use of the word "phylogeny" has become so ambiguous that I shall avoid it altogether.

Cladistics frequently is misunderstood because it is not fully realized that classifications based either in clades or on grades alone generally are completely different. So crocodiles belong to the reptilian grade, but form a clade together with birds. The difference is comparable to that between so-called vertical and horizontal classifications.

Another misunderstanding concerning cladistics is the belief, held by many taxonomists, that cladogenies cannot be known without a complete fossil record. Methods of deducing branching sequences in cladogenesis, based on contemporaneous species, have been developed independently by several authors (W. Hennig, 1965, "Phylogenetic Systematics," *Ann. Rev. Ent.* 10:97–116; E. Wilson, 1965, "A Consistency Test for Phylogenies Based on Contemporaneous Species," *Syst. Zool.* 14:214–220; J. H. Camin and R. R. Sokal, 1965, "A Method for Deducing Branching Sequences in Phylogeny," *Evolution* 19:311–326). In a paper just published (H. Gisin, 1967, "La systématique idéale," *Z. Zool. Syst. Evolut.-forsch.* 5:111–128) I have tried to contribute to a synthesis of these methods.

The main difficulty in deducing cladogenies arises from the frequency of parallel evolution. The latter is mostly due to directed selection pressure acting on parallel lineages. Selection acts on adaptive characters; that is, the definition of adaptive characters. Conversely, adaptive characters are the basis for the study of the course of anagenesis. Thus, cladogenesis should be deduced essentially from nonadaptive characters in order to be sure to distinguish it from anagenesis. This is a basic sort of *a priori* weighting of characters used in evolutionary studies.

The synthetic theory of evolution teaches us that the majority of characters are adaptive. This in turn explains why the results of anagenetic, conventional, and phenetic classifications are so similar—they are based either on all characters or on a majority of characters, whereas a cladogenetic classification is based on a minority of other nonadaptive characters. This explains further why cladogenies remain so often highly speculative—namely, through lack of dependable characters. An anagenetic classification has a higher information content, and thus has the advantage over a cladogenetic one.

It seems, therefore, that while cladistics is a very interesting by-product of systematics, the unilateral basis that it provides is too small for proper classification.

Another misunderstanding is reflected in the assertion that any biological definition of taxonomic categories is completely nonoperational. So, the biological species concept is currently, though unconsciously, applied in vast fields of systematics. The existence of reproductive isolation in sympatric, bisexual animals is inferred from existing discontinuities in the character distribution among animals (H. Gisin, 1964, "Synthetische Theorie der Systematik," *Z. Zool. Syst. Evolut.-forsch.* 2:1–17). The criterion "reproductive isolation" has such an essential, biological meaning that it cannot be ignored even though it is not universally applicable or operational. A purely phenetic species definition would be biologically meaningless; the same is true for purely phenetic definitions of any category. Therefore, I proposed (H. Gisin, 1966, "Signification des modalités de l'évolution pour la théorie de la systématique," *Z. Zool. Syst. Evolut.-forsch.* 4:1–12) both operational and biologically meaningful definitions of the principal taxonomic units. The limits of taxa are defined, indeed, by phenetic discontinuity, but their rank is defined by certain biological properties. These biological properties qualify the nature of the discontinuities–reproductive isolation for species, adaptation to broader ecological niches for genera and families, differences affecting form and function of homologous organs for orders and classes, and, finally, different organizations for phyla. These definitions are not more objectively operational, in all cases, than is the biological species concept, but they show the meaning that has been attached, more or less unconsciously, to these categories by generations of biologists.

It is true that no single hierarchical system can simultaneously express the paths taken by cladogenesis and anagenesis, but a system should express the result of the combined effect of both evolutionary processes. The question is how can this be better achieved than by an entirely subjective compromise.

Cladogenetic evolution without powerful anagenetic influence would, at most, produce closely related species. For more pronounced divergence and higher levels of evolution, or adaptive shifts, anagenesis is of foremost importance. Still, the process is continuous, and to establish limits seems quite artificial. Nevertheless, discontinuities exist, and very likely they have their origin in unequal rates of evolution. Simpson calls "quantum evolution" the kind of anagenesis responsible for the observed discontinuities in the fossil record and between contemporaneous groups of species. In other words, quantum evolution provides the biological explanation for the phenetic discontinuities that allow relatively nonarbitrary delimitation of taxa. The nature of the evolutionary quanta, after stabilization, furnishes the basis for a natural ranking of taxa. The aim of systematics could then be defined as that of the discovery, description, and classification of evolutionary quanta.

I feel that the controversy on taxonomic principles could be resolved by recognizing that the best of each theory has its place in systematics, not in a subjective compromise, but with each having a definite function. Phenetics shows discontinuities and therefore the limits of taxa, but not their rank; cladistics reveals the genealogical history, but not the natural system; conventional taxonomy, largely on an anagenetic basis, classifies evolutionary quanta.

Informal Discussion

FARRIS: Dr. Ghiselin, you stated that the natural classification was the classification that utilized all characters, and you also said that there is no such thing as "all characters." This seems to be a contradiction.

GHISELIN: It is necessary to make some sort of selection among the characters, even if the selection is, to some extent, arbitrary. We must select a few principles, or facts—for example, genealogy or degree of evolutionary advance—to be included in the classification system. When there are no objectively real unit characters, we have to accept some other concept as a basis of classification. The notion that there is a contradiction in my position seems to result from improper handling of the logic of conditional statements. One might just as well argue: if someone owns a unicorn, he must necessarily own a quadruped and the fact that there are no unicorns contradicts the possibility of owning a quadruped. In other words, I did not assert that a system is natural *if and only if* it uses all attributes, or even that one need accept such a thesis, but only maintained that merely trying to utilize all attributes presupposes a metaphysical position that many biologists would not find acceptable. My actual position is that as there is no "over-all similarity," there must be some selection of attributes, although such choice is not arbitrary.

FARRIS: Do you believe that there is such a thing as an order-quantifiable, or order-specifiable–metric or pseudometric–over-all similarity over some specified and finite set of characteristics of organisms?

GHISELIN: I think it is reasonable to take a set of kinds of properties in order to create a scale that is useful for certain purposes. For example, an IQ test contains certain kinds of selected attributes that, when placed in a certain order, are used for certain purposes. But such a test does not correspond to anything objectively; it is a scale that we use for a particular purpose, and I would say the same for a phenetic system. One takes a sample, admits that it is a sample, manipulates it, and tries to learn something from it that would allow one to predict something about the organisms. I have no objection to thinking this way; but I do object to saying that we are getting something more fundamental than a useful and expedient kind of sample.

FARRIS: Of course, in any particular sample you really have no more information than the sample originally contained; however, you may realize the data in such a way that certain statements that go beyond the scope of the sample itself have a high probability of being true. For example, numerical taxonomic analysis of some set of characteristics make it possible to say that a particular configuration of organisms has the maximum probability, given that available data, of being the true phylogeny of the organisms. I see nothing philosophically indefensible about that position.

GHISELIN: Absolutely not. You say, in effect, "Let us use induction. Because induction has proven useful in a variety of sciences, why not in taxonomy?" I merely am objecting to some of the excesses, amounting to metaphysical notions, that have crept into some of our theoretical discussions. Such notions have been more confusing than one might think because there has been a lack of rigor and consistency. I believe that numerical taxonomy and biochemistry are useful techniques, but I hope we will not read into them more than is really justified.

WARREN H. WAGNER, JR.

The Construction of a Classification

More and more, the distinction between "systematics," the study of relationships between organisms, and "taxonomy," the classification of organisms, is becoming accepted (cf. Michener, 1963:151, 161). In this symposium, more of the contributions deal with systematics than with taxonomy. My subject, however, does concern taxonomy, and this paper is devoted primarily to the matter of classification. How do we use systematic data in taxonomy? How do we construct a system of relationships? And, finally, how do we apply the taxonomic categories to express these relationships? The answers to these questions invoke practically all of the thinking of systematic biologists from the beginnings of the discipline, and the problems are far from being resolved. We can only hope that the debates currently raging in the pages of journals such as *Systematic Zoology* and *Taxon* will have constructive results.

The state of affairs is not ideal. How are most classifications actually constructed? Historically, a given classification began on the basis of a few key characters and was "improved" by successive workers who considered more and more characters. Each generation of taxonomists modifies previous classifications, adding here, subtracting there. Today if one picks up a taxonomic revision fresh off the press, he generally reads that the group in question was "previously in a state of flux," or that its "classification was poorly understood," or similar phrases. Practically always, the implication in a typical taxonomic revision is "now the problems are straightened out"; and the author presents a nicely graded series of categories—species, genera, families, and classes. The very critical authors use "sub" categories—subspecies, subgenera, subfamilies—and other refinements.

In the average new taxonomic revision, what improvements actually are made? First and foremost, new systematic data are added to the knowledge of the group, and these probably are the most valuable biological contributions. Previously overlooked or recently discovered taxa are added. Realignments are inevitable and necessary, for sometimes the author has discovered that a genus was placed in the wrong family, or a species in the wrong genus. The nomenclature has been corrected once again, and the author has discovered the legally valid first name that accords with the rules. The final "improvement" is to reclassify, to apply the categories differently, to "cut the pie" in a different way. In practically all cases, the categories are inflated. This "hierarchical inflation" (Wagner, 1961) takes the form of raising subspecies to species, subgenera to genera, and so on.

In terms of the numbers of biologists involved and the professional interest generated, the study of systematic data and the patterns thereof attracts vastly more attention than do actual theories of constructing classifications. Most active taxonomists are so busy that they have little time to contemplate the philosophical foundations of their calling. They are too preoccupied with the act of classification to be burdened with the ideas behind it or to devote themselves to developing a consistent theory. Those taxonomists who have become involved in theories of classification usually have endeavored to promote a particular viewpoint. Perhaps the most out-of-favor view today is the one that states that classification of organisms does nothing more than provide "pigeon-holes" or "tags," i.e., that the important thing is to get a name on everything, get it identified, and place it in a family. A number of authors have stressed the importance of "maximum information content"—a classification should be based entirely upon resemblances and differences, the more variables the better, and evolutionary considerations are irrelevant. On the contrary, evolutionists (systematic biologists in the purest sense) feel that classifications not aimed at expressing evolutionary relationships are unacceptable. Some go even further. Some biogeologists, for example, seem to think that the most important goal of classification is to fit living organisms into the fossil record, as if fossils are better indicators of evolutionary relationships than are living organisms.

It should be apparent that the problems in constructing classifications are deep and numerous and that they cannot be resolved readily. They must be faced, however, and taxonomists must arrive at some concordance about them if there is to be any utility and stability in classification. As to our use of characters: Should we weight them? If so, how? As to the purpose of classification: What is classification for? For identification? To express evolution? As to the application of categories: Where and why do we cut off species, genera, and so on? Can we ever achieve any semblance of stability in classification? (I am not now concerned with nomenclature; that is a purely legalistic business that takes care of itself.) Should we even worry about whether we can achieve stability in classification? In the following discussion I shall try, wherever possible, to affirm my own stand on the questions involved rather than make an equivocal review of the viewpoints of others.

One of the healthiest recent developments in systematic biology is the increasing recognition that *a priori* conclusions should be avoided. As much as possible our procedures should be inductive, and conclusions should be reached *a posteriori* after all the evidence is ordered and processed. Recent discussions concerning homology illustrate this point nicely, although some critics reject the arguments as useless semantics, a time-consuming word play. The problem is roughly as follows: In making comparisons we should use only homologous phenomena, for these are the only ones that are similar. The trouble is that we can conclude only that phenomena are homologous because they are similar. We cannot conclude that they are similar because they are homologous. Homology is thus a conclusion and not a datum. I think, therefore, that it would be more logical to say that we compare intrinsically similar structures or functions in obtaining the data of systematics. The degree to which the phenomena compared prove to be homologous or analogous can be concluded only after correlating the data. Homology and analogy, and all shades of conditions between, are systematic conclusions (cf. Sokal, 1964). The same is true of many other evolutionary phenomena—adaptation, animal and plant migration, and speciation. If we agree that a classification should express evolutionary pathways, we cannot permit *a priori* ideas about what these pathways have been to influence us in interpreting data.

Only the trends and patterns shown by the data themselves can be applied in constructing an evolutionary classification.

The ability to quantify comparative data in a detailed way is still far off. The most nearly accurate quantification is that among closely related organisms, such as subspecies and interspecific hybrids, in which remarkably accurate extrapolations can often be made, as shown in the classic works of Edgar Anderson. Even so, such values as we obtain for the measurements taken are probably only crude indexes of the real genetic factors involved, and when characters of species and hybrids are being compared, there is always the danger that dominance will enter the picture (e.g., Panigrahi and Manton, 1958).

As characters have no obvious built-in values, a common tendency today is simply to count all characters as equal, and approach credited to Michel Adanson. No differential weighting is allowed because we do not know whether petal length is equal to, greater than, or less than flower color. The idea of weighting characters, however, appeals intuitively to all practicing plant taxonomists. Such weighting as is used in routine identification is focused on "key" or "useful" characters, those that are striking or gross, like the visible parts of a flower. Also, those characters that are uniform because of resistance to environmental modifications or strictness of genetic control are valuable for identification. Most systematists today would tend to disagree, I believe, with the idea that mere grossness or convenience of a character necessarily gives it a greater value in working out relationships than a technical or microscopical one. For example, chromosomes have proved to have immense value, especially in plant systematics, but they are tiny objects not readily observed in the field or on herbarium sheets.

Problems of whether to weight characters and, if so, of how to weight them, have led to some of the liveliest arguments in recent literature. The numerical taxonomists, of course, have led in the battle for nonweighting. Others, especially the evolutionists, have supported the idea that some weighting has to be done. A number of different reasons other than those pertaining to identification have been proposed for weighting. For example, Kendrick (1965) has suggested that complexity of characters must be considered. If a character needs to be described by using other "subsidiary" characters, then that character is primary, and the subsidiary ones are secondary. Thus a leaf is characterized by a number of properties, such as shape, length, color, or hairiness, all of which are dependent upon the primary character of leaf. Kendrick concludes that primary features should be given more weight than secondary features.

Another type of weighting has to do with functional correlation. If, in order to have a particular function, it is necessary that correlated changes occur in two or more characters simultaneously, then the individual changes themselves are not as heavily weighted as a solitary change would be. For example, in plants, parasitism is correlated with loss of chlorophyll, adnation of stamens mostly coincides with fusion of petals, and the evolution of the pollen type of spore is correlated with the evolution of the seed. It is not yet known to what extent it is justifiable to work out intricate methods of weighting based upon complexity of characters and functional correlations of characters, or both, but these matters deserve careful consideration.

In the assessment of evolutionary relationships, only those data showing probable evolutionary trends can be utilized. It is important to know whether the evidence used displays logical patterns of primitiveness or specialization. At the species level, for example, diploidy is a primitive condition, and, as a rule, polyploidy is a specialized condition; and an elaborate form of apomixis, such as nucellar embryony, is a more specialized reproductive system than typical asexuality. On the contrary, if we have no basis to judge whether one condition or another of a character is primitive, then we cannot use that character in evaluating evolutionary relationships. If it is a 50–50 chance whether the original chromosome number of a group of organisms was 12 or 13, then we cannot use this comparison for judging the most probable evolutionary pathways of the organisms. Accordingly, in this case, we must eliminate that character until more evidence comes along. This is called residual or rejection weighting (Davis and Heywood, 1963, p. 49).

Before actually constructing a classification, one should develop a system that encompasses the organisms in question—a "system" in the sense of the underlying pattern of an interdependent group of organisms that, through their relationships, form a unified whole. The most satisfactory way of accomplishing this seems to be by some sort of visual graph, such as a type of dendrogram or cladogram. Once the system is worked out, it might appear relatively easy to "taxonomize" it, but, as we shall see later, this is by no means the case. As a matter of fact, most of the classifications available to us were not preceded by any logically derived systems. Most are intuitive. As indicated above, most classifications simply become "improved" by successive generations of workers, who modify here and there. Thus, most are re-evaluations of pre-existing ones, and a classification representing a complete reanalysis of a group from the ground up is a rarity.

Nonevolutionary classifications are ones based on purposes other than the embodiment of evolutionary relationships. If such classifications happen to show evolutionary groups and connections (and they usually do), this is merely incidental to other goals. The classifications of alpha taxonomy are devoted mainly to identification, as, for example, in manuals of flora and fauna, and in many revisions, especially those of poorly known tropical genera and families. Alpha classifications correspond to those of classical, pre-Darwinian taxonomy. Practitioners of alpha classifications are worried mostly about correct nomenclature, good descriptions, and useful keys. In spite of criticisms commonly leveled at "workers who are satisfied with this approach," biologists often fail to realize how valuable this effort is to the progress of their science. Alpha taxonomists are the pioneers and explorers who lay the groundwork necessary for more analytical systems and classifications, and their diligent efforts will be needed for a long time to come. Indeed, much of what the taxonomic theorists propose for improved classifications is highly idealistic and unrealistic. Our knowledge of most organisms is still much too scant to achieve truly thorough treatments.

The purely phenetic systems of the numerical taxonomists are based approximately on the following ideas:

1. Relationships are determined on coefficients of resemblance.
2. All characters are used and, in general, the more that are used the firmer will be the conclusions.
3. All characters are equal in value.
4. Evolution is usually unknowable with any certainty, so we substitute "maximum information content" as the basis for evaluating distance of relationship.

Different numerical taxonomists harbor different views on these points, but in a broad sense these are the basic tenets. The primary goal is to produce a repeatable assortment of organisms, and some taxonomists believe that using these procedures will lead to stability in classification.

Unquestionably, numerical taxonomy does lead to some extent to evolutionary groupings and branchings. On theoretical grounds it is even possible that, given enough data on the organisms being classified, the systems of the pheneticists and the evolutionists might coincide. But we do not know this yet. Furthermore, in most groups of organisms we simply do not have the data, and we are not likely to have them in the near future. In my own work on ferns, I have repeatedly found that we do not have the facts we need for making classifications. Many species critical to the study are rare or little known; the life cycles of many common and well-known sporophyte ferns have not been examined or reported; and technical data on cytogenetics and biochemistry are vanishingly sparse. Perhaps it is these "practical" considerations that lead many biologists to ignore, or deplore, the taxonomies of the pure pheneticist. In botany, at least, it may be that purely phenetic systems, no matter how detailed, will *not* produce results that coincide with evolutionary relationships. This possibility very much needs to be tested.

I am concerned, as are most botanists of higher plants, with parallelisms and convergences. It seems very likely that seeds have arisen at least twice, heterospory six times, and water-conducting vessels eight times. "Good" changes like those in the origin of the carpel, the embryo sac, the tricolpate pollen grain, the bitegumentary ovule, and parasitism, contrast with such fluctuating ones as those involving laticifers, habitat, stipules, leaf form, deciduousness, inflorescence structure, floral symmetry, and pollination system, or such extremely variable ones as hairiness, glandularity, flower color, plant habit, epidermal cell shape, time of flowering, and so on—parallelisms all too familiar to plant scientists. We have great difficulty, therefore, in discerning the main lines of evolution; all large groups reveal extensive series of fluctuating and parallel character changes. In seed plants, the wind-pollinated woody dicots called Amentiferae are classic. Such heterogeneous plants as mulberries, hickories, and silk-tassel trees were thus grouped together on the basis of many points of floral similarity. Our systematic concepts in higher plants have had to depend on the withdrawal of threads of consistency from the tangle of irregular fluctuations and parallelisms. Can all characters be equal? The evolutionary systematist says no.

The tenets of evolutionary classification differ sharply from those of purely phenetic classification:

1. Relationships are determined solely on the basis of the most probable evolutionary trends and branchings.
2. Only those characters that show trends can be used. Characters that are likely to give the wrong picture must be eliminated.
3. Some characters, therefore, must be given values, and others must be rejected.
4. Evolution is knowable to a greater or lesser extent, depending upon the availability of sufficient and reliable evidence.

The taxonomic goal of the evolutionist is a classification that expresses by categories the most probable evolutionary system.

There are, of course, some serious problems in evolutionary classification that have not been resolved. Even the word "evolution" itself is used in many senses, including some pertaining to processes and some to the actual patterns of change. For my purposes here, I define it simply as "the amount, direction, and sequence of biological change in populations" (cf. Hennig, 1966:197ff.). Evolution in this sense, then, deals with the actual pathways, transformations, specializations, and modifications that organisms have undergone in all phases of their biology. In this restricted definition, the place and time of evolution and the reasons for the changes are not involved. True, these are related subjects of great phylogenetic interest, but they are subsidiary to the primary questions: How much change has occurred? What characters were involved; that is, in what directions did the changes go? In what order did the changes occur? A question like "How fast did the changes occur?" is a secondary one that can be answered only after the evolution has been worked out. The same is true for "Why did the changes occur?"

Whether we can work out an evolutionary system at all depends in large part on the evidence available. The ideal might be to classify whole lines of evolution, but this is made difficult, if not impossible, by the presence in the living and fossil worlds of large gaps in the lines. In fact, much of classification is based upon gaps, and if these gaps did not exist, our classifications would probably be very different indeed. To the question of whether we should classify on the basis of gaps or on the basis of lines, it seems to me the answer is that we must compromise somewhere between these two alternatives if we are to be at all practical.

Assuming that we agree that classification must express evolution as accurately as possible and that it must reveal both the pathways of change and the gaps that exist in the record, how do we go about evaluating our characters—those that we can use as evidence in deriving the system? Here in particular I would argue that *a priori* judgments concerning characters should be avoided. Purely deductive theories such as the "Telome Theory" of Zimmerman place great emphasis on one or, at best, a few hypothetical characters like branching patterns of vascular tissue and spore-case position. Strict telomists adjudge evolutionary position in part or in whole upon whether the vascular tissue forms a forking pattern or a pinnate pattern, or whether the spore-cases are located at the ends of veins or on the sides of veins, or whether they are located on leaf-like structures or on stem-like structures. H. J. Lam (1948) produced an extraordinary classification of vascular plants based almost entirely upon the telome theory of plant evolution, which finds acceptance today mainly in the fraternity of paleobotanists.

Weighting of characters in favor of those that show or seem to show definite adaptive values and against those that do not has long been a matter for debate. Some workers feel that, theoretically, all characters may be regarded as adaptive; others believe that some are adaptive and some are neutral. Features such as flight, parasitism, and angiospermy occur as fairly clear-cut, new biological changes, often accompanied by rather profound remodeling of the organism. Gisin (1966) has grappled with this problem in his idea of evolutionary "quanta." In his "Quantum Theory" the species is distinguished by reproductive isolation; the genus and family, by their "adaptive facies"; and order and class, by differences in form and function of homologous organs. The value of characters, then, depends in large part upon how profound has been the change. Does the change, or do the changes, lead to a new adaptive zone or level? If we emphasize the value of "adaptive" characters and character complexes, our classification will tend to approximate steps or levels rather than lines of evolution, and grades rather than clades. The classical breakdown of vascular plants into pteridophytes, gymnosperms, and angiosperms is now considered by most botanists to be an excellent example of a "levels" classification. The categories of pteridophytes and gymnosperms are regarded as successive adaptive levels or grades, the former more primitive and showing fertilization separate from the parent plant, and the latter more specialized and showing fertilization through the agent of a pollen tube entering an enclosed female gametophyte parasitic on the mother plant. Practically all botanists today reject pteridophytes and gymnosperms as taxonomic categories on the grounds that they do not express natural evolutionary lines, merely levels. In Lam's telomic classification, mentioned above, even the angiosperms were interpreted as a level, arrived at biphyletically from different source stocks ("Angiospermae stachyosporae" and "Angiospermae phyllosporae"). It is my impression that, in recent plant classification at least, general opinion supports an emphasis on lines and gaps in the diversity rather than an emphasis on levels.

In my opinion, neither time nor place of evolution should enter the picture when one is constructing a classification. There seems to be much disagreement on this point. The primary goal of the evolutionary systematist is to analyze and correlate his knowledge of organisms to find the most probable relationships and then to express them in a classification. Only after this is done can we correlate the patterns of diversity with geological strata and geographical area. It would be illogical to attempt this in reverse; and furthermore I do not see how time and place have any role in the system itself. There are two questions we must ask. What are the known organisms and their properties, in terms of their phenetic resemblances and differences? These are the data. How are the organisms related to each other in the evolutionary sense? This is the system of relationships we seek. It is expressed only in terms of patristic distance or divergence index (the amount of change that has occurred) and cladistic branchings (the directions and sequences of changes as the populations diverge from each other). Absolute time is irrelevant; the only significant measure is that of evolutionary change.

Other, secondary questions also may be asked. When did these evolutionary changes occur during geological time? The answer to this type of question is simply arrived at: The system (e.g., as a diagram, or as a classification) is plotted on a time scale. When a cladogram that follows strictly the measure of patristic distance is plotted on a geological scale, however, the true evolutionary values will inevitably be distorted because of the differing rates of evolution. It is not possible to plot evolutionary relationships on a vertical two-dimensional time scale. Cladistic relationships can be shown, but patristic relationships cannot. The question of where the evolutionary changes occurred, so dear to the biogeographer, also can be answered simply. The system can be plotted on a map. Again, as before, it will be found that patristic distance will not correspond to migration distance. In some cases, one or a few closely related species may extend over enormous distances with little or no evolution taking place, while in another case, a single species may give rise to a series of highly differentiated species or even genera in a very small area and over short migration routes (e.g., in Hawaii). The question of why the evolutionary changes occurred is of special interest to ecologists and students of adaptation. Obviously, however, this question cannot be answered until the basic estimates of patristic and cladistic relationships have been made. What was the nature of the changes and how did they take place? Only after we have some idea of the answers to the previous questions can we ask why they took place. There is no reason that any of these secondary questions of when, where, and why should be included in a classification.

Thus, it is my firm belief that the only legitimate questions in the construction of a classification are those of what and how. Patristic distance, not the lapse of chronological time, is what should be embodied in an evolutionary system. It is not clear to me why it must be re-emphasized so often that rates of change in organisms differ. The actual rates of change, the numbers of generations involved, do not correspond to the evolution, and there is no reason why they should. Figure 1 illustrates diagrammatically how an earlier event, evolutionarily speaking, can occur later in actual time than an evolutionarily later event. If each of the numbers in the evolutionary graph shown at the top represents existing populations of organisms, the origin of $2'$, which from the standpoint of biological change is an earlier event, will be seen to have occurred following the origin of $3'$ and $3''$ in chronological time. This might be well illustrated by cultivated plants, which evolve under the influence of man. Long after the origin of highly specialized cultivars, the wildtype (the primitive population) may be induced and selected to give rise to new cultivars specialized in different respects. In wild organisms, this

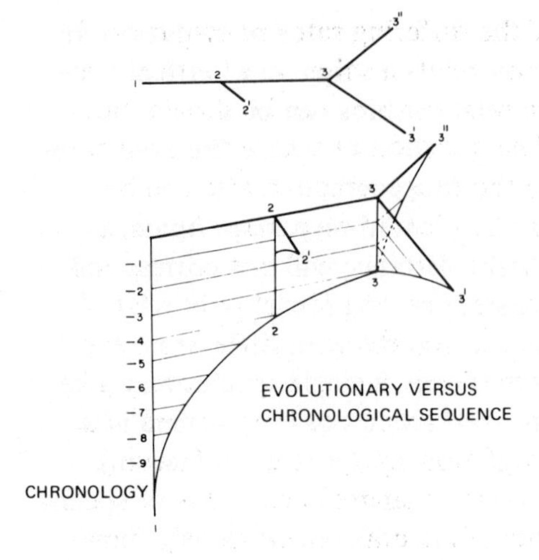

FIGURE 1 How an earlier evolutionary event can occur later in actual time than a later evolutionary event. The vertical axis represents actual time, and 1, 2, and 3 on the horizontal axis represent, respectively, the persistent ancestor, an intermediate taxon, and a specialized taxon.

type of noncorrelation between chronology and evolution probably has existed in all groups throughout their phylogeny. It is largely because of the persistence of conservative and primitive types on the earth today that our understanding of the pathways of evolution are as good as they are. In plant systematics, one need mention only such genera as *Marattia, Osmunda, Degeneria,* and *Drimys* to remind us of the value of so-called "living fossils."

Part of the problem in untangling evolution from chronology stems, very likely, from a preoccupation with fossils and with the idea of ancestry, genealogy, and antiquity. The fact is that many fossils were much more highly specialized than are organisms existing on the earth today. In plants, the fossil record is so poor for the most part that, at least in two large groups, the ferns and the flowering plants, the fossils have been of practically no help at all. One frequently hears such statements as, "The angiosperms have no fossil record, and that is why we cannot work out their origin and relationships." The truth is that the angiosperms have an extensive fossil record. The statement is misleading because it emphasizes the wrong thing. What is missing is not fossils *per se* but the all-important connecting links to fill in the enormous gaps between angiosperms and other kinds of vascular plants. The critical connecting links have not been found either in the fossil record or in the living record of evolution. The nearest thing to connecting links that we have to work with are the living woody Ranales, as was shown in the distinguished research of the late Irving W. Bailey.

If we really did have a neatly graded series of taxa in the over-all evolutionary record of angiosperms taken from living and fossil populations, that connected, perhaps, to some seedfern-like, or cycad-like plant, our evolutionary conclusions would be firm and no one would be likely to question their validity. Most of our conclusions in systematics have a factor of probability involved, and we encounter all degrees of certainty. I cannot accept the extreme view that evolution is unknowable, or even that our conclusions are necessarily highly speculative. It is my strong conviction that as methods become more and more refined and as information on the living world becomes more complete, evolutionary systematics will improve the probability of valid conclusions even to the extent of our being able to state, with fair accuracy, just how probable a particular conclusion is. At present, just how likely is it that our evolutionary inductions are correct? This depends in large share upon the availability of evidence—the completeness of the record and absence of overwhelming gaps—and the detail in which we know our organisms, including data from all aspects. But the probabilities contained in our conclusions depend also upon the logical validity of our methods of analysis and synthesis. For example, if we use characters for which there are no probable trends demonstrable, then we can only reduce the likelihood that our conclusions will approximate the actual evolution.

I should like to give one example of a method for working out evolutionary relationships that I devised some years ago. It is based upon a rationale developed in the study of the fern genus *Diellia* (Wagner, 1952, 1953), which was standardized, codified, and improved for teaching students of systematic botany how to analyze and correlate data for evolution into a coherent system. This method probably has no one part that is new, but it combines, in a particular way, many of the different techniques and ways of thinking that have been familiar to systematists over the years. Ideally there should be three steps: phenetic classification, character analysis and evaluation, and correlation into a pattern showing cladistic and patristic relationships. My method has been useful as a teaching device for presenting the concepts of evolutionary induction, and it has been used in one form or another by more than two dozen monographers since 1955 (e.g., Hardin, 1957; Hauke, 1959; Lellinger, 1965; Mickel, 1962).

This method, which I call the "groundplan/divergence method," has been described elsewhere, so I shall emphasize here only its philosophical basis. It is based on the idea of a groundplan (Danser, 1950) which—although rejected by some authors (e.g., Sporne)—is, I believe, the most fundamental indicator of primitiveness that we have. Generalized characters are primitive. Figure 2 illustrates the theoretical model. Each letter represents a character, with lower case representing the primitive condition of the ancestral stock and upper case representing a derived condition. The amount of change (i.e., patristic distance) is measured by the number of different characters that become specialized. Direction of change refers to the specific characters that become altered; for example, the leaves may become specialized in one line and the roots in another. Sequence of change is represented in two ways—by the presence of known intermediate forms on a single line and by the cladistic branchings determined by the common characters of related forms. Obviously, a classification induced on the basis of this model cannot accommodate reticulate relationships, so in order for it to work it is necessary to remove all species and genera of hybrid origin. Hybrid taxa must be fitted in later, after the basic divergent taxa are correlated.

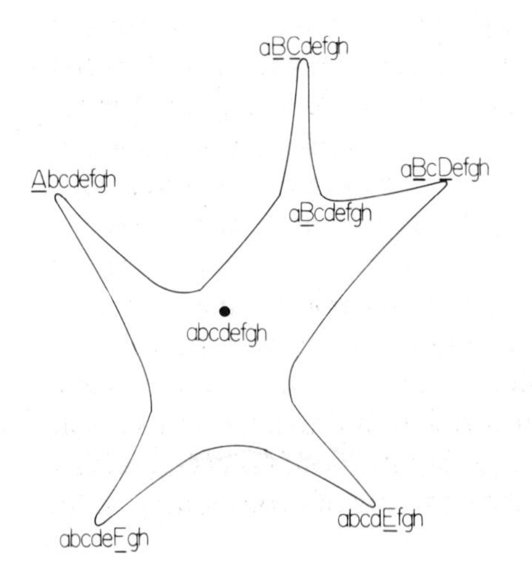

FIGURE 2 Theoretical model of the Wagner groundplan/divergence method for determining evolutionary relationships.

The specialized attributes are those that are least frequent, least generalized; the primitive attributes tend to be those that are most widespread. A character state found in all members of a group is the most certain primitive condition of that character for the group; and it is probable that the immediately ancestral populations from which the group diverged possess, or possessed, that state. For example, if all members of a group have $n = 9$ chromosomes, that number probably characterized the basic stock. On the other hand, if all members of a group have $n = 9$ chromosomes except one which has $n = 8$, the certainty is not so great. It is *probable* that $n = 9$ is primitive, but this must be checked. Accordingly, it is necessary to seek outside evidence. If we are working with phenetic genus *A*, for example, we must check its nearest allies among other genera—*B, C, D,* and so on. If we find that $n = 9$ in all or most of the other genera, then the evidence is very good that this is the primitive chromosome number; but if the predominance of distribution of chromosome numbers in the related genera is $n = 8$, it is likely that this is the primitive state even though it appears in a minority in the particular genus we are investigating. Good examples of the latter situation are found in such attributes as eusporangia (vs. leptosporangia) among ferns, and monocolpate pollen (vs. tricolpate pollen) in dicotyledonous angiosperms.

Figure 3 illustrates how we evaluate character states, which are represented by the symbols above the taxa shown in the phenetic dendrograms. Let each group represent a genus, and each of the in-

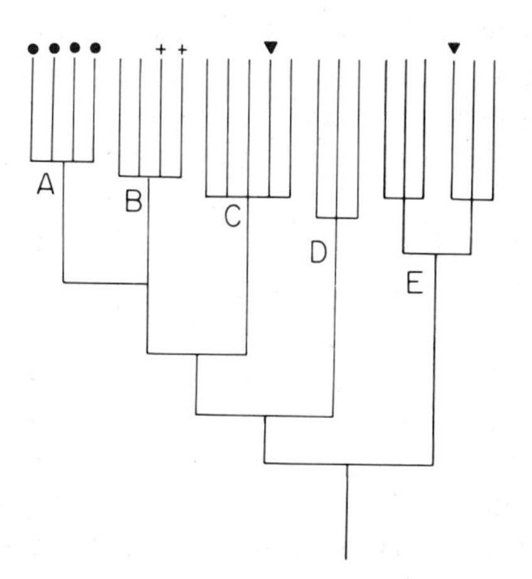

FIGURE 3 How character states are evaluated as to their probability of being primitive or specialized on the basis of their incidence within and between taxa.

dividual taxa a species. If, as shown in genus *A*, all species possess a given attribute, that attribute is primitive for the genus even though it is specialized for the family. If half the species of a genus (e.g., *B*) possess an attribute not possessed by the other half or by the members of any other related genus, then that attribute probably is specialized. One of the corollaries of the groundplan concept is the tendency of primitive character states to coincide with other primitive character states more often than with specialized ones. Primitive attributes tend to show a positive correlation with other primitive attributes. Specialized attributes, on the contrary, do not tend to coincide with other specialized attributes, unless there is a functional correlation (e.g., pollen tube and seed, wind pollination and loss of nectaries). Practically all systematists consciously or unconsciously use this rationale in evaluating characters as to their primitive and specialized states.

In addition, patterns in the character states themselves should be studied. In a linear series of changes, such as chromosome numbers of $n = 9, 18, 27, 36, 45$, and 54, the most economical conclusion is that the numbers form a natural series that runs either from 54 down to 9 or from 9 up to 54. These alternatives are more probable than that the series starts with one of the middle numbers; that is, that 27 or 36 is primitive, and has given rise to two lines of change, one downward in number and the other upward. From what we know of chromosomes, in this case it is most likely that the primitive haploid number is 9 rather than 54. In many cases, the series not only are linear but they branch in different directions.

As illustrated in Figure 4, the different kinds of forked leaves in megaphyllous vascular plants form a pattern radiating from the most logical central type, which also happens to be the groundplan leaf architecture. The Occam's Razor interpretation of the known diversity of forked leaves in ferns and flowering plants is the one shown in the figure. That any of the types of forked leaves is ancestral or basic to all the other types is very unlikely; if any were, a more complex hypothesis would be required.

If the primitive and specialized states of a character can be evaluated on the evidence of its incidence within the group in question and in related groups, and in terms of its own properties and trends, then that character can be used. Since I do not believe that we are in a position at present to weight more critically than this, for each taxon I as-

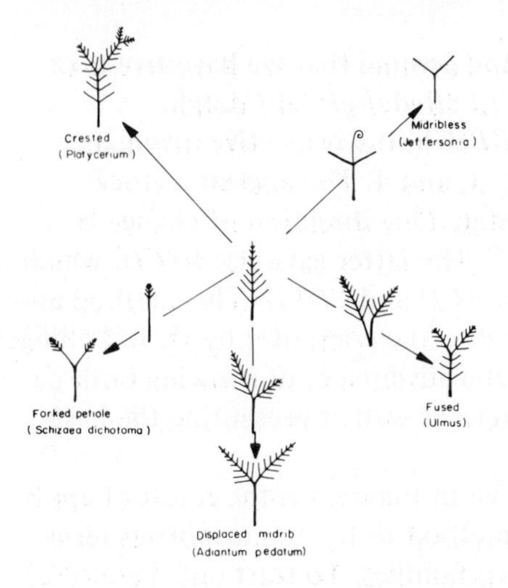

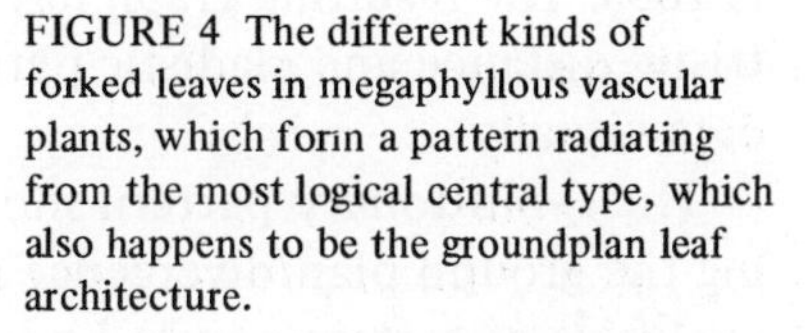
FIGURE 4 The different kinds of forked leaves in megaphyllous vascular plants, which form a pattern radiating from the most logical central type, which also happens to be the groundplan leaf architecture.

sign a value of "0" to each character showing the primitive state and a value of "1" to each character showing the specialized state. All characters for which we have little or no evidence of trend must be eliminated from the final synthesis. Inconclusive characters cannot be used as evidence because of the likelihood of introducing error. This is not to say that clearly defined and recognizable parallelisms cannot be used, as shown by *C* and *E* in Figure 3. Specializations that recur on two or more evolutionary lines are extremely common in plants. As long as their incidence and correlation with other characters makes it clear which attributes of a character are primitive and which are specialized, that character can be used in spite of the fact that it may reappear as a parallel development in several lines.

In essence, we attempt to extract from the data all characters that show clear-cut directions of change; then we reorganize the taxa according to the way these trend-showing characters correlate. The more usable characters we find, the more dependable will be the evolutionary system resulting from their synthesis. The synthesis itself is accomplished by plotting the taxa on an ordinary target graph according to amount of evolutionary change, the patristic distance determined by the sum of specializations (each equaling 1), and the cladistic pattern determined by divergences at the common groundplans of successive taxa. The use of a target graph may distort patristic distances slightly, but the method is convenient. If we let capital letters symbolize the specialized states of characters, and lower case letters the primitive ones, and assume that we have five taxa with the formulas, respectively, of a*B*cde*F*g*H*, ab*C*defgh, ab*CD*efgh, *A*b*CD*efgh, and ab*CDE*f*G*h, the respective divergence indexes of these taxa are 3, 1, 2, 3, and 4. The ancestral stock probably had the formula abcdefgh. One direction of change is that of *BFH;* the other, that of *C.* The latter gave rise to *CD,* which in turn gave rise in one direction to *ACD* and *CDEG.* This method and its refinements have been adapted to the computer by D. B. Lellinger (1965). The resulting graph has the advantages of showing both patristic distance and cladistic pattern as well as presenting the basic data visually.

The evolutionary pattern shown in Figure 5 is the result of applying the ground plan/divergence method to the homosporous ferns, exclusive of certain poorly known families. To start out, I chose 23 taxa based on the families of Copeland (1947), with modifications based upon more recent works by other authors. The taxa are shown in the graph with their divergence formulae; the names used are those of the typical genera. Of over 60 characters examined at the outset, only 45 proved to show patterns definite enough to be used as evi-

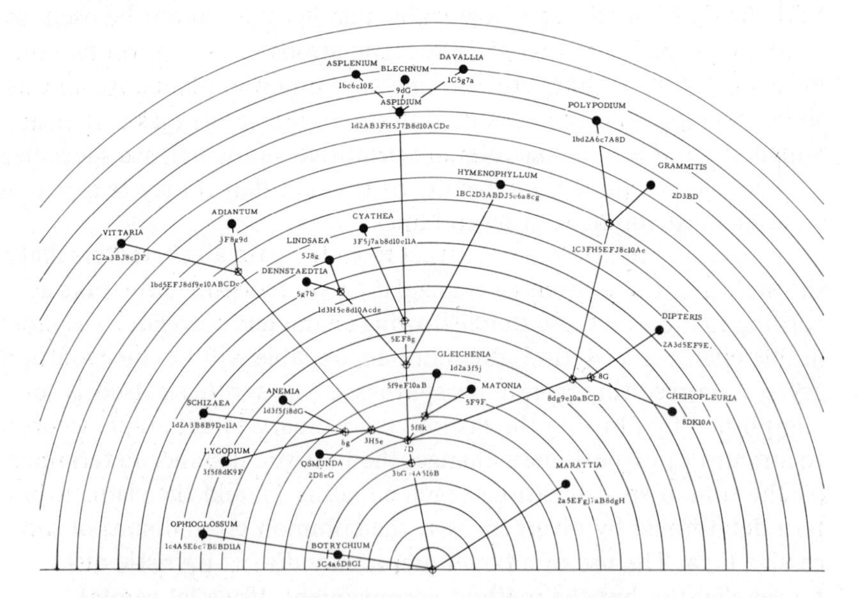

FIGURE 5 Evolutionary pattern that resulted from applying the groundplan/divergence method to homosporous ferns.

dence. If a given character was only partly specialized in a taxon (i.e., only in some of the members, or partly but not yet fully changed in any members), it was scored one half. Many characters that traditionally had been held to demonstrate definite trends in the ferns did not prove to do so when I used the procedures described earlier. I was unable, for example, to find any definite patterns for the stem as to whether the upright or creeping type of stem was primitive, or whether the protostele or dictyostele was primitive. The evidence also was inconclusive with regard to the position of the sorus—whether terminal or lateral on the veins. It is possible that the alternate conditions occurred and fluctuated even in the ancestral stock.

The resulting system, shown in Figure 5, reveals a number of interesting correlations. The chromosome number was not used in developing the chart, but it proved to correlate quite well with the pattern. Certain small groups, such as the traditional Schizaeaceae and Ophioglossaceae, seem to be much more divergent among themselves than the large groups of Aspleniaceae, Aspidiaceae, Davalliaceae, and Blechnaceae. The system as shown here is tentative and is undergoing further improvements; it is by no means final. Even as it stands, however, this chart is probably more objective and detailed than any other yet published.

I now come to the most difficult problem of all. Let us assume that we are able to make a very thorough phenetic classification, to analyze our characters to determine what trends are shown, and then to correlate them into a groundplan/divergence chart showing the most probable evolutionary relationships. Having accomplished this, perhaps it would seem simple to apply appropriate categories to best express the relationships in a taxonomic hierarchy. Nothing could be further from the truth. There are all sorts of ways to apply the categories, and there is no agreement whatsoever. The major problem is "hierarchical inflation"—the tendency of practically all workers to raise species groups to genera, generic groups to families, and so on. In 1938, Copeland completed his years of study of Hymenophyllaceae, the filmy-ferns, the group he came to know better than any other. He concluded that there were 34 genera, not 2. Like most workers, he raised the rank as he found more and more differences. But now the use of genera in the Hymenophyllaceae becomes out of phase with the generic concept in other families. At the family level in ferns, Christensen's Polypodiaceae, with 15 subfamilies, was raised to 5 families and 11 subfamilies by Holttum; to 9 families and no subfamilies by Copeland, and to 33 families and no subfamilies by Ching (Wagner, 1965). So far, authors dealing with the ferns have not invaded the ordinal level to any great extent, but we can expect that they will.

In angiosperms, on the other hand, writers have been having a field day by increasing the numbers of orders. The famous system of Bessey (Figure 6a) had 23 orders, which made it convenient. In more recent times, Cronquist (1964) doubled this number, and Hutchinson (1954) had created even more. Even the divisional level in higher plants has come in for inflation. Tippo's well-known system had only one division for vascular plants, but Bold's more recent system has nine. There is no question in my mind that such hierarchical inflation tends to destroy the usefulness of a classification system.

To illustrate how one may retain taxa at the convenient size more or less traditional prior to 1925, I attempted to make a diagram like

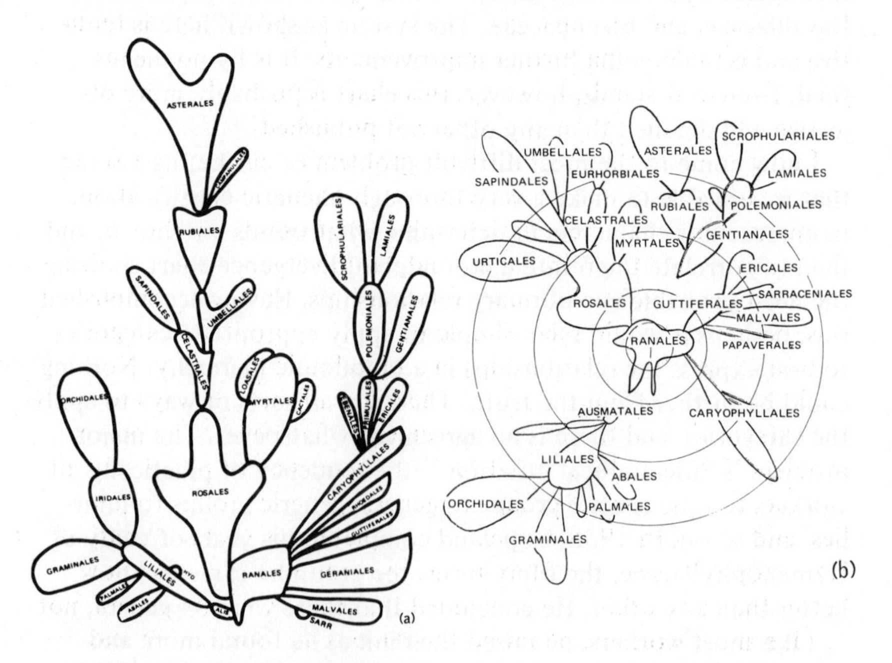

FIGURE 6 (a) C. E. Bessey's (1915) system of angiosperms, with 23 orders. (b) Wagner's revised system.

that of Bessey in style and size of orders but making revisions to accommodate recent correlations by Cronquist for the dicotyledons and by Hutchinson for the monocots. The results are shown in Figure 6b. I have used this diagram for several years in teaching and have found it infinitely more useful than the multiplicity of orders adopted by my authorities. My orders of angiosperms probably are no less accurate, evolutionarily speaking, than those of Cronquist and Hutchinson. I have simply tried to "cut the pie" so as to be more closely in accord with tradition, consistency, and usefulness.

So that we can sense the problems of applying the categories, let us use the cartoons of the groundplan/divergence graph of the ferns described earlier (Figure 5) and assume that the graph represents a fair estimate of the evolutionary lines and distances. How should we classify it? The main problem has to do with the so-called "higher ferns," traditionally classed in the Polypodiaceae. As early as the 1920's, the famous British fern authority F. O. Bower argued that the higher ferns, those with typical leptosporangia, presented a level of specialization and did not constitute a natural taxon because they contained several polyphyletic elements. When we set up families on our groundplan/divergence chart by using the concept of Polypodiaceae, we get a very unnatural picture indeed, as shown in Figure 7a. If we follow Copeland's (1947) classification, the picture shown in Figure 7b is created; note that his constitution of Pteridaceae (to include what most other authors regard as separate families–Adiantaceae, Dennstaedtiaceae, and Lindsaeaceae) also appears to be an artificial grouping. If we simply make every group a family (as shown in Figure 7c) no relationships of a linear nature are contained in the taxon; this seems to be much too finely divided, although the classifications of at least two authors, Ching (1940) and Pichi-Sermolli (1958), approach this. In my opinion, such a classification would emphasize gaps and overlook important resemblances and trends. If, on the contrary, it is lines that we wish to emphasize, the picture shown in Figure 7d would represent what might be called a "purely cladistic" classification. Another way of approaching the problem of applying the categories is seen in Figure 7e, where an arbitrary patristic distance was selected to separate the categories. My own interpretation of the classification of homosporous ferns is shown in Figure 7f, where I have tried to compromise between traditional views and the evo-

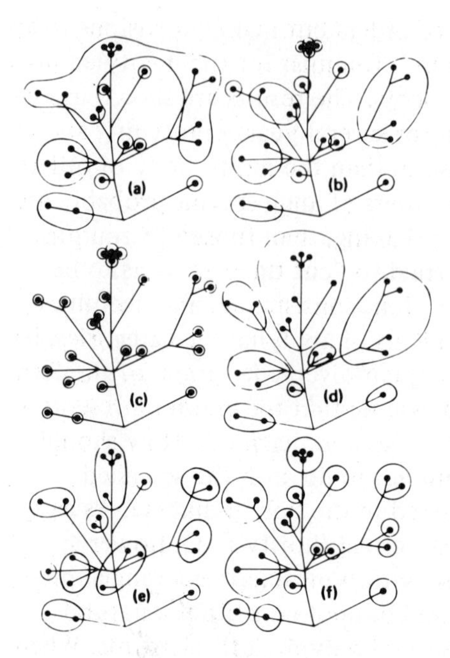

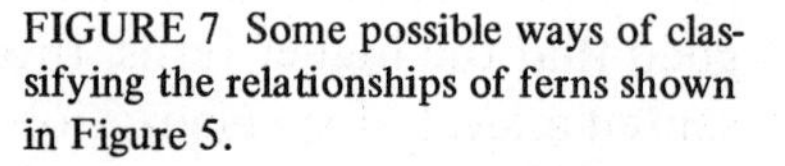

FIGURE 7 Some possible ways of classifying the relationships of ferns shown in Figure 5.

lutionary relationships revealed in the groundplan/divergence graph. I am not at all sure, however, that it represents a classification that is better or worse than those shown in Figures 7c or d.

I am not convinced that there is any generally acceptable guide for how one should apply the categories; it seems to be a matter of taste, and no two people will do it alike. Thus, the application of categories is a wholly arbitrary matter, whether we are dealing with a patristic cladogram, such as we have used for illustration here, or a purely phenetic dendrogram.

I realize that it has been impossible to give a truly exhaustive review of the problems of construction of a classification. Indeed, I have found it necessary to limit the subject to my own viewpoint; thus, this review is one-sided in many respects. I do believe, however, that certain points have emerged in boldface. For example, it is obvious that each person who constructs a classification has his own individualistic ideas of how it should be done. Michener (1963, p. 171) writes, "Taxonomists should indicate the criteria they use in recognizing species." It seems reasonable to expect that each person who works out *any* system of relationships would state the premises upon which he based his system—whether purely phenetic or evolutionary—and explain his theoretical and operational approach. He should clearly state what his characters were, how he interpreted them, and how he made his correlations. Finally, when it comes to the vexing problem of applying the categories, he should state how he went about applying the categories—whether it was entirely by degree of resemblances between the taxa, thus emphasizing the gaps; entirely by cladistic pattern; by patristic distance; or by some combination of these approaches.

In my opinion, the system of relationships should be based only upon those data that show the most probable evolutionary trends. Inconclusive data must be rejected, even though they may have initial objective value in showing phenetic relationships. The best system of classification is one that shows evolutionary relationships with the highest degree of probability. Questions of when, where, and why evolution took place are secondary ones; they may be of great interest in themselves, but they have no place in classification.

There is no agreed-upon way to guide us in applying the taxonomic categories—as to whether we should emphasize phenetic, cladistic, or patristic relationships, or whether we should construe our taxa broadly or narrowly, lump or split. Our only criteria lie in tradition, consistency, and usefulness; and such criteria must be subjective in every respect.

The current situation of hierarchical inflation in plants is very bad, and it may be hopeless. One wonders whether, in future, we may not totally abandon the dream of using the categories in a consistent way and resort to some other method. Stability in classification may not be so important a goal as many biologists seem to think. To those who consider it crucial that we do achieve stability, I must say that it is not yet clear to me how this can be done. Perhaps some statistically inclined biologist will come up with an agreeable factor based upon patristic distance or some other dimension that will serve to standardize our categories. Until that time, I can only suggest submitting all new classifications to *ad hoc* panels of experts for evaluation and approval.

REFERENCES

Bessey, C. E. 1915. The phylogenetic taxonomy of flowering plants. Ann. Mo. Bot. Gard. 2:109–164.

Ching, R. C. 1940. On natural classification of the family "Polypodiaceae." Sunyatsenia 5(4):201–260.

Copeland, Edwin B. 1938. Genera hymenophyllacearum. Philip. J. Sci. 67:1–110, plates 1–11.

Copeland, Edwin B. 1947. Genera filicum. Chronica Botanica Co., Waltham, Mass. 247 p.

Cronquist, Arthur. 1964. The status of the general system of classification of flowering plants. Ann. Mo. Bot. Gard. 52(3):281–303.

Danser, B. H. 1950. A theory of systematics. Bibl. Biotheor. 4(3):115–180.

Davis, P. H., and V. H. Heywood. 1963. Principles of angiosperm taxonomy. Van Nostrand, New York.

Gisin, Hermann. 1966. Signification des modalités de l'évolution pour la théorie de la systematique. Zeitschr. Zool. Syst. Evolutionforsch. 4(1-2):1–12.

Hardin, James W. 1957. A revision of the American Hippocastanaceae. Brittonia 9(3):134–171.

Hauke, R. F. 1959. A taxonomic monograph of the genus *Equisetum* subgenus Hippochaete. Doctoral thesis, Univ. of Michigan.

Hennig, Willi. 1966. Phylogenetic systematics. Univ. of Illinois Press, Urbana, Ill.

Hutchinson, J. B. 1954. The families of flowering plants. 2nd ed. Oxford Univ. Press, Oxford, England.

Kendrick, W. B. 1965. Complexity and dependence in computer taxonomy. Taxon 14(5):141–154.

Lam, H. J. 1948. Classification and the new morphology. Acta Biotheor. 8:107–154.

Lellinger, David Bruce. 1965. A quantitative study of generic delimitation in the adiantoid ferns. Doctoral thesis, Univ. of Michigan.

Michener, Charles O. 1963. Some future developments in taxonomy. Syst. Zool. 12(4):151–172.

Mickel, John T. 1962. The fern genus *Anemia,* Sect. Coptophyllum. Iowa State J. Sci. 36(4):349–382.

Panigrahi, G., and I. Manton. 1958. Cytological and taxonomic observations on some members of the *Cyclosorus parasiticus* complex. J. Linn. Soc. Bot. 55(363):729–743.

Pichi-Sermolli, Rodolfo E. G. 1958. The higher taxa of the Pteridophyta and their classification. Acta Univ. Upsaliensis 1958 (6):70–90.

Sokal, Robert R. 1964. The future systematics, p. 33–48. *In* Charles A. Leone [ed]. Taxonomic biochemistry and serology. Ronald Press, New York.

Wagner, W. H., Jr. 1952. The fern genus *Diellia.* Univ. Calif. Publ. Bot. 26(1):1–212, plates 1–31.

Wagner, W. H., Jr. 1953. An *Asplenium* prototype of the genus *Diellia.* Torrey Bot. Club Bull. 80:76–94.

Discussion

Herbert H. Ross

I commend Dr. Wagner for a forthright account of what we actually do about classifications. The classifications that we construct are strictly operational arrangements of concepts that fill the needs of individual investigators.

I would like to comment on two problems concerning stability in classification. Any classification consists of two parts, (1) the biological concepts that it embraces and (2) a set of names applied to these concepts according to some rules of nomenclature that govern the names as names rather than as biological concepts. These two facets of classification, biological and nomenclatorial, present different problems concerning stability.

Arguments about nomenclature, involving practically every rule and recommendation of all three biological codes, have resulted in a tremendous amount of instability. Because this is purely a bookkeeping operation, I think it is high time that zoologists, botanists, and bacteriologists worked out a single nomenclatorial code for all living things and established a paid executive secretariat to keep the names straight and to ensure prompt settlement of such nomenclatorial problems as arise.

At present a phylogenetic classification and a stable classification are mutually exclusive. Phylogeny is a dynamic field of investigation into which additional species, additional characters, and new ways of regarding old species and characters are constantly entering. It is becoming more and more obvious that phylogenetic trees are the best tools yet devised to express geographic dispersal, physiological and biochemical evolution, ecological evolution, and other types of change associated with the progress of phylogenetic lineages through time. Such trees also provide the simplest means of comparing happenings in one group of organisms with those in another. It should, therefore, be no surprise that classifications tend to follow phylogeny. But we must be very careful that, if this is done, the innate stultifying influence of classification does not become a nonscientific deterrent to phylogenetic investigation.

Let us not worry, therefore, about stability as it applies to biological concepts in classification; rather, we should be concerned about ways of achieving better phylogenetic analyses. Only as phylogenetic analyses progress toward an ever greater degree of probability in expressing the actual path of evolution will our classifications become increasingly stabile.

Discussion

Mortimer P. Starr and Helen Heise

We come to the problems inherent in the construction of classifications with the biases of a bacteriologist and of a philosopher who are collaborators in studies on the philosophical grounds of biological taxonomy.

Our first comment on this section of the Conference program deals with the very title of the preceding paper by W. H. Wagner, Jr., namely, "Construction of Classifications". Does the word "construction"* in the title stem from a no-contest decision on a basic philosophical question as to whether classes exist in nature or whether they are indeed constructs of the human mind?

Suppose we wanted to say that classifications are not constructed, but rather that classes are discerned. What is the distinction between the two? 'Constructing a classification'* seems at least to suggest, if not entail, that our concepts and conceptual techniques are the sole source of the classes that constitute a constructed classification. 'Discerning classes', on the other hand, means that the classes or the traits for forming classes are given or presented in nature. (By "classes" is meant "sets, groups, or assemblages"–the more general meaning–rather than specifically biological taxa or categories.)

When one discusses the problems of classifying, one wants to say of course that the traits are indeed found in nature and that

*There is a significant logical difference intended by our usage of single quotes (indicating a concept) and double quotes (indicating the very words).

NOTE: At the insistence of the authors this paper is published without editorial modification.

any single trait or any set of traits found in nature may be used to form a real class. Scientists do not conceive of disputing this position except when they get into a conceptual bind and then say that only individuals are real—which notion certainly contradicts their practice, depending as the latter does upon the real existence of traits or classes. So, the problem is not ontological (i.e., as taxonomists, we do not usually discuss whether a plurality of individuals—a class—possessing that set of traits really exists in nature), but rather the problem is methodological (i.e., we concern ourselves with the choice of a set of traits which will usefully divide the multiplicity of individuals).

There are various ways of manipulating traits to delimit classes and to construct classifications—dependent in part on one's purpose(s). For example in polythetic classification, a set of traits—no one of which is necessary, but a proportion of which is necessary and sufficient—is used for determining class membership. But, unless—as is clearly not possible—one could use, as a basis of classifying, all traits of the organisms being grouped, which traits should be used can always be disagreed upon. To offer a polythetic classification, though the technique is indeed a refinement, does not obviate the problem of which set of traits is to be used, since the method of polythetic classification does not make any easier or more obvious the selecting of the traits that are to be class-determining. Though there are significant conceptual and procedural differences between monothetic and polythetic classifications, the differences do not consist in or include any greater degree of necessity of the traits chosen. The important difference between a monothetic classification and a polythetic classification is that in a monothetic classification a single trait or a set of traits is said to be necessary and sufficient to determine class membership, whereas in a polythetic classification no one of the set of traits is necessary but a proportion of the set is both necessary and sufficient to determine class membership (see Beckner, 1959: p. 22–23; Sneath, 1962: p. 291; Sokal and Sneath, 1963: p. 12 ff.). One understands why degree of phenetic similarity as the basis of classifications is so repugnant to some taxonomists, since the degree of phenetic similarity between groups may seem to vary depending upon which set of traits is the basis of comparison. (It clearly is not possible to use all traits, even of a simple organism!)

It might look as if investigator I says–on the basis of traits-set *a*–that group *x* is more like group *y* than like group *z;* and investigator II says–on the basis of traits-set *b*–that group *x* is more like group *z* and less like group *y*. Then, how is one to decide whether set *a* is more significant, important, or revelatory of reality than set *b* is? And if one asserts that no set of traits is epistemologically paramount to any other, then the stability of the system may be endangered. This consequence would disturb those who would like the taxonomic scheme to be based on that which can assure some degree of stability, rather than to have the system based on what does not claim to offer any assurance of stability at all.

Methodologically superior to using a set of traits concerning the selection of which there may be controversy would be using a single trait which everyone could agree to be class-determining, since then there would be no disagreement. To find such a trait among organisms is not impossible, and possibly not even difficult. (Lest you expect a solution, here and now, to all the problems of classifying, be forewarned that selecting a class-determining trait is not the same as being able to decide whether the trait obtains in any particular case.) If descent is taken to be a single trait, then the methodological problem of finding a single class-determining trait is solved. Unfortunately, some biologists would say that this single trait, descent, can only be inferred from a set of phenetic traits–in which case there is no practical methodological advantage. But even if there is no practical methodological advantage, there is a systematic or theoretical advantage which can be expressed in the following way. Claims concerning similarity of organisms depend upon the traits being used as the basis of comparison. So the claims regarding similarities have to be qualified by stating the traits which were used to make the comparison. That is, claims about similarity are conditional–the conditions being how *we* are looking at the organisms. The descendent connection between organisms–how one organism came from another organism (in the case of asexual reproduction) or from two other organisms (in the case of sexual reproduction)–is a hard or brute fact; that is, in nature it could have obtained in only one way. So assertions about descent do not need the kinds of conditions which make explicit the set of traits on the basis of which the comparison has been asserted, as assertions about similarity do, because the basis of the progenitor-offspring claim is clear, namely, descent. Either the birds developed from reptilian ancestors or they did not. No further qualification—like "depending on how one looks at it"—is needed. But birds may be considered to be phenotypically more like bats or like snakes, depending upon which traits one looks at.

It has been said that the classifying of non-organismic entities is significantly different from the classifying of organisms (although the opposite opinion could also be defended). This distinction can be interpreted here in light of what we have been discussing. In the case of non-organismic objects which cannot reproduce themselves, the single trait, descent, cannot be used in the same sense as in the case of organisms. For though it is true that one can trace developmental connections between non-organismic objects, say, car models (Rowland, 1968), still the cars do not themselves determine the variations and permutations to follow. Earlier car designs may give rise to later car designs, but earlier car designs give rise to later car designs only via some person's concepts; there is no direct and necessary connection between the earlier car and the later car. An earlier car does not strictly determine the later car. No one is shocked, incredulous, or even surprised when one model of car differs markedly from the previous model. Comparisons of degree of similarity—which was the original problem we started with—are difficult, but one might say that there is less difference possible between biological progenitors and immediate descendants than between successive models of a car. It is more likely that 1961 Lincoln Continentals could be followed by what look like 1962 Volkswagens than that tall Caucasoids could consistently give rise to Negroid pygmies, which latter event most biologists would want to say is impossible and has no likelihood at all.

Thus, the assertion that organisms are different from non-organismic entities in respect to the methods of classifying can be given at least this true interpretation: in the case of organisms, appearances (or phenotypic traits) need not be the sole basis for classifying them. What more may be used is dependent on their being self-reproducing, which self-reproduction provides a brute fact not dependent on differing viewpoints, as are claims about phenetic similarity. ("Self-reproduction" is used here to mean "the production of a complete, new organism of the same kind as the one or two progenitors it comes from".)

In addition to these observations concerning the logic of monothetic and polythetic classifications, we should like to make another, rather obvious, suggestion about method. When it is technically possible, similarity of the genetic material, known directly (as distinct from indirectly through phenotypic expression) could be the grounds of our classifications. Presumably, one would have to determine the degree (range?) of genetic similarity between interbreeding organisms producing fertile offspring, and this degree of similarity would then constitute the species level. It may very well be the case that this degree of similarity need not be the same from one species to another. Lesser degrees of similarity might be used to decide other taxonomic levels; perhaps these levels would coincide with current genera, families, orders, etc., or perhaps levels would have to be chosen *de novo* by taxonomists.

That it would be advantageous for taxonomists to rely on the degree of similarity of genetic materials–known not indirectly through phenotypic expression but directly–no doubt is obvious to everyone. But all the same, it may not be superfluous to point out explicitly some of the advantages. The first advantage, which we might label systematic, consists in there being a single basis for determining all taxonomic levels, which presumably would differ only by degree of genetic similarity. Secondly, one could make both clear and precise the grounds for demarcating each taxonomic level. Thirdly, species in groups which do not reproduce sexually could also be determined by the degree of genetic similarity, which would be a decided boon for bacteriologists.

Whether or not a single set of classifying principles and methods can be applied to any organisms whatsoever will be decided only after making explicit and comparing the problems, principles, and methods of the several areas of biology. In bacterial taxonomy there are problems and limitations which seem different from those faced by botanists and zoologists; we shall mention eight of them.

First–The discovery of microbes occurred only after the invention of the microscope. Microbes are microscopic organisms, that is, they are so small that they could not be known without special optical devices. So there was no long history of their being classified, no practical taxonomic system which required only refinement, as was the case with higher plants and animals.

Second–The smallness and resultant simplicity of the bacteria preclude the presence of certain kinds of properties. An obvious lack: bacteria cannot—or more cautiously, so far as we know, do not—make noises, so we have no songs, calls, or sounds of any kind to use in classifying them. (Imagine a field ornithologist in a world of soundless birds!) Further, an individual bacterium has no readily discernible tactile properties; only masses of bacteria have some texture which is discernible to us. Of course, important morphological properties are visually perceptible, which properties might also be tactile if the organism were large enough to be touched with a finger. But since bacteria are not large, visual properties—as opposed to tactile or aural ones—have an epistemological primacy.

Third—The ordinary bacteria are rather monotonous in morphology [although some morphologically unusual bacteria are known (Starr and Skerman, 1965)]; hence, an unusually heavy reliance is placed on functional (physiological, biochemical) traits as taxonomic characters of bacteria.

Fourth—In addition to the greater reliance on functional traits, almost all of the traits used for classifying bacteria are observed as the sum or mean of the functional abilities of very large and genetically diverse populations rather than of individuals. The significance of this fact perhaps can be more forcefully expressed by an analogy. Suppose one could not make any assertions about individual persons but only about national groups, e.g., the people of country A are more refined and less hard-working than those of country B. Of course, such predicates are not applied to bacteria, but the individual exceptions to the assertion about the two national groups may alert us to similar exceptions applying to bacteria. One may also see that the plasticity of the genetic material of bacteria must be even greater than appears at the population level, which gives us the sum or mean of the individual variations under the existing environmental conditions.

Fifth—The remarkable plasticity of the bacterial genes and the phenotypic expressions thereof (in part controlled by the environment) lead some bacteriologists to view the kinds of bacteria as constituting overlapping clusters or an n-dimensional continuum, rather than discontinuous groups.

Sixth—By and large, bacteria reproduce asexually, so that what are called species of bacteria cannot be defined in the sense of "potentially or actually interbreeding populations." What sexuality exists (Jacob and Wollman, 1961) seems to be facultative rather than obligatory.

Seventh—Related to the preceding two factors is another, namely, there is much confusion as to the nature of the basic unit, the bacterial species (Ravin, 1960). The species level is not tied to interbreeding groups, and the limits of a species seem to depend on the taxonomist's preferences and purposes, restrained only by what Benecke (1912) called "wissenschaftlicher Takt". Though it may sound facetious, there is considerable truth to Cowan's (1962) description of the practice: "a species is what a competent worker says is a species". His assertion that "the microbial species does not exist; it is impossible to define except in terms of a nomenclatural type, and it is one of the greatest myths of microbiology" is provocative. Further, some bacterial taxonomists tend to elevate bacterial groups to overly high categories in the systematic hierarchy; that is, to promote practically every clone to a species—actually, to what Ravin (1963) calls a nomenspecies.

Eighth—A factor giving rise to special difficulties in the constructing of bacterial classifications is the virtual absence of a fossil record (Bisset, 1962; but see Marshall, *et al.*, 1964; Barghoorn and Schopf, 1966; Jackson, 1967) or even a hint about "which way is up" in the time scale of bacterial evolution. As a result, conventional paleontological support for so-called phylogenetic schemes of bacteria is unavailable and such schemes, initially criticized or slavishly accepted, ultimately have been discredited or abandoned. Coming into the picture is the idea that we may learn to rely upon molecules as "documents of evolutionary history" (Jukes, 1967).

In spite of these difficulties, there is reason to expect that the taxonomy of bacteria may one day approach the mainstream of evolutionary taxonomy. Traditionally, classifications of bacteria have been based largely on selected segments of the phenotype. With the development of molecular taxonomy, and a slight shift in viewpoint to include *in vitro* genetic homology as the bacterial counterpart of a "potentially or actually interbreeding population", we can go a long way towards giving a base to bacterial taxonomy which is equivalent to the grounds used in the evolutionary taxonomy of higher organisms. Because the genetic make-up of bacteria is simpler, the prospect of using genetic material directly as the grounds of classification is less distant than might be the case with the genetically more complicated higher plants and animals. This genetic homology of organisms is not, as such, sufficient to show descent of organisms which—as has been said innumerable times—is presently an inference based on other kinds of data. Concerning any claims for bacterial descent and its role in the construction of bacterial classifications we can at this point be only agnostic.

REFERENCES

Barghoorn, E. S., and J. W. Schopf. 1966. Microorganisms three billion years old from the Precambrian of South Africa. Science 152:758–763.

Beckner, M. 1959. The biological way of thought. Columbia University Press, New York. 200 p. [Reprinted, 1968, by the University of California Press, Berkeley & Los Angeles.]

Benecke, W. 1912. Bau und Leben der Bakterien. B. G. Teubner, Leipzig. 650 p.

Bisset, K. A. 1962. The phylogenetic concept in bacterial taxonomy. Symp. Soc. Gen. Microbiol. 12:361–373.

Cowan, S. T. 1962. The microbial species—a macromyth? Symp. Soc. Gen. Microbiol. 12:433–455.

Jackson, T. A. 1967. Fossil actinomycetes in middle Precambrian glacial varves. Science 155:1003–1005.

Jacob, F., and E. L. Wollman. 1961. Sexuality and the genetics of bacteria. Academic Press, New York and London. 374 p.

Jukes, T. H. 1967. Molecules and evolution. Columbia University Press, New York. 285 p.

Marshall, C. G. A., J. W. May, and C. J. Perre. 1964. Fossil microorganisms: possible presence in Precambrian shield of Western Australia. Science 144:290–292.

Ravin, A. W. 1960. The origin of bacterial species. Genetic recombination and factors limiting it between bacterial populations. Bacteriol. Rev. 24:201–220.

Ravin, A. W. 1963. Experimental approaches to the study of bacterial phylogeny. Am. Natur. 97:397–398.

Rowland, R. 1968. Evolution of the MG. Nature 217:240–242.

Sneath, P. H. A. 1962. The construction of taxonomic groups. Symp. Soc. Gen. Microbiol. 12:289–332.

Sokal, R. R., and P. H. A. Sneath. 1963. Principles of numerical taxonomy. W. H. Freeman, San Francisco. 359 p.

Starr, M. P., and V. B. D. Skerman. 1965. Bacterial diversity: the natural history of selected morphologically unusual bacteria. Ann. Rev. Microbiol. 19:407–454.

Informal Discussion

CRONQUIST: Dr. Wagner referred to making *a priori* assumptions and fitting the facts to them. He has given us an example of this in his historical survey of the inflation of the orders of Angiospermae, where he transposed two systems in time. The Hutchinson system, which has the most orders, chronologically is between the Bessey system and my own.

Also, Dr. Wagner noted that the problem of categorical inflation tends to be especially severe when a botanist is dealing with the group he knows best. I believe that his efforts to dismember the Polypodiaceae provide an excellent example of what he was talking about. I would be receptive to a system that would dismember the Polypodiaceae and put every genus in its proper place in a coherent scheme, giving us families that could be used and recognized. However, that has not been done yet, and until it is done, I, as a conservative taxonomist, will probably continue to recognize the Polypodiaceae in the traditional sense.

WAGNER: To your first point, Dr. Cronquist, all I can say is touché. I have indeed provided a fine example of what I am condemning.

As to the second point, I should probably say touché as well, but for different reasons. My "cartoon" of how the classical Polypodiaceae would plot on a groundplan/divergence graph illustrates the problem, which was first brought up by Bower. According to him and practically all subsequent workers in the past half century, the Polypodiaceae resulted from homoplastic evolution and constitutes a polyphyletic taxon, actually an evolutionary level. This is why the ferns so nicely illustrate the problems of the construction of a classification. I am making every effort to "put every genus in its proper place in a coherent scheme." What you are asking for, however, is "families that can be used and recognized." If by this you mean families that are easily described and keyed out, then we have a serious problem because of the extent of parallelism and diversity at this level.

I believe it is appropriate at this point to ask Mr. James Farris to make some comments. He is the statistical consultant of the Evolutionary Biology Training Program here at the University of

Michigan, and is especially interested in the mathematical and computer program aspects of evolutionary induction. He is also attempting to develop methods by which we can stabilize categorization for taxonomic purposes.

FARRIS: In my method I consider two aspects of relationships between organisms: the cladistic relationships, or the order of splittings of phyletic lines, and the patristic relationships, which depend on the amount of evolution along the phyletic lines. On these diagrams (Figure 1), the cladistic relationships are represented by the branching form of the tree, and the patristic relationships are represented by the lengths of the branches. We decide on the contents and ranks of taxa by requiring all taxa to be monophyletic groups and by designating taxa to be of the same rank if the operational taxonomic units (OTU's) they contain display about the same amount of evolutionary divergence from one another.

This diagram (Figure 1A) shows a monophyletic group that could be considered a valid evolutionary taxon of some rank. The next diagram (Figure 1B) indicates a group that is polyphyletic,

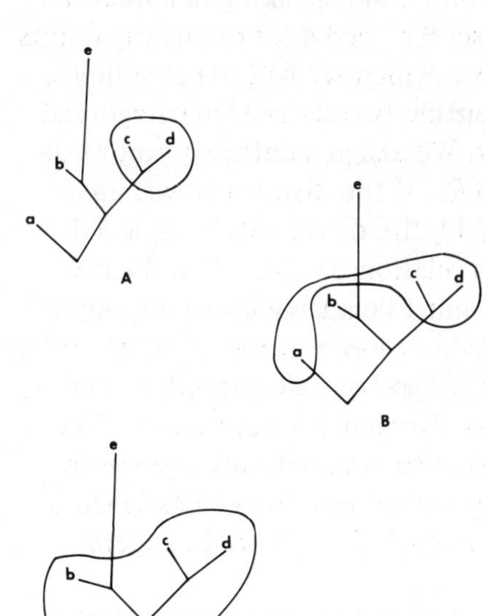

FIGURE 1 A: A monophyletic group containing OTU's *c* and *d* is circled. B: A polyphyletic group consisting only of OTU's *a, c,* and *d.* C: The boundaries of the group in B have been changed so that the group is now monophyletic and contains OTU's *a, b, c,* and *d.*

and hence cannot be an evolutionary taxon at all. But any set of OTU's we please can be included in some monophyletic group, if we just extend the boundaries of the group far enough down the phyletic tree. The last diagram (Figure 1C) shows a monophyletic group that includes the polyphyletic assemblage from the previous drawing (Figure 1B).

We can make any taxon monophyletic by changing its boundaries, but in doing so we may include new OTU's so diverse that the rank of the taxon may have to be increased. In the case of the Polypodiaceae, we cannot use that family, as it is classically understood, as a valid evolutionary taxon because it is polyphyletic. We can construct a new taxon that is monophyletic and contains most of the same OTU's as the classical Polypodiaceae, thus arriving at a new, evolutionarily valid taxon that we may be able to call "Polypodiaceae". But it may also happen that the new "Polypodiaceae" contains too many diverse OTU's to be considered a reasonable family of plants. I suspect that this will happen.

How do we decide on the rank of a taxon? I suggest that the criterion of divergence between the OTU's in the taxon be used. This is not the same as Dr. Gisin's earlier point that the *kind* of divergence indicates the rank of the group. I am speaking in a quantitative, rather than a qualitative sense. We need a set of cutting points for levels of divergence within taxa, which we will use as follows. Let R and R-1 be integers representing two sequential categorical ranks, such as suborder and order. We assign a cutting point of divergence to each value of R as $cd(R)$. If the divergence within a taxon is between $cd(R)$ and $cd(R-1)$, the taxon will be assigned rank R. Now we need to choose a relation between R and $cd(R)$. To do this, we note that a family must be a large enough group so that, if necessary, it can contain two or more subfamilies. An order must be big enough to contain, if necessary, two suborders, and so on. If a taxon of smallest rank has divergence k between its OTU's, the next higher rank will correspond to taxa with divergence between k and $2k$; the rank one step higher again will be assigned to taxa with divergence between $2k$ and $4k$; and so on. In general, $cd(R) = k2^R$.

We still must choose the value of k, and we must establish the correspondence between integer ranks, R, and classical categories; that is, establish which integer corresponds to phylum, which to order. These problems should be resolved by picking values that give the best fit to existing classifications. Actually doing this still lies in the future, but I think that these general methods are adequate to resolve objectively the controversies that arise over whether a given set of organisms is indeed a taxon and whether a given taxon has some particular rank.

ROBERT ORNDUFF

The Systematics of Populations in Plants

Before entering into the main body of my talk, I would like to discuss three key words in my title. "Plants" is one of these terms. When a botanist uses the word "plant" he usually means a vascular plant. This may be justified since there are more species of vascular plants known than there are species of nonvascular ones. However, the fact that when most of us say plants we really do not mean *all* plants illustrates a point I want to make—that the terminology used by systematists to describe population phenomena often is an oversimplification of the diversity of conditions that exist. When we use such terms, we use them as absolutes, whereas they often, if not usually, cover only common or average situations, and in some instances they may not do even that.

There are several reasons why this is true. One is that generalizations or terms are often generated on the basis of one or a few observations, yet we assume that the phenomena they describe are of general occurrence. In this respect I think we tend to underestimate the versatility of nature. Second, many of our concepts concerning natural populations are based on observations of populations under artificial conditions, such as those that exist in the experimental garden, greenhouse, growth chamber, or cage. These conditions and the structure and behavior of such populations usually are much simpler than they are in the field. It is uncertain just how far we can go in extrapolating from behavior under such artificial conditions. Third, many of our population concepts have issued from theoretical models, which are of great importance in orienting our thinking but frequently oversimplify what occurs in nature.

Another word used in the title of my talk is "systematics." This term is widely used by both botanists and zoologists as a synonym for taxonomy. Many of us would rather be called systematists than taxonomists, since in some circles the latter carries with it connotations of anachronism. The word "taxonomy" seems to have been invented by a botanist, the elder De Candolle. In an extensive discussion of this and related terms, Mason (1950, p. 207) states that the objective of taxonomy is ". . .the classification of plants into a system that expresses their interrelationships." However, the interrelationships among plants are so complex that any single taxonomic system that attempts to express these relationships probably will fail to do so. In my own limited taxonomic experience, I have found that the more I learn about the plants I am studying, the harder it is to construct a satisfactory taxonomy for them. Heslop-Harrison (1953) and Simpson (1961) define taxonomy as the study of classification, including its bases, principles, methods, and rules. However, Heslop-Harrison (p. 128) uses the term "systematics" to refer to the actual practice of ". . .describing, naming, and classifying living things." I would include this as a part of the definition of taxonomy, so that the term applies not only to the study of classification but to the practice of classifying, using the conventional taxonomic terminology.

The term "systematics" seems to have originated at about the same time as the word "taxonomy." Its casual usage in the term "systematic botany" by Lindley in 1830 (*fide* Mason, 1950) suggests that the word was in current usage even earlier in the nineteenth century. Since then, systematics and taxonomy frequently have been used interchangeably. In recent texts I find a general, although not universal, agreement that the two terms have different but related meanings. Mason (1950, p. 197) defines systematic botany as ". . . comparative studies of a systematic unit, utilizing research techniques of any division of botany . . . [its] objective will be the establishment of botanical facts upon which concepts of relationship are based." Porter (1967, p. 5) views systematics as "the fact-finding field" of taxonomy. These definitions seem to agree fairly well with the proposal by Simpson (1961) that systematics should be used to include, among other things, the study of any and all relationships among taxa.

It is clear that in light of these definitions a systematist may at times not practice taxonomy as such, since it is possible to carry out a systematic study without making any formal taxonomic judgments. Nevertheless, it is to the mutual advantage of both systematics and taxonomy that plant systematists generally do consider a taxonomic revision to be a logical outgrowth of their research, or, at least, they try to arrive at stated taxonomic conclusions.

"Population" is the third and last term that I want to discuss. All of us use this word but, like Humpty-Dumpty, when we use the word it means what we choose it to mean, neither more nor less. A number of current texts use the word without defining it. Possibly that is best. Nevertheless, if we talk about the local population as the "basic evolutionary unit," it is important that we agree generally on what it is we are talking about. The term "population" occasionally has been used to refer to all individuals of a species occupying a continent. At the other extreme, it has been used to refer to a segment of what seems to be a more or less continuous aggregation of interbreeding individuals. It may refer either to a single-species aggregation or to a multiple-species aggregation. In the latter usage it is similar to the ecological term "community." An ecologist may wish to define a population with respect to topographical or environmental factors; a geneticist, with respect to an accessible gene pool; and a taxonomist, with respect to morphological characters of component members. In systematics there is a strong tendency to emphasize interbreeding as a criterion for the recognition of a population. In this respect, the term "population" comes close to equivalence with the term "species" as defined by some. I would prefer to view a species as generally composed of populations that might be recognized on the basis of one or more of several attributes, and this recognition of the populations is dependent on which of these attributes one wishes to emphasize at the moment. This viewpoint is similar to that expressed by Gilmour and Gregor (1939), who proposed the term "deme" as a neutral suffix to which prefixes can be added to describe various characteristics of the population in question. In zoological usage, the term "deme" seems not to be used in this original sense but in the sense of a local, interbreeding community (Mayr, 1963). From an evolutionary standpoint, all the various kinds of populations are important, including the local interbreeding one.

If, as Mayr (1963, p. 136) states, "... the local population is by definition and ideally a panmictic unit ...," this definition prevents a number of organisms from forming local populations. Apomictic plants (not common to be sure) are not allowed to form local populations, and some would question even whether it is proper to speak of species of such plants (see Bennett, 1964)! Such asexually reproducing plants have spawned prodigious numbers of "species." Approximately 1,100 binomials reportedly have been given to the apomictic hawthorn genus *Crataegus* in eastern North America alone. The dandelion genus *Taraxacum* is overloaded with names; 4,000 binomials have been given to the blackberry genus *Rubus* in Europe; and perhaps as many as 10,000 names to the hawkweed genus *Hieracium.* Apomicts may form local populations that are more or less homogeneous but that differ slightly from adjacent populations morphologically. This seems to be a common pattern and one that explains the taxonomic excesses committed in such genera. On theoretical grounds it seems likely that (using population in a broad sense) apomicts may also form populations that are heterogeneous internally and in which numerous phenotypes exist that show minute but abrupt discontinuities with the other plants that grow with them. Such a pattern seems less likely to attract taxonomic attention than the same magnitude of difference expressed between populations, but it is not clear from the literature that this is indeed the case.

The asexual breeding system that defines apomixis would promote both kinds of variation patterns described above. Although apomixis allows such patterns to develop, it does not create them. If we examine the mode of origin of apomixis, we can see the causes of this variability. Apomictic plants are frequently of hybrid origin; they are often polyploid; and they are seldom, if ever, completely asexual. With this combination of ingredients, it is no wonder that apomicts cause taxonomic headaches. We are all familiar with the problematical variation patterns resulting from hybridization and from polyploidy. Add to this the variation pattern promoted by the perpetuation of numerous heterozygous genotypes via asexual reproduction, on the one hand, with the sporadic bursts of recombination associated with periodic sexuality. Apomicts expectedly would show some characteristics of hybrid swarms, polyploid complexes, and inbreeders all rolled into one. The resultant variation patterns perplex taxonomists, but much of the basis for these patterns lies in the mode of origin of apomixis rather than in the operation of apomixis *per se.*

Because apomicts are taxonomic nuisances, some of us prefer not to think about them very often. Furthermore, they are said to be evolutionary dead ends, so why bother with them? I suggest the contrary: the built-in mechanism of propagating certain genotypes asexually is an admirable breeding system when we realize that many apomicts can also produce recombinants by sexual means as well. Since most flowering plants produce tremendously more seeds than are necessary to produce the next generation, natural selection determines for apomicts how many recombinants and how many asexually produced progeny will make up the next generation. In retrospect, apomixis seems an ideal mode of reproduction, and, as Ehrlich and Holm (1963, p. 296) have put it, if dandelions were authors ". . . one might find sexual reproduction discussed in the literature as a rare and imprudent luxury." What led to this digression into apomixis was my concern that—according to some systematists—apomicts form neither local populations nor species. Actually, they, or rather taxonomists dealing with them, form all too many of the latter.

Autogamous plants might be excluded from forming populations for the same semantic reason as apomicts because they also are in infrequent genetic contact with their neighbors. Like apomicts, inbreeders cause taxonomic headaches, although much of the reason for this is not due to intrinsic properties of the breeding system itself. For example, Lewis (1963) has suggested that inbreeding does not in itself contribute to morphological complexity but that it is the hybridization between different inbreeding lines that causes the problems. This observation seems confirmed by the work of Winge (1940), who showed that by crossing various races of the autogamous crucifer *Erophila verna* it was possible to get myriads of new morphological and cytological races that were true-breeding. By the time of Schulze's monograph published in 1927, the number of taxa described in the genus was between 200 and 300 (*fide* Winge, 1940); many of these undoubtedly arose via hybridization between different autogamous variants.

In the late nineteenth century and early twentieth century, such workers as Jordan, Kerner, Bonnier, Massart, and Turesson concentrated their attention on the biology of plant populations. The eventual result of their studies was the formulation by Turesson of the ecotype concept, which emphasized interpopulation variation within species and interpreted such variation in terms of genotypic response to environmental factors. But, as Bennett (1964, p. 53) points out,

> . . . on the one hand Turesson's papers might reasonably be regarded as experimental starting points for the synthesis of the evolutionist and mutationist viewpoints at least equal in importance to the works [of Haldane, Fisher, and Wright, but] it might also—equally reasonably—be held that as a consequence of his comparison of the ecospecies with the Linnaean species, they were probably the origin of the future taxonomic-biological species controversy which is still with us today. . . .

This controversy is at the root of what came to be called the "conflict of categories" (Heslop-Harrison, 1955). An imposing amount of literature dealing with this and the related "species problem" has developed in the past four decades. At one extreme, some biologists hold that a species should be defined on basically morphological-geographical criteria, and at the other extreme it is maintained that the most important feature of a species is interbreeding (actual or potential) among its members and genetic isolation from other species. I suspect that the latter pair of criteria were initially *a posteriori* characterizations of species—explanations of why species could be recognized by taxonomists. But gradually these characterizations were transformed into testable, *a priori* criteria that were used to define species. Before the biological species concept developed, speciation—that is, the formation of species—was an intellectual process that went on in the minds of taxonomists; afterwards, speciation was viewed as an evolutionary process that occurred in nature.

Arguments have been offered repeatedly in favor of setting up parallel sets of terms to characterize species or their component populations. Proponents of this viewpoint suggest that the orthodox taxonomic terminology should continue in use; the so-called orthodox taxonomist would formulate his taxonomic schemes on the basis of morphological and geographical characteristics, proceeding on an intuitive basis. The experimental taxonomist—or whatever term you wish to apply to him—would utilize all methods available to him in working out relationships. In this role he would function as a systematist, and his taxonomic efforts, if any, would attempt to integrate all his data into a scheme that might use the conventional taxonomic hierarchy, or that might use some of the various parallel terminologies suggested by workers such as Turesson, Danser, Gilmour and Gregor, Camp and Gilly, and others.

Some believe that the conventional taxonomic categories, such as species, subspecies, and so on, have pragmatic value, but are too few in number and too ambiguous in past usage to convey specific information about the organisms to which they refer. A more moderate view has been expressed by Lewis (1963, p. 38), who has stated that "Classification by its very nature requires that some level of detail be omitted in the designation of classes" and (p. 39) that "One cannot . . . combine, in the same system, categories based on genetic relationship with categories based on breeding habit or manner of reproduction." For these as well as other reasons, various workers have suggested that special-purpose categories should serve in the latter role (cf. Gregor, 1963; Heslop-Harrison, 1953; Bennett, 1964). This would help resolve the conflict of categories, allow the conventional terminology to be continued in use, and allow for additional terminologies to be used when appropriate.

One result of the use of parallel categories is the belief on the part of some taxonomists that taxonomy is thereby freed of typologies. The use of these categories may, indeed, free us from the rigidity that has been called "typological thinking," but it hardly rids us of typologies. It merely supplants old typologies with new ones. It is true that the experimental categories do give us greater descriptive flexibility than the traditional taxonomic terminology, but this is because there are more of these experimental categories and because they are not necessarily members of a hierarchical series. It has recently been estimated that at least 100 "experimental" terms have been coined to apply to such relationships at the infraspecific level alone (Bennett, 1964). Nevertheless, there are still too few terms to describe the spectrum of relationships existing among individuals within a population and between populations, but, at the same time, there are too many terms available for general comprehension and use. The existence of these terms and the orderly, compartmentalized and sometimes rigid concepts they reflect have a strong influence on how we view populations, how we describe them, and, most important, how we study them. Close adherence to these conceptual restrictions may cause us to be blind to significant populational events. This point may be obscure, so in the remaining time I will give a brief account of some recent investigations that will illustrate current trends in population studies of plants and will show that some of our population concepts are a bit outdated.

If, as Bennett suggests, the Turessonian terminology and its associated concepts are at the root of some of our past systematic difficulties, it might be worthwhile to discuss some of these concepts in the light of recent investigations. In Turesson's sense, an ecotype refers to infraspecific populations that are recognized on morphological grounds and that occupy distinct habitats. In the late 1930's, some workers considered that ecotypes were more or less equivalent to taxonomic subspecies (e.g., Clausen, *et al.*, 1939). Many subspecies of plants probably are ecotypes in the Turessonian sense, but it does not follow that ecotypes are always morphologically distinct, nor does it follow that when morphological characters are associated with ecotypes these characters have any specific adaptive relationship to local habitat features. Nevertheless, we still encounter the practice of calling a morphologically different population (or group of populations) of a species that occurs in a specific habitat an ecotype without any real evidence of genecological status.

The work of Kruckeberg (1951, as discussed by Constance, 1953) has shown the impracticability of using the term ecotype as an unqualified, infraspecific taxonomic term. He demonstrated that within a single climatic ecotype of *Achillea borealis* there were serpentine and nonserpentine ecotypes. If this species were subdivided into ecotypes on the basis of edaphic adaptation, the clustering of its populations would display a pattern very different than would be shown by subdivision on the basis of climatic adaptation. As Constance (1953, p. 645) puts it, ". . . the occurrence of ecotypes within ecotypes, the existence of climatic seasonal, edaphic, and biotic ecotypes . . . raises a serious question as to whether or not they afford any reliable basis whatsoever for taxonomic classification." The term "ecotype" is still convenient to use, but it should be prefaced by an adjective specifying to which of the multitudinous environmental conditions the plant under consideration is adapted.

A number of workers continue to emphasize that ecotypic variation is clinal rather than discontinuous. Yet, many edaphic conditions such as the occurrence of serpentine are sharply discontinuous. Going back to Kruckeberg's work, the distribution of serpentine outcrops in the West resembles numerous islands in a sea of less stringent soil types. One would expect serpentinophilous edaphic ecotypes to show discontinuous distributions corresponding to the distribution of serpentine soils. Many of the serpentine populations are in close proximity to conspecific populations that are on non-serpentine soils. What is the expectation concerning the genetic discontinuities in a plant species that occurs in a more or less continuous population extending across such a sharp edaphic boundary? We might expect that outbreeding plants would have difficulty in developing or maintaining genetic discontinuities related to their edaphic adaptations because of gene flow between plants on the two substrates.

A decade ago, Jowett (1958) showed that lead-tolerant races of several species of the grass genus *Agrostis* occurred on the lead-rich soils around mine workings in Britain. Individuals obtained from normal soils adjacent to the mine workings were susceptible to the toxic effects of lead when grown in the leaden soils. The lead-tolerant and lead-intolerant plants appear to form one continuous population, yet the individuals seemingly do not intergrade with respect to lead tolerance. Plants were either tolerant or nontolerant, and their response to lead was related to the origin of the plants. These grasses are mostly self-incompatible and are wind-pollinated. Therefore, extensive gene flow throughout the population would be expected, but apparently it does not occur. More recently, Gregory and Bradshaw (1965) made similar observations on *Agrostis tenuis* with respect to toxic metals in the soil, and genetic discontinuities over a small area also were evident in this species.

Many evolutionists have argued that spatial barriers are necessary to maintain slightly divergent gene pools in conspecific populations. Yet there are now numerous examples, such as the ones I have cited, where slightly different populations or subpopulations of a species occur within a few meters of each other and continue to maintain their respective genetic integrities. In the grass *Agrostis stolonifera,* Jain and Bradshaw (1966) observed that as much as 25 percent gene flow may occur between adjacent pasture and cliff populations of this species without measurable effect on the composition of either population. This pattern of discontinuity exists not because of lack of interbreeding among these two races and not because of lack of seed dispersal; it exists because stringent selection operates at the time of germination, or shortly thereafter, to prevent the establishment of an individual with the wrong genotype–habitat interaction. The intensity of selection under these circumstances must be exceedingly strong.

Each of the grass species discussed above appears to form a more-or-less continuous population that spans edaphic or climatological discontinuities. It would be convenient to call these aggregations single populations but, from a genecological standpoint, such aggregations should be viewed as two contiguous Mendelian populations that apparently are strongly isolated with respect to gene exchange. Even though these two adjacent populations have a common gene pool, breeding is not at random but is effectively restricted to individuals within each population. Since the lead soils mentioned above have appeared within historic times, the development of such ecological races must have occurred recently and rapidly and should be viewed as an example of sympatric race formation. It is possible that inbreeding within each of the two contiguous but ecologically restricted populations may eventually lead to the accumulation of morphological differences that would supplement the physiological differences now extant, but at present these metal-ecotypes are not morphologically distinguishable. Nevertheless, the concept of ecotypic differentiation still carries with it a strong morphological flavor. As Gregor and Watson (1961, p. 167) state: "If ecotypic differentiation were always or even generally correlated with sets of taxonomically useful attributes, the determination of ecotypic patterns would present no novel problem." But we must realize that a large number of important adaptive attributes of plants are not reflected in their morphology and can be recognized only after experimental studies.

The work of Turesson and many of his successors suggests that ecotypic differences are genetically fixed with a high degree of precision. An extension of this suggestion is that the range of phenotypic plasticity of an individual is narrow, and if a species occupies a wide range of habitats, it does so because it is composed of numerous ecological races, each of which has a narrow tolerance. Yet, most ecological races seem to have left an open door that allows for flexibility of both the individual and the race. For example, Kruckeberg (1951) demonstrated that a few individuals of a predominantly nonserpentine race of *Achillea borealis* grew as well on serpentine as did the serpentine races. Although this nonserpentine race generally is not adapted for survival on serpentine, it could easily spawn a serpentinophilous offspring race should an occasion arise.

Although we often think of ecological races as narrowly adapted, Gregor and Watson (1961, p. 170) have pointed out that, on the contrary, "... it may well be a cryptic feature of ecotypic selection to favor genotypes with a high plasticity potential." Nelson's (1965) interesting work with *Prunella vulgaris* has shown that this weedy species is made up of genetically fixed, dwarf lawn races as well as phenocopies that mimic the lawn races. He points out that this phenocopy response is as effective an adaptation to the environment as is the genetically fixed response. Gregor and Watson (1961) and Nelson (1965) emphasize that such phenotypes eventually may achieve genetic fixity via a Waddingtonian route, but it is reasonable to assume that, under some conditions, high plasticity may continue to exist more or less permanently.

Another population phenomenon that interests the evolutionist but frustrates the taxonomist is natural hybridization. The positive evolutionary consequences of hybridization in plants are now generally accepted (see Anderson, 1949; Stebbins, 1959; and Anderson and Stebbins, 1954). Nevertheless, a few things remain to be said on the subject. We must realize that what we commonly call interspecific hybridization consists of two sequences. The first sequence is the actual interspecific pollination, fertilization, and seed formation; if any of these events fails to occur, hybridization has not taken place. The second sequence is the germination, growth, and maturation of the hybrid individual. The result of the second sequence may be called hybrid establishment, even though, incorrectly, it often is called hybridization. It is merely the usual and chief evidence that hybridization has taken place.

Making a distinction between these sequences is important because our estimates of the degree of interspecific hybridization in the field most often are based on the results of hybrid establishment rather than on observations of hybridization itself. The extent or rates of these two processes in populations may be unequal. Observations by a few workers on such diverse genera as *Ceanothus* (Nobs, 1963, and unpublished data), *Chaenactis* (Kyhos, 1965), and *Papaver* (McNaughton and Harper, 1960b) suggest that hybridization between various sympatric species of these genera occurs at a relatively high frequency but that successful hybrid establishment is a rare event. Although these observations require further documentation, they serve to emphasize the important role of the environment in selecting plants with specific genetic qualifications for occupancy of a site.

In these and other examples the hybridizing species may or may not be interfertile, and hybridizations may be made easily under garden conditions; however, from the standpoint of population biology, what occurs in the field is more important than what occurs in the experimental garden. The habitat plays an important role in determining the effective breeding pattern of a population. It also plays an important role in determining what effect hybridization will have on the populations involved. Briggs (1962) has shown that hybrids between species of Australian *Ranunculus* occur over a very small zone of interspecies contact that may be as narrow as 1 meter. Despite the abundance and high fertility of these interspecific hybrids, there is no evidence of backcrossing with the parental species. As Bigelow (1965, p. 451) points out, "Overemphasis on 'interbreeding' seems to spring from the assumption that hybridization always tends to make the gene pools of divergent populations progressively more similar . . .." It will do so, however, only if the difference between these populations is eroded by an increasing interflow of genes. My point is that hybridization may occur continually between different species with no apparent effect. That this is so aids the taxonomist in clearly delimiting his species, but what does this do for the species themselves?

We might expect this gametic wastage to result in the rapid buildup of genetic isolating mechanisms. As systematists, we emphasize the positive value of strong barriers preventing interbreeding between species. Yet, at the same time, we are confronted with an array of evidence indicating the strong role that the breakdown of isolation has played in evolution: polyploidy, introgression, stabilization of hybrids at the diploid level, and apomixis are all consequences of hybridization. We should assume that the ability to hybridize may have a positive selective value in many evolutionary lines. For example, Harlan and deWet (1963) have proposed the concept of the compilospecies, which is a species or species complex (usually widespread) that hybridizes locally and widely with various of its relatives and assumes some of the characteristics of each of these species from region to region. They (p. 499) dramatically characterize a compilospecies as " . . . genetically agressive, plundering related species of their heredities, and in some cases it may completely assimilate a species, causing it to become extinct." This statement does not emphasize, however, the increase in local adaptive range that is a consequence of such "genetic plundering." These authors also make the interesting point that plant species that are themselves derivatives of wide crosses tend to make wide crosses more readily than those species having more restricted germ plasm. Thus, once successful interspecific hybridization has occurred in the history of a species, the derivatives of the hybridization may have increased potentiality for occasional subsequent hybridization long into the future.

Rattenbury (1962) has suggested that reproductive isolation has not developed between many New Zealand species and that occasional interspecific hybridization is responsible for the polymorphism characteristic of so many taxa in that interesting insular flora. His explanation of why hybridization is so extensive in New Zealand is complicated, but it is related to the ability of plants to make rapid adaptive responses to the pronounced climatic changes in New Zealand in the Pliocene and Pleistocene. The present members of the New Zealand flora successfully made such responses. (Otherwise, they would not be members of the flora at present!) This seems to have been accomplished via genetic recombination resulting from cyclical hybridization. Similar events also may have occurred in Australia, where periodic aridities alternated with wetter periods, resulting in cyclical expansion and contraction of plant populations. These occasional and continued interspecies contacts during periods of expansion increased the opportunity for hybridization. From the resultant hybrids and their segregates, populations were derived that had new adaptive modes in response to the changed ecological conditions.

The net effect of periodic large-scale hybridizations is that many large genera in both New Zealand and Australia are characterized by weak interspecific isolating mechanisms. These include ecologically successful genera such as *Hebe* (*Veronica*), *Eucalyptus, Senecio,* and many others. Although we often think of interspecific genetic isolation as a means of allowing species to maintain their identity, it is the extensive history of hybridization in these antipodean genera that has led to the development of a multiplicity of species. The presence of strong isolating mechanisms may enhance species formation, but so does the absence of these mechanisms. As systematists, we should not view interspecific hybridization as a bothersome accident but rather as a genetic phenomenon of positive evolutionary significance. As Raven (1960, p. 98) has stated, " . . . the evidence appears strong that [interspecific hybridization] provides a most significant evolutionary pathway and it should therefore be regarded as an integral part of the adaptive systems in many groups of higher plants."

Our estimates of the degree and patterns of hybridization are based largely on morphological considerations. From the evolutionary standpoint, the features that ultimately determine the fate of hybridization are the adaptive traits of the hybrids and their derivatives. These traits may or may not be associated with morphological features. Therefore, our descriptions of hybridization, which are based largely on morphological studies, may, in fact, give us little insight into the actual changes in adaptive patterns resulting from hybridization. McHale and Alston (1964) have found that some plants of *Baptisia* that seemed, on the basis of reliable biochemical evidence, to be hybrids showed no morphological indication of this origin and would certainly have been overlooked in a morphological survey of the population. Similarly, Brehm and Ownbey (1965) have identified what they term "chemical introgressants" in *Tragopogon* that also provide no morphological documentation of their origin. In Oregon, I have found some populations of morphologically "typical" *Impatiens ecalcarata* occurring in the habitat characteristic of *I. capensis.* The genetic differences between these strikingly distinct species are probably rather simple. I have suggested that these ecologically aberrant populations of *I. ecalcarata* may be introgressants that possess only the "ecological" genes of *I. capensis* (Ornduff, 1967). Such a suggestion is plausible because these two species hybridize extensively in the area studied.

The morphological orientation that we have toward studying natural hybridization perhaps is reliable much of the time, but we may be overlooking one of the most important consequences of hybridization; namely, changes in adaptive ranges, since such changes may have no morphological expression.

The final point I wish to make about hybridization as a population phenomenon is that increasing evidence suggests that our ideas on the intermediacy of hybrids and hybrid segregates are too restrictive. We now know many examples of interspecific hybrids, between quite different species, that resemble one or the other parent so closely that the hybrids risk being undetected. This seems to be the case in the hybrids between *Papaver rhoeas* and *P. dubium* in Britain (McNaughton and Harper, 1960a) as well as in the interploid hybrids within the grass genus *Holcus* (Carroll and Jones, 1962) and the fern genus *Cyclosorus* (Panigrahi and Manton, 1958). Expected morphological patterns may be further complicated by transgression, in which a segregant genotype exceeds both of its parents in one or more characteristics. This is defined in terms of the F_2 or later generations, but something similar to transgression also may occur in morphological characters (Ornduff and Crovello, 1968) and biochemical characters (Brehm and Ownbey, 1965) at the F_1 level.

Emphasis in much of the preceding discussion has been on the evolutionary importance of the breakdown of isolation between species. I will now change emphasis and discuss intraspecific isolation and its probable consequences. I have talked about intraspecific isolation within populations, so my emphasis now will be on interpopulation isolation within species. Species are often characterized as consisting of populations that are actually or potentially interbreeding. Few plant systematists have had occasion to make extensive intraspecific crosses between populations to verify this statement; but when such crosses have been made, the results have often been rather unexpected. At one extreme, the expected occurs: full crossability and fertility exists between populations of a species. Somewhat lower on the fertility scale, Levin (1966) found a slight decrease in pollen fertility of interpopulation hybrids in *Phlox pilosa* as compared with intrapopulation hybrids. At the bottom of the scale, the interpopulation crosses within the tarweed species *Holocarpha virgata* and *H. heermannii* produced no F_1 plants (Clausen, 1951). Perhaps these tarweeds are unique, however, in their high degree of intraspecific karyotype variability.

In the middle of the scale, Mosquin (1966) has found variable results in *Clarkia rhomboidea.* Some populations of this widespread western annual are interfertile, others are not. Fertility of interpopulation hybrids ranges from 0 to 100 percent. Mosquin states (p. 211) that "Pollen fertility depends not only on the population but also on the particular parental individual of a population used in the cross." Some individuals and populations of this species are reproductively isolated, and others are not. It is clear that reproductive isolation ranging from none, to partial, to absolute exists within this species, but it does not provide a consistent basis for subdividing the species taxonomically.

As I discussed above, a series of related events in sequence often are lumped together under the inclusive term "hybridization." This is also true of the word "interbreeding." First in the sequence is the actual pollination, fertilization, and maturation of seed; the degree to which this can be accomplished I would term "relative crossability." Second, there is germination, growth, and maturation of the offspring; this is progeny establishment. Third, there is the measurement of the "fertility" of the progeny.

It is often assumed that crossability and interfertility are correlated positively, and for this reason the two terms and concepts are not always clearly separated in the literature. A lack of correlation between the two phenomena is probably quite common. This was convincingly demonstrated by Nygren (1957), who reported that after trying for several years to make hybrids between *Lychnis flos-cuculi* and *Melandrium rubrum* for genetic analysis he finally succeeded in getting hybrid seed and quite fertile F_1 progeny. These two species have very low crossability but high interfertility. Clausen (1951) reports that it is harder to make hybrids between populations of *Holocarpha virgata* than it is to cross this species with *H. heermannii,* even though the two species have different chromosome numbers. The different populations of

H. virgata certainly must have a very similar genetic code, even though the distribution of the code in the chromosomes is sufficiently different from population to population to cause a high degree of sterility of interpopulation hybrids of this species.

In my own studies of the composite genus *Blennosperma* I have found a peculiar set of relationships among populations (Ornduff, 1963). *Blennosperma nanum* is a widespread, spring-flowering annual that occurs throughout much of cismontane California. It forms series of large but spatially discontinuous populations. I have made intraspecific hybridizations among individuals originating in 13 populations of this relatively uniform species from throughout its range. With few exceptions, interpopulation crossability proved to be rather low, as most of the crosses produced less than 30 percent seed set. Yet, in general, these few seeds produced highly fertile offspring. In this species, therefore, interpopulation crossability is very low, but interpopulation hybrid fertility is generally very high. In contrast, crossability between the California composite species *Lasthenia fremontii* and *L. conjugens* is very high, yet pollen fertility of the hybrids is less than 30 percent, and seed set is even lower (Ornduff, 1966). Crossability of these species is high, but hybrid fertility is low.

In our systematic studies of populations, we are interested not only in the degree of genetic isolation between populations, but also in the genetic similarities among populations. Genetic isolation can be measured first by relative crossability; second by hybrid fertility. Genetic similarity can be measured only after obtaining hybrids, but a low yield of hybrids is not necessarily a clue to how fertile these hybrids may be. The evolutionary significance of strong interpopulation isolation in such species as *Blennosperma nanum, Clarkia rhomboidea,* and the tarweeds is not clear, but each of these species may be well on its way toward completely cutting off its component populations from genetic contact with each other. In the long run this could lead to extinction of a major proportion of the component populations, if not of the species itself.

This interpopulation isolation may, in fact, account for the near extinction of the closest relative of *Blennosperma nanum,* which is *B. bakeri,* now known from two subpopulations of a single population in central California. It is possible that if this species was more widespread at one time, its demise was initiated when population barriers became developed to the extent that the species was unable to adapt to the rapid climatic changes in California during and after the Pliocene. When we encounter unexpected population phenomena such as that exhibited by the species I have just discussed, we search for some positive evolutionary significance for such phenomena. But perhaps in many of these cases we should be willing to accept the view that these species survive not because of these phenomena but in spite of them.

The way we view populations is reflected in the terms we use to describe them, but this terminology is often formulated before we have sufficient sampling to indicate whether we have observed and described general patterns. For example, the terms allopolyploid and autopolyploid were at one time the only two terms generally used to describe polyploids. It took several years before the numerous intermediate conditions between autoploidy and alloploidy were accommodated by additional terms. Eventually Stebbins (1947) added two new terms: "autoallopolyploid" and "segmental allopolyploid." Whereas the spectrum of polyploid conditions was previously described by two terms, four were now available. Since then additional terms have been coined, but they are not yet in general use.

In applying the terms "autopolyploidy" and "allopolyploidy" we often mix taxonomic and cytological concepts. For example, *Galax aphylla* often is cited as an example of a species having natural autotetraploids. The populations of this species with $n = 12$ are considered autoploid derivatives of the diploids with $n = 6$. These are called autoploids because there is only one species of *Galax*. Or perhaps we could say these are autoploids because they are so similar to the diploids that no other species could have been involved in their origin. If these are, in fact, autoploids, we would expect each chromosome homologue to be represented four times, and might expect multivalent pairing to be prevalent during meiosis. However, in his original report of tetraploidy in *Galax*, Baldwin (1941) stated that only bivalents were observed in the few tetraploid meioses he examined. Is *Galax aphylla* an autoploid or an alloploid?

Because we are led to believe that autoploids are sterile due to multivalent formation, we naturally conclude that the majority of fertile, natural polyploids are alloploids. On the basis of recent work, however, this conclusion may be misleading. A number of examples are now known where the pairing behavior of chromosomes is under either genetic or cytological control. For example, Riley and Chapman (1958) have demonstrated that hexaploid wheat—known to have a large measure of chromosomal duplication—has diploid behavior at meiosis that is under genetic control. On the basis of chromosomal relationships alone, the proportion of multivalents should be very high, but it is not. Although the control of pairing in wheat seems to be genetically controlled, some years ago Upcott (1939) suggested a plausible cytological mechanism that also prevents multivalent formation. She observed that an autoploid tulip (*Tulipa chrysantha*) had normal bivalent formation and was fertile. This normal chromosome behavior was attributed to the restriction of chiasmata to only one per chromosome pair, so multivalent formation was not possible, despite chromosome duplication.

There are suggested examples of naturally occurring, fertile, meiotically regular autoploids that are now allopatric with their parent diploids (e.g., Torres, 1964). Such situations may be rare exceptions. However, Böcher (1961) has suggested that if the analysis of the chromosome number of a species is extended so that many populations from the whole range are sampled it will be possible to find occasional tetraploids in most diploid species. If most of these autoploids are sterile, they will probably have little evolutionary significance except to reinforce our notions about the negative role of autoploidy in evolution. Nevertheless, even sterile autoploids may have an evolutionary future because there is good evidence that in the initially sterile autoploid *Fagopyrum esculentum* (Sacharov, *et al.*, 1944), *Festuca pratenis* (Wöhrmann, 1960), and some other species selection may result in the production of meiotically regular, fertile derivatives as early as the F_2 generation or shortly thereafter. Because it is generally accepted that gene exchange among polyploids occurs more readily than among diploids of a genus, autoploidy may have a substantial role not only in producing stable races or species of autoploid origin, but also in allowing genetic exchange of basically diploid genomes at the polyploid level. If the genetic and cytological mechanisms that I have discussed are at all common, we will have to re-evaluate our ideas concerning the role of autoploidy in evolution.

We often think of polyploidization as an irreversible process. Once a polyploid is formed, we consider it to be isolated genetically from its parents, even though initially such polyploids may coexist sympatrically with the parents. This is probably a true characterization of the relationships among polyploids and diploids most of the time, but there are several instances known where this isolation or irreversibility does not exist. Three decades ago Randolph and Fischer (1939) showed that tetraploid races of maize occasionally spawned fertile diploids. Maize is normally diploid, of course, and the tetraploids used by these workers were artificially created. Later, Müntzing and his co-workers (Müntzing, *et al.*, 1963) observed that plants with $2n = 28$ were present in plots of octoploid *Triticale* with $2n = 56$. These "diploids" were partially fertile, and they produced offspring. Thompson (1962) has demonstrated that polyploids of *Rubus* at the 7-ploid and 8-ploid levels could produce viable offspring with diploid chromosome complements as well as offspring with still higher ploidy levels. A recent review by Kimber and Riley (1963) discusses several other examples of similar phenomena.

Most of these examples of the derivation of polyhaploids are from cultivated plants and have been investigated by workers having little concern for the evolutionary implications of their observations. Therefore, it was not until very recently that Raven and Thompson (1964) emphasized the possible evolutionary significance of polyhaploidy by stating (p. 252),

> We can no longer assume that polyploids are an evolutionary "dead end," connected only tenuously to the main evolutionary line of diploids by the rare exchange of genetic material . . . . The shift back and forth between the diploid state and the tetraploid state might serve as a mechanism for adjusting the balance of fitness and flexibility for the organisms of that group through selection.

Furthermore, polyploids may not be as genetically isolated from their diploid parents as we generally believe. Many years ago Müntzing (1937) pointed out that natural triploid hybrids between diploid and tetraploid races of the orchard grass *Dactylis glomerata* are pollen-sterile but can form seeds when appropriately pollinated. According to Zohary and Nur (1959), these triploid hybrids apparently produce a large number of unreduced triploid eggs. If these eggs are fertilized by sperm from tetraploid plants, the resultant offspring are sterile pentaploids, but if they are fertilized by haploid sperm from diploids, the resultant offspring are tetraploid. Zohary and Nur collected seed (in Israel) from two naturally occurring *Dactylis* triploids that produced a large number of tetraploid progeny. As they pointed out (p. 317), "By producing a large proportion of vigorous tetraploid progeny, triploids can serve as an efficient bridge for one-way gene flow from diploid level to tetraploid level." The resultant pattern would appear to be one of introgression of the tetraploid races by the diploid races. It is easy to say that this is a rare occurrence, yet we know of many cases of persistent natural triploids occurring with their parents (cf. Carroll and Jones, 1962), and these triploids, especially in the case of perennials, may serve as an effective bridge for gene flow between the parents.

Finally, I wish to point out that our measure of sterility in flowering plants is usually based on estimates of pollen viability rather than of seed production. Sterility of pollen, however, need not be associated with equivalent seed sterility, as demonstrated by the *Dactylis* work discussed above. We should also remember that the term "sterility" is a relative one and that interspecific hybrids that we consider sterile can serve, in time, as a substantial genetic bridge between their parents. The example in *Elymus* discussed by Stebbins (1959) is an excellent illustration of this possibility. In California, two distinctive perennial rye grasses, *Elymus triticoides* and *E. condensatus,* hybridize readily when populations of the two come into contact. The interspecific hybrids are vigorous, but they have 1–5 percent stainable pollen and do not set seed in cultivation, although in the field they apparently do so on a very small scale. Nevertheless, clones are found in the field that include the whole spectrum of variability from *E. triticoides* to *E. condensatus,* indicating that either backcrossing or segregation of the F_1 hybrids has occurred extensively. Again, events of low probability can be shown to have far-reaching effects, and Stebbins believes that situations such as the one he describes are not uncommon.

It is clear from the preceding discussion that much is still to be learned from intensive studies at the population level. Evolutionary change is initiated within populations and studies at this level should provide valuable new insights into the evolutionary process itself. However, tradition, orthodoxy, descriptive terms, and preconceptions dealing with population phenomena have a strong influence in shaping our investigative methodologies and on how we interpret the results of our studies. If, indeed, the systematist is a student–if not *the* student–of evolution, he must discard or broaden many of his conceptual straightjackets and approach evolutionary problems with a truly open mind.

REFERENCES

Anderson, E. 1949. Introgressive hybridization. John Wiley & Sons, New York. 109 p.

Anderson, E., and G. L. Stebbins. 1954. Hybridization as an evolutionary stimulus. Evolution 8:378–388.

Baldwin, J. 1941. *Galax:* The genus and its chromosomes. J. Hered. 32:249–254.

Bennett, E. 1964. Historical perspectives in genecology. Scottish Plant Breeding Sta. Rec. 1964:51–115.

Bigelow, R. S. 1965. Hybrid zones and reproductive isolation. Evolution 19:449–458.

Böcher, T. 1961. The development of cytotaxonomy since Darwin's time, p. 26–43. *In* P. J. Wanstall [ed.]. A Darwin centenary. London, Bot. Soc. British Isles.

Brehm, B. G., and M. Ownbey. 1965. Variation in chromatographic patterns in the *Tragopogon dubius-pratensis-porrifolius* complex (Compositae). Am. J. Bot. 52:811–818.

Briggs, B. G. 1962. Interspecific hybridization in the *Ranunculus lappaceus* group. Evolution 16:372–390.

Carroll, C. P., and K. Jones. 1962. Cytotaxonomic studies in *Holcus.* III. A morphological study of the triploid F_1 hybrid between *Holcus lanatus* L. and *H. mollis.* New Phytol. 61:72–84.

Clausen, J. 1951. Stages in the evolution of plant species. Cornell Univ. Press, Ithaca. 206 p.

Clausen, J., D. D. Keck, and W. M. Hiesey. 1939. The concept of species based on experiment. Am. J. Bot. 26:103–106.

Constance, L. 1953. The role of plant ecology in biosystematics. Ecology 34:642–649.

Ehrlich, P. R., and R. W. Holm. 1963. The process of evolution. McGraw-Hill, New York. 347 p.

Gilmour, J. S. L., and J. W. Gregor. 1939. Demes: A suggested new terminology. Nature 144:333.

Gregor, J. W. 1963. Genecological (biosystematic) classification: The case for

special categories. Regnum Vegetabile 27:24–26.
Gregor, J. W., and P. J. Watson. 1961. Ecotypic differentiation: Observations and reflections. Evolution 15:166–173.
Gregory, R. P., and A. D. Bradshaw. 1965. Heavy metal tolerance in populations of *Agrostis tenuis* Sibth. and other grasses. New Phytol. 64:131–143.
Harlan, J. R., and J. M. J. deWet. 1963. The compilospecies concept. Evolution 17:497–501.
Heslop-Harrison, J. 1953. New concepts in flowering plant taxonomy. W. Heinemann Ltd., London. 135 p.
Heslop-Harrison, J. 1955. The conflict of categories, p. 160–172. *In* J. E. Lousley [ed.] Species studies in the British flora. London, Bot. Soc. British Isles.
Jain, S. K., and A. D. Bradshaw. 1966. Evolutionary divergence among adjacent plant populations. I. The evidence and its theoretical analysis. Heredity 21:407–441.
Jowett, D. 1958. Populations of *Agrostis* species tolerant of heavy metals. Nature 182:816–817.
Kimber, G., and R. Riley. 1963. Haploid angiosperms. Bot. Rev. 29:480–531.
Kruckeberg, A. R. 1951. Intraspecific variability in the response of certain native plant species to serpentine soil. Am. J. Bot. 38:408–419.
Kyhos, D. W. 1965. The independent aneuploid origin of two species of *Chaenactis* (Compositae) from a common ancestor. Evolution 19:26–43.
Levin, D. A. 1966. The *Phlox pilosa* complex: Crossing and chromosome relationships. Brittonia 18:142–161.
Lewis, H. 1963. The taxonomic problem of inbreeders or how to solve any taxonomic problem. Regnum Vegetabile 27:37–44.
Mason, H. L. 1950. Taxonomy, systematic botany, and biosystematics. Madroño 10:193–208.
Mayr, E. 1963. Animal species and evolution. Belknap Press of Harvard Univ. Press, Cambridge. 797 p.
McHale, J., and R. E. Alston. 1964. Utilization of chemical patterns in the analysis of hybridization between *Baptisia leucantha* and *B. sphaerocarpa.* Evolution 18:304–311.
McNaughton, I. H., and J. L. Harper. 1960a. The comparative biology of closely related species living in the same area. II. Aberrant morphology and a virus-like syndrome in hybrids between *Papaver rhoeas* L. and *P. dubium* L. New Phytol. 59:27–41.
McNaughton, I. H., and J. L. Harper. 1960b. The comparative biology of closely related species living in the same area. III. The nature of barriers isolating sympatric populations of *Papaver dubius* and *P. lecoqii.* New Phytol. 59:129–137.
Mosquin, T. 1966. Toward a more useful taxonomy for chromosomal races. Brittonia 18:203–214.
Müntzing, A. 1937. The effects of chromosomal variation in *Dactylis.* Hereditas 23:113–235.
Müntzing, A., N. J. Hrishi, and C. Tarkowski. 1963. Reversion to haploidy in

strains of hexaploid and octoploid *Triticale*. Hereditas 49:78–90.
Nelson, A. P. 1965. Taxonomic and evolutionary implications of lawn races in *Prunella vulgaris* (Labiatae). Brittonia 17:160–174.
Nobs, M. 1963. Experimental studies on species relationships in *Ceanothus*. Carnegie Inst. Washington Publ. 623:1–94.
Nygren, A. 1957. A fertile hybrid *Lychnis flos-cuculi* and *Melandrium rubrum* and its sex segregating offspring. Kungl. Lantsbrukshögsk. Ann. 23:413–421.
Ornduff, R. 1963. Experimental studies in two genera of Helenieae (Compositae): *Blennosperma* and *Lasthenia*. Quart. Rev. Biol. 38:141–150.
Ornduff, R. 1966. A biosystematic survey of the goldfield genus *Lasthenia*. University California Publ. Bot. 40:1–92.
Ornduff, R. 1967. Hybridization and regional variation in Pacific Northwestern *Impatiens* (Balsaminaceae). Brittonia 19:122–128.
Ornduff, R., and T. J. Crovello. 1968. Numerical taxonomy of Limnanthaceae. Am. J. Bot. 55:173–182.
Panigrahi, G., and I. Manton. 1958. Cytological and taxonomic observations on some members of the *Cyclosorus parasiticus* complex. J. Linn. Soc. London. 60:729–743.
Porter, C. L. 1967. Taxonomy of flowering plants. 2nd ed. W. H. Freeman Co., San Francisco. 472 p.
Randolph, L. F., and H. E. Fischer. 1939. The occurrence of parthenogenetic diploids in tetraploid maize. Proc. Nat. Acad. Sci. U.S. 25:161–164.
Rattenbury, J. A. 1962. Cyclic hybridization as a survival mechanism in the New Zealand forest flora. Evolution 16:348–363.
Raven, P. H. 1960. Interspecific hybridization as an evolutionary stimulus in *Oenothera*. Proc. Linn. Soc. London 173:92–98.
Raven, P. H., and H. J. Thompson. 1964. Haploidy and angiosperm evolution. Am. Natur. 98:251–252.
Riley, R., and V. Chapman. 1958. Genetic control of the cytologically diploid behavior of hexaploid wheat. Nature 182:713–715.
Sacharov, V., S. L. Frolova, and V. Mansurova. 1944. High fertility of buckwheat tetraploids obtained by means of colchicine treatment. Nature 154:613.
Simpson, G. G. 1961. Principles of animal taxonomy. Columbia Univ. Press, New York. 247 p.
Stebbins, G. L. 1947. Types of polyploids: Their classification and significance. Adv. Genet. 1:403–429.
Stebbins, G. L. 1959. The role of hybridization in evolution. Proc. Am. Phil. Soc. 103:231–251.
Thompson, M. M. 1962. Cytogenetics of *Rubus*. III. Meiotic instability in some higher polyploids. Am. J. Bot. 49:575–582.
Torres, A. 1964. The chromosome races of *Zinnia juniperifolia*. Am. J. Bot. 52:760–765.
Upcott, M. B. 1939. The genetic structure of *Tulipa*. III. Meiosis in polyploids. J. Genet. 37:303–327.
Winge, Ö. 1940. Taxonomic and evolutionary studies in *Erophila* based on

cytogenetic investigations. C. R. Lab. Carlsberg, Ser. Physiol. 23:41–73.
Wöhrmann, K. 1960. Samentragsanalyse von di- und tetraploiden Wissenschwingel (*Festuca pratensis* Huds.). Z. Pflanzenzücht. 42:93–102.
Zohary, D., and U. Nur. 1959. Natural triploids in the orchard grass, *Dactylis glomerata* L., polyploid complex and their significance for gene flow from diploid to tetraploid levels. Evolution 13:311–317.

Discussion

Kenton L. Chambers

Dr. Ornduff has tried to make us feel a little uncomfortable, a little less than self-satisfied with our categories and concepts for classification of plant populations. As evolutionists, we approach the study of populations in terms of *processes*—factors that allow populations to persist, change, migrate, and adapt in endless subtle ways to their surroundings. As taxonomists, we feel obliged to translate our observations into *categories*—to say there is a limited number of patterns into which populations may be arranged.

In warning us about possible "conceptual straightjackets," Dr. Ornduff is saying that the categories and special classifications that have been erected—for example, the categories of experimental taxonomy, of genecology, of cytogenetics—should not form the starting points of population research. We cannot make much progress or expect to detect the novel and significant features of plant populations, if we set out only to show or reaffirm the presence in them of orthodox patterns and particular defined categories.

Some remarkable advances in our understanding of populations have come from inspired generalizations based originally on research with limited numbers of plant groups. The concept of distinct ecotypes, for example, came from the work of Turesson with certain plants of southern Sweden. But as we know, ecotype variation can fall into a very large number of patterns, and the categories proposed by Turesson have been much modified as additional groups of plants have come to be thoroughly known. Lately a suggestion has come from Langlet that it may no longer be scientifically useful to attempt to classify population systems in terms of ecotypic categories.

In our work as evolutionists, we ought to be interested in how particular attributes of plants act in maintaining population adaptedness or in allowing for genetic change; and we ought to be less concerned with how to stretch previously established population categories to fit our various observations. A difference in the breeding system of two groups may be correlated with differences in their variation pattern that are predictable, at least in part; and useful categories might be constructed on this basis. Probably we cannot generalize about specific factors: Does apomixis always tend to produce similar variation patterns, for example? However, we can compare different plants whose "way of life" is similar in certain respects, to detect interacting or correlated factors that may comprise an adaptive syndrome.

The caution to be kept in mind, I believe, is that we be alert to new possibilities, and not routinely interpret the populations we study in terms of rigid *a priori* categories. The focus should be on the biological attributes of individuals, and whatever significance we can make of these in our attempts to understand the evolutionary processes in plant populations.

Discussion

H. J. Thompson

One of the recurrent points of Dr. Ornduff's paper was a plea for the systematists to continue to assess the classifications that they use in their attempt to understand the overwhelming diversity of the biological world. Classifications, in this context, refer not only to the hierarchical classification from species to phylum of all living organisms but include such classifications as kinds of isolating mechanisms and hybridizations, types of polyploidy, and the elaborate classifications of kinds of species into morphological, ecological, and even biological species. Dr. Ornduff's points are particularly appropriate for a symposium of this sort, for although stemming from work on vascular plants, his remarks are of interest to all systematists and are not dependent on interests and knowledge of the detailed characteristics of some particular group of organisms.

My comments on this aspect of Dr. Ornduff's talk will emphasize that the many different schemes of categories of the systematists are really hypotheses constructed to accommodate facts about organic diversity. These schemes should not be judged on how well they accommodate these facts but by their fruitfulness, that is, by the extent to which they generate meaningful questions about previously unrecognized aspects of biological diversity. As Dr. Ornduff implied, and as I would emphasize, systematists have not always treated their schemes as hypotheses that will generate new questions—that will lead to new facts and, in turn to new hypotheses—but have tended to consider them an inflexible component of their science, an end in themselves. As evidence for this I submit that it is the practice of most systematists to avoid studying groups of organisms that other systematists are working on or that have been recently monographed. Too often a taxonomic monograph is thought of as the last word, not merely the latest word. Let me indicate briefly why I think systematists differ from other scientists in this regard and why systematics sometimes is considered an art. First, our classification of all organisms into species, genera, families, etc., is so useful for storing information and arranging specimens in museums and herbaria that we are reluctant to consider newer, more meaningful classifications. Second, the rules of nomenclature, so necessary for uniformity and stability of names, impress their resistance to change on all classifications that systematists use. These two constraints in systematics, though vitally important, permeate the discipline so that we are less able than most scientists to change our classifications and concepts—our hypotheses—even when there is no practical value in their retention. Two examples will serve to clarify this point.

In studying groups in which polyploidy is involved, we are compelled to ask if the process was alloploidy or autoploidy. Our answer, whatever it might be, serves as a releaser, a displacement activity, that diverts us from a more original way of understanding polyploidy. The clear demonstration, several decades ago, of the mechanism of doubling chromosome numbers has been incorporated into systematic concepts in the form of a dogma—that tetraploids arise from diploids but diploids cannot be derived from tetraploids. Although many of the patterns of variability in polyploid groups make attractive the idea of diploids being derived from tetraploids, only recently, with stimulus from geneticists, have systematists considered this reversal pathway to be important. It remained for geneticists, with a more open-minded approach to polyploidy, to develop the idea of the reverse pathway.

For a second example, I draw on Dr. Ornduff's remarks about our difficulties in dealing conceptually with hybridization. When we encounter a situation where two recognizably different groups of individuals are connected by individuals intermediate in character, we respond in ways largely determined by our previous experience as systematists. If we find the intermediates relatively scarce, we may describe the situation that keeps the hybridization at a minimum. We may call this genetic interaction between two populations an isolating machanism. We even go on to classify isolating mechanisms, forgetting that isolation is only the comparative view of the reproductive coherence of two different populations. Perhaps we chose to think in terms of isolating mechanisms because, as systematists, we emphasize the differences and look "between" populations rather than into them. Had systematists done the initial studies on the formation of raindrops they probably would have thought in terms of the isolating mechanisms between them rather than of the cohesive force of water.

The many different kinds of classifications used by systematists help us to understand what we know about organic diversity. They are powerful tools of summary and integration. There is every reason to expect these schemes of categories to raise fruitful questions about organic diversity. There is little reason to expect them—and no reason to require them—to participate in the understanding of the new information to which they lead.

Informal Discussion

CRONQUIST: All three of these speeches were very interesting and useful. I have no criticism of the things that were said, but I want to comment on some of their taxonomic implications. Almost anything that you can sit down in your armchair and dream up as a breeding behavior happens in something, somewhere. As a result, any attempt at a precise definition of the species, or of this or that infraspecific category, will work on only a limited segment of the actual cases. From a practical taxonomic standpoint, we are forced to accept the concept that has been advocated by Mason, among others, that a species is a *kind*—the smallest kind that you just have to recognize. From there on we can talk about this feature and that feature, that in one group the species have this characteristic, and in another group some other characteristic, but essentially the species is the smallest group that you just cannot ignore. Further elaboration is useful and necessary, but that is where we have to start.

DONALD W. TINKLE

Evolutionary Implications of Comparative Population Studies in the Lizard *Uta stansburiana*

A small iguanid lizard, *Uta stansburiana,* has been the subject of intensive study by me and a number of my graduate students for the past six years. Investigations have been made of the population structure and reproduction of the species (Tinkle, 1961; Cuellar, 1966; Hahn, 1964); of home range and movements (Tinkle, *et al.*, 1962; Tinkle and Woodard, 1967); of behavior (Ferguson, 1966 a and b; Irwin, 1965); of the relation of photoperiod, temperature and fat storage to reproduction (Tinkle and Irwin, 1965; Hahn and Tinkle, 1965); and of the variation and detailed systematics of the species (Knopf, 1963; Ballinger and McKinney, 1967; Ballinger and Tinkle, in manuscript). Finally, data have been presented on the demographic properties of populations of *Uta stansburiana* by Tinkle (1967) to which the reader is referred for detailed documentation of some of the statements made in this paper.

Comparative studies, whether of morphological, physiological, or behavioral traits, properly may be considered systematics because they contribute information of value for understanding the taxa considered in regard to their relationships and the evolution of their attributes. The present study is concerned with the relation between certain population characteristics, such as density, age structure and size structure, and the evolution of such individual characteristics as degree of aggression, age-specific fecundity, size, sexual dimorphism, and behavior in different populations. The origins of characters that have taxonomic significance as well as ecological importance ultimately must be found at the level of evolving populations, and it is there that this study is focused.

MATERIALS AND METHODS

Uta stansburiana is a small (maximum length, 60 mm from snout to vent) ground-dwelling lizard of the western United States and Mexico (see map, Figure 1). Within this area several geographic races have been described, and at least four of these races are valid. The distribution of the three U.S. races is shown on the map. This paper is concerned almost entirely with the northern race (*U. s. stansburiana*) and the southeastern race (*U. s. stejnegeri*).

Uta s. stansburiana is small, with little or no pattern, and with little sexual dimorphism in color; *U. s. stejnegeri* is larger, patterned, and strongly dimorphic (Figure 2). Despite these striking differences, there is some evidence of intergradation, at least between the southwestern (currently considered *U. s. stejnegeri*) and northern races (see Figure 1).

The ecological data presented here were collected through intensive field studies in two Texas populations of *U. s. stejnegeri* over a five-year period and from a much less extensive two-year study of one Colorado population of *U. s. stansburiana.*

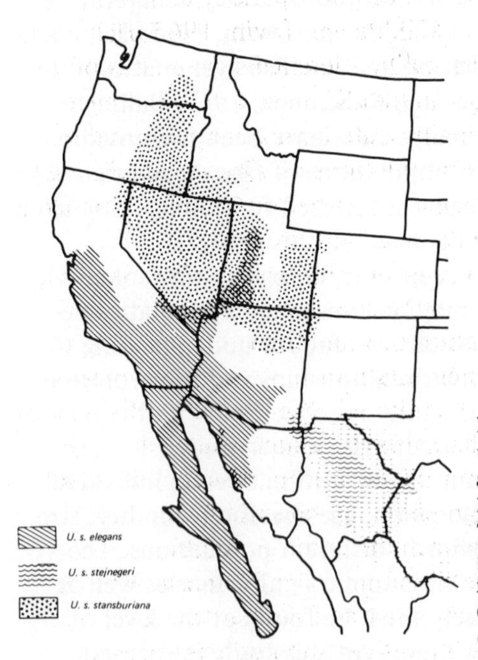

FIGURE 1 Geographic distribution of the three major mainland races of *Uta stansburiana* (data chiefly from unpublished records of Royce E. Ballinger). The range of the southwestern race should extend slightly farther south into northern Sinaloa than shown (Royce Ballinger, personal communication).

FIGURE 2 Male and female *U. s. stansburiana* (A) from Mesa County, Colorado, with male and female *U. s. stejnegeri* (B) from Winkler County, Texas.

In both Texas and Colorado, two-acre (300 by 300 feet) study areas were gridded with numbered stakes. All adult lizards and the young they produced were marked. They were recaptured at intervals, and their behavior and social interactions were followed closely. Some field experimentation was carried out, but most of the data herein were derived from the mark-recapture program. It is important that nearly all lizards in the study areas—not just a sample of them—were registered each generation.

RESULTS

TERRITORY SIZE AND INDIVIDUAL FITNESS

Both sexes in the Texas population are highly aggressive, and their aggressive defense of an area is not limited to small regions of the home range but extends to the perimeters. Females are much more sedentary than males; because of this, and because of their aggressive nature, there is little overlap in home ranges. This is documented in Figure 3, which shows the dispersion of females in one of the Texas study areas during a year in which adult density was high.

In a recent work (Tinkle, 1965) it was shown that, by marking the young lizards at or near the time of hatching, one can determine the probable parents of most of the young lizards. By following these young to sexual maturity it could be shown which females produced the most surviving offspring. By assigning each female a gametic contribution of 1.0 for each offspring that survived to maturity, the total genetic contribution of each resident female to the next generation was estimated, and this figure was used as the measure of individual fitness.

I chose to measure fitness in this way because I think the term has no evolutionary significance if it is defined in any other way. Alleles for various traits usually increase in frequency because of differential reproduction and survival of the animals that carry

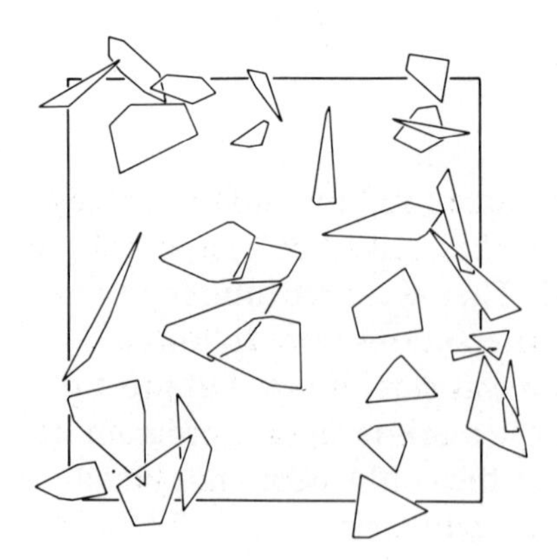

FIGURE 3 Diagram of home ranges (minimum polygon method) of female *Uta stansburiana* on one Texas study area during a year of high adult density.

those alleles. I assume that living to sexual maturity is tantamount to passing genes to the next generation.

Assuming that the ultimate function of territorial defense is to increase fitness, there should be a positive correlation between size of territory held and fitness of the individual. Territory size can best be estimated by the mean recapture radius (see Tinkle and Woodard, 1967). One would not expect perfect correlation, because the variance in fitness is affected by other factors, such as quality of the habitat, food supply, and availability of shelter. However, there is a highly significant ($P \cong 0.001$) positive correlation (Figure 4).

The degree of correlation was greatly increased by comparing years when density of adults and their offspring during the reproductive season was higher and lower than the median of 83 per acre.

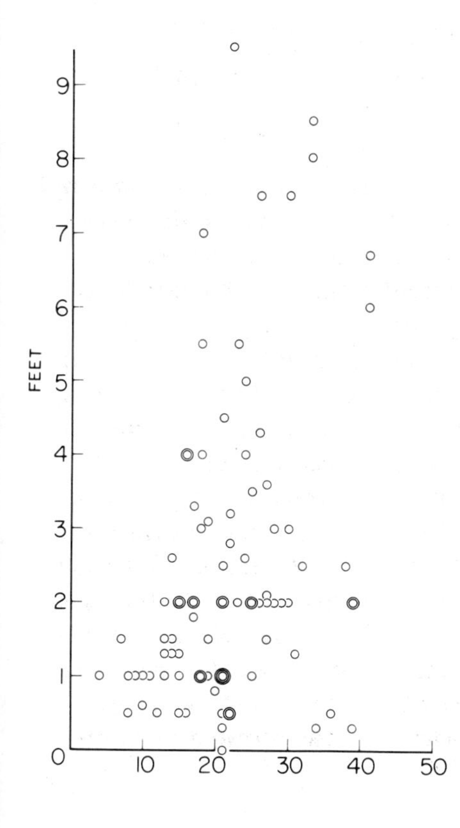

FIGURE 4 Relationship between mean recapture radius (abscissa) and gametic contribution (ordinate) in females of *Uta stansburiana* from two Texas populations over a period of three generations.

The results, together with the correlation coefficient between recapture radius and fitness for each year, are shown in Table 1.

TABLE 1 Relationship between density (per acre) of adult and juvenile *Uta stansburiana stejnegeri* and the correlation coefficient (r) between territory size (recapture radius) and fitness for three years of above-median density and below-median density. Also shown are figures for the number of young produced per acre in each year by the resident females.

		Density per Acre	r	Number of Young per Acre
LOW-DENSITY YEARS	1964, Area I	69	0.05	119
	1962, Area II	77	0.23	150
	1961, Area I	81	0.29	190
HIGH-DENSITY YEARS	1963, Area I	84	0.30	152
	1961, Area II	86	0.44	215
	1963, Area II	113	0.56	230

When data from all low-density years are combined and compared with similarly lumped data from the high-density years, there is a correlation of 0.05 between fitness and recapture radius in low-density years (not significantly different from 0), but a correlation of 0.50 ($P \cong 0.001$) in high-density years.

The data indicate that it is nearly always advantageous to the animal to be aggressive, but that the advantage is greatest in those years when competition between the many young and between young and their parents presumably is most intense. Because these lizards in Texas have an essentially annual turnover (more than 90 percent), failure to reproduce during the first breeding season is equivalent to leaving no alleles in the gene pool of the next generation. Obviously, genes for aggressive behavior generally will increase due to the strong correlation between reproductive fitness and degree of aggressive behavior, at least as the latter is indicated by size of the territory held; by bold and conspicuous coloration of the males; and by aggressiveness of the lizards toward intruders, as demonstrated by numerous field experiments (Tinkle, 1967).

BREEDING STRUCTURE OF THE TEXAS POPULATIONS

The high degree of aggressive behavior between individuals of the same sex results in a type of facultative monogamy in which each lizard tends to be restricted to a single mate because interpair mating is discouraged by the territoriality of both members of each pair. However, since the males continually court any female they encounter, polygyny probably occurs, but it has not been observed in nature.

Because of the strong territoriality and the pair system, it has been possible to estimate the effective breeding size of the population as contrasted with the actual number of sexually mature residents of the study area. As has been pointed out, some females (and presumably the males associated with them) produce a disproportionate share of the breeding stock of the next generation, at least in some years. One would expect, then, that in years when reproduction was particularly disproportionate (high-density years) there should be a smaller effective breeding size than in years when the females made essentially equal contributions to the next generation. To test this hypothesis, I calculated the ratio of effective breeding numbers to actual numbers (see Tinkle, 1965, for details) for low- and high-density years:

Low-Density Years	Ratio of Effective Number to Actual Number	High-Density Years	Ratio of Effective Number to Actual Number
1964, Area I	1.1	1963, Area I	0.6
1962, Area II	1.5	1961, Area II	1.1
1961, Area I	0.8	1963, Area II	0.4

These figures differ somewhat from those of a previous work (Tinkle, 1965) because I have been more rigorous here in defining the number of residents (Tinkle, 1967). These data generally are in agreement with the hypothesis; the two lowest ratios did occur in years of high density, and there is certainly a difference in the mean of the ratios for high-density and low-density years. A paired t-test gives $t = 13$ ($P < 0.01$).

AGGRESSIVE BEHAVIOR AND BREEDING STRUCTURE IN THE COLORADO POPULATION

One of the surprising early observations on lizards in the Colorado population, both in the field and in the laboratory, was the apparent absence of social interactions between individuals of the same sex. These observations, together with the fact that the home ranges of several individuals of the same sex are frequently congruent, led Tinkle and Woodard (1967) to suggest that the animals were nonterritorial.

In Colorado during the summer of 1966 I carried out experiments with social behavior and made observations of natural interactions. That sexes are aggressive was proved by the introduction of nonresidents into the visual field of residents. However, in Colorado the aggression is weaker, and fighting is rarer than in Texas; and a resident will tolerate a nonresident if the latter adopts a submissive posture. There is evidence of social hierarchies in which the older adults are dominant.

Because of the great overlap in home ranges, it was impossible to determine the relative fitnesses, as was done in Texas. Breeding may be restricted primarily to the dominant animals in the hierarchy, but I have no evidence of this. However, the difference in aggressiveness between the Texas and Colorado animals does seem real, and the existence of social hierarchies presumably results from the reduced aggression. I think that this difference in behavior of the Colorado and Texas lizards can be explained in part by reference to the details of demography of these two populations and to differences in the reproductive effort (Williams, 1966) of the females.

In Texas there is a consistent turnover of 90 percent or more of the adults each year. The peak of hatching is in July, and the young grow rapidly and reach sexual maturity in the fall, when the males undergo spermatogenesis and the females store large quantities of fat that will be utilized in egg production the following spring (Hahn and Tinkle, 1965). During the breeding season each adult female lays at least three but probably four or more clutches averaging four eggs each, and then usually disappears from the population (presumably dies) in late summer and fall. Therefore, there is little overlap of adult age classes, and an individual has essentially only one opportunity (season) to reproduce. Furthermore, a female laying four clutches must synthesize an amount of material for eggs that nearly equals her own body weight, and she must defend a territory at the same time. It seems clear that the amount of reproductive effort in a single season is very high, and in order to yield dividends of surviving offspring, this effort must be accompanied by strong territoriality, as Williams (1966) has suggested.

The data for the Colorado population are not so comprehensive, but are sufficiently so that certain comparisons can be made. The breeding season begins in early April and ends in mid-July, so it is shorter than in Texas by at least a month. A female that is mature at the onset of the season may lay three clutches of three eggs each, but many females reproducing for the first time may lay only two, so that there is presumably less total effort per reproductive season than in Texas. Furthermore, in Colorado nearly one third of the adults of one season will live to reproduce during another season (see Figure 5 for survivorship curves), and their age-specific fecundity will increase slightly. Many females reproduce for three seasons.

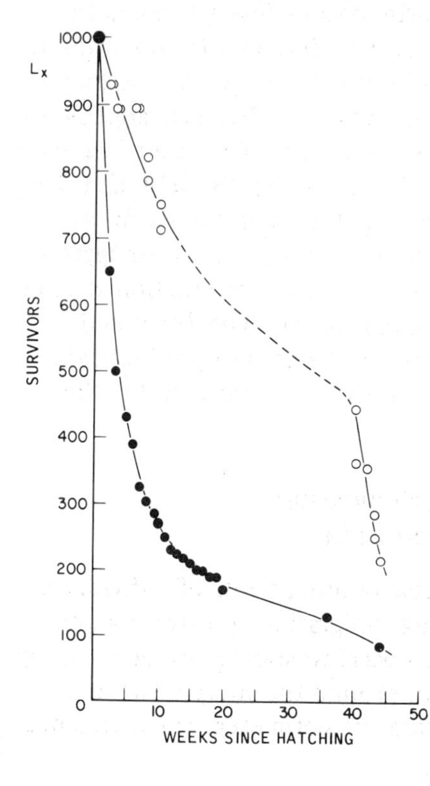

FIGURE 5 Survivorship curves for Texas (solid) and Colorado (dashed) *Uta stansburiana* based upon pooled data for several generations of lizards marked at hatching. Abscissa, weeks since hatching; ordinate, number (of 1,000) alive at each age interval. The dotted portion of the curve for Colorado is an extrapolation in the absence of data for the time period.

Williams (1966) has provided a set of criteria for reproductive effort and has predicted that total effort will be found to be greater in short-lived than in long-lived animals and that aggressive behavior should be expected to be at a peak in the former. He also has provided an equation to which the reproductive effort might be expected to conform.

I have used the criteria of Williams by assigning a value of one to each criterion and obtaining a total effort figure for Colorado and Texas lizards as the sum of the criteria met in each of the two populations. The sums of those criteria applicable to these two populations were five for Texas and two for Colorado. The equation provided by Williams indicates an effort by Texas lizards about four times greater than that by Colorado animals.

With only the above facts, the differences in behavior in Texas and Colorado may be explained. If an animal is aggressive and if this behavior has a genetic basis, it may be expected to leave more surviving offspring and presumably increase the frequency of its genes in the population if, by its intimidation, less-aggressive animals were prevented from mating or were forced into suboptimum home ranges where their survivorship or that of their young might be impaired. However, if some less-aggressive individuals are able to produce more offspring than the aggressive ones (by extending their reproduction over a greater period, behaving submissively, and perhaps thereby being less exposed to predation than the more conspicuous aggressive ones), then selection can scarcely favor aggression to the degree possible in situations where reproduction is denied or strongly limited in nonaggressive individuals. The Texas and Colorado populations seem to approach the above hypothetical extremes, and their comparative behavior is in accord with the theoretical expectation.

DEGREE OF EMIGRATION AND OF COLOR DIMORPHISM IN TEXAS AND COLORADO POPULATIONS OF *UTA*

In both Texas and Colorado the relative movements of individuals were studied in detail. Long-distance emigration—greater than one half the diameter of the study area—was investigated by periodically and systematically collecting lizards around the study areas to a distance of several hundred feet from the perimeter. The difference in the recorded frequency of these unusually distant movements by individuals in Texas and Colorado is striking. Over a period of four generations in Texas, I recorded fewer than 10 individuals (0.2 percent), of 3,500 marked, that were distant emigrants (see Tinkle, 1967, for further discussion). Yet, in Colorado nearly 10 percent of all lizards marked made such movements, and all of them were young adults; that is, they were adults in their first breeding season. These differences cannot be attributed simply to sampling bias. The margins of the areas were much more intensively investigated and over a much longer period of time in Texas than in Colorado.

I want to make it clear that I realize such differences in degree of emigration may reflect differences in habitat stability, differences in the degree of uniformity of the habitat, and differences in the probability of an animal's finding an unoccupied breeding site (Murray, 1967). The differences in frequencies of emigrants may also be due to demographic differences between the two populations. In Texas, a lizard that emigrates may in fact not better its chances to reproduce; it may sacrifice the single chance that it has. In Colorado, a lizard unable to achieve dominance in a social hierarchy may lose little by emigrating, and it may gain if it is able to reproduce elsewhere and does not shorten its life expectancy by moving.

In other words, the probability of emigrating and breeding is equal to the product of the probabilities of emigrating and surviving; of finding a suitable unoccupied territory, or of being able to displace or to dominate a resident; and of living more than a single breeding season. There are some data that might allow a rough calculation of some of these probabilities.

In a recent study (Tinkle, 1967) I defined an emigrant lizard as a young animal marked within the study area and last recorded outside the study area. Mature lizards were considered emigrants if they were marked within the area when young but established home ranges outside the area as adults. Of 1,077 young lizards marked within the Texas study areas from 1961 to 1963, 132 were emigrants, but fewer than 1 percent of the 1,077 made major emigrations. These data indicate that the probability of emigrating a long distance and surviving may be roughly 0.01. The probability of displacing a resident must be nearly zero, and few unoccupied territories would exist in the rather dense Texas populations; a low, but generous, probability estimate would be 0.05. The probability of living to more than one breeding season is 0.10. The product of these probabilities is 5×10^{-4}. In Colorado, corresponding probabilities determined in the same way would be 0.05 for emigrating and surviving, perhaps 0.5 for finding an unoccupied site because of the hierarchical system, and at least 0.3 for surviving to a second breeding season. The product of these probabilities is roughly 8×10^{-3}. These figures should not be taken too seriously, but they do suggest that selection against emigrators is likely to be less severe in the Colorado than in the Texas populations. However, the really critical problem is whether a Colorado lizard might, under certain conditions, increase its fitness relative to a nonemigrator by moving. I have no data to support or refute that possibility.

If such tendencies toward emigration are characteristic of the northern populations of *Uta* one might predict (other things being equal) that interpopulation divergence would be less in *U. s. stansburiana* than in *U. s. stejnegeri.* Such a comparison really requires very fine scale sampling, but some indication might be gained by comparing certain populations for which adequate data are available from large samples.

Royce Ballinger has examined large samples of *U. s. stansburiana* from Mesa, Montezuma, Rio Blanco, and San Juan Counties of southwestern Colorado and northwestern New Mexico; and of *U. s. stejnegeri* from Winkler, El Paso, Chaves, and Otero Counties of western Texas and eastern New Mexico. Each of the populations of each race was compared with all other populations of the same race on the basis of 28 quantitative characters. The total number of traits that differed significantly ($P < 0.01$) between the four populations of each race was divided by the number of possible interpopulational comparisons within the matrix to obtain an index of interpopulational divergence.

The calculated indices support the opposite hypothesis: that there is greater average interpopulational divergence (10.3) between the northern populations than between the southern (5.3). However, the average distance from the geometric center of the four localities is 135 miles in the north as compared to 85 in the south.

There seems to be little point in pursuing this comparison further in the absence of large, equally spaced, randomly chosen samples. I think such a fine-scale sampling experiment is worth carrying out, and I predict that the hypothesis of less interpopulational divergence in the northern race would be verified.

There are, likewise, reasons to consider the degree of sexual dimorphism to be correlated with the differences in behavior. If a lizard must be aggressive to reproduce, it would seemingly be advantageous, at least for the male, to be brightly colored or patterned. This would be true as long as the advantage gained by the male was greater than the risk involved in being conspicuous in color and behavior. The advantage would be that such advertisement might be effective in territorial defense without actual fighting, and also it might be advantageous in attracting females. As discussed earlier and as shown in Figure 1, sexual dimorphism in pattern and color is striking in Texas but is very much reduced in Colorado. This difference is consistent throughout the ranges of both races, although the degree of difference is variable.

Ferguson (1966a) has demonstrated that in the Texas population sex discrimination by a male lizard is made, in part, on the basis of the color and pattern of the other animal. Again, I would expect selection to favor the ability to discriminate quickly when both individuals are highly aggressive, because aggression exhibited toward a potential mate certainly would lower the fitness of the individual. The fact that pattern seems to be important in this discrimination suggests that contrasting patterns might be advantageous for the reasons advanced above.

There are other possible reasons for differences in the patterns. Background matching by the predominantly saxicolous Colorado lizards might be more important than in Texas. The presence of other species with patterns that might be confusing in mate recognition might result in selection for pattern differences if the mistaken recognition resulted in gametic wastage, particularly by the female. In the Texas population, the species *Holbrookia maculata* and *Sceloporus graciosus* are similar to *Uta* in size. *H. maculata* is extremely rare in the immediate vicinity of the study sites but is common to the north and west. *S. graciosus* is more common, but its distribution is extremely spotty. It has never been recorded in the study area. The Colorado population is sympatric with three other common iguanid lizards, *Urosaurus ornatus, Sceloporus undulatus,* and *Sceloporus graciosus. U. ornatus* is common on cliffs and huge boulders, and presumably is in less direct contact with *Uta* than the other two species. *S. undulatus* is a much larger species than *Uta. S. graciosus* is distinctly striped and is somewhat larger than *Uta.* The two are in frequent contact; if intermatings occur, selection would presumably favor those individuals of *Uta* that look less like *S. graciosus,* i.e., unstriped individuals.

From the above discussion there is reason to suggest that if mechanisms exist whereby a male is able to distinguish between a female of his own kind and one of another, such discriminatory ability should be better developed in Colorado lizards than in Texas lizards. The degree of discrimination has been tested by Gary Ferguson and Charles McKinney, who have kindly allowed me to cite their unpublished results. When Texas males in the field were given a simultaneous choice of a Texas and Colorado female, their response was random. In six tests they chose the Texas female, in six the Colorado female. Fourteen tests were run in the field in Colorado where the males chose their own female in 12 of the tests. These data seem to support the hypothesis that the Colorado lizards have greater ability ($P < 0.05$) to discriminate. It should be noted, however, that these were male choice experiments whereas female choice is probably more important in nature, but more difficult to investigate experimentally. The evolutionary history of the group deserves consideration at this point because most of the apparently primitive species and populations in the genus *Uta* are also monomorphic. Inasmuch as the Colorado populations evidently are representative of this primitive stock, the degree of sexual dimorphism may have little to do with the current selective forces operating within those populations. This, however, is unlikely because of the degree of interpopulation variation in the expression of sexual dimorphism in pattern and color in this species.

OTHER BEHAVIORAL DIFFERENCES BETWEEN TEXAS AND COLORADO LIZARDS

Much more positive information can be presented on differences in behavior patterns of northern and southern *Uta* that might be important in inhibiting interbreeding of the two forms if they were sympatric.

One such difference is the pattern of push-ups, or bobs, performed by most iguanid lizards. Such bobs are assumed to be species-specific, but their function is unknown, although some experimental evidence suggests that they may play a role in species recognition (Hunsiker, 1962). Ferguson, using a modification of the technique of Carpenter and Grubits (1961), has filmed in the lab and field many bobbing sequences of the Texas and Colorado lizards. I have selected one of each (Figure 6) to illustrate similarities and differences. The time required for each component is quite similar, but the entire bob sequence in Colorado lizards is longer, and there is an average of five component movements compared with four in Texas. The bob of the Colorado lizards is also more shallow, but this is of dubious importance.

Similarities exist in the courtship patterns of most iguanid lizards. The male's peculiar shuddering motion and his bobbing, circling, and licking of the female are common components. The male's preliminary display to the female is more elaborate in Texas, where it almost always involves considerable bobbing, circling, and shuddering. The approach of the Colorado male is more direct, faster, and he engages in faster licking and nipping of the female than does the Texas lizard. The number of copulatory thrusts made by the Texas male is only three to six over a period of less than 10 seconds, and the male

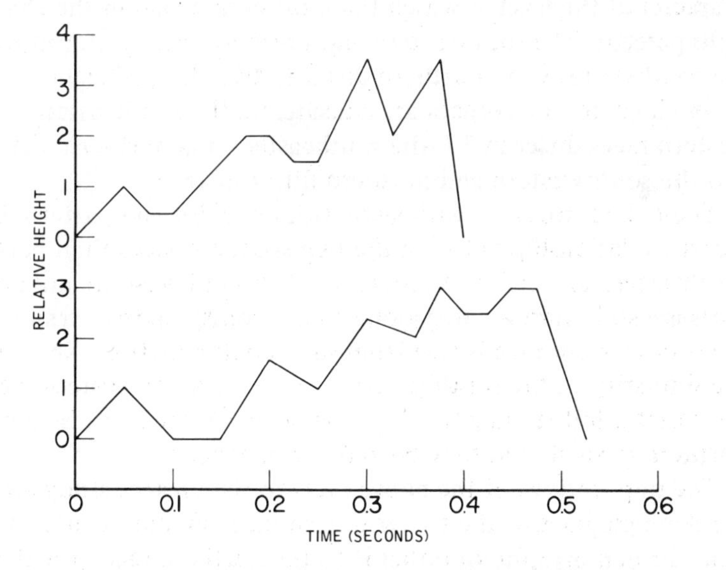

FIGURE 6 Pattern of the bobs or push-ups performed by *Uta stansburiana* from Colorado (bottom) and Texas (top). Abscissa, time in seconds; ordinate, relative height of push-up. (Based on film records provided by Gary W. Ferguson.)

and female rarely remain for long *in copulo* after thrusting has ceased. Colorado males thrust 10 or more times over a period of almost 20 seconds, and the pair remains *in copulo* for a minute or longer.

Fortuitously, selection at the individual level in the two populations obviously has affected traits that not only are of taxonomic importance but that might partially limit interbreeding of these two populations should they become sympatric. The degree of limitation to interbreeding already evolved is now being tested, and much more detailed comparative information on several populations is being obtained by Gary Ferguson; in the meantime, it is instructive to consider again the taxonomic status of the Texas and Colorado populations.

The map shows that the subspecies *U. s. stejnegeri,* which includes the Texas population, is at present allopatric from both the southwestern race (currently considered *U. s. stejnegeri,* also) and the northern race (*U. s. stansburiana*), which includes the Colorado population.

Coefficients of difference (Mayr *et al.,* 1953) in 28 characters show that the southeastern and southwestern races differ in only one character at the level at which the joint nonoverlap in the character is 90 percent. The southeastern and northern races differ in four, and the southwestern and northern differ in two. If significant ($P < 0.01$) *mean* character differences are considered, the southeastern and southwestern races differ in 17, the southeastern and northern differ in 21, and the southwestern and northern differ in 18.

These data, together with similarities in color and pattern, indicate a closer relationship between the two southern races than between the southeastern and the northern races. The southwestern and northern races are still interbreeding along an apparently narrow transect, but the southeastern race is free from such contamination. Nevertheless, the similarity of the southeastern race to the southwestern race suggests that interbreeding would occur between the southeastern and northern races should they become sympatric.

The implications of the above facts to the present study are that the demographies of the two southern races should be more similar than the demography of either is to the northern race. Furthermore, if the features I have mentioned—such as behavior, clutch size, and body size—have a genetic basis, then comparative study of populations in areas adjacent to the zone of intergradation between the southwestern and northern races would be useful. Some of the biological differences between the races are of such magnitude that there might be some incompatibility between the races because of genetic differences related to their behavior and ecology, a possibility also suggested by the present narrow boundaries of the zone of intergradation.

The Texas (southeastern race) and Colorado (northern race) populations apparently have no opportunity to interbreed at present, although there is only a short geographic distance between their range limits. The three races involved seem clearly in different stages of evolution, and in two of them the process has been interrupted by secondary contact. The opportunity to study the degree of mating and reproductive incompatibility among the three is being investigated. I emphasize again that some of the most striking differences between these populations are color, pattern, size, and behavior. These differences are explicable on the basis of the ecological differences between them. These characteristics are the ones that most likely are involved in the complex of isolating mechanisms between lizard species, and this study indicates how such differences may arise between allopatric populations, but not in the context of isolating mechanisms.

THE EVOLUTION OF REPRODUCTIVE RATES

As already noted, the clutch sizes of Texas and Colorado lizards are different. The number of clutches laid is also different. In Texas the actual number of young produced per female has averaged 15 over four generations. Only seven per female were produced in the Colorado populations during the single generation studied there. This figure is well below the minimum observed in Texas.

Presumably, both populations have been maintaining relatively stable numbers, despite the great difference in birth rates. Thus, it is not surprising that the mortality rates among young are lower in Colorado (Figure 5) than in Texas. Likewise, it is not surprising that the adults in Colorado live longer than those in Texas. There is, however, little likelihood that selection can favor an increase in clutch size directly *because of* high mortality rates, so another explanation must be sought for the obvious differences.

It is well to consider again some implications of a detailed taxonomic study of *Uta* (Ballinger and Tinkle, in manuscript). The Texas race (*U. s. stejnegeri*) presumably evolved in the Chihuahuan desert and is essentially restricted to that area. Consequently, it is reasonable to suppose that it always has been a southern form not exposed to the type of climatic conditions that exist in Colorado. The stock of the Colorado race (*U. s. stansburiana*), on the contrary, at one time occurred much farther south, as indicated by the presence of relict populations of a similar type of lizard (*Uta s. taylori*) in the southern Sonora Desert of Mexico. The *U. s. stansburiana* populations presumably are secondarily of northern restriction so we may assume that whatever adjustments they have made in reproductive rate may have been made under the direct selective influence of the northern climate. This assumption is not essential to the argument to be presented, but it is consistent with the clues of past distributions gained from a detailed study of many mainland populations of *Uta stansburiana,* which suggest that *U. s. stansburiana* has been restricted to its northern distribution in very recent times (Royce Ballinger, personal communication).

Females in the Texas populations of *Uta* hatch in early summer, mature by fall, and evidently are protected from entering upon an unseasonal estrus by a period in the fall during which they are refractory to external stimuli known to stimulate estrus at other times of the year (Tinkle and Irwin, 1965). After December, the females can be made to reproduce in the laboratory at a time they do not reproduce in the field, indicating that they are physiologically mature by that time after hatching. However, females of 40-mm snout-to-vent length or less cannot be induced to enter estrus in the laboratory, indicating that they are physiologically immature at that size. Furthermore, no indication of estrus, such as follicles undergoing vitellogenesis, has been seen in hundreds of such small females from natural populations. However, by the onset of the breeding season in March almost all females have attained a minimum size of sexual maturity.

Because of the shorter growing season, the situation in the Colorado population is quite different. The young are not produced in number until late July, and most are not mature by late fall; in fact, only about 40 percent of those hatched in the summer reach mature size by the start of the breeding season the following spring.

This is true despite the fact that sexual maturity is reached at 37-mm snout-to-vent length, considerably smaller than in Texas. If individual females in Colorado had to reach the same size at maturity as those in Texas, almost no female would be capable of reproducing during its first season.

I think that the reduced birth rate in Colorado has, nevertheless, resulted in an increase in individual fitness. Selection has favored a smaller size at maturity in Colorado because females capable of reproducing at a small size there have an enormous reproductive advantage over those that are not so capable. However, in almost all species of lizards the small females have smaller clutches than do large females; consequently, selection for a small size at maturity has resulted in reduction in number of eggs per clutch. The egg weights of Colorado and Texas lizards are the same ($\bar{x}$ = 0.2 g); therefore, we may also infer that selection has not led to smaller eggs in Colorado lizards.

From all of this it is assumed likely that the differences in size of Colorado and Texas lizards are genetic, but more rigorous proof might be provided by transposing lizards of the two areas so that one could determine if a Colorado lizard, for example, would mature at a larger size in Texas.

DISCUSSION

In a paper of this sort, one feels obligated to compare the explanations set forth for one species with the situation that exists in other species. I think there may be sufficient data to indicate that most species of lizards studied show the expected inverse relationship between degree of aggressiveness and adult life expectancy. On the other hand, the clutch size of a species is frequently,if not usually, larger in the northern part of the range than in the south (Tinkle, 1967).

There is so little precise data available on the demographic properties of reptile populations, however, that any sort of comparison is doomed to flounder at certain points. This fact can be illustrated simply. I have taken a sample of 50 papers on the biology of lizards and extracted from them the information that would be of value in deriving certain generalizations of the ideas presented in this paper. This is a biased sample because I chose all of the best papers on lizard life histories. I chose 12 topics—such as age at first breeding, age-specific fecundity, adult life expectancy, and degree of aggression—and determined the frequency with which each item was reported in the papers examined. From these data I calculated the probabilities of occurrence of such information in the literature. The probability of a paper's having data on age-specific fecundity, for example, was 1 to 10; for degree of aggression, 5 in 10. By multiplying the various probabilities I could determine the probability of finding all of these pertinent points in any particular study as 8.2×10^{-5}. This probability is indeed low, and it is found to be even more seriously low when one considers that these data are drawn from the best studies, which have covered only a fraction of 1 percent of the total number of lizard species. Any generalization made on the basis of such paltry data is fraught with hazard.

Much more could be said on this subject; and some further generalizations might be made as working hypotheses, but this will be the subject of another paper on the evolution of reproductive types and rates in lizards. Consequently, I will leave this point with a simple urging for more detailed life history studies that include information usually lacking in such investigations.

I am certain that a much greater understanding of the process and result of natural selection is to be gained by demographic studies. My own studies have suggested that a thorough knowledge of the taxonomic status and evolutionary history of the populations studied may be essential to understanding some of the biological traits of populations as well as the morphological ones upon which taxonomic judgments so often rest. By the same token, the origin and significance of characters important in systematic studies may be suggested from ecological studies of populations in which data on demographic properties are collected. More importantly, the accumulation of comparative demographic information will allow us to understand the diversity of life history types in animals and to make predictions about them.

It must be obvious also that most of the ideas presented here could be subjected to an experimental test. Indeed they should be, but this must be done in the field and is not feasible until enclosed, protected areas are available in several regions of the range of the species. In the absence of such facilities, comparison of the characteristics discussed in this paper in several different populations will substitute for experimentation and will increase the circumstantial evidence for a cause-and-effect relationship between morphological and behavioral traits and the structure and demography of the populations in which they occur. With this comment I stress again what I said at the beginning concerning the importance of the comparative method in biology.

ACKNOWLEDGMENTS

I thank Michael Sabath and James Platz for help in the field and Gary Ferguson, Royce Ballinger, and Charles McKinney for supplying details of some of their studies of *Uta.* James S. Farris aided me with mathematical analyses.

Data reported for the first time in this paper were derived from research supported by National Science Foundation Grants GB-4396 and GB-5416x.

REFERENCES

Ballinger, R. E., and C. O. McKinney. 1967. Variation and polymorphism in the dorsal color pattern of *Uta stansburiana stejnegeri.* Am. Midland Natur. 77:476–483.

Carpenter, C. C., and G. Grubits, III. 1961. Time–motion study of a lizard. Ecology 42:199–200.

Cuellar, O. 1966. Delayed fertilization in *Uta stansburiana.* Copeia 1966: 549–551.

Ferguson, G. W. 1966a. Releasers of courtship and territorial behavior in the side-blotched lizard *Uta stansburiana.* Anim. Behav. 14:89–92.

Ferguson, G. W. 1966b. Effect of follicle stimulating hormone and testosterone propionate on the reproduction of the side-blotched lizard, *Uta stansburiana.* Copeia 1965:495–497.

Hahn, W. E. 1964. Seasonal changes in testicular and epididymal histology and spermatogenic rate in the lizard *Uta stansburiana stejnegeri.* J. Morphol. 115:447–460.

Hahn, W. E., and D. W. Tinkle. 1965. Fat body cycling and experimental evidence for its adaptive significance to ovarian follicle development in the lizard *Uta stansburiana.* J. Exp. Zool. 158:79–86.

Hunsiker, D. H. 1962. Ethological isolating mechanisms in the *Sceloporus torquatus* group of lizards. Evolution 16:62–74.

Irwin, L. N. 1965. Diel activity and social interaction of the lizards *Uta stansburiana stejnegeri.* Copeia 1965:99–101.

Knopf, G. N. 1963. Sexual, geographical and individual variation in three Texas populations of the lizard, *Uta stansburiana stejnegeri.* Am. Midland Natur. 70:74–89.
Mayr, E., E. G. Linsley, and R. L. Usinger. 1953. Methods and principles of systematic zoology. McGraw-Hill, New York. vii + 328 p.
Murray, B. G., Jr. 1967. Dispersal in vertebrates. Ecology 48:975–978.
Simpson, G. G. 1961. Principles of animal taxonomy. Columbia Univ. Press, New York. x + 247 p.
Tinkle, D. W. 1961. Population structure and reproduction in the lizard *Uta stansburiana stejnegeri.* Am. Midland Natur. 66:206–234.
Tinkle, D. W. 1965. Population structure and effective size of a lizard population. Evolution 19:569–573.
Tinkle, D. W. 1967. The life and demography of the side-blotched lizard. Misc. Publ. Mus. Zool. Univ. Michigan. No. 132, 1–182.
Tinkle, D. W., D. McGregor, and S. Dana. 1962. Home range ecology of *Uta stansburiana stejnegeri.* Ecology 43:223–229.
Tinkle, D. W., and L. N. Irwin. 1965. Lizard reproduction: Refractory period and response to warmth in *Uta stansburiana* females. Science 148:1613–1614.
Tinkle, D. W., and D. W. Woodard. 1967. Relative movements of lizards in natural populations as determined from recapture radii. Ecology 48:166–168.
Williams, G. C. 1966. Adaptation and natural selection. Princeton Univ. Press, Princeton. x + 307 p.

Discussion

Robert F. Inger

I will try to show how Tinkle's paper fits into a general framework in animal systematics and to point to some potentialities of this kind of study.

We have been saying for a long time that systematics should use every conceivable character, from the molecular level up, as parameters of taxa. In his work Tinkle takes advantage of the higher levels of organization to define and delimit taxa; but he does a bit more, and that bit more is important.

Systematists, it seems to me, should look at populations not merely as sources of taxonomic information but as a level of organization worthy of study for its own sake. I am not talking now about taxonomy in the usual sense of determining the average morphological characteristic of demes, but about such things as breeding structure, population size and fluctuation, movements and distribution of individuals, and gene flow in wild populations. Systematists, by virtue of their intellectual and practical field experience, can make their own distinctive contribution to population biology.

There probably are a few purists tucked away in odd corners of some museums and universities who will be horrified at the thought of obscuring the boundaries separating taxonomy, ecology, and genetics. That should not bother us here. What should concern us is how small is the number of systematists who take advantage of their opportunities to work on these aspects of population biology.

If I had to single out just one aspect of population biology to which systematists should give emphasis, I would name fluctuation in population size. Except for a few economically important arthropods and fishes, we have almost no sound data on variation in numbers.

Such data are crucial if we are to develop sound concepts of community evolution. One of the common elements in the more popular, or respected, hypotheses of ecosystem evolution is that stability or resistance to perturbation increases during community evolution. To many people, this suggests that population size fluctuates less widely in communities of greater species diversity. Is this supposition valid? Data available are far too scanty to permit even a tentative answer.

Phenomena related to fluctuations in population size also are extremely important to evolutionary processes; so they are of immediate concern to systematists. Examples of such phenomena are changes in aggressiveness, the impact of such changes on interspecific interactions, and the relation of population size to gene flow and rates of evolution. These are not unstudied relationships, but our information is restricted to very few kinds of organisms. Our understanding is correspondingly limited. One of the exciting possibilities that investigation of these relationships holds is that evolution, at least below the generic level, often proceeds at a much faster rate than we have generally thought.

Fortunately, systematists are becoming more interested in these aspects of population biology. The paper we have just heard is an excellent example of what can be done. Dr. Tinkle is neither so foolish nor so immodest as to think he has solved the major problems of the population biology of these lizards. But I think he can justifiably feel that he not only has made a very good beginning but that he has hit upon a very fruitful biological system to investigate.

Now I want to ask Dr. Tinkle two questions.

One of the more interesting matters of your work will ultimately concern the extent to which the interpopulational differences in individual behavior (in aggressiveness, extent of movements, etc.) represent genetic differences between populations. Do these individual behavior patterns change in time within populations as population size and density change? Are these genetic changes? Do you have any evidence that would bear on these problems?

TINKLE: I do not have evidence that would be satisfactory to a geneticist. But I do have evidence of at least a circumstantial nature. For an example, I refer to degree of aggression, which can be modified quite effectively in the laboratory but cannot be modified in the field. Furthermore, it can be shown in the field that there is a correlation between the degree of aggressive behavior and the likely fitness of the individual that exhibits it. So, I think on that basis such behavior is likely to be genetic. In regard to differences in size at reproductive maturity, we can bring lizards of the southern population into a state of estrus in midwinter, when ordinarily they are not reproducing in the field; but we cannot do this with individuals that are smaller than the size at sexual maturity that we find during the breeding season. That at least is evidence that the difference in size at maturity probably is genetic. The bob patterns of these animals are quite specific. They are given by young animals and hatching animals as well as by the adults, and I think this, also, is likely to be genetic. But I am not satisfied that this sort of knowledge can tell us definitely whether these patterns are genetic. These things can be tested experimentally, but it has to be done in the field and not in the laboratory. As to variability, I would say that with a nearly annual population turnover considerable genetic change can occur in a short period.

INGER: Can you relate differences in breeding structure to differences in variability in population parameters as well as in morphological parameters?

TINKLE: I cannot. I prefer not to speak on that question because it is a very complicated one and we do not have any good data in that area. The only data relevant to the question are those presented on behavioral and sexual differences that appear to be related to differences in population structure.

Discussion

Allen Keast

Dr. Tinkle's paper demonstrates that species are far from the uniform typological entities of the classical taxonomists. It emphasizes, like other modern works in its field, how far we have come from the days when the emphasis was on the discovery of species and, later, when workers concentrated on describing and delimiting races with little or no attempt to explain or understand their characteristics. Such studies as the present extend back only for a couple of decades. In this respect the work of two other herpetologists, Gustav Kramer, who worked on the lizards of the Mediterranean region, and R. C. Stebbins in California, must be mentioned.

Regional populations are shown to differ by a complex combination of ecological, physiological, behavioral and morphological characters. Color and color pattern are considered relative to camouflage, heat exchange, species recognition, sex recognition, and individual aggressiveness and dominance. This approach obviously gives us a new appreciation of the significance and importance of color characters. Principles once established can be extended to other species and groups. Again, it is essential to distinguish basic and primitive characteristics, or both, that can be used in classification from those that represent minor adaptive trends and are of little significance.

Physiological differences between regional forms were ignored, or at least not appreciated, by earlier taxonomists, even though it has long been known that within certain bird species, for example, some races are migratory and others are not and that the migrants from different areas may winter in different places. Seasonal movements in birds are part of a whole adaptive complex that includes breeding times, molting times, and the annual behavior cycle. Yet, interestingly, they serve to restrict the development of what might otherwise be advantageous local adaptations in that they tend to accelerate gene flow between individuals from different parts of the species range. These trends reach a peak in the avifauna of the dry interior of Australia where, because of low and unpredictable annual rainfall, a majority of species are nomadic, moving over wide areas in the course of the year and concentrating to breed wherever conditions happen to be best. As a result they have few morphologically differentiated isolates (distinctive populations building up genetic distinctness behind distributional barriers and hence representing the first stage in the speciation process). The 99 nomadic species in the 531 breeding land and freshwater birds of Australia (23 percent of the total) average only 0.07 isolates per species, compared with 0.65 per species in resident species. A high level of seasonal mobility is, of course, an adaptation available to birds but not the dry-country lizards studied by Dr. Tinkle. The attributes of the group determine the mechanisms available to it for handling a particular environmental situation.

Another aspect of evolution at the population level that is not treated in the present study is the influence of the associated fauna. This is a much neglected area of study, yet one that is of fundamental importance in explaining race characteristics, at least to those of us who see species as "adaptational peaks" and still believe that the Gause concept of "one species, one niche" is substantially correct. It might not be out of place for me to comment on some recent comparative studies I have been carrying out on the passerine birds of Tasmania and southern Victoria.

Like many islands, Tasmania, which is isolated from the mainland by 130 miles of sea, lacks a number of basic ecological types of birds. The extent of its faunistic impoverishment can be seen from its having only 40 passerine species, compared with 87 in equivalent habitats in Victoria. In 65 percent of the species common to the two areas the Tasmanian population is distinct on structural grounds (mostly in size of bill, tarsus, hallux, and wing). This percentage is significantly higher than in mainland localities a thousand or two miles apart. The degree of difference is, moreover, much greater.

Field studies show that the explanation lies in fundamental resorting of the available ecological niches and life opportunities on the part of many of the Tasmanian populations. In any fauna, each bird species has its own characteristic feeding zone or level. Some species are entirely, or largely, foliage gleaners. Others do their feeding on the branches and trunks, in shrubs, or on the ground.

Twenty-five percent of the Tasmanian populations were found to utilize (at least in part) a zone different from their mainland counterparts. The absence of trunk-feeding nuthatches, creepers, and shrike-tits, was made good by four species (*Melithreptus validirostris, Meliphaga flavicollis, Colluricincla harmonica, Sericornis magnus*) whose mainland populations feed only incidentally from trunks and that now obtain a significant proportion of their food there. A robin (*Petroica rodinogaster*) was found to be largely a ground feeder (its mainland relative, *P. rosea,* feeds in foliage and branches) in the absence of the common terrestrial feeder of the mainland forests (*Eopsaltria australis*). In each case the morphological shifts in the insular populations (e.g., stronger legs and longer bills in the trunk-clingers) were obviously directly adaptive to their new roles.

Our deeper knowledge of population characteristics, however fundamental to an understanding of evolutionary processes, presents nomenclatorial problems. The trinomial system has long been plagued by trivial disagreements as to just how well differentiated a given form must be to warrant naming. Even today minor color forms, the results of Gloger effects, rank alongside populations characterized by much more important morphological differences in our taxonomic schemes. I do not say that such forms should not bear race names, but I do feel that climate-induced color effects occupy a low position in the hierarchy of race characters.

In the last decade or two, in certain widely distributed species, it has been recognized that clines may run in several directions at once. When local adaptations are added to this, the net effect is that of a mosaic of regional populations, each with its own characteristics. When physiology, behavior, and ecology are considered, the problem is further compounded. Fortunately, detailed studies make it possible to distinguish fundamental characters. The new sophistication, stemming from our knowledge of how adaptation at the population level operates, permits the taxonomists to work in a much more positive fashion.

Informal Discussion

BESCHEL: I should like to ask Dr. Tinkle to compare his ideas about selection mechanisms working in the lizard populations he has studied with the selection mechanisms advocated by Wynne-Edwards, especially in the latter's study of the red grouse. Are there any freely moving, nonterritorial animals that are nonbreeders? If so, is anything like that happening in the lizards too?

TINKLE: I do not think that is true at all for the females. It may be true for some males, but the only place it would be true would be in the north. In the social hierarchies that exist in the northern populations it is possible that only the animals at the upper levels of the hierarchy would be able to reproduce; however, if that is the case, I do not think my explanation of the low degree of aggression would hold true. So I think they must be reproducing; furthermore, we know that all the females, regardless of their position in the social structure, are producing eggs. I do not know to what extent breeding is limited to dominant males.

BLAIR: I commend Dr. Tinkle for his interesting line of research, which is a start in the direction toward which we must look to find the origins of differences in populations that lead to species. One thing that bothers me, though, is this: Dr. Tinkle, the measure of fitness you are using is the size of the area occupied by the females and the number of young in that area that reach sexual maturity. If there were a very early dispersal that was undetected, I think you would have an incorrect correlation. In other words, how certain are you when you make the assumption that the young animals you find in the home range of the female actually are her offspring?

TINKLE: Obviously, I have no proof that the assumption is true, but I have measured the degree of movement by individuals from the time of their hatching through all the various sizes and ages of their lives. A week or two after hatching, when they measure about 25 mm, the average distance they are away from the hatching site is 10 feet. If that represents the normal movements of young animals in a population, I would say that the movements of dispersing or emigrating young must be very low; and, therefore, most of the animals I am studying must be animals that were produced by the females in the area. In your own studies of *Sceloporus* you found that the females move well outside their ordinary home ranges to lay their eggs. If individuals in populations of *Uta* did that, I could be in serious error, but we have no evidence of such behavior.

A. R. KRUCKEBERG

Ecological Aspects of the Systematics of Plants

Labels like "ecology" and "systematics" have an annoying way of conjuring up still more labels. My reaction is to reach for two more open-ended word pictures—"evolution" and "taxonomy." All four of these interpenetrating concepts will have to be tapped in order to examine the ways in which the systematics and ecology of plants mutually interpenetrate. I will assume from the start that out there in the real world living things are interacting systematically and ecologically. What I really must discuss is the common ground—actual and yet untrod—where systematists and ecologists might meet.

The moment the systematist goes beyond the classification of organic diversity to seek causal relationships, he is drawn into the ecological-evolutionary drama. The synthesizing theme goes something like this: The units of systematics are stages or end products of the evolutionary process. That process, evolution, occurs through the interplay of hereditary potentialities (or their expressions) and the impinging environments. Therefore, the objects of systematic studies (individuals, populations, discrete-formal taxa, etc.) are shaped by their past and present ecologies. To accept this argument is to be enveloped by the whole of evolutionary biology. This is the worldwide arena where evolving organisms are meeting and reacting to their animate and inanimate environments at all interfaces.

A hasty retreat from the all-embracing view stated above is called for. A more practical and containable piece of this "big picture" must be framed for this presentation. What kinds of problems and questions can be practically dealt with under the broad umbrella of "ecoevolutionary systematics"?

There is substantial precedent for encouraging greater rapport between the two integrative disciplines, ecology and taxonomy. Constance (1953) reviewed from a taxonomist's vantage point the potential for fruitful contact. He espoused an increased communion between plant taxonomist and ecologist in three general areas of mutual concern: (1) the description, verification and classification of ecotypic variation, (2) the ecological basis of hybridity, and (3) the ecological barriers to interbreeding. The timeliness of his paper is both a tribute to a penetrating analysis and to the fact that his plea for *rapprochement* is still viable. At about the same time, an ecologist took up the plea for effective dialogue. McMillan (1954) assessed the need for greater ecological bias in the thinking of taxonomists. He argued that both taxonomy and ecology attempt the integration of basic biological and environmental data into the framework of form and function. McMillan proposed, therefore, that the research objectives and the operational outputs of the two formal disciplines can be usefully and mutually shared. A decade or so later, I am induced to take up many of the ideas developed by Constance and McMillan. For, although plant ecology and systematics have made substantial strides since then, the gaps between the two areas are still there.

What I propose then is to restate some major points of articulation—actual and potential—between higher plant systematics and ecology.

AREAS OF MUTUAL CONCERN AT THE ECOLOGY-SYSTEMATICS INTERFACE

Assuming an intricate intertwining of the attributes of ecology, evolution, systematics, and taxonomy, are there operational interactions among them that provide useful feedback? We may also anticipate that there are areas of disparate and nonoverlapping concerns in both ecology and systematics.

There should be generalizations in both ecology and systematics that have mutual applicability. From the crucible of systematics come the concepts and tools for ordering discontinuity and diversity, the bases and criteria for classification, the determinants of relationship, and the technologies for nomenclature. In return, the ecologist can assist the systematist in his quest for cause-and-effect relationships. Such concepts as interaction (e.g., mutualism, interference, competition, parasitism, etc.), ecophysiological tolerance ranges, community structure and pattern, and succession can be exploited in aiding the systematist's search for the environmental limits in the distribution of taxa.

I suspect that some generalizations (conceptual products) of ecology and systematics have only unidirectional utility. The taxonomies of the systematist are freely utilized by floristically oriented ecologists, but the classifications developed by the ecologist appear to have little interest for the systematist—or do they?

Both ecologist and systematist operate at several hierarchical levels of complexity. The individual, the population, and the species are three levels of mutual interest for the two disciplines. At higher levels, the common meeting grounds become less obvious. I wonder if this decrease in mutual concern is not a product of the disparate qualities or special-purpose nature of the higher units of ordering in systematics and ecology. Synecological units, from association to ecosystem, cannot be usefully juxtaposed to the higher taxonomic units, i.e., genus to kingdom. I propose that we look at existing and prospective ways in which the various hierarchical levels in the two disciplines can interact. Are there areas of useful contact and information-sharing, let us say, between minor and major taxonomic categories and the successive levels of the synecological hierarchy? We could well profit by an analysis of similarity and difference in the composition, function, etc., of an ecosystem as compared with a taxonomic family or order. I believe a useful comparison could be made of the dynamics of vegetation change and speciation or evolution above the species level.

EXAMINATION OF SOME INTERACTIONS BETWEEN ECOLOGY AND SYSTEMATICS, OR BETWEEN ECOLOGISTS AND SYSTEMATISTS

It remains now to particularize some of the problems and questions generated when ecology and systematics are brought together for heuristic contact. The way in which ecology and systematics are formalized, both in organization and in process, will be probed. As this symposium seeks to clarify the goals and activities of systematics, I will emphasize those areas in ecology that can enrich systematics.

EVOLUTIONARY STUDIES

Ecology can contribute to the interpretation of evolutionary process and, hence, to the systematics of intergroup relationships in several ways and at several levels. The moment the ecologist seeks particular environmental explanations for discontinuities in structure, function, and distribution of organisms, he is in the evolutionary domain. Adaptive and nonadaptive shifts in gene frequency occur largely through intrinsic, ecological differences. Micro- and macroevolutionary changes thus are traceable to ecological changes in space and time. The most fundamental questions for the ecologist who seeks evolutionary explanations of adaptive ecological specialization are in the realm of natural selection. What are the operational components of the total environment that elicit nonrandom, selective changes in the biologies of organisms? Plant ecologists have barely begun to examine the larger dimensions of this question, yet, some progress in evolutionary plant ecology is being made. Genecology, pollination and seed-dispersal ecology, and the ecology of isolating mechanisms are areas in which substantial contributions are evident.

Ecotypic Variation

Genecology constitutes, to date, the greatest point of contact between ecology and plant systematics. Genecological concepts and their applicability and limitations for systematics are thoroughly aired by Davis and Heywood (1963). We may look upon genecology as a special branch of microevolutionary study; it seeks to establish the nature of the genotype–environment interactions. As I see it, the genecologist's major contribution has been to identify and assess the role of local adaptation of a species to its total, heterogeneous habitat. This so-called ecotype variation is what Goldschmidt (1952) called existential adaptation and what the neo-Darwinian zoologists have long recognized as local microevolutionary fitness of wide-ranging species.

The major contribution of genecology to plant systematics has been to instill an awareness of a multidimensional, holocoenotic effect of environments on local fitness within Linnean species. Local and regional climate, soil, and other organisms can all produce ecotypic responses and must inevitably do so in one and the same population. The most relevant effect on systematics of an awareness of multidimensional ecotypic response is in the evaluation of variation. Continuous or discontinuous variation becomes readily explainable in the microevolutionary terms of genecological behavior of populations along gradients—abrupt or gradual. Reciprocally, ecology can benefit from an infusion of genecological practice and orientation (McMillan, 1954; Kruckeberg, 1959). Rarely are the elements of communities that extend over substantial geographic areas genotypically identical. Ecotypic differentiation adds a complicating but essential component to evaluations of community composition.

Attempts to formalize the ecotypic response of plants as systematic units have been largely abandoned. What was a conflict in categories with lively debate on both sides has now subsided. Ecologic races, clines, ecotypes, and all the rest have vastly increased our appreciation of the complexity of discontinuity in the time–space–habitat dimensions. As Erna Bennett (1964) says in her perceptive review of genecology, the recognition of finer and finer ecotypic differences will go on as long as the technology of science provides the means. Systematics can draw upon these findings in diverse ways. Genecological data can illuminate the nature of patterns of diversity, can give substance to causal relationships, and can fortify the basis for making taxonomic judgments. Ultimately, however, whether to formalize the detected variants by nomenclature will be determined by the needs of the system of classification. For a general-purpose classification (Gilmour and Walters, 1963), physiological, biochemical, or biotic variants may serve little practical purpose. The contrary view is justified if a special-purpose taxonomy is required. I would prefer, however, a nomenclature that does not add burdens to the system of Linnean taxonomy.

A type of genecological study that correlates environmental controls with morphological expression is related by Haller (1965), who made a broad survey of the temperature and moisture regimes

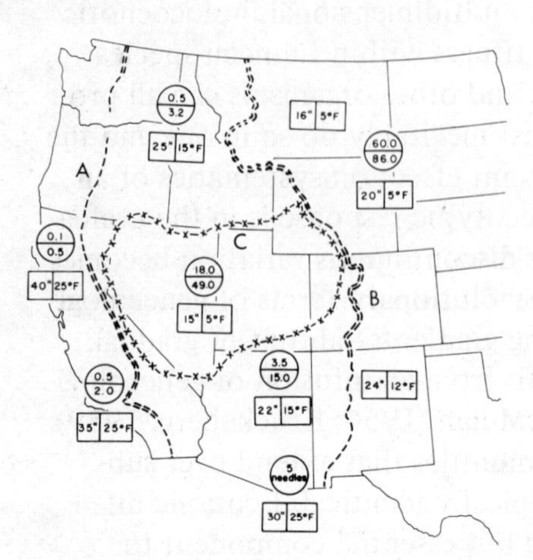

FIGURE 1 Generalized distribution of 2-needle fascicles, precipitation, and winter temperatures within the range of *Pinus ponderosa.* Dashed lines indicate the principal dividing ranges: *A,* Sierra-Cascade system; *B,* Continental Divide (Rocky Mts.). Double dashed lines indicate continuous high ridges. Line *C* marks the approximate limit of the Great Basin region. Representative frequencies of 2-needle fascicles are enclosed by circles: mature trees in upper half, young trees in lower half. Climatic data, interpolated from U.S. Weather Bureau records, are enclosed by rectangles: mean annual precipitation to left, mean January minimum temperature to right. Figure and caption from Haller (1965: 379).

that coincide with various populations of *Pinus ponderosa.* The critical morphological expression is needle number (Figure 1); it is evident that moisture stress favors the two-needle over the three-needle fascicles. Here then, a fundamental taxonomic character appears to respond directly (and genotypically?) to environmental restraints. Haller suggests that his results point to a possible mode of origin for distinct species of pines, as in the pinyon pines of the southwestern United States.

The most elegant studies in genecology are now revealing ecotypic variation at the physiological and biochemical levels. Instead of the gross yardsticks of vigor or survivability in contrasting environments, the contemporary genecologist is looking for variations in specific physiological responses to detect the ecotypic response to local selective forces. Work of this nature has been reviewed recently by Hiesey and Milner (1965). Clearly, species of broad distribution show specific and adaptive response in function to a wide spectrum of environmental and physiological factors. Soil nutrients, moisture stress, photoperiodism, temperature effects, photosynthesis, and respiration all have elicited racial differentiation in a variety of seed plants. The studies of Bjorkman and Holmgren (1963) exemplify the new breed of genecologists. They find that the photosynthetic apparatus has been subjected to selection so as to yield adaptive variation in the mechanism for optimal function in sun versus shade. Variations in this physiological adaptation can occur within short distances; also, as Turreson (1922) found many years earlier, ecotypic differentiation is often polytropic, for the same physiological response to light intensity can occur in ecologically similar habitats, though they may be separated by many miles.

As might have been predicted, the ultimate in the reductionist approach (*sensu* Simpson, 1963) to physiological accommodation is currently being sought. If we learn that physiological processes are ecotypically variable, then we would expect tissues, organelles, and even macromolecules to be genecologically discrete in different populations. Following the lead of Mooney and Billings (1961), who found metabolic differences between arctic and alpine populations of *Oxyria digyna,* Klikoff has isolated mitochondria from populations of diverse habitats. His studies on temperature dependence of mitochondrial respiration support the view (Klikoff, 1966:529) "that plants of colder regions, arctic or alpine, have higher respiratory rates at a given temperature than those from more moderate regions." It remains now to fix the differentiating metabolic mechanism more precisely. I am confident that, in due time, cytochrome, enzyme, and even DNA variables will be found that correlate with the physiological adaptations in question.

I am inclined to the view that this sort of refined comparative "ecophysiology" is of but limited value to systematics. To be sure, by such studies we are given the penultimate cause-and-effect basis for microevolutionary differentiation. We are indeed impressed with the finely graded response to habitat differences. No two collections of a species are likely to be physiologically identical. However, the utility of such an atomistic view to formal classification is nil. The views of Langlet (1963:348) on the inadvisability of incorporating genecological data into formal taxonomies are worth repeating in this context:

> There is no possibility of classifying the manifold patterns of ecological variability in the rigid system of acknowledged subdivisions of a species. It seems just as futile to construct special terminologies in order to summarize, and at the same time discriminate between, the various patterns which may occur. The ecological variability and its patterns in different species of animals and plants vary in such a multitude of combinations and degrees that every effort to force them into one or another terminological system will inevitably result in violating the facts and thus substituting artefacts for the real thing.

I am not forgetting that the genecologist has indeed given us overwhelming evidence of multidimensional, clinal, ecotypic variation (differentiation) within species. What the systematist might expect for the future would be a more "systematic" search for the fundamental differentiating ecophysiological and biochemical criteria that have yielded the adaptive radiations at higher levels—within genera and families.

Ecology and Isolating Mechanisms

Differentiation into detectable, discontinuous groupings is the evolutionary level that comes under the purview of the systematist. That stage in evolutionary divergence at which isolation achieves a recognizable hiatus in the biological continuum provides the systematist's *raison d'être.* Every possible ecological barrier can initiate the evolution of definable segregates. We will examine a few of these as they relate to the systematics of angiosperms.

Unfortunately, the systematist's deep involvement in identifying ecological isolating factors has not been fully complemented by thorough ecological studies. Most often it is the systematist who has to make observations and judgments on particular ecological conditions that may promote isolation. The systematist can recognize the general relevance of such factors, but can he be expected to quantify them or particularize about them? Without ecological training or the aid of an interested ecologist, judgments on the action of ecological isolating mechanisms must remain tentative. Not many plant ecologists have concerned themselves with these types of problems; evolutionary autecologists who would direct their attention to the ecological basis of isolation between plant populations would find it a fascinating and fertile field of investigation. I will discuss two such areas of evolutionary ecology as they relate to the origin of discontinuities: edaphic specialization and biotic selection, both of which generate a multitude of adaptive responses and yield products dealt with by the systematist.

The edaphic factor—physical and chemical properties of soils—can elicit sharp discontinuities in plants. Some of the richest floras in the world owe their diversity to the complex mosaic of edaphic differences. Sharp discontinuities between soils of highly contrasting lithological origin exert marked selective effects on flora. A list of such substrates would include limestones, dolomites, serpentine and other ultramafics, highly acid sands and other siliceous substrates, guano deposits, and others. Where such nonzonal or exceptional substrates locally outcrop or interdigitate with more "normal" soils, a strong selective action can be expected.

Exemplifying the effect of substrates on systematics are the impressive lists of edaphic endemics and the singular floristic responses recounted in reviews by Krause (1958); Stebbins and Major (1965); Mason (1946); Kruckeberg (1954) and Whittaker (1960). I will select three examples from the most recent studies that illustrate a complementary interplay between systematics and edaphic ecology. Gankin and Major (1964) have found an ecological explanation for the remarkable endemism of *Arctostaphylos myrtifolia* in California. This distinctive manzanita occurs locally in nearly pure stands on Eocene laterite and sericitic schists in the Sierra Nevada foothills. The species is the dominant plant in this azonal acid heath association that abruptly interposes itself within the regional climax vegetation. Thc authors find evidence to support the thesis that the high soil acidity and high aluminum content favor the Ione manzanita and exclude elements of the surrounding flora. The ecological explanation for this case of edaphic endemism is not solely based on adaptation to a unique substrate. In fact, Gankin and Major derive a broader explanation from the Ione manzanita case that applies to other examples of endemics that are edaphic specialists. The authors develop a common causal explanation, as follows (Gankin and Major, 1964:803).

Once this principle of disjunct and endemic plant occurrence on non-zonal soil sites is accepted, examples become almost too numerous. In all these cases explanations of why the rare plants occur where they do in terms of plant physiological reactions are completely lacking. Judging from the cases cited, they would have to be conflicting. The only explanation which fits the diversity of facts—that is, plants occurring at higher or lower altitudes than normal, in wetter habitats or drier, with less calcium or more—is in terms of plant competition. All the cases fit the conclusion that rare or disjunct (non-zonal) plants can occur in a given area where competition is decreased by some kind of extraordinary soil parent material or other continuously effective disturbance of climax vegetation development.

Another example of the fruitful contribution of edaphic ecology to systematics bears directly on the ubiquitous phenomenon of vicarism in plant genera. When two closely related species have a similar but not wholly confluent distribution, we suspect habitat specialization to have produced the discontinuity. Within the complex lithology of the White Mountains of eastern California, two highly contrasting types of bedrock support distinctly different vegetation. A bristlecone pine community is largely restricted to dolomite, while sagebrush dominates on sandstone. Among the species that show strong preferences for one or the other of the two soils are two closely related species of *Erigeron* (Compositae). Mooney (1966) has studied the two species both in the field and under experimental conditions. Combining data from these studies with an analysis of the physical and chemical features of the dolomite and sandstone soils has provided an unexpected explanation for the vicarism of the two species. The soil preferences shown by these two species are not direct responses to just the chemistry of the substrates. Rather, distinct microclimatic differences resulting from "compensations provided by substrate color, temperature, moisture, and soil chemistry" serve to separate the two species. The systematist would be grateful for more studies that provide sound ecological explanations for the habitat preferences of closely related "semipatric" species. Tansley (1917), the celebrated British ecologist, initiated such comparative ecological studies with his work on the calciphile and calciphobe galiums; similar comparisons since then have been anything but plentiful. By such an approach, the plant ecologist, capitalizing on the initial observations of field-oriented systematists, would be in a position to define more properly the ecological niche for higher plants. Niche specialization and its counterpart, competitive exclusion, have been difficult to apply in dealing with plants. I see in Mooney's work provocative insight.

Much species diversification in plant genera must be a result of adaptive radiation in terms of specific ecological preferences. Germane to our discussion of the edaphic factor and systematics are those cases in which species multiplication is related to substrate diversity. Here again we have to be content, for the most part, with the systematist's necessarily superficial account of substrate specificity for species of a genus. An ecologist with a systematic bent could provide us with some crucial environmental circumscriptions of plant groups that have developed edaphic specialists.

For some years I have been looking at a group of crucifers that have developed a high degree of edaphic specialization. The genus *Streptanthus* of the western United States (in the broadest sense to include *Caulanthus*) consists of about 40 species. In their edaphic tolerance, they range all the way from broad generalists (*S. glandulosus, S. cordatus, S. tortuosus*) to a group of about four species that occur only on serpentine soils (exclusively in California and southern Oregon). The serpentine specialists can be either very local endemics (e.g., *S. niger* on Tiburon Peninsula, San Francisco Bay, *S. batrachopus* on Mount Tamalpais, and *S. insignis* in the New Idria area) or more wide-ranging species that are, nevertheless, obligate to serpentine (e.g., S. *breweri,* S. *howellii,* and *S. drepanoides*). In this group of serpentine endemics we have the proliferation of discrete taxa on a single substrate. The key to this is surely the highly discontinuous distribution of serpentine outcrops throughout the range of the California-Oregon area. Work in progress is attempting to correlate the edaphic ecological attributes of the species with their genetic relatedness. Determinations of specific soil tolerances are being combined with hybridization studies to determine the systematic relationships of the narrow serpentine endemics to the more broadly tolerant species. Ecotype differentiation into serpentine-tolerant and serpentine-intolerant races already has been detected in *S. glandulosus* (Kruckeberg, 1957, 1958); also it has been confirmed recently for *S. tortuosus* (Kruckeberg, unpublished). The occurrence of ecotypic variation within species gives a promising lead on the possible steps in species formation. Some edaphic races are strongly isolated from each other genetically, and reduced gene flow, accentuated by edaphic and spatial isolation, is likely to lead to speciation. That it already has done so in one case is clearly indicated for the narrow endemic *S. niger,* which is now spatially and genetically cut off from its nearest morphological congener, *S. glandulosus pulchellus* (Kruckeberg, 1957).

Could catastrophic selection have brought about some of the amazing diversification in *Streptanthus?* Raven (1964) thinks so. He reminds us that Lewis (1962) developed the concept of catastrophic selection to account for rapid speciation from ecologically peripheral populations of the genus *Clarkia* (Onagraceae). Lewis suggested that under conditions of severe drought all but a few uniquely preadapted genotypes may be eliminated. Raven applies the idea to edaphic endemics by proposing that the preadapted types are edaphic specialists. Surely the environmental conditions in much of the range of *Streptanthus* heighten the opportunity for catastrophic selection. The dry, inner Coast Ranges of California, both north and south of San Francisco Bay, are complex mosaics of contrasting lithology; ultrabasic rocks like serpentine are prime ingredients in the pattern. Speciation in *Streptanthus* is richest precisely in these areas. For example, in the South Coast Range country from Mount Diablo down to New Idria there are no less than nine species, four of which are restricted to serpentine. I would propose that the "color-spot" endemics (S. *insignis* and *S. "lyoni"*) are derived from *S. coulteri* and *S. glandulosus* via catastrophic selection. What we are particularizing for serpentine endemics as a singular kind of evolutionary response is but one possibility when a biota encounters environmental extremes (Detling, 1948a, 1948b; Mason, 1946; Stebbins, 1952).

Ecological Aspects of Biotic Isolation

Discontinuity in physical factors of the environment serves to isolate flora as well as species or other infraspecific elements of phylogenetically related groups. Climatic and soil differences are the broad categories of such isolating factors. Both synecologists and autecologists have been probing these issues for decades, and phytogeography, floristics, and subfamilial systematics all have profited from the work of the environmentalists. But no less significant in controlling the spatial and ecological distribution of plants is the plenitude of plant-to-plant and plant-to-animal interactions. Thus, the biotic environment through all ontogenetic stages as well as the evolutionary history of plants has provoked responses that lead to discontinuities. Extrinsic isolation resulting from biotic interactions may be expressed as taxonomic discontinuity. Here again the systematist, more often than the ecologist, has sought the causal relations that may explain cases of obvious interference or cooperation.

A given set of biotic interactions that achieve ecological integrity (and isolation) for plants are complexly and holocoenotically interrelated with the physical environment as well as with all other biotic intercourse. To simplify the matter for discussion, I would compartmentalize organism-to-organism interactions into two ontogenetic stages, vegetative and reproductive.

Interactions during the vegetative stage of plant life histories immediately thrust us into that arena of debate circumscribed by the word "competition." Rather than be boxed in by the polemics that using the term competition may arouse, I would prefer to look at biotic interactions from the standpoint of their relationship to taxonomic discontinuities. As I view it, the phenomena of competition or interference (*sensu* Harper, 1961), as well as cooperation, operate at the physical and chemical levels and, in turn, express themselves both in terms of natural selection (yielding adaptation and evolution) and community organization. What are some ways in which biotic interactions may achieve discrete, systematic effects at progressively higher hierarchical levels? Competition, including chemical inhibition as well as cooperation, influences the outcome of vegetation change through the process of replacement or succession. Any seral species is likely to have a set of vegetative characteristics different from those of a climax species. Interactions and their effects at the population and community levels certainly go beyond the purely plant-to-plant type. Plant-to-animal (e.g., herb–herbivore) and plant-to-microbe situations must be reckoned with in the context of interspecies mutual responses. The ultimate result is significant not only for community development and structure but has import for coevolution of mutual plant–animal–microbe adaptive synergisms.

I am afraid that if a plant systematist should ask of an ecologist "What is a seral species?" he would get only a superficial answer. The resource and spatial limitations imposed on a seral dominant by later invaders is said to eliminate the seral species; impermanence is the criterion. But this explanation is only a panchreston; many additional problems are posed by such a facile answer. What are the particular physiological and environmental factors that restrict the species to its sere and cause it to disappear late in its particular seral state? How can seral species continue to survive in the face of repeated eliminations during succession? And then we are led to the larger evolutionary-genetic question raised by John Harper in his provocative review of plant competition (Harper, 1961): "Why doesn't the seral species climb its own sere?" Surely one would expect natural selection to promote progressive fitness to enable a species to pass successfully into later stages of succession. The plant systematist and ecologist could better understand seral species if there were cases where closely related species of a genus do indeed occupy successive seral stages in a given ecosystem. Although I have not encountered any case of this sort, a somewhat negative counterpart does exist. Species of the legume *Lespedeza,* which are confined largely to the southeastern United States, apparently are all successful occupants of early successional stages (Clewell, 1966). Several species are sympatric in the sandy soils of the Deciduous Woodland Formation. However, all the colonizers of open and disturbed areas are tolerant of fire, and they persist only through the early seral phase of pine savannah. More extensive hybridization among the sympatric species is thus prevented by their short-lived seral nature. Fire and other types of repetitive disturbance thus keep these seral gene pools alive. Recognition that these species of *Lespedeza* are seral illuminates their evolutionary-systematic status in the genus.

The portrayal of a prairie continuum in Wisconsin by J. T. Curtis (1955) gave both ecologists and taxonomists a tantalizing glimpse of how synecological studies can delimit the environmental amplitudes of related taxa. Curtis used the set of presence index curves (Figure 2) for species pairs to illustrate divergent ecological patterns of species in the same genus. But one is struck with the cases of close ecological convergence between species of a genus (e.g., in *Baptisia, Lithospermum, Desmodium,* and *Silphium*). Plant taxonomists could well heed the urgings of Dansereau (1952), reiterated by Curtis (1955:565):

> . . . the full description of a given taxon must include a measure of its ecologic adaptations as well as its morphology and its genetics. Preparation of similar behavior diagrams for all communities of occurrence of a given species or for similar gradients in other portions of its geographical range would contribute as much to our understanding of the species as would the most comprehensive monographic treatment based on morphology alone.

The ecological attributes of closely related species that permit their coexistence should be important concerns of the systematist. Outstanding studies of species interactions continue to come from John Harper and his plant ecology group at Bangor, Wales. In a series of papers under the general title "The Comparative Biology of Closely Related Species Living in the Same Area," Harper and his colleagues have looked at a host of physical and biotic factors that permit coexistence: physical variations in such biotic factors

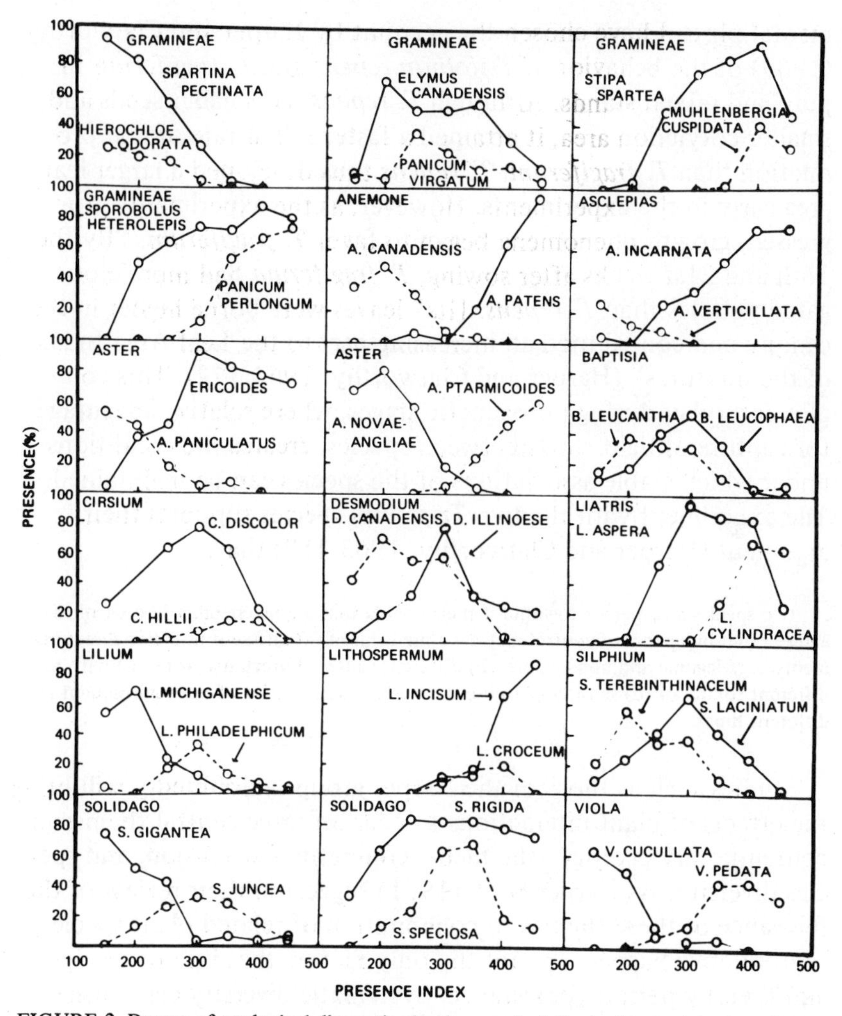

FIGURE 2 Degree of ecological discontinuity (or overlap) for various pairs of species in genera of the Wisconsin prairie. Occurrence is expressed as presence (in percent) along a prairie continuum. Figure from Curtis (1955:563).

as population density, relative seed size, phenotypic plasticity (or, physiological adaptation), and "safe-site" preferences for germination as well as in parasitism, predation, and growth differences (expressed both morphologically and physiologically).

As an example of the complex interactions that can take place between two congeneric species even in relatively simple experimental plots, I have chosen the account by Harper and Clatworthy (1963) of the behavior of *Trifolium repens* and *T. fragiferum* in pure and mixed stands. Although *T. repens* has smaller seeds and smaller cotyledon area, it attained a faster initial rate of leaf production than *T. fragiferum; T. repens* thus developed a larger leaf area early in the experiments. However, as the experiments progressed, growth phenomena began to favor *T. fragiferum.* "By the 18th and 21st weeks after sowing, *T. fragiferum* had more elongated petioles than *T. repens,* [its] leaves were borne higher in the canopy and contributed an increasing part to the Leaf Area Index of the mixtures" (Harper and Clatworthy, 1963:172). This complex interplay during ontogenetic stages, where relative advantage for capture of light shifts between species, creates the conditions under which stable associations of the species can be maintained. The experiment with the two *Trifolium* species supports their argument (Harper and Clatworthy, 1963:189) that:

> . . . two species may persist together if their populations are independently controlled and . . . that independent control may take the form of (a) different nutritional requirements, e.g., legume and non-legume, (b) different causes of mortality, (c) sensitivity to different toxins, or (d) sensitivity to the same controlling factors of the environment at different times.

Studies such as those of the Harper group undoubtedly will bring the effects of plant interactions to bear on three central themes in contemporary ecology—the niche, competitive exclusion, and species diversity. As Harper *et al.* (1961) suggest in their review of the relevance of these themes to cohabitation of related plant species, reproductive barriers are not the only factors that isolate species and thereby permit coexistence. Systematic diversity can persist only if differentiating biological properties of the species *other than* reproductive ones function to promote coexistence.

At this point in the discussion of coexistence it is appropriate to query botanists on the subject of character displacement. The phenomenon is generally accepted for animals (Brown and Wilson, 1956; Mayr, 1963), though questions of interpretation of species coexistence (character displacement versus introgression) are not always easily resolved. The essence of the idea is that two species are more distinct when they are sympatric than when they are allopatric. Why, then, should not two species of plants when rejoined in secondary sympatry show exaggerated character discontinuity? At first glance, the plant systematist is likely to predict the outcome of secondary sympatry to be genetic contamination by introgression or alloploidy. But there should be certain conditions under which selection would favor ecophysiological as well as morphological divergence of the "sympatriates." Selection might take the specifications of a closed, highly competitive plant community where hybrids would not be tolerated, coupled with rather specific pollination ecologies to promote character displacement between plant species. Genera of temperate latitudes where one might look for the phenomenon would include *Penstemon, Ophrys, Habenaria, Calochortus, Gilia, Oenothera, Clarkia,* and others where zoophilous flowers predominate. As to character displacement in tropical plant groups (orchids, bromeliads, gesneriads, aroids, etc.) we may speculate that exaggeration of character differences may have been an adaptive response long before ecosystem stability was obtained. Subsequent elimination of the allopatric segments of the species could have left the products of character displacement as the singularly divergent taxa of the present.

In the past, it was understood that the interactions between prey and predator were purely in the domain of zoological ecology. Yet in contemporary ecology it is not surprising to see the plant ecologist using the term "prey" for plants and showing an active interest in their responses to animal predators. Most contemporary studies on the ecological and microevolutionary interactions between herb and herbivore illustrate adaptive differences at the infraspecific level. These indeed should be of intrinsic interest to biosystematists. Yet of even greater moment for systematics would be studies on herb–herbivore interactions at higher taxonomic levels. We may ask, has speciation—and even adaptive radiation at the generic and familial level—been promoted by herbivore pressure? Since phylogenetic plant taxonomy at the level of genus and family is predisposed to differentiate taxa by reproductive structures (and function, i.e., pollination and dispersal mechanisms), the search for major systematic discontinuities brought about by predation has been limited. The now classic paper by Kemp (1937) illustrates the effect of grazing on microevolutionary divergence. Pasture grasses developed marked ecotypic differences depending on the presence or absence of grazing. More recently, Jones (1962) has described a case of heritable polymorphism in *Lotus corniculatus* that appears to have selective predation as its basis. Local polymorphism for levels (or presence/absence) of cyanogenic glucosides in herbage of *Lotus* elicits selective predation by snails, slugs, and voles.

Mechanical "predation" (mowing, harvesting, etc.) can also produce evolutionary differentiation. The famous cases of "crop mimics" associated with cultivated flax come first to mind; the story has been reviewed by Stebbins (1950). Here, selection favoring vegetative and reproductive similarity to the crop plant (flax) has created species mimics out of unrelated species; e.g., *Silene linicola* in the Caryophyllaceae and *Camellina sativa* var. *linicola* in the Cruciferae. Harper (1964) cites another case—discovered years ago by Salisbury—in which two weed species of grain fields developed dwarf strains. In so doing, the weeds survived harvesting operations and were perpetuated as stubble forms in the seed crop.

I have no doubt that many weedy and ruderal species as well as species of natural communities owe their survival to mechanisms evolved to escape or avoid predation. Spines, raphides, tough tissues, etc., are the morphological indicators, while secondary metabolites, so richly diverse in plants, are the chemical indicators that may lead us to discoveries of singular import to both ecology and systematics. A provocative case of biochemical selectivity is being studied at the University of Washington by two animal ecologists (G. Orians and R. Paine, unpublished) who have exposed to slug predators various strains of *Nicotiana tabacum* of differing nicotine content. Under controlled greenhouse conditions, they find suggestions of selective predation correlated with nicotine content: The slugs tend to avoid plants with high nicotine. In other experiments, it appears that different species of slugs have remarkably distinct degrees of preference for a given plant (seedlings of *Agrostis* sp.). I would envision selective predation entraining a continual coevolutionary drama: The prey (plants) are apt to respond adaptively to the predator, and the predator, in turn, to react adaptively so as to keep up with changes in plant palatability, etc. On the other hand, possible extinction of prey or predator species could terminate the coevolutionary race.

Biotic interactions surely will have to be reckoned with in any satisfactory attempts to explain species diversity in ecosystems, particularly in the tropics. Again, this is another problem whose resolution will be aided by mutual cooperation between ecologists and systematists. In a paper of great clarity and simplicity, Gillett (1962) sets forth an imaginative hypothesis to account for the origin and perpetuation of high levels of species diversity. Gillett was led to this view by cases of pest–host interactions where the host is most vulnerable when numerically dominant in the plant community. This state of affairs evoked for Gillett the Roman dictum *Debellare superbos, et subjectis parcere* ("spare the scarce but beat down the dominant species."). He explains the mystery of evolutionary diversification within plant groups as follows (Gillett, 1962:40): "Pest pressure is the inevitable, ubiquitous factor in evolution which makes for an apparent pointless multiplicity of species in all areas in which it has time to operate." I would like to add a postscript to this challenging idea. I believe a known mechanism can be adduced to account for adaptation to pest pressure. Apostatic selection (Clarke, 1964) is a type of negative feedback in populations wherein the occurrence of various morphs is frequency-dependent. Coupled with isolation and reduced gene flow, rare morphs could further diverge to form species. Rarity then becomes a premium for success at the species level.

Ever since the landmark studies of Gray and Bonner (1948) and Muller (1953) on the effect of herbage leachates on the growth of plants, plant ecologists have been expecting such chemical inhibitor studies to have far-reaching implications for interpreting community organization. Assuming that exocrines (substances excreted by plants) are part of the inherited and evolved character complex of species and larger groups, they surely come within the purview of the systematists. Muller (1964, 1965) and his associates, working on California *Salvia* species, and Baker (1966) working with *Eucalyptus,* have shown that volatile exocrines are toxic to other vegetation and that this toxicity has ecological significance. Pattern, spacing, and species composition of local communities often are influenced dramatically by the species that secretes the volatiles.

Exocrines need not act only as chemical inhibitors in plant communities. One can imagine that interspecific associations may be enhanced by a kind of chemical symbiosis. That this can occur between different genotypes of the same species is reported by Roy (1960), who made a most provocative discovery: interplantings of two varieties of rice influence the yield of one another. As the mixtures are included in the same aqueous environment (water plots bordered by a dam), the influence appears to be transmitted in the water. Under some mixture regimes, especially with varieties in alternate rows, the yield was 126 percent of mean yield. Cooperative interaction, by whatever means (chemical, physical, biotic) has import not only for the study of plant communities. I would envision the strengthening of interactions, say, between morphs of the same species, etc., by natural selection such that their interdependence becomes obligate. In fully documenting the comparative biology of taxa, the systematist cannot fail to recognize the significance of this sort of mutualism.

Ecological Aspects of Reproductive Isolation

Discontinuities, produced by whatever cause, isolate gene pools. Thus, reproductive hiatus is at the heart of discontinuity, is the promoter of diversity, and hence gives the systematist his neverending *raison d'être.* Although reproductive isolation in plants is to be discussed by several of us at this symposium, it could stand scrutiny from the ecological point of view.

Purely for convenience, I have dealt first with ecological factors that determine a plant's habitat. The initial selective pressures act during the vegetative phase. However, the various physical, spatial, and biotic influences that shape discontinuity in the vegetative stage can continue to do so during reproduction. In fact, reduced reproductive exchange between populations often is the supreme arbiter of ecological preference. Continued gene flow, despite ecological specialization, would be the rare exception.

Reduction or cessation of gene flow due to ecological specializations of vegetative growth are not the only kinds of barriers to reproduction. Reproductive mechanisms themselves serve in many, often bizarre ways to isolate populations and species. The ecologist who becomes curious about comparative reproductive biology enters a rich and fascinating field of study. Unfortunately, there is little evidence that plant ecologists have preoccupied themselves with floral ecology. As in other contacts between ecology and systematics, it has been the nineteenth-century naturalists and the twentieth-century biosystematists who have dominated the field of ecological reproductive biology of higher plants.

Floral or pollination ecology seeks to define the physical and biotic environments that promote or inhibit the transfer of pollen. Where effective pollen transfer is wholly infraspecific, the reproductive isolation between species is complete. The ecological barriers to pollination are seasonal (timing) differences, spatial limitations (within or between habitats), and pollen vector specificities. The literature, both modern and classical, on pollination ecology has become so rich that a textbook treatment was inevitable. The latest and certainly the most comprehensive treatment of the subject is that by Faegri and van der Pijl (1966). I need not reexamine the ground so expertly covered by these two authors.

The significance of pollination ecology for systematics is self-evident. That evolutionary diversification has been marvelously complicated and elaborated by coevolutions of flowers and pollen vectors has been amply documented (Faegri and van der Pijl, 1966; Leppik, 1957; Ehrlich and Raven, 1965; Grant, 1949, 1950; and others). But how might this impressive body of information be utilized by the plant ecologist? For instance, does community composition owe some of its character to the pollination ecology of a number of plant and animal species? Coexistence of two closely related plant species (and their pollen vectors of similar taxonomic propinquity) largely may be the result of specific pollination syndromes. In fact, I would speculate that the essential niche specificity of some species is determined by the pollination function. Community ecology stands to benefit from pollination ecology in other ways. I would envision such synecological phenomena as species diversity, pattern (spacing, aggregation, etc.), dominance (common versus rare species), and successional and climax community composition to be conditioned in part by the ecology of pollen transfer.

Should pollination ecology shed light on some of the aforementioned problems in community ecology, then in gratitude the ecologist should offer his services to the systematist who uses pollination data. The many elaborate flower–vector syndromes have yet to be analyzed thoroughly in terms of the physiological ecology of the flower and behavioral ecology of the vector. For example, in tropical orchids we would like to know more about the role of microhabitat (temperature, light, position in the forest canopy, etc.) and about the nature of the chemical, mechanical, and visual stimuli that attract the vector as well as having more specific and detailed studies of behavior and population biology. Pollination biology's traditional base in systematics should be substantially broadened by wider interest on the part of physiologists, ecologists, and animal behaviorists.

Just to suggest a provocative approach, cooperative ecological and behavioral studies could be brought to bear on the vast problem of hummingbird pollination. Karen Grant (1966) offers the challenge; she hypothesizes that red coloration of flowers serves as a recognition sign attracting migrating hummingbirds to local feeding sites, and that subsequent foraging need not be restricted to red flowers. She thus discards the widely held view that red is the sole color detected by the birds. Foraging behavior and floristic composition in each major biotope along the migration routes of the birds would have to be studied in order to particularize the "homing" function of red coloration.

Another intriguing possibility of significance for systematics needs further investigation by pollination ecologists. Verne Grant (1949) contended that in areas where flower-constant bees are common, and hence promote floral isolation, the regional flora should have undergone greater speciation than in areas dominated by plants that rely on wind or promiscuous animal pollination. Since his data were purely statistical and were gathered in only one area, Southern California, it would be useful to test the argument in other floras—tropical and temperate. For instance, is the richness of the Himalayan-Western China flora—where some genera (*Rhododendron, Gentiana, Primula, Meconopsis, Lilium,* etc.) have gone on a speciational rampage—partly attributable to floral isolating mechanisms created by specific pollination ecologies?

Plant Ecology and Dispersal Types

The obvious counterpart to pollination ecology is dispersal-unit ecology. As in pollination, successful dispersal has put a premium on the evolution of highly adaptive devices for particular ecological circumstances. Though the morphology of dissemules is of great value in plant systematics, the biology of dispersal can provide much more in the realm of causation. The biology of diaspore dissemination is of mutual concern to ecology and systematics in two ways. First, the systematist seeks to know some of the environmental parameters that control effective dispersal. Ecogeographic discontinuity, isolation, and speciation are some of the consequences of barriers to unlimited dispersals. Thus, a host of questions could be put to the ecologist: What are the microclimatic (wind, temperature, etc.) factors that abet specific dispersals? What are the physical, mechanical, and physiological explanations for wind, water, and animal dissemination? How do such physiological phenomena as viability and dormancy relate to successful dispersal? Then, reciprocally, the ecologist will seek from the systematist information on the taxonomic significance of dispersal types as they relate to ecological life histories in species and higher categories and to the process and structure in plant communities.

I must resist the temptation to examine in depth the manifold ways in which dissemination of diaspores (dispersal units) brings ecology and systematics of plants together. From the classic treatments of Kerner and Oliver (1902) and Ridley (1930) to the more contemporary studies by Salisbury (1942) and Carlquist (1966 a and b), the reader can develop the sense of ecoevolutionary and systematic interrelatedness that plant dispersal evokes. From the systematics standpoint, salient evolutionary trends are associated with adaptive radiations of dispersal type. Ehrendorfer (1965) develops the theme in his discussion of the evolution of colonizing types in the Dipsacaceae, Rubiaceae, and Compositae. Carlquist (1966b) portrays the ultimate in the bizarre with his account of loss of dispersability in insular endemics of the Compositae. Thus, for many large genera or families of flowering plants, it is not surprising to find circumstantial evidence of evolutionary and systematic response to the ecological demands of dispersal.

The ecologist could well ask how dispersability and its evolutionary-systematic proliferation might be significant in shaping the composition of plant communities. For instance, are not seral stages, edaphic climaxes, local and endemic floras, and regional climatic climax communities all likely to have different diaspore spectra (*sensu* Raunkiaer, 1934 and Dansereau and Lems,

1957)? Salisbury's book, (1942) with its statistics on diaspore types for various plant communities in Britain, contributes importantly to this problem. Also, the ecological classification of diaspore types by Dansereau and Lems (1957) provides a basis for dealing with dispersal as an "important force in the internal dynamics of each stand of vegetation."

A pair of miscellaneous conjectures should indicate how plant ecology might profit (and, to my knowledge has not yet profited) by a recognition of the significance of diaspore dissemination. The first conjecture concerns primary and secondary succession versus climax: Are seral species more likely to have diaspores of light and easy dispersability versus heavier or otherwise less mobile diaspores for climax species? The second conjecture relates to aggregation, sociability, and other pattern-forming phenomena in communities, as well as continuous to discontinuous plant associations: How does relative, species-specific dispersability influence these synecological characters?

Ecology, the Disturbed Habitat, and Hybridization

Hybridization and the disturbed habitat is an area of plant systematics in which the ecological approach could be of real value. Strong taxonomic and cytogenetic evidence supports the view that hybridization followed by introgression (Anderson, 1936, 1948, 1949 and 1953; Heiser, 1949b) or by allopolyploidy (Clausen *et al.*, 1945; Stebbins, 1950) accounts for many of the blurred species boundaries in vascular plants. The biological success of interspecific hybridization usually is attributed to the availability of intermediate or pioneer habitats (Anderson, 1936, 1948; Stebbins, 1950, 1959a); that is, the result of natural or man-made disturbance. It usually is assumed that the hybrid genotypes find a hospitable habitat that is different from the habitats of the parental species. But who has yet answered the ecological question: What is a "hybrid" habitat?

We inevitably turn to Edgar Anderson for his imaginative ideas on the relation between hybridity and the habitat. In his paper entitled "Hybridization of the Habitat" (Anderson, 1948) and in Chapter 2 of his book "Introgressive Hybridization" (Anderson, 1949), he has set forth the ecological basis of hybrid survival. The crux of his argument is derived from the presumed diverse ecological requirements of later generation progeny from an interspecific hybrid. "The second generation will be made up of individuals each of which will require its own peculiar habitat for optimum development" (Anderson, 1948:4). Using a simple system of three ecological variables, each with two contrasting states, he suggests that in addition to the six recombination or "hybrid" environments many other variant habitats will be required to meet the phenotypic requirements of the hybrid plants. The number of appropriate habitats will increase as the diversity of the segregating progeny gets more complex. Anderson further asserts that the actual number of environments will be far more limited than the number required by recombination phenotypes of the F_2 generation. Therefore, backcross (introgressed) progeny that most closely approximate one or the other parent are more likely to find suitable habitats; that is, habitats that are merely modified parental habitats.

Several ecological questions should be studied in efforts to account for habitat suitability of F_1, F_2, and introgressants. What are the ecological characteristics of an intermediate habitat, a recombination habitat, a disturbed habitat, etc.? To what extent do physiological adaptability (phenotypic plasticity of physiological traits) or broadened tolerance spans of hybrids reduce the need for a specific habitat? Does the hybrid (F_1, F_2, backcross, etc.) always require a disturbed habitat? And then, a final question: Is survival of the hybrid associated more with reduced competition, by whatever cause, than with some particular recombination of physical attributes of the habitat? I fear that biosystematists concerned with natural hybridity have not adequately answered these and other relevant ecological questions. Anderson's provocative theme, the "hybridized habitat," still needs ecological amplification.

Some insights into the possible ecological causes of successful gene flow between species can be gleaned from the recent literature. From a sampling of papers on natural hybrids especially, I have searched for statements on the ecological conditions that may have facilitated the hybridity. One of three or four general kinds of ecological conditions usually is described: (1) The hybridization is fostered by human disturbance (e.g., *Tradescantia* in Anderson, 1936; *Helianthus* in Heiser, 1949a; *Phlox* in Anderson and Gage,

1952; *Crataegus* in Bradshaw, 1953; *Vaccinium* in Ritchie, 1955; *Hemerocallis* in Kawano, 1961; and *Hieracium* in Kruckeberg, 1967b; (2) the hybridization follows natural disturbance (*Hieracium* in Anderson and Stebbins, 1954; and *Purshia* and *Cowania* in Stebbins, 1959a); (3) there is disturbance but no extensive hybridization (*Primula* in Clifford, 1958; and Woodell, 1965); and (4) the hybridity ranges from rare F_1's to extensive introgression in natural, undisturbed habitats (*Salvia* in Epling, 1947b; *Arctostaphylos* in Epling, 1947a; *Epilobium* in Lewis and Moore, 1962; *Oenothera* in Raven, 1961; *Polystichum* in Wagner and Hagenah, 1954; *Dryopteris* in Wagner and Hagenah, 1962; *Ononis* in Morton, 1956; *Trillium* in Matsuzaka and Kurabayashi, 1959; *Lewisia* in Tucker, *et al.*, 1964; *Quercus* in Stebbins, *et al.*, 1947; and *Juniperus* in Hall, *et al.*, 1961).

In all of these examples, for which either disturbance or lack of disturbance is associated with some degree of hybridity, I find a common denominator. The hybrid genotype, like any other segregating progeny, must have *lebensraum* for germination and establishment. Thus, by whatever cause, freedom from competition, or the lack of interference, permits the establishment of progeny. Disturbance may indeed open up "new" or mongrelized habitats, but I would contend that disturbance—natural or human—creates the openness in the biotope, freedom from interference. Even for cases of hybridity without disturbance, conditions of reduced competition may be discovered. Some natural habitats like rock talus, screes, and other pioneer communities with plants widely spaced, or habitats with a mosaic of microenvironmental differences are sufficiently "open" that hybrid progeny can get a toehold in the absence of competition. Such an ecological interpretation can be given the cases of hybridity in *Lewisia, Epilobium, Juniperus,* and *Trillium* mentioned above. I realize that by invoking reduced competition as favoring hybridization in addition to the widely held idea that intermediate habitats are made available, we merely add one more hypothesis to be tested. Both views still await adequate ecological study.

Indeed, a beginning has been made. The ecological approach to determining the role of the habitat in natural hybridity is nicely developed in a recent paper by Brayton and Mooney (1966). Two species of *Cercocarpus*—*C. intricatus* and *C. ledifolius*—occur sympatrically in undisturbed habitats of the White Mountains in eastern California. The two species, however, are largely separated altitudinally and coexist only where the pinyon woodland and the subalpine forest zone meet as an ecotone. Careful analysis of the morphological traits of the two species and of their putative hybrids as well as of the ecological parameters (elevation, slope, rock cover, substrate) of the three habitats has provided an entirely

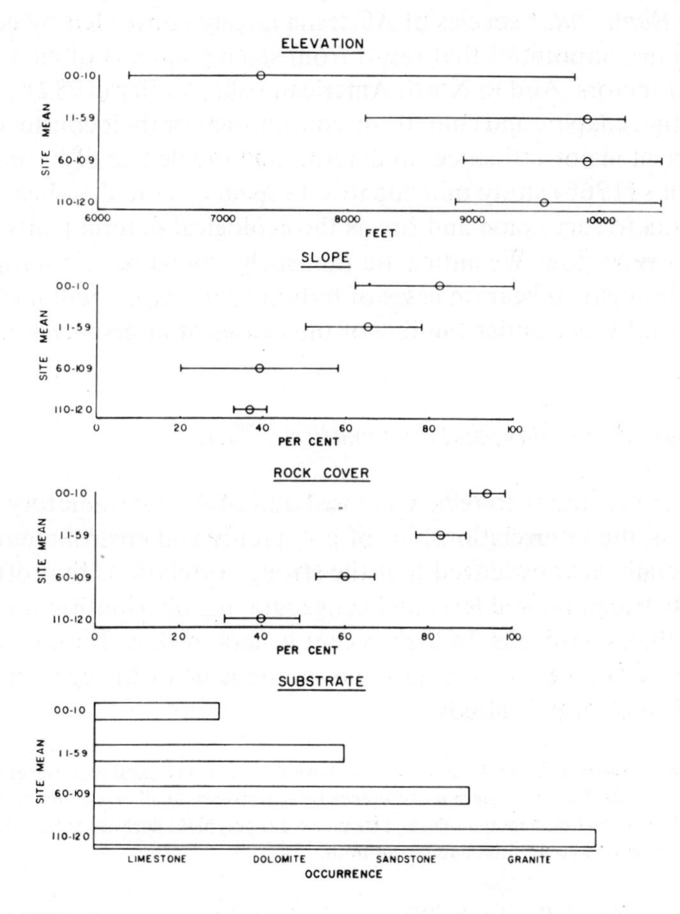

FIGURE 3 Relationship of certain environmental parameters of habitats to hybridity in the genus *Cercocarpus*. "Site mean" (vertical axis) refers to four hybrid index values. The extreme values are for *C. intricatus* (0.0–1.0) and *C. ledifolius* (11.0–12.0); the intermediate values are for populations of putative hybridity. Figure from Brayton and Mooney (1966:389).

plausible solution (Figure 3). The ecotone is indeed a "hybrid" habitat, intermediate between the pinyon woodland and the subalpine zone. Though uninfluenced by human disturbance, the ecotone occupied by the hybrids is believed to be unstable; that is, the ecotone is shifted upwards or downwards with each major shift in regional climate.

Three other papers are cited as sources of ecological documentation of hybridization in nature. Briggs (1962) finds hybridity in alpine *Ranunculus* species of Australia largely controlled by ecological discontinuities that result from steep gradients of environmental factors. And in North American oaks, Muller (1952) contends that edaphic and climatic discontinuities, or their confluencies, have been major influences in determining the degree of hybridity. Clewell's (1966) study of sympatric Lespedezas, cited earlier, clearly points to succession and fire as the ecological determinants that restrict gene flow. We anticipate that such ecological orientation, when brought to bear on cases of hybridity in nature, will increase significantly our understanding of the causes of interspecies gene flow.

Ecology, Polyploidy, and Systematics

It is not my intent to review the vast and often contradictory literature on the interrelationships of polyploidy and environment. It is generally acknowledged that the strong correlations that often exist between ploidal level and ecogeographic distribution are more than fortuitous. In their recent general review, Johnson *et al.*, (1965:507) take a moderate stand on the issue of the ecological significance of polyploidy:

> In polyploid series, polyploids almost always have different ecological requirements than related diploids, but the pattern of difference is inconsistent. In all cases, the diploid is adapted to an environmental mode, and its successful polyploid derivatives have occupied colder-wetter or warmer-drier habitats or both.

Thus where alloploidy "freezes" a hybrid genome, we would expect the ecological amplitude of the polyploid to differ from the parental diploids. Either through hybrid vigor or by the joining of two modes of adaptedness the alloploid is likely to be suited to environments differing from those of its parents. The difficulty comes in defining the ecological boundaries of the particular diploid-to-polyploid case history. Little ecological analysis has been offered to support the biosystematic hypothesis of change in ecological tolerance. As Johnson *et al.*, (1965) point out, much remains to be done in specifying the interplay between the polyploid genome and the environment. However, Johnson and Packer (1965) do offer an example of how intensive ecological study of a particular local flora can account for pattern of polyploid distribution. They find that diploids and polyploids are distributed locally (in the Ogotoruk Creek area, northwestern Alaska) along environmental gradients. Gradients in soil texture, soil moisture, soil temperature, permafrost, and disturbance are related, in a consistent fashion, to changes in frequency of polyploidy for a large number (89 percent) of the monocot and dicot members of the flora (Figure 4). Other studies such as this will be needed to support any particular hypothesis purporting to explain the causal relation between polyploidy and environment.

Ecology and the Diversification of Genera and Families

I have taken as axiomatic the view that much diversification of angiosperms and their present systematic organization is the evo-

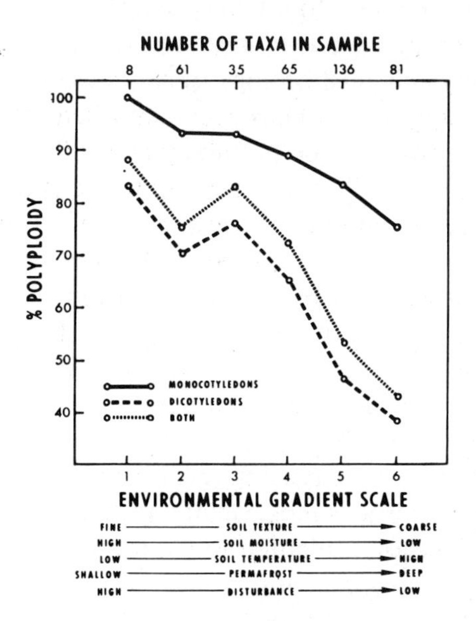

FIGURE 4 Relationship of the frequency of polyploidy to environmental gradients in the angiosperm flora of the Ogotoruk Creek Valley, Alaska. Figure from Johnson and Packer (1965:238).

lutionary response to ecological heterogeneity, fluctuating in time and space. It seems as if we should be able to glimpse salient ecological restraints or stimuli that have molded at least some major systematic groupings. The range of our concern here runs the gamut from adaptive radiation within genera to the origin of angiospermy itself.

Any genus of angiosperms with more than two or three species can be said to have diversified. Just how much of this diversification is due to adaptive responses to discrete ecological pressures (biotic and physical) and not solely to spatial discontinuity? I contend that nearly all species of a genus that are distinguished on fairly substantial morphological and physiological characters, or both, are the result of ecological selection. Only the trivial vicariants would be excluded. Then we would ask the ecologist: What are the distinguishing ecological parameters of species within genera? Here we confront a vast area of the unknown. Ecological life histories are known for only a few species, and there has been little attempt to approach this sort of study systematically throughout a genus. The British Ecological Society, however, has been doing ecological life histories under the continuing title "Biological Flora of the British Isles"; thus, a few species in *Ranunculus, Rumex, Juncus,* and other genera can be compared ecologically.

Another approach—the first of its kind, to my knowledge—deals with ecology of the several species of a genus represented in a regional flora. The comparative physiological ecology of seven closely related species of *Eriogonum* (Polygonaceae) has been described by Cole (1967), who made comparisons between populations of different species in the same habitat, as well as between populations of a given species occurring in different habitats. Using a roadway transect through several plant communities in the Santa Monica Mountains, California, Cole recorded environment, distribution patterns, ecological life-history data, and other autecological information for the seven species. His study reveals that some adaptive radiation into discrete habitats can be detected even within a limited region and for only a part of the generic diversity in *Eriogonum.* This is true for the three wide-ranging species and the four local species studied. However, Cole's most significant discovery was that different species become adapted to the same habitat through what he calls physiological convergence. That is, common ecological stresses lead to ecotypic convergence; thus, "populations of different *Eriogonum* species in a common habitat show more physiological resemblances among themselve than between populations of the same species in different habitats" (Cole, 1967:23).

Comparative physiological ecology at the generic level will have to be discriminating if it is to contribute significantly to our understanding of the total systematic biology of plant groups. To undertake such studies merely for the sake of "doing a genus" could become repetitive and delay by decades our quest for wider systematic coverage. I hope a concerted effort to do such ecologies on a preconceived plan can be undertaken. Such studies should aim at discerning ecoevolutionary pattern and process in the origin of life-form differences, the genesis of endemism, the spread into various life zones or into coevolutionary pathways with animals, microorganisms, etc. Also, comparisons between selected genera of major biomes–tropical and temperate–should be made. Here is a fruitful field for cooperative research between systematists and ecologists.

Quantum shifts in evolution are thought to be the opportunistic responses of selected preadapted populations to radically new habitats (Simpson, 1953). It should be possible to link major systematic "breakthroughs" in plants with similarly significant environmental events. For example, Axelrod (1966) has looked for causal explanations for the origin of the deciduous habit. He cites evidence that the deciduous condition is derived from the broadleaved evergreen habit of the tropics. Initially, the deciduous habit was an adaptation to periodic drought in the lower latitudes of subtropical climate. Since change from the evergreen to the deciduous habit has involved wholesale systematic innovation (new temperate genera and species from tropical ancestors), the latitudinal shift surely is an ecoevolutionary response of diverse phylads on a worldwide basis. That ancestral lines have evolved types that have penetrated to zones of greater environmental stress is inscribed in the early ontogenetic stages of many species. Stebbins (1952, 1959b) accounts for the shift from juvenile, mesic-type leaf structure to adult, xeric-type structure (and the reciprocal) as adaptive responses assumed by phylads as they entered new habitats.

At first glance, it seems utterly simplistic to account for the origin of a large segment of a continental flora on the basis of a single limiting ecological factor. The case for just this event is made plausible, however, by an Australian ecologist, N. C. W. Beadle (1966), who offers strong circumstantial and provocative experimental evidence that elements of the Australian flora have been guided in their migration and subsequent adaptive radiation by the limited quantity of phosphate in the soil. In his view, migration and evolution of diversified phylads found in xeric parts of Australian flora from rain forest families are promoted by low phosphate rather than by aridity. The evolutionary response in the face of low phosphate has been the increase in frequency of two vegetative characters, xeromorphy and sclerophylly. These traits can be experimentally "reversed" by addition of phosphate and nitrate. Surely, the development of other floras and systematic groups might be linked to similar highly selective factors of the environment. To name a few possibilities: ultrabasic soils and the endemic genera of New Caledonia, aridity coupled with edaphic and topographic diversity and the Cactaceae, pest pressure and tropical diversity, and coevolution of mutualistic associations between plants and animals.

The latter association, coevolution of plant–animal syndromes, brings to mind the exciting paper of Janzen (1966) on mutualisms between ants and acacias. Here is an extravagant case wherein the survival of ant and plant are irrevocably interlinked. With our eyes open for other cases of plant–animal mutualisms we may begin to detect much more subtle interactions. I would reiterate the suggestion that biotic interactions, both vegetative and reproductive, may be at the heart of major evolutionary events in higher organisms, viz., insects, birds, herbivorous mammals, and angiosperms.

The specification of the coevolutionary idea has come from several quarters in recent years. A provocative start was made by Grant (1949) and by Stebbins (1951). Both papers emphasized the probable adaptive nature of diagnostic familial characters in the angiosperm families. Grant and Grant (1965) were able to be more specific in view of coadaptations from their survey of the floral biology of the entire family Polemoniaceae. Then, beginning with Leppik (1957) and van der Pijl (1960, 1961), we see a resurgent interest in the natural history of floral mechanisms and its application to problems of phyletic evolution in the angiosperms. Yes, and even to the origin of the angiosperms themselves. The Ehrlich and Raven (1965) paper referred to earlier, is the latest contribution to documenting the thesis that "the plant–herbivore 'interface' may be the major zone of interaction responsible for generating terrestrial organic diversity."

Use of Ecological Data in Taxonomy of Higher Plants

Animal taxonomists give considerable weight to ecological data, either in the total diagnostic account of taxa or as delimiting features that separate closely related species. The principle of competitive exclusion is clearly involved here, and it is tacitly assumed to operate almost universally (Simpson, 1961:74). Minor and major categories have ecological attributes that can identify and distinguish them. Thus, orders of vertebrates as well as families, genera, and species of birds and mammals often can be circumscribed by their habitat or niche specializations. The counterpart in formal plant taxonomy either does not exist or has been overshadowed by the morphological characterizations that are used to delimit plant taxa. At least at the ordinal level of angiosperms there is little distinction between orders on the basis of ecological specialization. Of course, we can argue that sympetalous orders are ecologically distinct from polypetalous ones on the basis of floral ecology. But the formal character differentiae of the higher plant categories are *not* ecological. Why is this?

I think the answers stem both from intrinsic biological differences between plants and animals and from the precedents that issue from the history of plant taxonomy. The zoological principle stated by Simpson (1961), that each species "has a distinctive, unshared niche and that two or more associated species are usually rather sharply distinct," cannot be applied easily to plants. The niche concept has less applicability in autotrophic organisms; niche specificity is blurred by the common trophic base of green plants (Harper, 1961; Orians, 1965). Though there may, indeed, be an ecological specificity for plant taxa at various levels, traditionally, angiosperm taxonomy has been preoccupied with the separation of taxa on morphological grounds, even though the morphological differentiae often are the products of ecological selection.

"General-purpose" taxonomy (Gilmour and Walters, 1963) still is best served by the traditional use of morphological resemblances. I would propose, though, that much sharper definition could be given major and minor taxa of angiosperms if their ecological boundaries were circumscribed more closely. Convergence, parallelism, and broad tolerance ranges, of course, limit the utility of ecological circumscription for many plant taxa. But for plant species of restricted distribution—the endemics, plant indicators, and the like—salient ecological traits are likely to be coextensive with their taxonomic limits.

At levels of greatest inclusiveness, we would look for genera and families that are coincident with major world biomes. For the broadest ecological categories, tropical and temperate, Good (1964) lists 60 families and 305 genera as predominantly tropical but only 20 families and 90 genera as largely restricted to the temperate category. Then there are the Cactaceae and many genera of other families that are restricted to deserts, and such families as the Amaranthaceae, Chenopodiaceae, and Ericaceae, which have become edaphic specialists on saline, alkaline, nitrogenous, or acid soils. There is a meaningful idea to be derived from even these general tabulations: nearly all the constituent species in each category have their tolerance limits set by a climatic, edaphic, or biotic parameter.

What is being proposed here is that major angiosperm phylads (e.g., genera or families) are predisposed to display characteristic adaptive radiations. Some have diversified for desert life, others for aquatic, epiphytic, or parasitic life, and so forth. The radiations may be ecologically narrow (*Potamogeton* for fresh water, *Opuntia* for water stress, Balanophoraceae for parasitism, etc.), or the amplitude of the phylad may be ecologically broad (Rosaceae, Leguminosae, Compositae, Umbelliferae, *Carex, Ficus,* etc.). On the other hand, evolutionary opportunism surely has some finite ecological limits: Cactaceae are not likely to become hydrophytes, nor are tropical orchid genera expected to gain a foothold in the Arctic-Alpine. If this line of reasoning is valid, then the largest genera, especially ones that span many world biomes (*Senecio, Carex, Bromus, Rhododendron,* etc.), either must have made quantum shifts in evolution from one major biome to another or else they are artificial. Evolution, in which achievement of the improbable is commonplace, argues for the first possibility. This whole question of the adaptive nature of characters in higher plants as well as adaptive radiation in angiospermous families has been discussed at length in a recent paper by Stebbins (1967).

Ecological differentiation of taxonomic groups is most apparent at the species and infraspecific levels. Existential adaptations to the gamut of limiting factors and of factor complexes of an environment may become directly or indirectly manifested. As such, they are likely to be accorded taxonomic recognition as species or local variants in the regional flora.

My own predilections in plant ecology have led me into the area of edaphic factors and plant distribution. The number of edaphically specialized plants in the floras of the world is large; often, highly distinctive taxa are restricted to singular substrates. Limestone, dolomite, serpentine, siliceous sands, alumina-containing earths, and lead and zinc deposits are just a few of the parent materials that elicit sufficient ecological specialization to yield discontinuities recognized by the systematist. Ever since the classic paper by Franz Unger (1836) on the influence of soil type on plant diversity and distribution in the Tyrol, the examples of endemism, discontinuous distribution, vicariant taxa, and ecotypic specialization, among others, that stem from the edaphic factor have grown to substantial proportions. The review by Krause (1958) is an entrée to some of the literature on edaphic restrictions.

What features of taxonomic significance are evolved by stresses at the limits of ecological tolerance? I would take the stand that *all* characters or character complexes used by the systematist are in some way or in some degree the outcome of selection by prevailing ecological conditions. I must refrain from embarking on a defense of such an open-ended contention, but perhaps a look at the taxonomic consequences of addiction to serpentine soils will illustrate the way in which habitat and taxonomic criteria can be related. For years, students of local serpentine floras have called attention to the morphological singularities displayed by both serpentine endemics (*bodenstet* species) and indifferent (*bodenvag*) species (Kruckeberg, 1967a). Novak (1928) gave the name "serpentinomorphoses" to the particular morphological responses of plants to the serpentine habitat. Pichi-Sermolli (1948) identified as serpentinomorphoses the following morphological modifications: stenophylly (narrow leaves), glabrescence, and glaucescence. When one or more of these features is strongly accentuated, the distinction afforded the plant is often recognized taxonomically. The serpentinomorphs usually are varieties or vicariant species of nonserpentine relatives. Rune (1953) cites not only the cases of such taxonomic novelties in the Scandinavian serpentine flora, but also reviews the significance of serpentinomorphoses in other floras. Incidentally, he records the view that certain genera (e.g., *Dianthus, Alyssum, Potentilla, Euphorbia, Armeria, Stachys,* and *Galium* in the European flora) are particularly rich in serpentinomorphoses.

Beyond the genesis of existential adaptations in the form of serpentinomorphoses, we must suggest that the ecology of serpentines, coupled with their discontinuous distribution, can account for divergences of still greater magnitude. Evolutionary diversification in the California genera *Streptanthus, Navarretia, Linum,* etc., the occurrence of the monotypic borage *Halacsya sendtneri* in Yugoslavia (Krause and Ludwig, 1956), and the many endemic species in New Caledonia (Thorne, 1965) are indubitably the outcome of adaptive responses to the stringent serpentine habitat.

The association of infraspecific variants of species or of more inclusive taxa with the serpentine habitat by no means gives us a complete answer to the problem of adaptive significance of the modifications. What is true of the more general case where correlations exist between morphological specializations and habitat restrictions is true also of the specific serpentine case—experimental verification of the adaptive value of taxonomic characters is largely lacking. Examples of ecotypic variants to particular environmental stresses will be valuable tools in a combined ecological and genetic approach to the problem. It should be possible thereby to establish correlations between singular morphological expressions (or their physiological bases) and the ecological stimuli. The 1958 monograph by Clausen and Hiesey, "Genetic Structure of Ecological Races," was a solid beginning on the ecological genetics of plants. When extended to the many other areas of ecological specialization (xerophylly, serpentinomorphoses, gypsophily, epiphytism, calciphily, etc.) we may then begin to supply the causal basis of much taxonomic differentiation in flowering plants.

CONCLUSION AND RETROSPECT

Throughout this presentation I have taken the view that ecology and systematics of plants are two separate ways of life that appear reluctant to become integrated, even though they should. Somehow, we are "boxed in" by the semantics of biology and the effect that formalizing disciplines has in partitioning the biological continuum. Ecology, systematics, and evolution usually are practiced as separate disciplines, each with its own cadre of practitioners. The realities of nature surely are not compressed into the formal compartments of our science, though they may be dealt with operationally at levels of integration from individual to ecosystem. Some of the gaps in our knowledge of organismic and environmental biology really are the result of having created "no-man's lands" at the artificial boundaries between the three integrative disciplines. Thus the ecologist may stop short of real study of natural selection because this is the bailiwick of the evolutionist, or the ecologist hesitates to look systematically and comparatively at environmental tolerance limits within genera or families for fear of intruding on the systematist's domain. The biologist who dares to ignore the provincial boundaries, can, with broad training and insight, approach any of the limitless interfaces between ecology, systematics, and evolution. Then he can confront effectively the most fascinating problems of all—why organisms are where they are, and why they do what they do. In a nutshell, superintegration of the three fields of synthesis truly will give us a twentieth-century natural history. A modern natural history of the entire plant and animal world is a goal so unattainable as to be irrelevant. But broadly based biologies of critical plant or animal groups are both attainable and sorely needed. Aggregations that are unique in their position for a variety of reasons should be tackled on a multifaceted approach. Species threatened with extinction, having peripheral or aberrant distributions, occupying critical phylogenetic positions, or showing exceptional adaptive radiations—all are bases for the broadest biological investigations.

REFERENCES

Anderson, E. 1936. Hybridization in American Tradescantias. II. Hybridization between *T. virginiana* and *T. canaliculata.* Ann. Mo. Bot. Gard. 23:515–525.

Anderson, E. 1948. Hybridization of the habitat. Evolution 2:1–9.

Anderson, E. 1949. Introgressive hybridization. John Wiley & Sons, New York. 109 p.

Anderson, E. 1953. Introgressive hybridization. Biol. Rev. 28:280–307.

Anderson, E., and A. Gage. 1952. Introgressive hybridization in *Phlox bifida.* Am. J. Bot. 39:399–404.

Anderson, E., and G. L. Stebbins, Jr. 1954. Hybridization as an evolutionary stimulus. Evolution 8:378–388.

Axelrod, D. I. 1966. Origin of deciduous and evergreen habits in temperate forest. Evolution 20:1–15.

Baker, H. G. 1966. Volatile growth inhibitors produced by *Eucalyptus globulus.* Madroño 18:207–210.

Beadle, N. C. W. 1966. Soil phosphate and its role in molding segments of the Australian flora and vegetation, with special reference to xeromorphy and sclerophylly. Ecology 47:992–1007.

Bennett, E. 1964. Historical perspectives in genecology. Scottish Plant Breeding Sta. Rec. 1964:49–115.

Bjorkman, O., and P. Holmgren. 1963. Adaptability of the photosynthetic apparatus to light intensity in ecotypes from exposed and shaded habitats. Physiol. Plantarum 16:889–914.

Brayton, R., and H. A. Mooney. 1966. Population variability of *Cercocarpus* in the White Mountains of California as related to habitat. Evolution 20:383–391.

Bradshaw, A. D. 1953. Human influence on hybridization in *Crataegus,* p. 181–183 *In* The changing flora of Britain. Bot. Soc. British Is., London.

Briggs, B. G. 1962. Interspecific hybridization in the *Ranunculus lappaceus* group. Evolution 16:372–390.

Brown, W. L., and E. O. Wilson. 1956. Character displacement. Syst. Zool. 5:49–64.

Carlquist, S. 1966a. The biota of long-distance dispersal. I. Principles of dispersal and evolution. Quart. Rev. Biol. 41:247–270.

Carlquist, S. 1966b. The biota of long-distance dispersal. II. Loss of dispersability in Pacific Compositae. Evolution 20:30–48.

Clarke, B. 1964. Frequency-dependent selection for the dominance of rare polymorphic genes. Evolution 18:364–369.

Clausen, J., D. D. Keck, and W. M. Hiesey. 1945. Experimental studies on the nature of species. II. Plant evolution through amphiploidy and autoploidy, with examples from the Madiinae. Carnegie Inst. Washington Publ. 564. 174 p.

Clewell, A. F. 1966. Natural history, cytology, and isolating mechanisms of the native American lespedezas. Bull. Tall Timbers Res. Sta. 6:1–39.

Clifford, H. T. 1958. Studies in British Primulas. VI. On introgression between primrose (*Primula vulgaris* Huds.) and cowslip (*P. veris* L.) New Phytol. 57:1–10.

Cole, N. H. A. 1967. Comparative physiological ecology of the genus *Eriogonum* in the Santa Monica Mountains, Southern California. Ecol. Monogr. 37:1–24.

Constance, L. 1953. The role of plant ecology in biosystematics. Ecology. 34:642–649.

Curtis, J. T. 1955. A prairie continuum in Wisconsin. Ecology 36:558–566.

Dansereau, P. 1952. The varieties of evolutionary opportunity. Rev. Canadienne Biol. 11:305–388.
Dansereau, P., and K. Lems. 1957. The grading of dispersal types in plant communities and their ecological significance. Contrib. Inst. Bot. Univ. Montreal 71:5–52.
Davis, P., and V. H. Heywood. 1963. Principles of angiosperm taxonomy. Oliver and Boyd, Edinburgh and London, 556 p.
Detling, L. E., 1948a. Environmental extremes and endemism. Madroño 9:137–149.
Detling, L. E., 1948b. Concentration of environmental extremes as the basis for vegetation areas. Madroño 9:169–185.
Ehrendorfer, F. 1965. Dispersal mechanisms, genetic systems, and colonizing abilities in some flowering plant families, p. 331–352. *In* The genetics of colonizing species. Academic Press, New York and London.
Ehrlich, P. R., and P. H. Raven. 1965. Butterflies and plants: A study in coevolution. Evolution 18:586–608.
Epling, C. 1947a. Actual and potential gene flow in natural populations. Am. Natur. 81:104–113.
Epling, C. 1947b. Natural hybridization of *Salvia apiana* and *S. mellifera.* Evolution 1:69–78.
Faegri, K., and L. van der Pijl. 1966. The principles of pollination ecology. Pergamon Press, London and New York, 248 p.
Gankin, R., and J. Major. 1964. *Arctostaphylos myrtifolia,* its biology and relationship to the problem of endemism. Ecology 45:792–808.
Gillett, J. B. 1962. Pest pressure, an underestimated factor in evolution, p. 37–46 *In* Taxonomy and geography. Systematics Assoc. Publ. 4, London.
Gilmour, J. S. L., and S. M. Walters. 1963. Philosophy and classification, p. 1–22 *In* Vistas in botany, 4. Pergamon Press, New York and London.
Goldschmidt, R. 1952. Evolution as viewed by one geneticist. Am. Sci. 40:84–98.
Good, R. 1964. The geography of flowering plants. 3rd ed. Longmans, Green and Co., London, New York, Toronto, 518 p.
Grant, K. A. 1966. A hypothesis concerning the prevalence of red coloration in California hummingbird flowers. Am. Natur. 100:85–98.
Grant, V. 1949. Pollination systems as isolating mechanisms in angiosperms. Evolution 3:82–97.
Grant, V. 1950. The protection of the ovules in flowering plants. Evolution 4:179–201.
Grant, V., and K. A. Grant. 1965. Flower pollination in the *Phlox* family. Columbia Univ. Press, New York and London. 180 p.
Gray, R., and J. Bonner. 1948. An inhibitor of plant growth from the leaves of *Encelia farinosa.* Am. J. Bot. 35:52–57.
Hall, M. T., J. F. McCormick, and G. G. Fogg. 1961. Hybridization between *Juniperus Ashei* Buchh. and *Juniperus Pinchoti* Sudw. in southwestern Texas. Butler Univ. Bot. Stud. 14:9–28.
Haller, J. R. 1965. The role of 2-needle fascicles in the adaptation and evolu-

tion of ponderosa pine. Brittonia 17:354–382.

Harper, J. L., 1961. Approaches to the study of plant competition, p. 1–30 *In* Mechanisms in biological competition. Symp. Soc. Exp. Biol. 15.

Harper, J. L. 1964. The nature and consequence of interference amongst plants, p. 465–482. *In* Genetics today. Pergamon Press, Oxford.

Harper, J. L., and J. N. Clatworthy. 1963. The comparative biology of closely related species. VI. Analysis of the growth of *Trifolium repens* and *T. fragiferum* in pure and mixed populations. J. Exp. Bot. 14:172–190.

Harper, J. L., and J. N. Clatworthy, I. H. McNaughton, and G. R. Sagar. 1961. The evolution and ecology of closely related species living in the same area. Evolution 15:209–227.

Heiser, C. B., Jr. 1949a. Study in the evolution of the sunflower species *Helianthus annuus* and *H. bolanderi.* Univ. California Publ. Bot. 23:157–208.

Heiser, C. B., Jr. 1949b. Natural hybridization with particular reference to introgression. Bot. Rev. 15:645–687.

Hiesey, W. M., and H. W. Milner. 1965. Physiology of ecological races and species. Ann. Rev. Plant Physiol. 16:203–216.

Janzen, D. H. 1966. Coevolution of mutualism between ants and acacias in central America. Evolution 20:249–275.

Johnson, A. W., and J. G. Packer. 1965. Polyploidy and environment in arctic Alaska. Science 148:237–239.

Johnson, A. W., J. G. Packer, and G. Reese. 1965. Polyploidy, distribution and environment, p. 497–507 *In* The quaternary of the United States. Princeton Univ. Press.

Jones, D. A., 1962. Selective eating of the acyanogenic form of the plant *Lotus corniculatus* L. by various animals. Nature 193:1109–1110.

Kawano, S. 1961. On the natural hybrid population of *Hemerocallis.* Can. J. Bot. 39:667–681.

Kemp, W. B. 1937. Natural selection within plant species as exemplified in a permanent pasture. J. Hered. 28:329–353.

Kerner, A., and F. W. Oliver. 1902. The natural history of plants. Blackie and Son, London. Vol. 1, 777 p.; Vol. 2, 983 p.

Klikoff, L. G. 1966. Temperature dependence of the oxidative rates of mitochondria in *Danthonia intermedia, Penstemon davidsonii* and *Sitanion hystrix.* Nature 212:529–530.

Krause, W. 1958. Andere Bodenspezialisten, p. 755–806 *In* Handbuch der Pflanzenphysiologie. Springer-Verlag, Berlin.

Krause, W., and W. Ludwig. 1956. Zur Kenntnis der Flora und Vegetation auf Serpentinstandorten des Balkans. 1. *Halacsya sendtneri* (Boiss.) Dorfl. Deut. Bot. Ges. 69:417–428.

Kruckeberg, A. R. 1954. Plant species in relation to serpentine soils, p. 267–274. *In* The ecology of serpentine soils: A symposium. Ecology 35.

Kruckeberg, A. R. 1957. Variation in fertility of hybrids between isolated populations of the serpentine species, *Streptanthus glandulosus* Hook. Evolution 11:185–211.

Kruckeberg, A. R. 1958. The taxonomy of the species complex, *Streptanthus glandulosus* Hook. Madroño 14:217–227.
Kruckeberg, A. R. 1959. [Book review.] Ecological genetics. Ecology 40:519–520.
Kruckeberg, A. R. 1967a. Ecotypic response to ultramafic soils by some plant species of northwestern United States. Brittonia 19:133–151.
Kruckeberg, A. R. 1967b. A hybrid hawkweed from the Olympic Mountains of Washington. Madroño 19:126–129.
Langlet, O. 1963. Patterns and terms of intraspecific ecological virability. Nature 200:347–348.
Leppik, E. E. 1957. Evolutionary relationship between entomophilous plants and anthophilous insects. Evolution 11:466–481.
Lewis, H. 1962. Catastrophic selection as a factor in speciation. Evolution 16:257–271.
Lewis, H., and D. M. Moore. 1962. Natural hybridization between *Epilobium adenocaulon* and *E. brevistylum.* Bull. Torrey Bot. Club 89:365–370.
Mason, H. L. 1946. The edaphic factor in narrow endemism. II. The geographic occurrence of plants of highly restricted patterns of distribution. Madroño 8:241–257.
Matsuzaka, S., and M. Kurabayashi. 1959. Hybridization of *Trillium* in a habitat at Nanae. J. Hokkaido Gagugei Univ. 10:181–187.
Mayr, E. 1963. Animal species and evolution. Belknap Press of Harvard University Press, Cambridge, Massachusetts. 797 p.
McMillan, C. 1954. Parallelisms between ecology and taxonomy. Ecology 35:92–94.
Mooney, H. A. 1966. Influence of soil type on the distribution of two closely related species of *Erigeron.* Ecology 47:950–958.
Mooney, H. A., and D. Billings. 1961. Comparative physiological ecology of arctic and alpine populations of *Oxyria digyna.* Ecol. Monogr. 31:1–29.
Morton, J. K. 1956. Studies on *Ononis* in Britain. 1. Hybridity in the Durham Coast colonies of *Ononis.* Watsonia 3:307–316.
Muller, C. H. 1952. Ecological control of hybridization in *Quercus:* A factor in the mechanism of evolution. Evolution 6:147–161.
Muller, C. H., 1953. The association of desert annuals with shrubs. Am. J. Bot. 40:53–60.
Muller, C. H., 1964. Volatile growth inhibitors produced by aromatic shrubs. Science 143:471–473.
Muller, C. H. 1965. Inhibitory terpenes volatilized from *Salvia* shrubs. Bull. Torrey Bot. Club 92:38–45.
Novak, F. A. 1928. Quelques remarques relatives au probleme de la vegetation sur les terrains serpentiniques. Preslia 6:42–71.
Orians, G. H. 1965. On the theory of plant competition. [Mimeographed.] Univ. Washington, Seattle, Washington.
Pichi-Sermolli, R. 1948. Flora e vegetazione delle serpentine e delle altre ofioliti del 'alta valle del Tevere (Toscana). Webbia 6:1–380.
Pijl, L. van der. 1960. Ecological aspects of flower evolution. I. Phyletic

evolution. Evolution 14:403–416.
Pijl, L. van der. 1961. Ecological aspects of flower evolution. II. Zoophilous flower classes. Evolution 15:44–59.
Raunkiaer, C. 1934. The life forms of plants and statistical plant geography. Clarendon Press, Oxford. 632 p.
Raven, P. 1961. Interspecific hybridization as an evolutionary stimulus in *Oenothera.* Proc. Linn. Soc. London 173:92–98.
Raven, P. 1964. Catastrophic selection and edaphic endemism. Evolution 18:336–338.
Ridley, H. N. 1930. The dispersal of plants throughout the world. Kent, Ashford. 744 p.
Ritchie, J. C. 1955. A natural hybrid in *Vaccinium.* I. The structure, performance and chorology of the cross *Vaccinium intermedium* Ruthe. New Phytol. 54:49–67.
Roy, S. K. 1960. Interaction between rice varieties. J. Genet. 57:137–152.
Rune, O. 1953. Plant life on serpentines and related rocks in the north of Sweden. Acta Phytogeog. Suecica 31:1–139.
Salisbury, E. J. 1942. The reproductive capacity of plants. G. Bell and Sons, London. 244 p.
Simpson, G. G. 1953. The major features of evolution. Columbia Univ. Press, New York. 434 p.
Simpson, G. G. 1961. Principles of animal taxonomy. Columbia Univ. Press, New York and London. 247 p.
Simpson, G. G. 1963. Biology and the nature of science. Science 139:81–88.
Stebbins, G. L., Jr. 1950. Variation and evolution in plants. Columbia Univ. Press., New York, 643 p.
Stebbins, G. L., Jr. 1951. Natural selection and the differentiation of angiosperm families. Evolution 5:299–324.
Stebbins, G. L., Jr. 1952. Aridity as a stimulus to plant evolution. Am. Natur. 86:33–44.
Stebbins, G. L., Jr. 1959a. The role of hybridization in evolution. Proc. Am. Phil. Soc. 103:231–251.
Stebbins, G. L., Jr. 1959b. Seedling heterophylly in the California flora. Bull. Res. Counc. Israel 7D:248–255.
Stebbins, G. L., Jr. 1967. Adaptive radiation and trends of evolution in higher plants, p. 101–142 *In* Evolutionary biology. I. Appleton-Century-Crofts, New York. 444 p.
Stebbins, G. L., Jr., and J. Major. 1965. Endemism and speciation in the California flora. Ecol. Monogr. 35:1–35.
Stebbins, G. L., Jr., E. G. Matzke, and C. Epling. 1947. Hybridization in a population of *Quercus marilandica* and *Quercus ilicifolia.* Evolution 1:79–88.
Tansley, A. G. 1917. On competition between *Galium saxatile* L. (*G. hercynicum* Weig.) and *Galium sylvestre* Poll. (*G. asperum* Schreb.) on different types of soil. J. Ecol. 5:173–179.
Thorne, R. F. 1965. Floristic relationships of New Caledonia. Univ. Iowa Stud. Nat. Hist. 20:1–14.

Tucker, J. M., L. K. Mann, and S. L. Holloway. 1964. A natural hybrid in the genus *Lewisia.* Cactus and Succulent J. Am. March–April, 1964:47–50.
Turesson, G. 1922. The genotypical response of the plant species to habitat. Hereditas 3:211–350.
Unger, F. 1836. Ueber den Einfluss des Bodens auf die Verteilung der Gewaechse. Rohrmann und Schweigerd, Vienna. 367 p.
Wagner, W. H., Jr., and D. J. Hagenah. 1954. A natural hybrid of *Polystichum lonchitis* and *P. acrostichoides* from the Bruce Peninsula. Rhodora 56:1–6.
Wagner, W. H., Jr., and D. J. Hagenah. 1962. *Dryopteris* in the Huron Mountain Club area of Michigan. Brittonia 14:90–100.
Whittaker, R. H. 1960. Vegetation of the Siskiyou Mountains, Oregon and California. Ecol. Monogr. 30:279–338.
Woodell, S. R. J. 1965. Natural hybridization between the cowslip (*Primula veris* L.) and the primrose (*P. vulgaris* Huds.) in Britain. Watsonia 6:109–202.

Discussion

Calvin M. McMillan

The modern ecologist, who is less concerned with memorizing dogma than his predecessor, will applaud Dr. Kruckeberg's suggestions for needed ecological investigations and his pointing out a number of research areas where ecological–taxonomic interplay would be beneficial.

Where Dr. Kruckeberg has referred to ecological studies of species, the work applied only to certain populations. Available ecological data about species must be used with caution by taxonomists, because ecologists do not study species. Ecologists are interested in and study only a part of the species, the population. Although an ecologist may refer to his investigated populations by the species name, it should be emphasized that the primary ecological target is still the population. Even so-called ecological life histories of species are studies of, at most, a few populations. Studies labeled as species interaction are studies of population interaction. Ecological studies may contain information useful to taxonomists, but there appears to be little reason for ecologists to make systematic analyses of species unless they would serve an ecological goal.

As Dr. Kruckeberg has indicated, the interests of taxonomy and ecology converge on the population and the individual organisms that make up a population. The concept *population* as a unit of common interest cannot include adjectives, such as interbreeding or homogeneous, which indicate the kind of population. The population that is the common property of the taxonomist and the ecologist is that unit made up of individuals in a given area at a given time. The study of populations provides the basis for a taxonomic–ecological dialogue. Dr. Kruckeberg may have suggested more disagreement between taxonomy and ecology than is warranted because in much of his discussion he placed the emphasis on the species. It should be emphasized, however, that a single population is a part of a species and, at the same time, a part of a community. *Community* in this conceptual form refers to the total of organisms in a given area at a given time.

Systematic studies of populational differentiation are taxonomic or ecological, or both. The outlook and intent of a given study determines whether it fits into taxonomy or into ecology. For example, the studies of altitudinal differentiation in populations by Clausen *et al.* (1940, 1948) have been used primarily to investigate the nature of species. In contrast, studies by McMillan (1959, 1964, 1965), patterned after those of Clausen and co-workers but stressing latitudinal differentiation of populations in the grasslands of North America, have been used to understand the nature of the community. The data from both types of studies may be useful in either taxonomic or ecological analyses.

Dr. Kruckeberg has indicated some doubt about the usefulness of the concept *niche* for plant study. He has looked at niche from the viewpoint of species, where its usefulness is doubtful. The concept *niche* is useful in biology when it refers to the total set of relations, actual or potential, that an organism has, or may have, with its surroundings. It is meaningful as it merges the *hypervolume* concept of Hutchinson (1958) with the *operational environment* concept of Mason and Langenheim (1957). At the level of the individual organism, *niche* is a concept of great utility; at the level of the population, it is a useful concept; at the level of the species, it becomes a concept of limited value and may even be exceedingly misleading. I do not share the hope of some taxonomists that all species niches can be characterized, particularly among wide-ranging, genetically diverse species. When one considers the few environmental relations common to all individuals of an ecotypically differentiated species such as *Andropogon gerardii* Vitman, distributed from Manitoba to Mexico City and from montane New Mexico to the Gulf of Mexico, one wonders how the concept *niche* ever reached the species level. *Niche* is perhaps meaningful for a species that is restricted to a single or few genetically depauperate populations. Perhaps the niches of some of the narrowly restricted *Streptanthus* species mentioned by Dr. Kruckeberg might be characterized, but, in general, the niche at the species level includes only a small part of the niche of any individual organism.

As Dr. Kruckeberg indicated, taxonomists and ecologists are seeking information by using techniques of diverse disciplines. Ecologists have been most successful in finding causative relations in physiology; taxonomists have been more successful in using morphology. At the present time, studies of enzymes are being pursued by taxonomists and ecologists at the University of Texas and at other institutions. The ecologist is studying the organism and its enzyme activity in relation to a given range of temperature or to different light intensities. He views differences in enzyme activity as significant in understanding the adaptation of populations to diverse habitats. The taxonomist views differences in enzyme structure as a means of characterizing populations.

Taxonomists and ecologists are digging systematically into the same ground. Apparently, the tools in the hands of the ecologist are helpful in obtaining information about selection as it relates to populational adaptation; those in the hands of the taxonomist are advantageous in probing for information that will characterize populations, the results of selection. Hopefully, both can be applied systematically to dig new ground for the furtherance of population biology and to the advantage of both taxonomy and ecology.

REFERENCES

Clausen, J., D. D. Keck, and W. M. Hiesey. 1940. Experimental studies on the nature of species. I. Effect of varied environments on western North American plants. Carnegie Inst. Washington Publ. 520. 452 p.

Clausen, J., D. D. Keck, and W. M. Hiesey. 1948. Experimental studies on the nature of species. III. Environmental responses of climatic races of *Achillea*. Carnegie Inst. Washington Publ. 581. 129 p.

Hutchinson, G. E. 1958. [Concluding remarks.] Cold Spring Harbor Symposia on Quantitative Biology 22:415–427.
Mason, H. L., and J. H. Langenheim. 1957. Language analysis and the concept *environment.* Ecology 38:325–340.
McMillan, C. 1959. The role of ecotypic variation in the distribution of the central grassland of North America. Ecol. Monogr. 29:285–308.
McMillan, C. 1964. Ecotypic differentiation within four North American prairie grasses. I. Morphological variation within transplanted community fractions. Am. J. Bot. 51:1119–1128.
McMillan, C. 1965. Ecotypic differentiation within four North American prairie grasses. II. Behavioral variation within transplanted community fractions. Am. J. Bot. 52:55–65.

Discussion

Philip V. Wells

Genecology, the first topic reviewed by Professor Kruckeberg, is especially appropriate for further discussion because there are long-standing difficulties in the definition and understanding of some basic concepts in this area. A central point is the misleading distinction between an "environmentally induced" phenotypic modification (the "ecophene" of Turesson, 1922, also called phenocopy or ecad) and a "genetically fixed" ecological race (the "ecotype" of Turesson, 1922). Both ecophene and ecotype are phenotypic expressions of the interaction of genotype with environment. The distinction hinges on the degree of developmental modifiability or plasticity.

To use the terminology of a recent treatise on the systematics of plants (Davis and Heywood, 1963), an ecophene would be "euryplastic" (*eury* = broadly) while an ecotype would be relatively "stenoplastic" (*steno* = narrowly) in its developmental response to varying environment. The degree of plasticity is experimentally demonstrated by culturing in a uniform garden. One difficulty in this approach is the relativistic nature of the trial garden. An ecotypic race may undergo little modification if the environmental difference between garden and native habitat is not very great, but it will show some modification if the difference exceeds an environmentally controlled threshold of morphological or physiological response.

A significant but little emphasized aspect of the well-known investigations of ecotypic differentiation in plants by Clausen *et al.* (1940, 1948) is the euryplastic developmental response exhibited by lowland and midelevation races, in contrast to the relatively stenoplastic response of dwarf alpine races, when individual genotypes (clones) of the different races were divided and grown in trial gardens under widely different environments. Similar results were obtained with a number of taxa belonging to different families.

Some of the data derived from a detailed study of California yarrows (*Achillea*) are summarized in Figure 1. The frequency distribution plots show that samples of populations from various elevations have roughly normal curves of phenotypic variation when grown in the low-elevation garden at Stanford. The modes are shifted to different positions in ecotypically different populations, but there may be a broad overlap. The spread of the curves is wide for populations native to the milder climates of lower elevations, but it is very narrow in the samples from extreme alpine habitats. The important point is that the amplitude of phenotypic variation

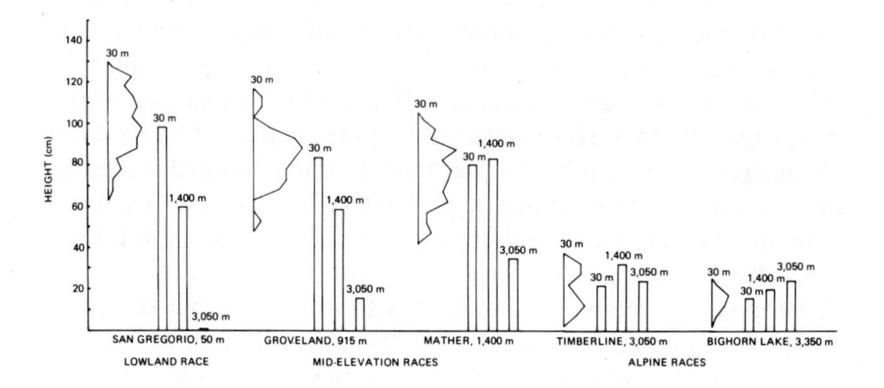

FIGURE 1 Phenotypic variation in height growth of five different climatic races of the perennial herb *Achillea.* Frequency distributions show population variability of samples grown in a low-elevation uniform garden (Stanford, at 30 m); bars show means of phenotypic plasticity responses of individual genotypes, based on divided clonal material of each race at three trial gardens spaced along a gradient of elevation in California (Stanford, Mather, and Timberline at 30, 1,400, and 3,050 m, respectively). The frequency diagrams were based on samples of about 60 individuals (fewer individuals in the alpine samples); plasticity responses were based on clones from about 30 individuals of each race. Taxonomically, the lowland race is *A. borealis* Bong; the other races are *A. lanulosa* Nutt. Figure adapted from Clausen *et al.*, 1948.

within ecotypically different populations is paralleled in another dimension: the developmental plasticity of individual genotypes. Clonal subdivisions of the same genotype were grown at widely different elevations. The individual developmental responses, presented as bars representing means of 30 individuals in Figure 1, show that only the alpine races can be termed stenoplastic with respect to growth in height; the other ecotypes are euryplastic.

These considerations focus attention on some superfluous and inadequate aspects of the concepts "ecophene" and "ecotype." On the one hand, the traditional distinction between ecophene and ecotype is analogous to the difference between phenotype and genotype (a point originally made by Turesson, 1922); on the other hand, the term "ecotype" encompasses a broad spectrum of plasticity of developmental response to varying environment.

In order to arrive at a better understanding of these phenomena, it is necessary to distinguish between "normalizing" and "canalizing" selection (Waddington, 1942, 1957, 1962). Normalizing selection narrows the phenotypic variation within a population to a normal distribution about an adaptive mode for the home environment, but it does not exclude morphological or physiological accommodation to other environments because the developmental pathways may not be genetically buffered or canalized. Canalizing selection increases the frequencies of genes that restrict the amplitude of developmental response to varying environment. As a result, the degree of developmental plasticity of the individual is decreased and the number of stenoplastic individuals is increased. When a developmental pathway is stabilized genetically so that a given trait has full penetrance over a range of environmental conditions, the development is said to be canalized with respect to that trait, and the process of canalization is called "genetic assimilation."

In Figure 2, a scheme for the canalization of a polygenic trait is outlined. The end-member phenotypes are designated "euryphene" (phenotype of a euryplastic genotype) and "stenophene" (phenotype of a stenoplastic, canalized genotype) in order to express a dimension—the degree of modifiability by environment—that the terms "ecophene" and "ecotype" themselves do not express adequately.

But one might ask: What is the advantage of being stenoplastic? On the surface, the euryplastic condition, normalized to an adaptive mode of phenotypic response, would seem to have the greater evolu-

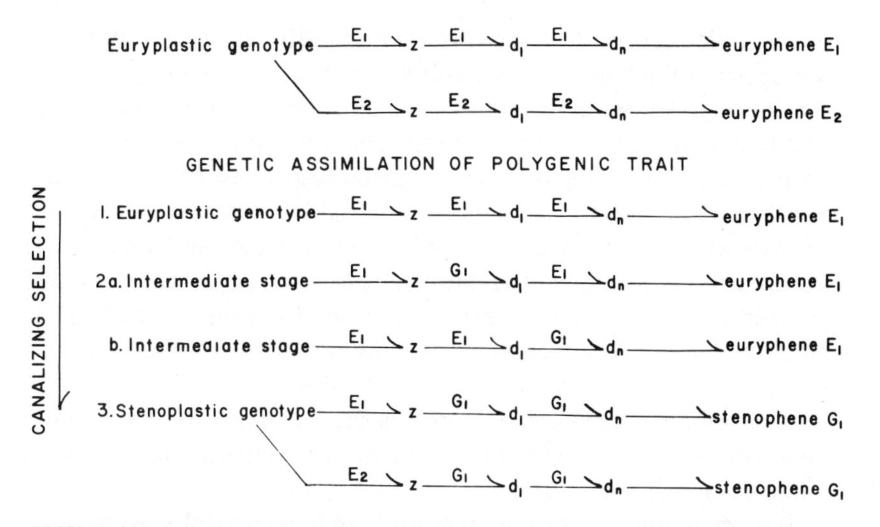

FIGURE 2 Scheme for the evolution of an ecotypic race with genetically canalized development, beginning with a phenotypic accommodation: z, d_1, d_n, developmental steps of polygenic trait (z, zygotic stage, d_1, d_n, postzygotic developmental steps); E, environmental programming; G, genetic programming; euryphene = phenotype of euryplastic genotype; stenophene = phenotype of stenoplastic genotype. Most internal factors in the developmental sequence are assumed to be controlled primarily by the genetic code; however, the programming of the sequence may range from primarily environmental to primarily genetic. Stage 1 represents a phenotypic accommodation to a new environment; frequencies of genes that could potentially canalize development are assumed to be very low. Stage 3 probably arises through recombination at stage 2, following an increase in the frequency of stabilizing or buffering genes due to selection.

tionary potential. However, the experimental evidence amassed by Clausen *et al.* (1940, 1948) supports the generalization that populations native to the severe, fluctuating alpine environment are stenoplastic, narrowly normalized, and that they constitute well-marked ecotypic races, while populations from milder climates at lower elevations are euryplastic and have broad and widely overlapping normal curves of phenotypic variation. These findings suggest a probable mechanism for rapid evolutionary shift from the euryplastic to the stenoplastic condition, involving one aspect of the Baldwin effect, and canalizing selection of a catastrophic nature:

1. Initial penetration of the severe alpine environment by colonizing individuals of a relatively tall but euryplastic race from a milder climatic zone at a subjacent elevation is made possible by

phenotypic accommodation (*inter alia,* modification of stature to the dwarf condition), which ensures survival in the new habitat long enough for selection to operate. This persistence of individuals by means of an adaptive phenotypic response, elicited by the environment from the array of potential responses inherent in the genotype, is the strategic aspect of the Baldwin effect (Baldwin, 1896; Huxley, 1942; Waddington, 1953). In rejecting Lamarckism on genetic grounds, it is important to remember that the environment is more than a mere sieve, sorting the fit from the unfit; it may play an equally decisive role in shaping the very phenotypes that are the raw material of natural selection.

2. Normalizing selection decreases the frequency of gene combinations interacting to produce phenotypes outside the adaptive mode of the alpine habitat.

3. Canalizing selection may operate in a catastrophic way (Lewis, 1962). One or more unusually mild seasons would tend to elicit a potentially disastrous overgrowth in the more euryplastic individuals, causing a rapid expenditure of food reserves. If a shift to the severe extreme of climate ensued, the more overgrown euryphenes would be "catastrophically" eliminated, but individuals with more canalized development would persist to form the nucleus of a race of stenoplastic alpine dwarfs, well-suited to existence in the seasonally fluctuating climatic extremes of the tundra environment.

REFERENCES

Baldwin, J. M. 1896. A new factor in evolution. Am. Natur. 30:445.

Clausen, J., D. D. Keck, and W. M. Hiesey. 1940. Experimental studies on the nature of species. I. Effect of varied environments on western North American plants. Carnegie Inst. Washington Publ. 520. 452 p.

Clausen, J., D. D. Keck, and W. M. Hiesey. 1948. Experimental studies on the nature of species. III. Environmental responses of climatic races of *Achillea.* Carnegie Inst. Washington Publ. 581. 129 p.

Davis, P. H., and V. H. Heywood. 1963. Principles of angiosperm taxonomy. Oliver and Boyd, London. p. 337.

Huxley, J. S. 1942. Evolution: The modern synthesis. Allen and Unwin, London. p. 304.

Lewis, H. 1962. Catastrophic selection as a factor in speciation. Evolution 16:257–271.

Turesson, G. 1922. The genotypical response of the plant species to the habitat. Hereditas 3:211–350.
Waddington, C. H. 1942. Canalisation of development and the inheritance of acquired characters. Nature 150:563–565.
Waddington, C. H. 1953. The "Baldwin effect," "genetic assimilation," and "homeostasis." Evolution 7:386–387.
Waddington, C. H. 1957. The strategy of the genes. Macmillan, New York. 262 p.
Waddington, C. H. 1962. New patterns in genetics and development. Columbia Univ. Press, New York. 271 p.

Informal Discussion

BESCHEL: I should like to ask Dr. Kruckeberg to criticize my opinion in regard to the question of why a seral species does not climb its own sere? I think this question is valueless because it is shrouded in the antiquated Clementsian terminology, which makes it a nonsense question in itself. As long as we have all kinds of different habitats available in one area, the species that is adapted to one kind of habitat can always go to that habitat by migration, by dispersal. So we have to think in terms of complexes in which each community, regardless of how ephemeral it is (e.g., fungi on dung) still finds its niche. Also, of course, we have to think of much longer survival times. A species can stay within its own sere because space and time are the same; it can really live on, and it does not have to climb its sere because it finds itself completely content where it is.

KRUCKEBERG: I do not think John Harper says it has to climb its sere. I think he is simply inquiring why we do not get some particular cases where the species have climbed their sere. The lespedeza case is an example where obviously there is a mechanism that holds species in their seral condition, the cyclical events of repeated secondary succession. But I think it is at least provocative to think of a possibility where speciation might be seral, or successional. Maybe I am looking for something that does not exist. Maybe Harper was too. If we could find a genus that has related species in different degrees of seral condition we might get some ideas about this.

SIBLEY: Dr. Kruckeberg asked a question obviously directed to the zoologists about character displacement. The reason that plants do not exhibit the kind of character displacement exhibited by animals is because they do not see and they do not move about in search of food. In animals, the characters usually affected by this phenomenon are those that are related to feeding and to reproduction. Competition for food often results in adaptive responses that reduce such competition while selection against hybrids will reinforce reproductive isolating mechanisms. In animals the senses of sight, hearing, and smell are often involved and thus visible, audible, or olfactory characters will respond, depending upon the species involved. I would suggest that the botanists might well look for character displacement in the feeding and reproductive structures in plants. Such displacements may be present, but they will take a different form and perhaps will be more subtle than in animals.

KRUCKEBERG: I wonder if Peter Raven might comment on this phenomenon as related to coevolution between herbs and herbivores. For instance, is character displacement relevant to the idea of coevolution in butterflies and plants?

RAVEN: I do not think so. I intend to discuss the subject of character displacement after presenting my prepared comments tomorrow.

ROBERT K. SELANDER

The Ecological Aspects of the Systematics of Animals

In this review I have selected several topics in which I have special interest or that I believe will continue to be prominent in systematic research in the next decade. I have tried to avoid undue overlapping with contributions to this conference that deal with behavior and population aspects. What duplication does exist serves to emphasize the impossibility of considering the ecology of animal diversity apart from genetical, behavioral, and morphological aspects.

ECOLOGICAL EVIDENCE IN SYSTEMATICS

The use of ecological characters in descriptive and analytical systematic research at all levels of classification is now so widespread that lengthy discussion of the subject seems unnecessary. Mayr *et al.* (1953) have suggested that ecological data are requisite for a complete species description, and many systematists believe that species groups, genera, and higher categories should be characterized in ecological as well as morphological terms. The weight given to ecological considerations in hominid systematics in recent years is a case in point. Thus, in defining the genus as "a group of species of common origin occupying the same adaptive zone that is not shared with other, related genera," Robinson (1967:95) lumps the omnivorous, arid-adapted "*Australopithecus*" with *Homo,* following Weidenreich (1945) and Mayr (1950), but retains the vegetarian, humid-adapted *Paranthropus* as a distinct genus on the basis that it and *Homo transvaalensis* (= "*Australopithecus*" *africanus*) were sympatric and adapted to different major ecological niches.

In view of the increasing use of ecological evidence in systematic research, it is worthwhile to note the warning of Cain (1959:311; see also Cain and Harrison, 1960) that ecological characters must be viewed with the same suspicion as other phenotypic characters. Systematists working at the species level must be especially discriminating in the use of ecological characters because many aspects of the ecology of allopatric populations may be no more relevant to the problem of systematic relationship than are morphological data. At this level any character is useful only insofar as it reflects mechanisms of genetical isolation. A case in point is Norris' study (1958) of the systematic status of the allopatric brown-headed and pygmy nuthatches (*Sitta pusilla* and *S. pygmaea*) in North America. This is an admirable example of the broad biological approach to systematics, integrating morphological, ecological, and ethological information, but much of the ecological evidence marshalled in favor of specific status–particularly that concerning population density, mortality rate, territory size, and clutch size–actually has little if any bearing on the problem at hand. Moreover, because the two nuthatch populations were studied in distinctly different habitats (humid coastal forest of Marin County, California, and longleaf pine forest of Georgia), there is no basis for judging how well the observed differences characterize the supposed species populations as wholes.

SOME ECOLOGICAL ASPECTS OF SPECIES

The ecological aspects of species and speciation, recently reviewed at length by Mayr (1963), are so numerous that I cannot here attempt even a brief general summary. I shall limit my discussion to a few selected topics.

SIBLING SPECIES

Sibling species were the chief concern of several ecologically oriented systematists participating in the development of the "New Systematics." Thorpe's discussion of "Ecology and the Future of Systematics" (1940) deals almost entirely with morphologically similar forms that were first recognized as species on the basis of ecological differences. Diver's contribution (1940) is similar, although his approach was based on the mistaken but then current belief that methods of isolation between closely related sympatric species reflect modes of speciation involved in their origin. Today we are accustomed to the discovery of sibling species even in the taxonomically best-known groups of animals; for example, at least two have been unmasked in birds in the United States in the past decade (Selander and Giller, 1961; Stein, 1958, 1963). Although the detection of sibling species remains an important aspect of systematics, major research emphasis in *causal* systematics (Mayr, 1959) has shifted to the evolutionary aspects of competition and other ecological and behavioral interactions among sympatric species.

Although sympatric sibling species are known in all animal groups, they appear to be more frequent in some groups than in others. This is due in part to the systematist's having greater difficulty recognizing species in groups utilizing chemical rather than auditory or visual signal systems (Mayr, 1963), but there is a more important reason. From an ecological standpoint, the requirements for sympatric sibling species are that they exploit different niches through adaptations not involving conspicuous differentiation of morphological characters (Kohn and Orians, 1962). Ecological theory predicts a high frequency of sibling species among small animals that are likely to adapt for ecological coexistence through niche divergence involving physiological specialization for particular sets of environmental conditions (Hutchinson, 1961) or specialization for particular types of food. Thus the ecologist sees sympatric species as an ecological problem, the frequency of their occurrence depending upon the possibilities of ecological coexistence. It is not surprising to find them relatively more common in insects than in birds and mammals (Hutchinson, 1959).

THE GENETICAL AND ECOLOGICAL ASPECTS OF SPECIES

The dual nature of the "species problem" is indicated by the comment of Simpson (1961:9) that it is "fundamentally a genetic problem," and by the suggestion of Pitelka (1951:195) that it is "even more ecological than genetical." Of course, the species problem is both genetical and ecological; Pitelka (1951), as an ecologist, is simply making the point that, while the current "biological" species definition is strictly genetical (Simpson, 1961; Cain, 1959), in theory, species can be defined by ecological as well as by genetical criteria. I agree with Simpson (1961:150, footnote) that the designation "biological" species is misleading since any relevant designation for a category of groups of organisms cannot be anything but biological. The term "biosystematics" is similarly redundant. The ecological-genetical viewpoint, first developed in detail by Lack (1944, 1949), emphasizes the fact that speciation involves the attainment by populations of both reproductive (genetical) and ecological isolation (compatibility in sympatry). Where differences in habitat selection or time of occurrence limit contact between individuals of two incipient species in secondary contact, thereby promoting genetical isolation, the genetical and ecological isolating processes are related. But the distinction becomes apparent where populations have achieved reproductive isolation but not the ecological isolation that would permit sympatry. This consideration may be of practical importance to the systematist in defining species limits, for there is the chance that populations that actually meet the "biological" species criterion of reproductive isolation will be relegated to the status of subspecies because of their allopatric distributions (Vaurie, 1955; Hall, 1963; Selander and Giller, 1961).

The term "superspecies" is applied to groups of allopatric or largely allopatric populations ("semispecies") that are known or thought to be reproductively isolated. An important problem in systematics is to test the "competitive displacement hypothesis" (or "competitive exclusion principle") and to determine how frequently allopatric distributions can be correctly attributed to competitive interactions. The evolutionary importance of this phenomenon is that, unless sympatry can be effected, interspecies interaction cannot operate to produce niche shifts (Lack, 1944, 1949; Brown and Wilson, 1956). Often it may not be possible to explain just why a pattern of allopatry or parapatry persists after genetical isolation is achieved (Mayr, 1963:81–82), but sometimes there is good reason for believing that competitive interaction of the species populations precludes sympatry. Other cases are known in which species, although macrogeographically sympatric, are, in a sense, microgeographically allopatric since their territories are mutually exclusive (Orians and Willson, 1964). Genetically they are two species, but ecologically they behave as a single species. The converse situation is exemplified by certain species in which the sexes behave ecologically as two species, as will be discussed later.

Among birds, woodpeckers as a group apparently experience special difficulties in effecting sympatry because of the specialized feeding niches they exploit (Schoener, 1965). In the *Centurus carolinus-aurifrons-uropygialis* complex of woodpeckers, as in the genus *Centurus* as a whole, the evolution of reproductive isolating mechanisms tends to proceed more rapidly than does the evolution of ecological isolation, with the result that the distribution pattern of the species is predominantly allopatric or parapatric (Selander and Giller, 1959, 1963). Species ranges meet in bands of sympatry only a few miles wide, within which bands the species manifest interspecific territoriality. The argument for ecological incompatibility is especially strong in the case of *C. aurifrons* and *C. carolinus,* since where the two species meet in Texas they are identical in size.

Opportunities for niche divergence are limited even more for species of pocket gophers (Geomyidae), all of which are herbivores exploiting essentially a single niche just beneath the soil surface. The only path open to them for ecological isolation is that of habitat divergence through specialization for different types of soils. Despite marked differences in body size and other morphological features, species manifest competitive displacement wherever they are in contact. According to Miller (1964), the four species occurring in Colorado can be arranged in a competitive series: *Geomys bursarius, Cratogeomys castanops, Thomomys bottae,* and *T. talpoides.* The first species replaces all others in optimal habitat (deep, light soils) but is competitively inferior in poor habitats, to which the last species is largely confined (Figure 1). As noted by Hutchinson (1965:36), this case exemplifies "the reciprocal relationship between adaptability (or large fundamental niche) and adaptation (or possessing of inherent competitive powers) . . . ."

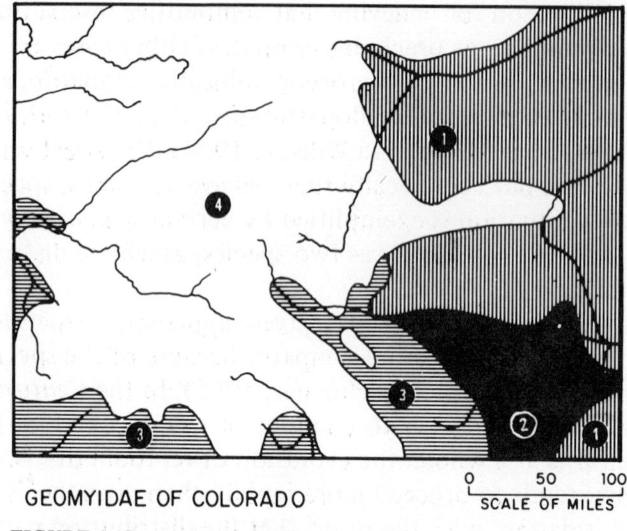

FIGURE 1 Geographical distributions of *Geomys bursarius* (1), *Cratogeomys castanops* (2), *Thomomys bottae* (3), and *T. talpoides* (4) in Colorado. (After Miller, 1964.)

Studies of the distribution and ecology of two of the parapatric species (*Thomomys talpoides* and *T. bottae*) in Colorado suggest that the interspecific interactions experienced by individuals of a mixed-species "population" are not different from those occurring between members of a single species (Vaughan, 1967). Both gophers are strongly territorial during most of the year—a single individual occupying a given burrow system. Territoriality limits population density, presumably in relation to amount of vegetation available, and the resource for which individuals compete is space. Vaughan (1967:156) notes that

> . . . in time, the population of one species is able to perpetuate itself in a given situation at the expense of the other species not because interspecific competition is more intense than intraspecific competition, but because as populations and individuals the two species are not ecologically identical.

Minor differences in productivity and behavior may tip the scale. Complex mosaic distribution patterns occur where the species meet, the borders of ranges sometimes shifting locally as much as one half mile per year. Generally, however, the border stabilizes in an area where habitat is patchy or where there are partial barriers to dispersal. A similar situation is described by Kennerly (1959) for the species pair *Geomys personatus* and *G. bursarius,* the ranges of which meet in Texas in an area where there is no abrupt environmental change.

A strongly allopatric pattern of distribution also is characteristic of the Eurasian fossorial rodents of the genera *Spalax* (family Spalacidae), *Cannomys, Rhizomys* (Rhizomyidae), *Myospalax,* and *Ellobius* (Cricetidae). According to information collated by R. S. Hoffman (in manuscript), in most areas of Europe and Asia only a single species of fossorial rodent is found, and in the better known situations where sympatry does occur, there are suggestions of species differences in habitat preference or body size. Similarly, species of the South American tuco-tucos (*Ctenomys*) are rarely sympatric, as shown by Pearson (1960:53–54), who interprets the allopatric distribution of subterranean rodents and the striking anatomical and ecological similarity of unrelated forms as evidence that "there is only one niche exploitable by subterranean, herbivorous mammals."

An unexcelled example of competitive displacement in ecologically homologous species is provided by DeBach and Sundby's (1963) field and laboratory studies of three species of Hymenoptera of the genus *Aphytis* that are ectoparasites on the California red scale insect (*Aonidiella aurantii*) infesting citrus groves in southern California (see Figure 2). As in the case of the pocket gophers, sympatry is precluded by a lack of opportunity for niche divergence—in this situation because no alternate hosts are available for the parasites. *Aphytis chrysomphali,* a native of the Mediterranean region, was accidentally introduced in California in 1900 and was found to be distributed generally in southern California citrus areas by 1920. From 1948 to 1950 *A. lingnanensis* from southern China was cultured and colonized throughout the same citrus areas, and by 1959 it had almost replaced *A. chrysomphali,* which appeared to be approaching extinction in southern California by 1963 (DeBach, 1965). Meanwhile, from 1957 to 1961, a third species, *A. melinus,* imported from India and West Pakistan, was cultured and colonized in the citrus area. Within one year (8 or 9 generations) *A. melinus* had displaced *A. lingnanensis* from the immediate environs of some colonization plots, and by 1961 it had replaced that species in the interior areas of southern California. Continuing

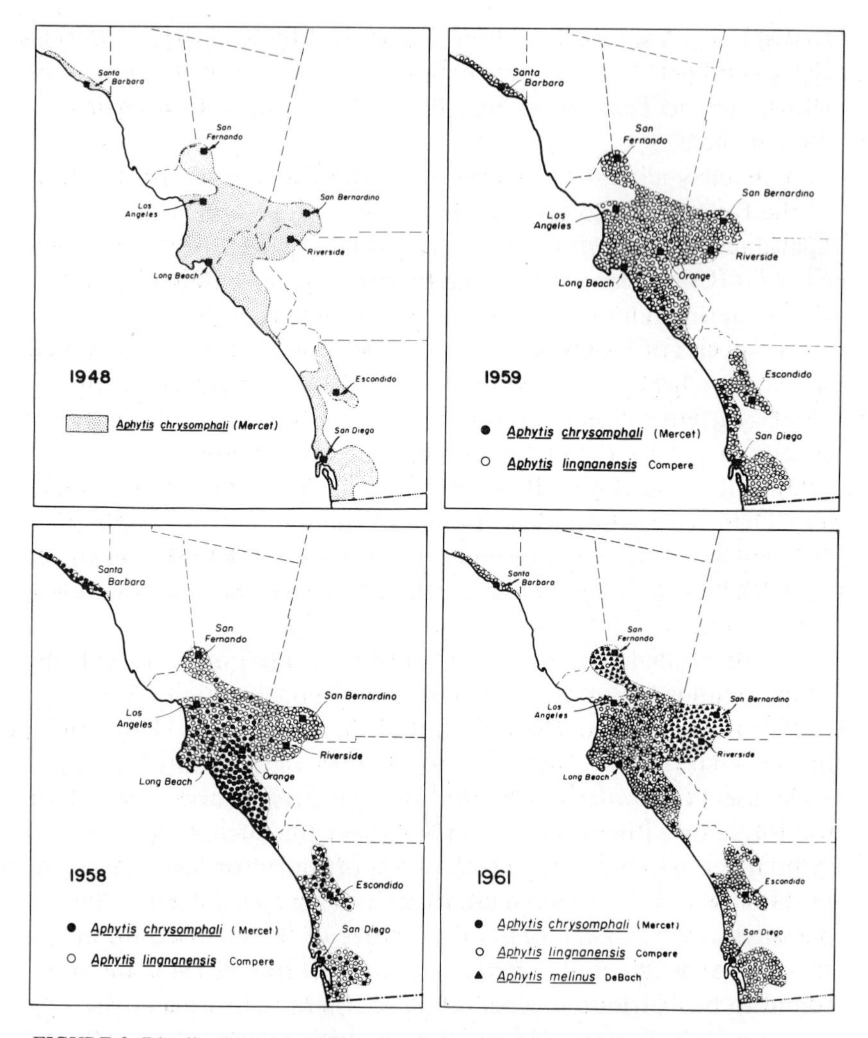

FIGURE 2 Distribution and relative abundance of species of *Aphytis* in citrus-growing areas of southern California. (After DeBach and Sundby, 1963.)

to spread, *A. melinus* has now eliminated *A. lingnanensis* everywhere except locally near Santa Barbara and San Diego (DeBach, personal communication).

Laboratory investigation of the mechanism of displacement in the three species of *Aphytis* suggests that species differences in relative fecundity of adults and survival of immature stages are critical in determining competitive ability. The three species vary somewhat in developmental rate, longevity, fertility, and tolerances to temperature and humidity but are identical in other aspects of their ecology. The larvae, which hatch from eggs deposited on the body of scale insects, feed in identical fashion by piercing the host body with their mandibles, and they are indistinguishable morphologically.

Interest in the evolutionary and systematic consequences of ecological interactions among closely related species in sympatry has centered on habitat divergency and on differential exploitation of food resources within the same habitat as means to alleviate competition (see, for example, MacArthur, 1958; Dixon, 1961; Kohn, 1959; Hamilton, 1962; Hutchinson, 1959; Willis, 1966). Admittedly, most of the evidence for competitive interaction is indirect, but in the opinion of many workers it is compelling, and only an occasional proponent of density-independent or "probabilistic" theories of population control continues to maintain that competition is not a cause of divergence of sympatric species (Bowman, 1961).

Considerable insight into the factors determining alternate methods by which sympatric species partition food resources is provided in an analysis by Schoener (1965) of bill-length ratios among sympatric congeneric species associations of 46 families of birds. Implicit in Schoener's approach, first suggested by Hutchinson (1959; see also Klopfer and MacArthur, 1961), is the assumption that differences in size of bill among species reflect differences in the nature of their food or in the methods of obtaining it. Ratios of bill length (length of larger bill/smaller bill) between species above 1.14 are thought to reflect significant differences in size or physical properties of the food or its immediate environment. Schoener finds that bill ratios usually are large (1) among members of certain families (for example, woodpeckers, Picidae) feeding on food of relatively low abundance; (2) among birds whose body sizes are relatively large in proportion to the total abundance of their food; and (3) in insular birds, especially those on small islands. These trends—explained by Schoener in terms of a model that considers the distribution of food biomass in relation to size—have systematic significance in accounting for generic and familial diversity in bill size and in methods of partitioning food. Among sympatric congeners, the smallest difference in bill size occurs in species feeding on abundant food, presumably because such species are able to partition food by foraging in different microhabitats or by using different feeding techniques within a major habitat, as do certain warblers (MacArthur, 1958) and titmice (Betts, 1955). But species exploiting less abundant food more frequently partition it by size, presumably because in any one narrow range of microhabitats food is not sufficiently abundant to support a population.

It is noteworthy that families of birds whose sympatric species are characterized by relatively great divergence in bill size also show relatively large degrees of sexual dimorphism in the bill. Apparently the very factors (food biomass distribution, etc.) that determine methods of interspecific partitioning of food also determine methods of partitioning by the sexes to avoid intersexual competition (R. K. Selander, 1966:142).

Adaptations to alleviate competition are, of course, not the only consequences of ecological interactions among sympatric species. Clarke (1962 a and b) has examined the evolutionary and systematic aspects of "apostatic selection," a concept based on evidence furnished by L. Tinbergen (1960), de Ruiter (1952), and others that predators develop "search images" that result in their taking proportionately low percentages of rare prey items. Within species populations this frequency-dependent aspect of predation provides a means of maintaining polymorphism in the absence of heterozygous advantage, and it has several additional consequences at the interspecies level. When two or more species share a predator that has a "search image" for one of the species, selection will favor variants in the other species that have the least likelihood of being confused with it. The expected effect of this selection is demonstrated by Clarke in two genera of snails, sympatric species pairs of which share homologous visible morph types. In mixed colonies of *Cepaea nemoralis* and *C. hortensis* occupying grassy and herbaceous habitats in the Oxford region, frequencies of the yellow morph are negatively correlated. And a negative correlation between percentages of banded morphs is evident in samples of *Partula suturalis* and *P. taeniata* from mixed colonies on Moorea Island in the South Pacific.

Where two prey species are extremely common and conditions do not favor apostatic selection, Clarke suggests that selection will act in each species to favor those variants that resemble the other, even when both species are highly palatable, since individuals of both species will benefit from the predator's "desire" for a mixed diet. This situation is the parallel, among palatable species, of Mullerian mimicry.

Brower (1958) has proposed a hypothesis implicating apostatic selection in the evolution of food plant specificity by phenotypically similar, procryptic, palatable insects preyed upon by birds. Whereas the scattering effect of polyphagy would be advantageous if only one prey species were present in an area, when two or more species are present, selection pressure exerted by predators concentrating on a common prey "search image" would favor individuals of the species occupying mutually exclusive plants. Thus, oligophagy could arise from polyphagy. An alternative adaptation would be the development of a polymorphism (for example, color pattern types for visually oriented predators) breaking the prey populations into several visible "species."

SYMPATRIC SPECIATION

Any discussion of the ecological aspects of systematics must include at least a reference to sympatric speciation (the "ecological speciation" of the early "New Systematics"), in which the initial division of the gene pool is attributed to ecological factors rather than geographical isolation. This old but persistent theme finds special favor among entomologists and others dealing with "host races" and other instances of narrow host specificity (Ross, 1962). While it is likely that sympatric speciation will be a subject of research for some time to come, it may, in the end, be extremely difficult if not impossible to demonstrate in natural populations. My own impression is that the readiness with which systematists invoke sympatric speciation varies inversely with their knowledge of the distribution and ecology of the taxonomic group concerned. Wherever modern, thorough analyses of distribution and variation have been made for groups of insects or other organisms in which this mode of speciation has seemed likely, the idea of sympatric speciation becomes less attractive in accounting for species diversity (R. B. Selander, 1960; Burns, 1964; Fisler, 1965; Bush, 1966). Regarding speciation in *Drosophila,* Patterson and Stone (1952:353–354) concluded:

> We find no evidence of sympatric speciation in Drosophila through ecological divergence or any other mechanism. The origin of related species which are found together might have occurred by sympatric divergence, but in no case is the alternate possibility of divergent evolution during (geographic) separation ruled out.

In a refreshingly coherent analysis of the subject stimulated by the work of J. M. Thoday and his colleagues (for example, Thoday and Gibson, 1962, and Thoday, 1965) on disruptive selection in laboratory populations of *Drosophila melanogaster*, Maynard Smith (1967) has defined a set of genetical and ecological conditions under which sympatric speciation might occur in natural populations. This is an extension of an argument presented by Clarke (1962b:61) in developing a model of sympatric speciation initiated by apostatic selection. In a heterogenous environment, a stable polymorphism involving alleles that adapt individuals to different ecological niches may develop if (1) the density-dependent factors regulating population size operate separately in the two niches, and (2) the selective advantages of the genotypes are very large. Given the stable polymorphism, reproductive isolation between "populations" in the two niches could evolve, provided there is assortative mating and some degree of habitat selection by the egg-laying females.* Since the frequency with which these several conditions will be satisfied is unknown, is it apparent, as Maynard Smith (1967:649) notes, that the analysis can be regarded equally well as an argument for or against sympatric speciation.

ECOLOGICAL ASPECTS OF ADAPTIVE RADIATION WITHIN POPULATIONS

Although it has been customary for systematists to think of adaptive radiation solely in terms of species, a growing body of evidence indicates that some degree of radiation occurs also within populations as individuals come to occupy different subniches or adaptive subzones, subdividing and perhaps expanding the total niche or zone utilized by the population. This concept has been developed not by ecologists but by population geneticists concerned with polymorphisms maintained by heterotic and diversifying selection. Several models

*Imprinting as a mechanism promoting the assortative mating necessary in sympatric speciation has been considered by several workers (O'Donald, 1960 a and b; Kalmus and Maynard Smith, 1966; Seiger, 1967). Given a polymorphism for use in mate discrimination in a population, absolute imprinting could split the population into two noninterbreeding subpopulations; if imprinting is partial, however, a balanced polymorphism results, and the population is not subdivided genetically. In assessing imprinting as a factor promoting assortative mating, one should remember that a preference for properties of the parents is likely only when there is parental care; and we have no evidence that the effect of imprinting on mate choice is absolute in any natural population (Seiger, 1967:54).

for the origin and maintenance of ecological polymorphism have been developed (Ludwig, 1950, 1954; Levene, 1953; Dempster, 1955; Levins, 1962, 1963; Levins and MacArthur, 1966). Much of the available observational and experimental data bearing on polymorphic variation comes from the studies of Dobzhansky, Beardmore, Stalker, Carson, and others on chromosomal inversions in *Drosophila* (see reviews by Dobzhansky, 1961, 1965), and from those of the Oxford school of ecological geneticists on visible and physiological polymorphisms in Lepidoptera and snails (see reviews by Ford, 1964, 1965). Recently developed electrophoretic techniques for detecting allelic variation at loci that control enzymes and other proteins make it possible to relate genic heterozygosity and ecological variation in natural populations (see Lewontin and Hubby, 1966).

Although research in ecological genetics suggests that adaptation of individuals to different aspects of heterogeneous environments is a major cause of genetic variation in animal populations (Van Valen, 1965:386), we actually know very little concerning the ways in which this type of adaptation evolves. This is due, in part, to the complexity of the problem of relating genetical polymorphism to ecological variables. For example, the mechanisms of selection maintaining color, banding, and physiological polymorphisms in the snail *Cepaea nemoralis* are only partially understood despite years of intensive genetical and ecological research by Cain, Clarke, Lamotte, Sheppard, Wolda, and others (see review by Ford, 1964, and more recent works cited by Clarke, 1966, and Wolda, 1967). Another example is seen in the major difficulties encountered in interpreting the relationship of chromosomal polymorphism to ecological "flexibility" or "tolerance" in *Drosophila.* Carson (1965) finds a reduction in chromosomal polymorphism in cosmopolitan species of *Drosophila,* which thus appear to have originated from homoselected isolates (Carson, 1959). Perhaps genic polymorphism rather than chromosomal polymorphism provides the seemingly necessary ecological "plasticity" of these widespread, colonizing species, or perhaps this adaptability is achieved by the evolutionary "mobility" of the chromosomally monomorphic, open system of recombination (Carson, 1967); but the situation is far from clear (Mayr, 1965). Only in the case of polymorphic mimicry (see reviews of ecological aspects by Sheppard, 1959, 1965) do we have some understanding of the function of polymorphism in increasing the size of the niche of a population (Hutchinson, 1965:66), and we know almost nothing of the adaptive relationships of continuous character variation with aspects of ecological diversity.

CONTINUOUS ECOLOGICAL VARIATION

I know of only one attempt to relate levels of continuous morphological variation and ecological amplitude of populations. Van Valen (1965) has compared levels of intrapopulation variation in bill width in passerine birds known to differ geographically in width of niche, as reflected in the variety of habitats occupied in local regions. His study dealt with five species occurring in England and on the Canary Islands and the Azores and with a sixth species (a mockingbird, *Mimus gilvus*) occurring in South America and on Curaçao Island. For five of the six species, the insular populations have been reported to inhabit a greater variety of habitats than do the mainland populations; and one species, the chaffinch (*Fringilla coelebs*), exhibits a narrower ecological range on the Canary Islands and a wider range on the Azores than on the mainland of England.

By applying a scaling correction for differences in means of bill width, Van Valen was able to obtain for each species unbiased estimates of the ratio of the intrapopulation variance on islands to that on the mainland. The results indicate that populations of these species are about twice as variable in bill width in the region where the wider niche is occupied. Significantly, *Fringilla coelebs* is least variable on the Canary Islands, moderately variable in England, and most variable in the Azores. Within sexes the distribution of bill measurements for the insular populations is unimodal, indicating that the greater variation is not achieved by a polymorphic system.

ECOLOGICAL SEXUAL DIMORPHISM

One aspect of ecological polymorphism that may readily be investigated is the relationship between sexual dimorphism of trophic structures and differential niche utilization by the sexes. This possibility was recognized by Darwin (1871) but has received little attention from systematists or ecologists. Neglect of this and other types of ecological variation within populations reflects a persistence of typological concepts. In focusing attention on the population as the unit of evolution and on the species as an objectively definable taxonomic entity–or even "the major evolutionary unit" (Solbrig, 1966:54)–systematists and ecologists may forget that the individual is the unit of selection and, hence, that it is the unit of adaptation. This tendency to ignore individual ecological variation has been promoted by proponents of theories of "population adaptation" and group selection, notably in recent years by V. C. Wynne-Edwards (1962, 1963, 1965), who erroneously regard the population as the unit of both evolution and selection (see critiques by Cain, 1964; Crook, 1964, 1965; N. Tinbergen, 1965; Lack, 1966; R. K. Selander, 1965b; Wiens, 1966; and Williams, 1966). It is in the area of the evolution and adaptiveness of social systems and mating systems that concepts of "biotic adaptation" have most impeded progress in understanding.

Hutchinson (1965) has recently discussed some ecological aspects of sexual dimorphism, particularly dimorphism in body size. As he notes, extreme cases of size differences between the sexes are found in certain insects, spiders, cladocerans, cirripeds, and isopods, and in oceanic angler fishes, in which small males are parasitic on females. In many of these cases, the smaller size of the male merely reduces competition without involving utilization of another niche. Hutchinson (1965:67–68) also discusses probable genetical, physiological, and other limitations on the extent of sexual dimorphism in animals.

As I have noted elsewhere (R. K. Selander, 1965b, 1966), evaluation of the ultimate causes of ecological sexual dimorphism is complicated by the fact that Darwinian sexual selection, by promoting sexual dimorphism in body size, may produce dimorphism in trophic structures, which will secondarily result in some degree of differential niche utilization by the sexes. For example, in many fishes of the family Gobiidae, the mouth of the male is disproportionately large (Breder and Rosen, 1966). In one species, *Microgobius gulosus,* Baird (1965) has shown that the mouth is used by males in agonistic behavior in connection with territory defense and in courtship. Here the sexual dimorphism in mouth size appears to be attributable primarily to sexual selection. But, as Baird has demonstrated, males are able to ingest larger items of food than females; thus, some degree of differential niche utilization apparently is associated with the structural dimorphism.

Whether sexual variation in niche utilization results from sexually selected dimorphism or is selected *per se* must be determined by investigations of the behavior and ecology of individual species. In some cases it is apparent that selection for optimal size of trophic structures opposes sexual selection for increased body size dimorphism. For example, among some omnivorous and insectivorous birds, especially small species feeding on abundant food, the bill is less dimorphic sexually than other structures, such as the tarsus or wing (R. K. Selander, in manuscript). Thus the house sparrow (*Passer domesticus*) is sexually monomorphic in bill dimensions but is dimorphic in body weight, tarsus length, wing length, and tail length (Selander and Johnston, 1967).

I have recently summarized the circumstantial and direct evidence bearing on the problem of methods by which intersexual competition for food is alleviated by birds (R. K. Selander, 1966). Here I shall be concerned only with one method, that of differential niche utilization by the sexes within a common home range or territory. This is appropriate in a paper on systematics because it is this method with which the greatest degrees of morphological dimorphism are associated.

To illustrate ecological sexual dimorphism, I propose to review my own work on two species of woodpeckers of the genus *Centurus*. First, however, I call attention to a classic example of this phenomenon provided by the extinct huia (*Neomorpha acutirostris*) of North Island, New Zealand, which has the greatest degree of bill dimorphism (39 percent in mean bill length) known in birds. The sexes are similar in body size (7 percent difference in mean tarsus length), but the short, thick bill of the male is adapted for digging in rotted wood for boring insects, while the long, slender, decurved bill of the female is adapted for probing in crevices. (The frequently cited anecdotal accounts of male and female working cooperatively in pairs probably should be discounted.) If the two bill types were represented in different species, avian systematists would be inclined to place them in different genera.

In many large families or genera of birds there is considerable interspecific variation in degree of sexual dimorphism in bill size.*

*Where there is a positive correlation between body size and degree of sexual dimorphism in bill size, the variation is sometimes attributed to allometric effects (Rensch, 1950, 1960), although this is an unsatisfactory explanation because of the necessary corollary that bill size is selectively neutral (see Amadon, 1959).

For example, among melanerpine woodpeckers dimorphism may be absent, moderate, or marked. The greatest dimorphism in bill size (21 percent difference in mean bill length and 96 percent joint nonoverlap between the sexes) occurs in *Centurus striatus,* a species endemic to Hispaniola and the only resident woodpecker on that island (see Figure 3). (*Melanerpes herminieri* of Guadeloupe Island and *M. portoricensis* of Puerto Rico are only slightly less dimorphic.) In another species of similar body size, *Centurus aurifrons* of Mexico and Texas, which is representative of the continental members of the species group, sexual dimorphism is moderate (9 percent difference in mean bill length and 83 percent joint nonoverlap). With regard to sexual dimorphism in the tongue (which functions importantly in feeding in woodpeckers), the difference between the insular and continental species of *Centurus* is even more marked (35 percent difference in mean tongue length in *C. striatus* and 9 percent in *C. aurifrons*). In both species (but to a much greater degree in *C. striatus*), as in woodpeckers in general, dimorphism is greater in trophic structures than in other body dimensions (Figure 3). Because the variances of bill and tongue dimensions are no smaller in the insular species than in the continental form, the greater sexual dimorphism of the former increases by approximately one third the total span of bill length represented in the adult segment of the population (Figure 4).

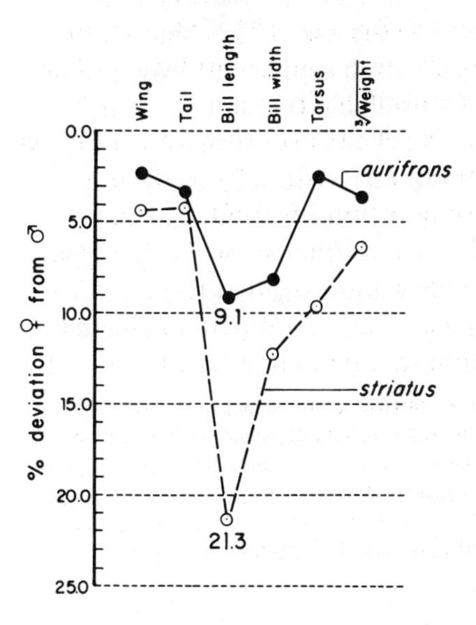

FIGURE 3 Sexual dimorphism in size in the Hispaniolan woodpecker, *Centurus striatus.* (Based on data from R. K. Selander, 1966.)

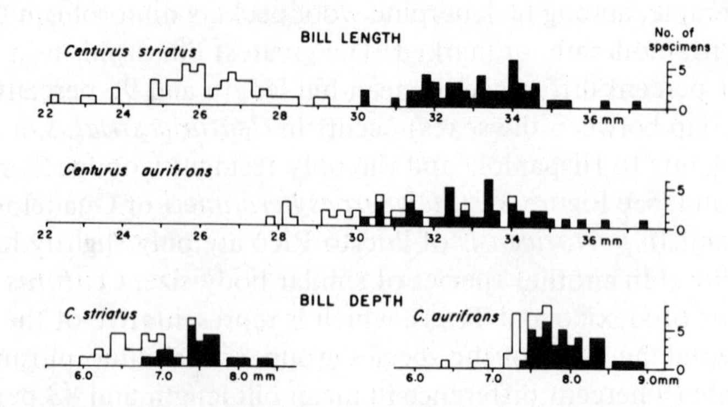

FIGURE 4 Individual and sexual variation in bill length in two species of *Centurus* woodpeckers. Solid histograms, males; open histograms, females. (After R. K. Selander, 1966.)

Records of foraging by *Centurus striatus,* from a study area in the Dominican Republic, demonstrate significant sexual differences in feeding technique and location in directions that would be expected on the basis of sexual differences in the feeding apparatus (Table 1). The male specializes in probing and the female in gleaning, although both sexes employ the same array of foraging techniques and forage at the same average height above the ground. The sexual difference in foraging behavior in the sexes of *Centurus striatus* is greater than that found in many sympatric species pairs of birds in continental North America (Brewer, 1963; MacArthur, 1958). In the less dimorphic *C. aurifrons,* a similar but less-marked difference in feeding is suggested by available foraging records.*

In developing a general hypothesis for the evolution of ecological sexual dimorphism, I have interpreted differential foraging as a means of alleviating intersexual competition for food. For the melanerpine woodpeckers, *C. striatus* and other strongly dimorphic woodpeckers of the West Indies, I have additionally attempted to relate the increased sexual dimorphism and accompanying increased sexual difference in niche utilization to a reduction in intensity of

*These findings for *Centurus* species have been verified and extended by R. A. Wallace (in manuscript), who also has demonstrated marked sexual differences in foraging behavior in *M. portoricensis.* Conspicuous sexual differences in foraging have been recorded in the strongly dimorphic, nonmelanerpine continental hairy woodpecker (*Dendrocopos villosus*), a species exhibiting 11 percent difference in mean bill length and between 92 and 95 percent joint nonoverlap (Kilham, 1965; see also R. K. Selander, 1965a).

TABLE 1 Sexual variation in foraging behavior in *Centurus striatus.*

	Males		Females	
Foraging Technique (and Location)[a]	Number of Records	Percent of Total	Number of Records	Percent of Total
Probing (in epiphytes, fruit, crevices, holes)	32	34.8	9	8.6
Pecking and excavating (on branches, trunks, seed pods)	30	32.6	26	24.8
Searching and gleaning (on leaves, twigs, branches, trunks, fruit)	30	32.6	70	66.6
TOTALS	92	100.0	105	100.0

[a] For distribution of records of foraging by the three techniques, $\chi^2_{(2)} = 28.54$; $P < 0.001$. (Data from R. K. Selander, 1966:124.)

interspecific competition resulting from the absence or rarity on Hispaniola (and Guadeloupe and Puerto Rico) of other woodpeckers and birds of similar adaptive type. Before developing this hypothesis, I want to make two points. First, there is considerable evidence from a variety of types of birds that unusually large degrees of sexual dimorphism in bill size occur more frequently on islands than on continents (see review in R. K. Selander, 1966, and a recent example in Snow, 1966:267). Second, it appears that many of the factors (including competition, isolation, and environmental heterogeneity) promoting adaptive radiation at the species level act similarly to promote adaptive radiation through ecological sexual dimorphism.

Whether the possibility for niche expansion is open to a species depends on the complex interaction of several factors. For example, there must be sufficient environmental heterogeneity to provide subniches for the sexes. Thus, opportunity for divergence depends upon the composition and structure of the biotic community and is influenced by the presence or absence of other species exploiting "adjacent" niches. In rich continental faunas it seems probable that the niche of a species is to some degree "contained" by the presence of other species with similar if not partially overlapping niches. For this reason the extent of sexual divergence in niche utilization that a species may achieve will vary regionally but generally will be limited in continental areas owing to the relative richness of the faunas. On islands, the opportunity for sexual divergence may be greater because of reduced numbers of competing species and the resultant vacant niches. Also, it is possible that on islands—especially on smaller ones—divergence of the sexes is selected more frequently because food items within any given size or type category are less abundant.

Current ecological theory holds that insular faunas are impoverished because not all species of adjacent continental faunas reach the islands and, of those that do, only some find habitats or niche requirements in sufficient quantity to permit long-term maintenance of populations. The result is that rare species are subject to periodic extinction (Serventy, 1951; Preston, 1962; Mayr, 1963; MacArthur and Wilson, 1963; Hamilton *et al.,* 1964). Consequently there is a chronic vacancy of ecological spheres, which permits adaptive radiation of species that are able to exploit the vacant habitats and niches in addition to their own preferred ones. Shifts in niche may be facilitated by the genetic lability experienced by small colonizing populations (Mayr, 1954, 1963) and, especially on small islands, by a weakening of the buffering or balancing effects of counterselection that typifies complex mainland ecosystems (Anderson, 1960). Where there is opportunity for speciation through geographical isolation, as in archipelagos, new species can arise to exploit unoccupied niches and habitats (Lack, 1947; Amadon, 1950). But even where there is no opportunity for speciation, as on single, isolated oceanic islands, some degree of adaptive radiation may be achieved by a single species population through an expansion of its ecological range and, as I have contended, an increase in individual or sexual variation in niche utilization.

The adaptive radiation achieved by *Centurus striatus* on Hispaniola is remarkable. The absence of competitors has favored increased ecological sexual dimorphism, and this, in turn, permits the species to maintain population densities far in excess of those known in any continental species of woodpecker. The colonial nesting habit of *Centurus striatus,* which is highly unusual for a woodpecker (R. K. Selander, 1966), also may be related to the increased ecological sexual dimorphism, if Ashmole (1967) is correct in believing that the exceptionally high densities maintained by the species make the defense of territories uneconomic. The species is exceedingly eurytopic, inhabiting all types of woodland from mangrove swamps on the coast to pine forests of the mountains. Through ecological polymorphism and an expanded range of habitat distribution, this single species manages to exploit its insular environment to a degree that in continental North America is achieved only by the combined efforts of several species of woodpeckers or other birds of similar adaptive type.

A strikingly parallel example of increased ecological sexual dimorphism in insular populations is provided by the work of A. S. Rand (in manuscript) and Schoener (1967) on *Anolis* lizards in the West Indies. Lizards of this genus occurring on the smaller islands in the absence of congeners are unusually dimorphic in size—the head length of adult males averaging 1.3 to 1.5 times that of females. This increased dimorphism has developed independently in at least seven stocks of *Anolis.* In a study of *Anolis conspersus,* the only species of the genus on Grand Cayman Island, Schoener (1967) demonstrated sexual variation in microhabitat occurrence and in insect prey size (Figure 5). Adult males, which tend to occupy larger perches and to perch higher than females, obtain 62 percent (by volume) of their food from insects over 15 mm in

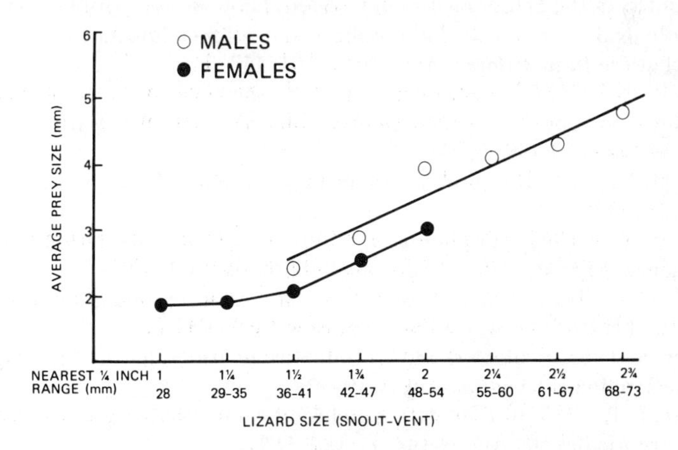

FIGURE 5 Relationship of predator size to prey size for *Anolis conspersus* on Grand Cayman Island. (After Schoener, 1967.)

length, whereas adult females obtain only 21 percent of their food from such large prey. Additionally, adult males take prey in a greater range of sizes than do females; the average range in prey size for 47 males was 12.6 mm; the average for 84 females was 8.2 mm. The degree to which the major quantitative and qualitative differences in the kinds of food ingested are explainable solely on the basis of sexual microhabitat differences is not clear. However, we have evidence in an insular population of a significant niche expansion achieved by differential adaptation of the sexes. As in the case of *Centurus,* it seems probable that a reduction in intraspecific competition resulting from ecological polymorphism permits the species to maintain extremely dense populations in the absence of competitors.

This work was supported by NSF Grant GB-6662 and NIH Grant GM-15769.

REFERENCES

Amadon, D. 1950. The Hawaiian honeycreepers (*Aves, Drepaniidae*). Bull. Am. Mus. Nat. Hist. 95:151–262.

Amadon, D. 1959. The significance of sexual differences in size among birds. Proc. Am. Phil. Soc. 103:531–536.

Anderson, P. K. 1960. Ecology and evolution in island populations of salamanders in the San Francisco Bay region. Ecol. Monogr. 30:359–385.

Ashmole, N. P. 1967. Sexual dimorphism and colonial breeding in the woodpecker *Centurus striatus.* Am. Natur. 101:353–356.

Baird, R. C. 1965. Ecological implications of the behavior of the sexually dimorphic goby *Microgobius gulosus* (Girard). Publ. Inst. Marine Sci. Univ. Texas 10:1–8.

Betts, M. M. 1955. The food of titmice in oak woodland. J. Anim. Ecol. 24:282–323.

Bowman, R. I. 1961. Morphological differentiation and adaptation in the Galápagos finches. Univ. California Publ. Zool. 58:1–326.

Breder, C. M., Jr., and D. E. Rosen. 1966. Modes of reproduction in fishes. Natural History Press, Garden City, New York. 941 p.

Brewer, R. 1963. Ecological and reproductive relationships of black-capped and Carolina chickadees. Auk 80:9–47.

Brower, L. P. 1958. Bird predation and food plant specificity in closely related procryptic insects. Am. Natur. 92:183–187.

Brown, W. L., and E. O. Wilson. 1956. Character displacement. Syst. Zool. 5:49–64.

Burns, J. M. 1964. Evolution in skipper butterflies of the genus *Erynnis.* Univ. California Publ. Entomol. 37:1–216.

Bush, G. L. 1966. The taxonomy, cytology, and evolution of the genus *Rhagoletis* in North America (Diptera, Tephritidae). Bull. Mus. Comp. Zool. 134:431–562.

Cain, A. J. 1959. Taxonomic concepts. Ibis 101:302–318.

Cain, A. J. 1964. The perfection of animals, p. 36–63 *In* J. D. Carthy and C. L. Duddington [ed] Viewpoints in biology. 3. Butterworths, London.

Caine, A. J., and G. A. Harrison. 1960. Phyletic weighting. Proc. Zool. Soc. London 135:1–31.

Carson, H. L. 1959. Genetic conditions which promote or retard the formation of species. Cold Spring Harbor Symposia on Quantitative Biology 24:87–105.

Carson, H. L. 1965. Chromosomal morphism in geographically widespread species of *Drosophila,* p. 503–531 *In* H. G. Baker and G. L. Stebbins [ed] The genetics of colonizing species. Academic Press, New York.

Carson, H. L. 1967. Permanent heterozygosity, p. 143–168 *In* T. Dobzhansky *et al.* [ed] Evolutionary biology. Vol. 1. Appleton-Century-Crofts, New York.

Clarke, B. 1962a. Natural selection in mixed populations of two polymorphic snails. Heredity 17:319–345.

Clarke, B. 1962b. Balanced polymorphism and the diversity of sympatric species. Syst. Assoc. Publ. 4:47–70.

Clarke, B. 1966. The evolution of morph-ratio clines. Am. Natur. 100:389–402.

Crook, J. H. 1964. The evolution of social organisation and visual communication in the weaver birds (Ploceinae). Behaviour, Suppl. 10:1–178.

Crook, J. H. 1965. The adaptive significance of avian social organisations. Symp. Zool. Soc. London 14:181–218.

Darwin, C. 1871. The descent of man and selection in relation to sex. John Murray, London.

DeBach, P. 1965. Some biological and ecological phenomena associated with colonizing entomophagous insects, p. 287–303 *In* H. G. Baker and G. L. Stebbins [ed] The genetics of colonizing species. Academic Press, New York.

DeBach, P., and R. A. Sundby. 1963. Competitive displacement between ecological homologues. Hilgardia 34:105–166.

Dempster, E. R. 1955. Maintenance of genetic heterogeneity. Cold Spring Harbor Symposia on Quantitative Biology 20:25–32.

Diver, C. 1940. The problem of closely related species living in the same area, p. 303–328 *In* J. Huxley [ed] The new systematics. Oxford Univ. Press, London.

Dixon, K. L. 1961. Habitat distribution and niche relationships in North American species of *Parus,* p. 179–216 *In* W. F. Blair [ed] Vertebrate speciation. Univ. Texas Press, Austin.

Dobzhansky, T. 1961. On the dynamics of chromosomal polymorphism in *Drosophila,* p. 30–42 *In* J. S. Kennedy [ed] Insect polymorphism. Symp. Royal Entomol. Soc. 1.

Dobzhansky, T. 1965. Genetic diversity and fitness, p. 541–552 *In* Genetics today. Vol. 3. Proc. XI Int. Congr. Genetics.

Fisler, G. F. 1965. Adaptation and speciation in harvest mice of the marshes of San Francisco Bay. Univ. California Publ. Zool. 77:1-108.

Ford, E. B. 1964. Ecological genetics. Methuen, London.

Ford, E. B. 1965. Genetic polymorphism. Massachusetts Inst. Technology Press, Cambridge, Massachusetts. 101 p.

Hall, B. P. 1963. The francolins, a study in speciation. Bull. Brit. Mus. (Natur. Hist.) 10:1-204.

Hamilton, T. H. 1962. Species relationships and adaptations for sympatry in the avian genus *Vireo.* Condor 64:40-68.

Hamilton, T. H., R. H. Barth, Jr., and I. Rubinoff. 1964. The environmental control of insular variation in bird species abundance. Proc. Nat. Acad. Sci. U.S. 52:132-140.

Hutchinson, G. E. 1959. Homage to Santa Rosalia *or* why are there so many kinds of animals? Am. Natur. 93:145-159.

Hutchinson, G. E. 1961. The paradox of the plankton. Am. Natur. 95:137-145.

Hutchinson, G. E. 1965. The ecological theater and the evolutionary play. Yale Univ. Press, New Haven. 139 p.

Huxley, J. [ed] 1940. The new systematics. Oxford Univ. Press, London. 583 p.

Kalmus, H., and J. Maynard Smith. 1966. Some evolutionary consequences of pegmatypic mating systems (imprinting). Am. Natur. 100:619-635.

Kennerly, T. E., Jr. 1959. Contact between the ranges of two allopatric species of pocket gophers. Evolution 13:247-263.

Kilham, L. 1965. Differences in feeding behavior of male and female hairy woodpeckers. Wilson Bull. 77:134-145.

Klopfer, P. H., and R. H. MacArthur. 1961. On the causes of tropical species diversity; niche overlap. Am. Natur. 95:223-226.

Kohn, A. J. 1959. The ecology of *Conus* in Hawaii. Ecol. Monogr. 29:47-90.

Kohn, A. J., and G. H. Orians. 1962. Ecological data in the classification of closely related species. Syst. Zool. 11:119-127.

Lack, D. 1944. Ecological aspects of species-formation in passerine birds. Ibis 86:260-286.

Lack, D. 1947. Darwin's finches. Cambridge Univ. Press. 204 p.

Lack, D. 1949. The significance of ecological isolation, p. 299-308 *In* G. L. Jepsen *et al.* [ed] Genetics, paleontology, and evolution. Princeton Univ. Press, Princeton.

Lack, D. 1966. Population studies of birds. Clarendon Press, Oxford. 341 p.

Levene, H. 1953. Genetic equilibrium when more than one ecological niche is available. Am. Natur. 87:331-333.

Levins, R. 1962. Theory of fitness in a heterogeneous environment. I. The fitness set and adaptive function. Am. Natur. 96:361-378.

Levins, R. 1963. Theory of fitness in a heterogeneous environment. II. Developmental flexibility and niche selection. Am. Natur. 97:75-90.

Levins, R., and R. MacArthur. 1966. The maintenance of genetic polymorphism in a spatially heterogeneous environment: Variations on a theme by Howard Levene. Am. Natur. 100:585-601.

Lewontin, R. C., and J. L. Hubby. 1966. A molecular approach to the study of genic heterozygosity in natural populations. II. Amount of variation and degree of heterozygosity in natural populations of *Drosophila pseudoobscura.* Genetics 54:595–609.

Ludwig, W. 1950. Zur Theorie der Konkurrenz. Die Annidation (Einnischung) als fünfter Evolutionsfaktor. Neue Ergeb. Probleme Zool. Klatt-Festschrift 1950:516–537.

Ludwig, W. 1954. Die Selektionstheorie, p. 662–712 *In* G. Heberer [ed] Die Evolution der Organismen. G. Fischer, Stuttgart.

MacArthur, R. H. 1958. Population ecology of some warblers of northeastern coniferous forests. Ecology 39:599–619.

MacArthur, R. H., and E. O. Wilson. 1963. An equilibrium theory of insular zoogeography. Evolution 17:373–387.

Maynard Smith, J. 1967. Sympatric speciation. Am. Natur. 100:673–650.

Mayr, E. 1950. Taxonomic categories in fossil hominids. Cold Spring Harbor Symposia on Quantitative Biology 15:109–118.

Mayr, E. 1954. Change of genetic environment and evolution, p. 157–180 *In* J. Huxley *et al.* [ed] Evolution as a process. George Allen and Unwin, London.

Mayr, E. 1959. Trends in avian systematics. Ibis 101:293–302.

Mayr, E. 1963. Animal species and evolution. Harvard Univ. Press, Cambridge, Massachusetts. 797 p.

Mayr, E. 1965. Summary, p. 553–562 *In* H. G. Baker and G. L. Stebbins [ed] The genetics of colonizing species. Academic Press, New York.

Mayr, E., E. G. Linsley, and R. L. Usinger. 1953. Methods and principles of systematic zoology. McGraw-Hill, New York. 328 p.

Miller, R. S. 1964. Ecology and distribution of pocket gophers (Geomyidae) in Colorado. Ecology 45:256–272.

Norris, R. A. 1958. Comparative biosystematics and life history of the nuthatches *Sitta pygmaea* and *Sitta pusilla.* Univ. California Publ. Zool. 56:119–300.

O'Donald, P. 1960a. Inbreeding as a result of imprinting. Heredity 15:79–85.

O'Donald, P. 1960b. Assortative mating in a population in which two alleles are segregating. Heredity 15:389–396.

Orians, G. H., and M. F. Willson. 1964. Interspecific territories of birds. Ecology 45:736–745.

Patterson, J. T., and W. S. Stone. 1952. Evolution in the genus *Drosophila.* Macmillan, New York. 610 p.

Pearson, O. P. 1960. Biology of the subterranean rodents, *Ctenomys,* in Peru. Mem. Mus. Hist. Natur. "Javier Prado" No. 9:1–56.

Pitelka, F. A. 1951. Speciation and ecologic distribution in American jays of the genus *Aphelocoma.* Univ. California Publ. Zool. 50:195–464.

Preston, F. W. 1962. The canonical distribution of commonness and rarity: Parts I, II. Ecology 43:185–215, 410–432.

Rensch, B. 1950. Die Abhängigkeit der relativen Sexualdifferenz von der Körpergrösse. Bonn Zool. Beitr. 1:58–69.

Rensch, B. 1960. Evolution above the species level. Columbia Univ. Press, New York. 419 p.
Robinson, J. T. 1967. Variation and taxonomy of the early hominids, p. 69–100 *In* T. Dobzhansky *et al.* [ed] Evolutionary biology. Vol. 1. Appleton-Century-Crofts, New York.
Ross, H. H. 1962. A synthesis of evolutionary theory. Prentice-Hall, Englewood Cliffs, New Jersey.
Ruiter, L. de. 1952. Some experiments on the camouflage of stick caterpillars. Behaviour 4:222–232.
Schoener, T. W. 1965. The evolution of bill size differences among sympatric congeneric species of birds. Evolution 19:189–213.
Schoener, T. W. 1967. The ecological significance of sexual dimorphism in size in the lizard *Anolis conspersus.* Science 155:474–477.
Seiger, M. B. 1967. A computer simulation study of the influence of imprinting on population structure. Am. Natur. 101:47–57.
Selander, R. B. 1960. Bionomics, systematics, and phylogeny of *Lytta,* a genus of blister beetles (Coleoptera, Meloidae). Illinois Biol. Monogr. 28:1–295.
Selander, R. K. 1965a. Sexual dimorphism in relation to foraging behavior in the hairy woodpecker. Wilson Bull. 77:416.
Selander, R. K. 1965b. On mating systems and sexual selection. Am. Natur. 99:129–141.
Selander, R. K. 1966. Sexual dimorphism and differential niche utilization in birds. Condor 68:113–151.
Selander, R. K., and D. R. Giller. 1959. Interspecific relations of woodpeckers in Texas. Wilson Bull. 71:107–124.
Selander, R. K., and D. R. Giller. 1961. Analysis of sympatry of great-tailed and boat-tailed grackles. Condor 63:29–86.
Selander, R. K., and D. R. Giller. 1963. Species limits in the woodpecker genus *Centurus* (Aves). Bull. Am. Mus. Natur. Hist. 124:213–274.
Selander, R. K., and R. F. Johnston. 1967. Evolution in the house sparrow. I. Intrapopulation variation in North America. Condor 69:217–258.
Serventy, D. L. 1951. Interspecific competition on small islands. West. Australian Natur. 3:59–60.
Sheppard, P. M. 1959. The evolution of mimicry; a problem in ecology and genetics. Cold Spring Harbor Symposia on Quantitative Biology 24:131–140.
Sheppard, P. M. 1965. Mimicry and its ecological aspects, p. 553–559 *In* Genetics today. Vol. 3. Proc. XI Int. Congr. Genetics.
Simpson, G. G. 1961. Principles of animal taxonomy. Columbia Univ. Press, New York. 247 p.
Snow, B. K. 1966. Observations of the behaviour and ecology of the flightless cormorant *Nannopterum harrisi.* Ibis 108:265–280.
Solbrig, O. T. 1966. Evolution and systematics. Macmillan, New York. 122 p.
Stein, R. C. 1958. The behavioral, ecological and morphological characteristics of two populations of the alder flycatcher, *Empidonax traillii* (Audubon). N. Y. State Mus. Sci. Serv. Bull. 371:1–63.

Stein, R. C. 1963. Isolating mechanisms between populations of Traill's flycatchers. Proc. Am. Phil. Soc. 107:21–50.
Thoday, J. M. 1965. Effects of selection for genetic diversity, p. 533–540 *In* Genetics today. Vol. 3. Proc. XI Int. Congr. Genetics.
Thoday, J. M., and J. B. Gibson. 1962. Isolation by disruptive selection. Nature 193:1164–1166.
Thorpe, W. H. 1940. Ecology and the future of systematics, p. 341–364. *In* J. Huxley [ed] The new systematics. Oxford Univ. Press, London.
Tinbergen, L. 1960. The natural control of insects in pinewoods. I. Factors influencing the intensity of predation by song-birds. Arch. Neerl. Zool. 13:265–336.
Tinbergen, N. 1965. Behavior and natural selection, p. 521–542 *In* J. A. Moore [ed] Ideas in modern biology. Natural History Press, Garden City, New York.
Van Valen, L. 1965. Morphological variation and width of ecological niche. Am. Natur. 49:377–390.
Vaughan, T. A. 1967. Two parapatric species of pocket gophers. Evolution 21:148–158.
Vaurie, C. 1955. Pseudo-subspecies. Acta XI Congr. Int. Ornith. 1954:369–380.
Weidenreich, F. 1945. Giant early man from Java and South China. Anthropol. Papers Am. Mus. Natur. Hist. 40.
Wiens, J. A. 1966. On group selection and Wynne-Edwards' hypothesis. Am. Sci. 54:273–287.
Williams, G. C. 1966. Adaptation and natural selection: A critique of some current evolutionary thought. Princeton Univ. Press, Princeton. 307 p.
Willis, E. O. 1966. Interspecific competition and the foraging behavior of plain-brown woodcreepers. Ecology 47:667–672.
Wolda, H. 1967. The effect of temperature on reproduction in some morphs of the landsnail *Cepaea nemoralis* (L.). Evolution 21:117–129.
Wynne-Edwards, V. C. 1962. Animal dispersion in relation to social behaviour. Oliver and Boyd, London. 653 p.
Wynne-Edwards, V. C. 1963. Intergroup selection in the evolution of social systems. Nature 200:623–626.
Wynne-Edwards, V. C. 1965. Social organisation as a population regulator. Symp. Zool. Soc. London 14:173–178.

Discussion

Lincoln P. Brower

Dr. Selander is to be congratulated for both the breadth and the depth of his contribution. Rather than give a general commentary,

I should like to discuss four points that seem to me to be of major importance.

Dr. Selander has presented most interesting evidence that insular populations of birds, particularly woodpeckers in the Caribbean islands, exhibit sexually dimorphic differences in their bills and tongues to a greater extent than they do on continental areas where more competing species are present.

My first point is merely an elaboration of one of Dr. Selander's. It would appear from the many studies of insular populations that the attainment of numerical abundance is of greater importance than morphological stability. Any means of increasing the abundance of the species, including ecological sexual dimorphism, polymorphism, or simply an increase in morphological variance in both sexes, is probably selectively advantageous. Undoubtedly, the reason for this is a highly exaggerated direct relationship between population size and survival on islands where periodic high mortality can lead so easily to extinction. In contrast, decline to a dangerously small population size can be compensated for in continental areas by migration from adjacent populations. Furthermore, this is not thought to be a group-selection process.

The second point is that the phenomenon of *ecological sexual dimorphism* may be much more widespread than has been realized. For example, if one examines museum collections of insects, one sex often greatly outnumbers the other; and, yet, when reared in captivity, the sex ratio is nearly always equal. The inference that I have made elsewhere (Brower, 1963) is that insect collectors have subniches that broadly overlap only one of the sexes of the insects.

My third point is this: Selection for morphological variation will affect not only food-getting ability but very likely will modify the ability of the sexes to recognize each other. In a continental area, a large variance in bill size, bill shape, and other characteristics among several species could lead to interspecies confusion in mate choice; but on an island where few or no other closely related species are present, the large ecological advantage of increasing the variance in bill shape could easily outweigh any disadvantage in courtship recognition.

A case in point that I have discussed elsewhere (Brower, 1963) is the evolution of *sex-limited mimicry* in butterflies. In these insects, mimicry is often limited to the female; but it is obvious that the mimicry also should be of advantage to the male. However, it appears that a change in color pattern in the male puts him at such a disadvantage in courtship that the mimetic advantage is outweighed. Consequently, only those genes that express mimetic coloration in the female sex can become established in the population.

Thus, it is important to consider sexual selection as well as ecological selection, because both factors can interact to produce a net selective advantage or disadvantage.

Finally, I believe that it is of great importance to consider competitive relationships not only within the context of a single trophic level in the food chain, as we have been doing so far, but also to remember that competition within and between species can be mediated via predators at higher levels in the food chain.

For example, in recent research we have discovered that the monarch butterfly is completely palatable to blue jays if reared on the milkweed genus *Gonolobus;* but if reared on *Asclepias curassavica,* one male monarch contains sufficient cardiac poison to cause vomiting in four birds! In Alabama, Knudsen (in Urquhart, 1960) has reported the monarch ovipositing on *Asclepias* and *Gonolobus* growing side-by-side. Thus, polymorphism involving oviposition choice in the adult female monarch will lead to a mixed population of butterflies, some palatable and others poisonous to their avian predators. As such, the monarch butterfly must be regarded as exhibiting the phenomenon of *automimicry* (Brower *et al.*,1967).

The selective factors promoting such a polymorphism most certainly involve a balance between the metabolic advantage and disadvantage of eating the two different plants and the advantage of being unpalatable to the birds. Here, we see how selection is operating between plant and herbivore and between herbivore and predator, i.e., at least three levels in the food chain are involved in a complex ecological interaction.

REFERENCES

Brower, L. P. 1963. The evolution of sex-limited mimicry in butterflies. Mimicry Symposium, Proc. XVI Int. Congr. Zool., Washington 4:173–179.

Brower, L. P., J. V. Z. Brower, and J. M. Corvino. 1967. Plant poisons in a terrestrial food chain. Proc. Nat. Acad. Sci. U.S. 57(4):893–898.

Urquhart, F. A. 1960. The monarch butterfly. Univ. of Toronto Press, Toronto.

Discussion

Bryan C. Clarke

I also congratulate Dr. Selander on a most interesting paper. In relation to it, there are three points I wish to discuss.

First, he has kindly mentioned some of my earlier work on *Cepaea* and *Partula.* The situation now seems to be more complicated than it did in 1962. With respect to the apparent interaction between *Cepaea nemoralis* and *C. hortensis,* some recent unpublished studies by Dr. M. A. Carter have suggested that the negative relations are characteristic of particular areas. Dr. Carter has found other areas among, and within, which the negative relations do not occur (as have Cain and Currey, 1963).

The negative correlations between *Partula suturalis* and *P. taeniata* were calculated from the data of Crampton (1932), who made collections on the island of Moorea. Each of his samples represents a large area, often several square kilometers. Dr. J. J. Murray, Jr., and I revisited Moorea in 1962 and found significant changes of gene frequency over distances of less than 10 meters. When we studied populations *within* Crampton's areas, no correlations were found between the two species. Here we have the intriguing possibility that interactions of the type discussed by Dr. Selander are effective at the level of the geographical "race" but not at the level of the individual population.

I should add that now there is further evidence of the importance of apostatic selection. John Allen, working at Edinburgh, has demonstrated strong "searching images" in wild passerines (including the song thrush, which is a major predator of *Cepaea*).

Second, Dr. Selander has discussed several related ecological factors that can influence genetic diversity within and between species. I would like to add another to the list–namely, disease, which may turn out to be one of the most important. I think it was Haldane (1949), in a rather inaccessible paper, who first emphasized the major role of disease as an evolutionary force. Curiously little work on the subject has been done since then, perhaps due to a reluctance on the part of systematic biologists to become embroiled in microbiology and biochemistry. In drawing your attention to the matter of disease, time allows me to make only a few dogmatic statements:

1. Disease can maintain polymorphisms by frequency-dependent selection (Haldane, 1949; Flor, 1956; Clarke, 1962; Damian, 1964; Person, 1966).
2. By the same process, disease can produce sympatric divergence between species.
3. Disease can bring about interspecific exclusion. As pointed out by Haldane, many of the African Artiodactyls probably owe their continued survival to the fact that they harbor trypanosomes. Exclusion of this kind can occur between species that do not exploit the same ecological niche, except in the widest possible sense of that term.
4. The evolutionary effects of disease will manifest themselves most evidently at the biochemical level. It is perhaps significant in this context that Kojima and Yarbrough (1967) have demonstrated frequency-dependent selection at the esterase-6 locus in *Drosophila melanogaster.*

My third point is a more general one. Within a single population, the effects of niche diversity, of predator behavior, and of disease will be detected as frequency-dependent selection. A measure of the importance of such selection within populations will give us an idea of the wider relevance of these factors to interspecific divergence.

I shall conclude by describing an experiment that has not yet been done. I can justify this unusual course only by saying that I hope to induce someone else to do it, as well as ourselves. It was conceived in discussion with Dr. Alan Robertson at Edinburgh. We propose taking an outbred population of *Drosophila* and from it producing a second population, thoroughly inbred. We then propose to grow the two populations together without allowing them to cross. The inbred population would be largely homozygous, and its effect on the outbred population should be to increase the effective frequency of particular alleles at any loci that show polymorphism. With respect to any polymorphisms that are maintained by frequency-dependent selection, the outbred population should "move away" from the inbred. At the end of the experiment we would survey both populations for enzyme and other protein variants, using the techniques described by Lewontin and Hubby (1966). The proportion of loci at which the equilibrium had moved away would give an estimate of the over-all proportion of loci at which frequency-dependent selection is important to the maintenance of polymorphism.

There seems to be no good reason, in principle, why similar experiments should not be carried out in the field. They might provide us with answers to some of the fascinating questions that have been raised by Dr. Selander.

REFERENCES

Cain, A. J., and J. D. Currey. 1963. Area effects in *Cepaea.* Phil. Trans. Roy. Soc. London B246:1–81.

Clarke, B. 1962. Balanced polymorphism and the diversity of sympatric species. *In* D. Nichols [ed] Taxonomy and geography. Systematics Association, Oxford.

Crampton, H. E. 1932. Studies on the variation, distribution and evolution of the genus *Partula.* The species inhabiting Moorea. Carnegie Inst. Wash. Publ. 410:1–335.

Damian, R. 1964. Molecular mimicry: Antigen sharing by parasite and host and its consequences. Am. Natur. 98:129–149.

Flor, H. H. 1956. The complementary genic systems of flax and flax rust. Adv. Genet. 8:29–54.

Haldane, J. B. S. 1949. Disease and evolution. La Ricerca Scientifica Suppl. 19:68–76.

Kojima, K. I., and K. Yarbrough. 1967. Frequency-dependent selection at the esterase-6 locus in *Drosophila melanogaster.* Proc. Nat. Acad. Sci. U.S. 57:645–649.

Lewontin, R. C., and J. L. Hubby. 1966. A molecular approach to the study of genic heterozygosity in natural populations. II. Amount of variation and degree of heterozygosity in natural populations of *Drosophila pseudoobscura.* Genetics 54:595–609.

Person, C. 1966. Genetic polymorphism in parasitic systems. Nature 212: 266–267.

Informal Discussion

BLAIR: I agree almost entirely with what Dr. Selander has said, and I congratulate him on a well-rounded presentation. I would like to take issue, however, on two points.

The first is on the emphasis placed on the kind of distribution of allopatric populations wherein two populations come into juxtaposition with essentially no overlap. Such cases are very rare in my experience, and, I think, Dr. Selander had to search hard to find some. They may be more common in birds than other kinds of animals, but even so, I think they are quite rare. The second point at issue concerns the example of the pocket gophers in Colorado. In this case we actually are dealing with three genera, each of which has evolved—as a complex of its own, as a genus or a taxon—a set of adaptive characters that determine quite well where these animals live. To call this competitive exclusion or competitive replacement, I think, is to beg the issue. I feel strongly, for example, that *Cratogeomys* would never occupy the Rocky Mountains whether any *Thomomys* were there or not. We are dealing here with high-level adaptation to particular physiographic and soil conditions, and I think that any kind of competition here is strictly out of the question. In regard to the gophers, I am surprised that Dr. Selander did not cite as an illustration Kennerly's work with two species of *Geomys* where a highway or a small Texas river might be the only barrier between the two populations. I would think that this type of example is very interesting and significant. In studying allopatric populations it seems that two populations either run out of something that they need as they approach one another geographically, so that they actually do not meet, or that they overlap to a considerable degree and interdigitate on the basis of the characters they already possess. I am not saying that there is no reinforcement of isolating mechanisms, and occasionally, then, the opportunity also for displacement of other characters; in general, however, I think Dr. Selander has tended to overlook what one population had to work with before it came into contact with the other population.

SELANDER: In my paper I do cite Kennerly's work, which I think is a fine example; but I had to skip many good examples. From what I have read of Miller's paper and of Vaughan's work on the gophers in Colorado, it seems that there must be some active competitive exclusion going on. For example, Vaughan notes that the borders of ranges shift back and forth as much as a half mile per year and that locally the species have a complex mosaic distribution. Individuals of both species are in the same burrow system and are in physical contact. I do not know enough about *Cratogeomys,* but from what I have read of Miller it seems that *Thomomys talpoides* could occupy the types of soils that *Geomys* is occupying if only *Geomys* were not there. What needs to be done, I suppose, is to remove one of them and then see if the other comes in. Whether or not there is a great deal of competition going on now, it is very impressive to me that no two pocket gophers are together, that is, sympatric. The distribution maps of pocket gophers indicate that they are parapatric.

BLAIR: In the Davis Mountains in Texas, and also in eastern New Mexico, I have seen the very deep burrows of *Cratogeomys* overlain by the very shallow burrows of *Thomomys* in the few places where they do get together. There is no indication whether the two are competing or not, but both are there. The point I want to make is that here are two very different adaptations. One is adapted for a deep burrow and the other for a shallow burrow; so they are able to live together, not because they are reacting with one another but because of something that is characteristic of the particular species.

SELANDER: But there, very locally, they have been able to split the niche, in a way. But where else?

BLAIR: I think the niche was split before they got there.

SHORT: One brief question, Dr. Selander. I think you implied that you could bring ecology into the genetic definition of species. Would you comment on how you would do this, especially in terms of niche? It would seem that you could not really establish the genetically determined spectrum of niches of any single species, because a species cannot be separated from the effects of competitors in its habitats.

SELANDER: Theoretically, I think there is almost as much reason to think of species in terms of ecology as there is to think of them genetically. For practical purposes it would be difficult to define species ecologically, and I do not advocate it.

ALEXANDER: I have a complex of questions about sexual dimorphism in bill length. You first spoke of this as an ecological adaptation, and then you added that it could be sexual dimorphism in regard to sexual selection. I think we might add another possibility: that to change the bill length is always a disadvantage in some groups of species that show exactly the relationships you have indicated between mainlands and islands, and so forth, but that this ecological disadvantage is outweighed by an advantage in terms of sexual selection. An ecological advantage to an individual of changing its bill size would either have to come directly to that individual—that is, enable it to outcompete—or come to its mate. If it is a monogamous bird, where the male does not compete with the female in which he has invested his reproductive effort, the advantage to the female would be an indirect advantage to him. Could it not be possible that in the case of increased population size on islands where there are no congeneric species, the cause-and-effect relationship is the reverse of what you have indicated? In other words, the large population size might increase the sexual selection issue and therefore cause divergence between the sexes or increase the likelihood of it.

SELANDER: That is the most complex question I have ever heard. As to the last part of the question, the situation could be the other way around, certainly. High densities would be expected to increase competition which then would be alleviated by the increasing dimorphism. I will have to talk to you about the first part, though. It seemed too complex for my limited powers at the moment.

ALEXANDER: If I may, I will try rephrasing the question. How do you know whether it is an *ecological* advantage for the island individuals to diverge their bill lengths?

SELANDER: Because I take it on faith that when we talk about advantage it has to be in terms of individuals. The idea of there being advantages for populations makes no sense to me.

ALEXANDER: I meant to contrast ecological advantage with advantage in sexual selection.

JOZEF DE LEY

Molecular Data in Microbial Systematics

The root of the present confusion in bacterial systematics resides in the small size of the organisms, their morphological similarity, and the invisibility of most of their features, usually revealed by physiological, biochemical, and serological tests. With higher organisms, on the contrary, many features can be visually observed.

The division of the class Schizomycetes into the orders Pseudomonadales, Eubacteriales, Beggiatoales, etc., is based mainly on morphology. The further subdivision into families uses morphological and a few physiological criteria. For the lower levels—tribes, genera, and species—physiological and biochemical features are used almost exclusively for differentiation. The total number of features studied down to the species level usually is less than 30. These properties, empirical and arbitrary, were discovered and selected by chance, and there is no guarantee that they comprise a representative choice with which a classification can be built. In addition, these criteria are weighted unequally as some are considered to be more important than others, but the meaning of "importance" has never been adequately specified, and what looks important for one investigator is not important for another investigator, and not necessarily for the bacteria themselves.

The unavoidable result is that bacterial systematics is very unstable, is biased, differs from one school to another, and does not necessarily represent the true degrees of relationship between the organisms. This is illustrated by comparing the three classical textbooks—Bergey's *Manual*, Prévot's *Traité* and Krassilnikov's *Diagnostik*. The classifications in these textbooks are drastically different. Subsequent editions of Bergey's textbook show strikingly how much the classification changed over relatively short periods, in spite of the fact that few new data were added. Quite frequently, the known criteria are merely shuffled into a different arrangement. Therefore, many taxonomists feel that this situation cannot continue and that new approaches are needed. From experience gathered over the last few years it appears that the molecular biological approach is called upon to improve and stabilize the existing microbial systematics.

Molecular applications now in use in bacterial systematics pivot on three centers: the size of the bacterial genomes; the DNA base composition; and the DNA homology.

SIZE OF THE BACTERIAL GENOME AS A TAXONOMIC CRITERION

Much can be learned from some simple considerations that have been made on the size and information content of bacterial chromosomes. The available data are summarized in Table 1. It has been demonstrated with several bacteria and phages that the chromosomal DNA is circular and, very likely, this will prove to be the case with all bacteria. The data in Table 1 represent the molecular weight of one chromosomal DNA molecule. Assuming that no nonsense DNA exists and that one cistron contains about 1,500 nucleotide pairs, one can make a good estimate of the maximal possible number of cistrons in each organism, which for bacteria is of the order of a few thousand. The estimate in Table 1 is quite acceptable because there are at least 1,000 cistrons needed for the manufacture of the different types of proteins alone. Some of the phenotypic features used in classification—for example, the presence of β–galactosidase and other tests for single enzymes—involve only one cistron; others, such as the fermentation of glucose, involve possibly some 20 to 30 cistrons. From other data it can be estimated that the morphology of the bacterial cell is dictated by less than 100 cistrons. Thus, the 30-odd orthodox taxonomic features involve, at most, a few hundred cistrons, or some 10 percent of the genetic

TABLE 1 The size of some bacterial genomes as calculated from data of various investigators. The number of nucleotide pairs per nucleoid was calculated by dividing the molecular weight of DNA per nucleoid by the molecular weight (618) of one nucleotide pair. The estimated number of cistrons was calculated on the assumption that there are some 1,500 nucleotide pairs per cistron.

Organism	Molecular Weight, Dalton	Nucleotide Pairs per Nucleoid	Estimated Number of Cistrons	Reference
Mycoplasma gallisepticum	ca. 0.2×10^9	ca. 0.3×10^6	200	Morowitz *et al.* (1962)
Haemophilus influenzae	0.72×10^9	1.2×10^6	800	Berns and Thomas (1965)
Aerobacter aerogenes	1.2×10^9	1.9×10^6	1,300	Caldwell and Hinshelwood (1950)
Pseudomonas campestris (xanthomonad)	$(2.1 \pm 0.3) \times 10^9$	3.4×10^6	2,300	Park and De Ley (1967)
fluorescens	$(2.5 \pm 0.7) \times 10^9$	4×10^6	2,700	Park and De Ley (1967)
putida	$(2.7 \pm 0.3) \times 10^9$	4.4×10^6	3,000	Park and De Ley (1967)
Bacillus subtilis	1.3×10^9	2.1×10^6	1,400	Dennis and Wake (1966)
	2.4×10^9	3.9×10^6	2,600	Data of De Ley and Park
	$(2–4) \times 10^9$	$(3.4–6.5) \times 10^6$	2,300–4,300	Massie and Zimm (1965)
Escherichia coli	2.8×10^9	4.5×10^6	3,000	Cairns (1963)
	$(3.1 \pm 0.2) \times 10^9$	4.9×10^6	3,300	Park and De Ley (1967)

information contained in the chromosome. So most of the properties of the organisms remain undetected, and it is no wonder that the usual classification results in a grossly distorted picture of the relationships among bacteria.

Numerical (Adansonian) taxonomy already has greatly improved the situation. Usually, from 100 to 150, and sometimes up to 200, features are included. On the reasonable assumption that some five cistrons are responsible for the average phenotypic feature, this method would cover up to 1,000 cistrons, or about one third of the genome. Molecular data and numerical taxonomy are mutually supporting, as we shall see from Figure 8 (page 266). The applications of the numerical method are still open to some improvements. The tendency to include too few features should be discouraged. Sometimes as few as 30 to 50 features are used, and the data are processed by a computer; yet this is still incorrectly called numerical taxonomy. Another weakness is to overemphasize a single aspect—for example, carbohydrate metabolism. The greatest weakness, however, is that numerical taxonomy of bacteria involves too few enzymatic tests. Physiological and biochemical tests rarely tell us anything about the enzymatic mechanisms, and those are the phenotypic expressions of the cistrons. It is hoped that in the future numerical taxonomy will evolve in this direction; it thus could become the direct phenotypic counterpart of molecular taxonomy.

BASE COMPOSITION OF BACTERIAL DNA AS A TAXONOMIC CRITERION

From the determinations of Lee, *et al.* (1956) and of Belozersky and Spirin (1960), it followed that the base composition of bacterial DNA (preferably expressed as molar percent guanine + cytosine, i.e., percent GC) ranges from 25 to 75 percent. The method of determination by paper chromatography is time-consuming and not very precise (mean error about 4 percent). Newer methods by density gradient centrifugation (Schildkraut *et al.*, 1962) and, in particular, the very precise method of thermal denaturation (Marmur and Doty, 1962) opened the way to accurate routine investigations of many strains. To be useful for taxonomy, DNA base composition of a taxon (species, genus, or higher) should be in a rather narrow range and preferably not overlapping from one taxon to another. It was known from the determinations by several authors that the percent GC of several strains of *Escherichia coli* is in the range 50 to 55, and the tabulation by Marmur *et al.* (1963) foreshadowed the concept that organisms from one genus also have related GC percentage values. However, the percent GC range of a taxon was not known at that time, and no taxonomic conclusions were drawn. The percent GC limits of a genus were first established by De Ley and Schell (1963), who showed that all organisms belonging to the genera *Acetobacter* and *Gluconobacter* have a percent GC within the range 59.7 + 4.3 and 60.3 + 3, respectively. The percent GC of about 2,000 different bacteria—belonging to some 120 different genera out of 200 listed in Bergey's *Manual*—is already known. Some of these data have been tabulated (Hill, 1966), and the taxonomic conclusions from them are presented below.

Different strains of the same nomen species have a DNA base composition in a more-or-less narrow range. Twenty-seven strains of *Escherichia coli* are in the range 50 to 55 percent GC; 28 strains of *Agrobacterium tumefaciens* are in the range 60 to 62.5 percent GC; and 14 strains of *Bacillus subtilis* are in the range 42 to 47 percent GC. Other nomen species have a greater range; for example, *Bacillus cereus* (15 strains) from 32 to 40 percent GC, *Bifidobacterium bifidum* (29 strains) from 57 to 64 percent GC, and *Lactobacillus plantarum* (102 strains) from 38 to 46 percent GC. The latter examples show that different strains belonging to the same nomen species may be very diversified genetically.

Within a genus, the GC percentage values of different nomen species frequently lie close together or overlap, so species differentiation on this basis alone is impossible. An example of this is *Rhizobium meliloti,* with a percent GC within the range of *R. leguminosarum* (De Ley and Rassel, 1965); only by numerical methods could this species be identified as a separate group (Graham, 1964), a situation later confirmed by DNA hybridization (G. Heberlein *et al.,* 1967). There appear to be some cases where nomenclatural species might be separated on the basis of their percent GC as in *Pseudomonas* (Mandel, 1966).

Different nomen species, known from morphological, physiological, and other data to be closely related and therefore grouped together in one genus, have related percent GC values. The GC range varies from one genus to another. The available data—those published by several authors and many of those gathered at our laboratory—are compiled in Figures 1–4.* The genus range may be rather

*The compilation summarized in Figures 1–5 includes all published data as well as considerable unpublished data from the author's laboratory that will be published in full elsewhere.

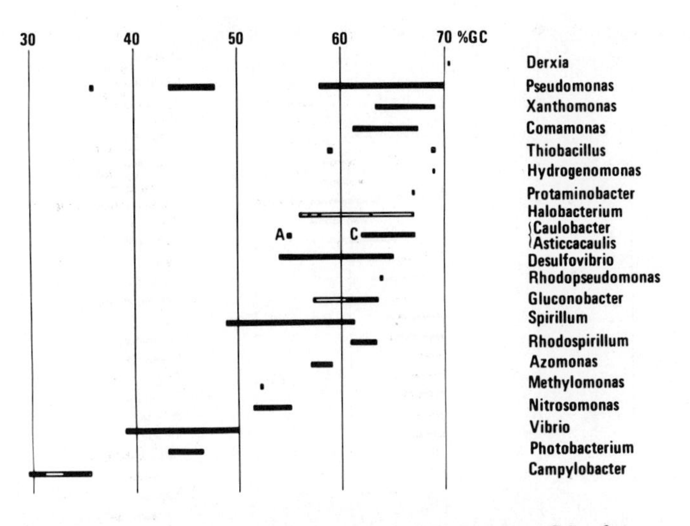

FIGURE 1 DNA base composition, expressed as percent GC, of several genera of Gram-negative, polarly flagellate bacteria. Explanation: Single dot (e.g., *Derxia*) indicates that only one strain of the genus has been studied; solid bars, several or many strains have been used; bars with open spaces, no strains have a GC percentage in the open range shown; and multiple bars (e.g., *Pseudomonas*), strains with percent GC aberrant from the main group that will have to be integrated in other genera.

narrow (a few percent GC in *Azomonas, Arthrobacter, Haemophilus,* etc., up to some 20 percent in *Bacillus* and *Betabacterium*). Future research on DNA homology will have to be done to clarify whether more than one genus is involved in the latter cases.

Some genera appear to extend fragmentarily over a very wide range. This situation is illustrated in Figures 1–4 by, for example, *Spirillum* and some actinomycetes, *Fusobacterium,* and *Flavobacterium.* The exceptional strains are indicative of wrong classification and will have to be removed from the main body of the genus. This is illustrated in the previously chaotic genus *Vibrio.* The redefined genus *Vibrio* is now well-delineated phenotypically (De Ley, 1964; Véron, 1965) and extends from 40 to 50 percent GC. *"Vibrio" cholinicus,* with 57 percent GC, was shown to be a *Desulfovibrio desulfuricans; "Vibrio" tyrogenus, cuneatus, percolans, neocistes, cyclocites,* and *alcaligenes* all have a percentage GC

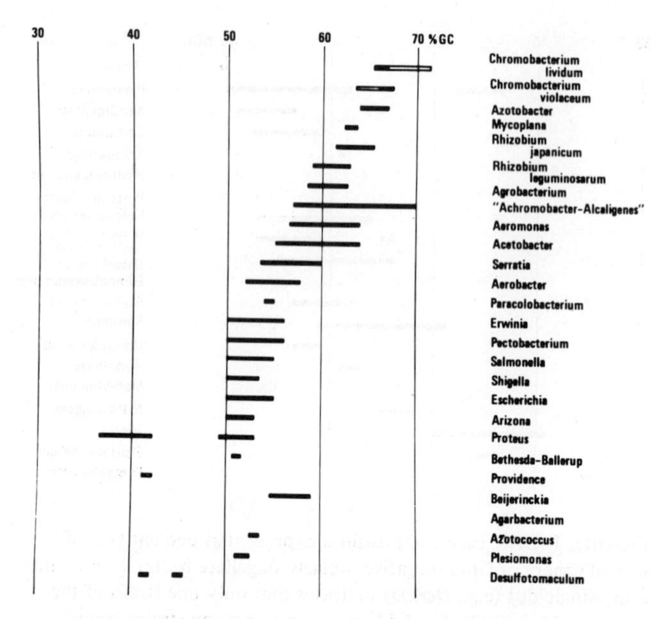

FIGURE 2 DNA base composition, expressed as percent GC, of several genera of Gram-negative, peritrichously flagellated bacteria. The genera of the motile *Achromobacter* and *Alcaligenes,* still poorly defined, are combined here. (For explanation see Figure 1.)

in the range 60 to 66 and are removed to the genera *Pseudomonas* or *Comamonas.* "*Vibrio*" *fetus* and "*V.*" *bubulus* with 30 to 35 percent GC are accommodated in a new genus *Campylobacter.*

Different genera that are known, or suspected, on phenotypic grounds to be related also have similar base compositions. The Enterobacteriaceae, with the possible exception of the low-GC *Proteus* and *Providence,* illustrate this point. Another example is the order Actinomycetales, nearly all members of which have more than 70 percent GC. *Mycobacterium,* with 60 to 70 percent, can be included in this order. *Streptosporangium* and *Thermomonospora* possess a few interesting strains with a GC percentage that is very far removed. These cases will have to be reinvestigated and, if confirmed, will deserve extensive study as examples of evolutionary divergency.

Sueoka (1961) has pointed out that two organisms with a mean difference of 10 or more in percent of GC have only a few DNA

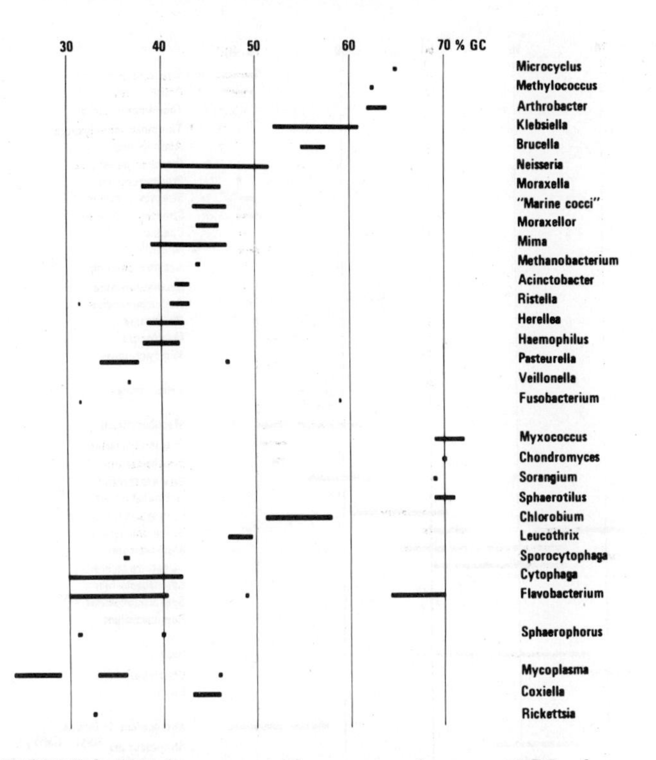

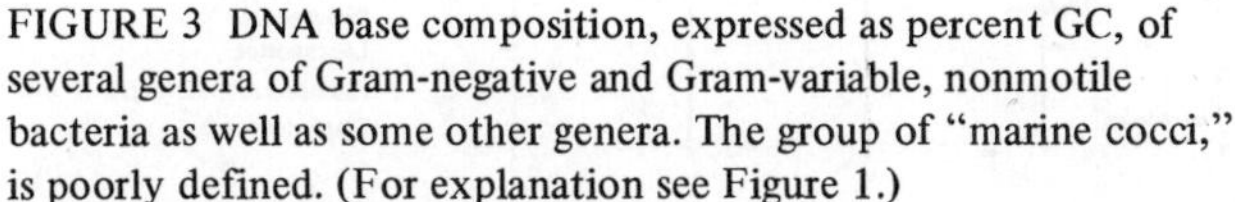
FIGURE 3 DNA base composition, expressed as percent GC, of several genera of Gram-negative and Gram-variable, nonmotile bacteria as well as some other genera. The group of "marine cocci," is poorly defined. (For explanation see Figure 1.)

stretches of the same percentage GC in common. More recent investigations (De Ley, unpublished data) have shown that the distance is somewhat greater and that organisms have to be 16 to 20 percent GC apart to share, at most, 4 percent of their cistrons. This is the molecular basis for the hypothesis that genera such as *Bacillus* and *Betabacterium* may, in the future, have to be split. Other examples can be given: The present genus *Proteus* consists of a group having 36 to 42 percent GC (*P. mirabilis, P. rettgeri,* and *P. vulgaris*) and the *P. morganii* group having about 52 percent GC. It seems nearly certain that both groups, having so few cistrons in common, will have to be separated by being given different generic status. The genus *Pseudomonas* contains, by definition, organisms with 58 to 70 percent GC. There is a small group consisting of organisms that

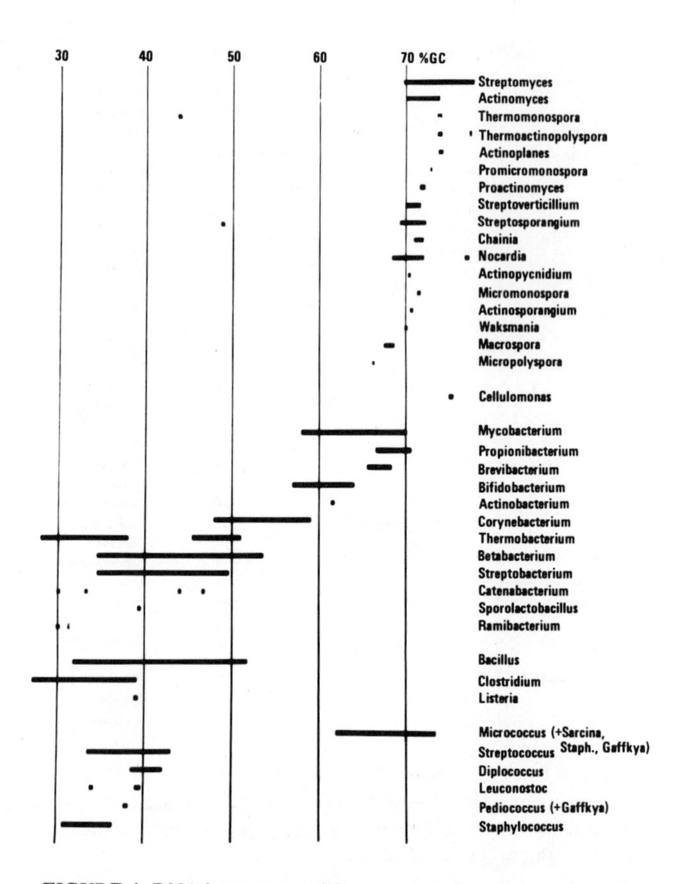

FIGURE 4 DNA base composition, expressed as percent GC, of several genera of Gram-positive bacteria. (For explanation see Figure 1.)

are likewise aerobic, Gram-negative, with polar flagella, but that have about 45 percent GC. Organisms in this group are *"Pseudomonas" rubescens, pavonacea, piscicida, azotogensis, natriegens,* and *putrefaciens.* They cannot belong in the genus *Pseudomonas;* so either they will have to be removed individually to other genera or—if it is shown that they are genetically and phenotypically related—a new genus name will have to be created for them.

These considerations will also have to be taken into account for the supergeneric classification. Figures 1–4 herein, in conjunction with Bergey's *Manual,* show that the validity of several families is highly questionable. For example, Bergey's *Manual* lists the Gram-positive "cocci" together in the family Micrococcaceae. Figure 4 shows that the genera *Streptococcus, Diplococcus, Leuconostoc, Pediococcus,* and *Staphylococcus* might belong in one family (depending on future results on DNA hybridizations), but that *Micrococcus* is so different that it clearly is in another family. It seems likely that in a future reconstruction of bacterial classification families can consist only of genera with related GC values. It is difficult to predict the permissible range, but 15 to 20 percent seems an acceptable estimate.

The GC percentage value of an organism is an average for the complete chromosomal DNA. Two organisms with a different set of cistrons and phenotypic characteristics may very well have identical GC percentage values, as evidenced by many examples in Figures 1–4. Therefore, it cannot be said that two organisms or two genera are related simply because they have the same or a similar percent GC. The relationship can be decided only by DNA hybridization or numerical analysis.

The DNA base composition method is now in its constructive phase, wherein the general limits are being laid down. Because of considerable overlapping of the genera, it is not possible to construct a bacterial classification on GC percentage values alone. Phenotypic data also are required. It seems preferable to use numerically studied groups for determinations of percent GC. Having a collection of new strains with similar percentages of GC but not knowing their phenotypic features, the molecular taxonomist cannot judge their taxonomic position, or whether one or more genera are involved; but if a certain strain is very different in percent GC from others in given genus, he can veto the inclusion of the strain in that group. The exclusion of low-GC *Pseudomonas*-like organisms from *Pseudomonas* proper already has been cited. Another example is the motile *Achromobacter liquefaciens* (Tulecke *et al.,* 1965) which has 44 percent GC. Many motile organisms in the genus *Achromobacter* were found in our laboratory to be in the range 57 to 70 percent GC. Thus the organisms called *A. liquefaciens* cannot be in the genus *Achromobacter.*

In the not-too-distant future the GC percentage values of nearly all bacterial genera will be known; then there will be a reshifting of organisms into their proper taxonomic positions, and the result will be a considerable clarification of the taxonomy. The data for

DNA base composition as indicated in Figures 1–4 will then be completed and will become the cornerstone of a much-improved taxonomy.

DNA base composition can also be used for rapid identification of bacterial genera. In our laboratory we proceed in the following way. We first establish the cell morphology and motility by phase contrast microscopy. Nonmotile cells also may be variants of flagellated organisms. The same slide is then used for the Gram stain. Flagella staining is done on another slide. In many cases the type of flagellation can be clearly established; for doubtful cases, electron microscopy is used. A few grams of cells then are grown on a suitably rich medium, pure DNA is prepared, and the percent GC is calculated from thermal denaturation. This value is then compared with the data in Figures 1–4. The number of possible genera can now be narrowed down to relatively few; all other genera shown on these figures are thereby excluded. For example, a Gram-negative, polarly flagellated, rod-like organism with 60 percent GC can be *Pseudomonas, Halobacterium, Desulfovibrio, Gluconobacter, Spirillum,* and, perhaps, *Rhodospirillum, Caulobacter,* or *Azomonas.* These genera are sufficiently different that a quick conclusion can be reached after a few tests. Because not all genera have been investigated and the figures are therefore not yet complete, in the present state of our knowledge it is quite possible that the properties of an unknown strain do not fit any of the above-mentioned genera. Obviously, then, one is thrown back on the uncertainties of the orthodox identification and classification. It is clear that in the near future, when all genera have been included in these figures, bacterial identification will have been considerably simplified and will be on a reliable and solid basis.

DNA base composition of organisms other than bacteria may be useful. The data available from published literature are graphically summarized in Figure 5. Although we are not concerned here with the vertebrates, invertebrates, and Embryophyta, it seems possible that molecular data may be useful in classification. Definitely, the situation is hopeful for the Thallophyta and Protozoa, where the GC value extends over nearly 40 percent in both groups. Too few data are available to reach the same wealth of conclusions as is possible for the bacteria, but Figure 5 clearly demonstrates that a rich taxonomic harvest awaits the molecularly inclined algologist, protozoologist, and mycologist.

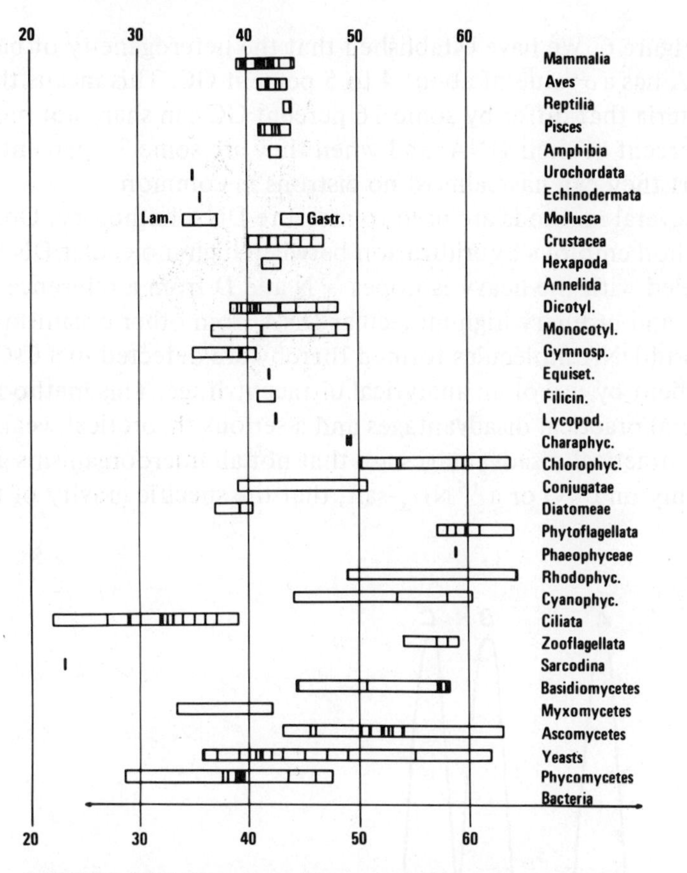

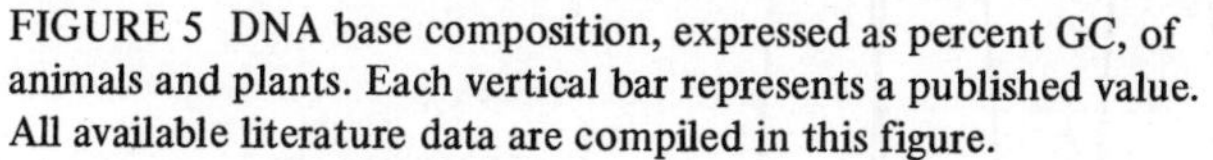

FIGURE 5 DNA base composition, expressed as percent GC, of animals and plants. Each vertical bar represents a published value. All available literature data are compiled in this figure.

DNA HOMOLOGY AS A TAXONOMIC CRITERION

In theory, a much more direct and quantitative measure of relatedness would be the number of genes or cistrons shared by a group of organisms. In practice, such determinations are not yet feasible; instead, measurements of the fraction of chromosomal DNA that has a similar nucleotide sequence can be used.

On theoretical grounds one can calculate the maximal possible DNA homology between two organisms if their percentage of GC, the GC heterogeneity, and the molecular weight of the chromosomal DNA are known. This is represented for a few simple cases in Figure 6. We have established that the heterogeneity of bacterial DNA has a σ value of about 4 to 5 percent GC. This means that two bacteria that differ by some 16 percent GC can share not more than 4 percent of their DNA, and when they are some 25 percent GC apart they can have almost no cistrons in common.

Several methods are used to measure DNA homology. One method employs hybridization between high-molecular DNA, labeled with the heavy isotopes ^{15}N and D from a reference organism, and ordinary high-molecular DNA from other organisms; the hybrid DNA molecules formed thereby are detected in a CsCl gradient by use of an analytical ultracentrifuge. This method has several practical disadvantages and a serious theoretical weakness. The practical disadvantages are that not all microorganisms grow readily on D_2O or a $^{15}NH_4$-salt, that the specific gravity of the

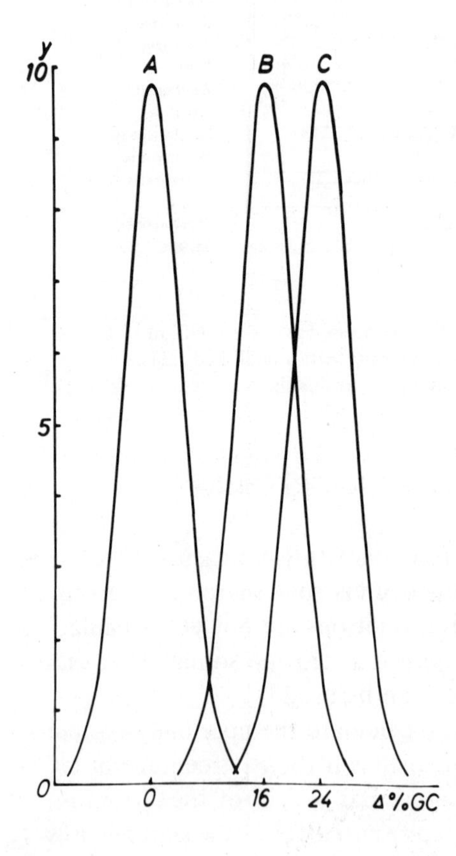

FIGURE 6 Theoretical maximal possible DNA homology between three organisms (*A*, *B*, and *C*) deduced from the compositional distribution of the GC percentage values within the chromosomal DNA. The *x*-axis represents the distance in percent GC between the DNA of the organisms; the *y*-axis represents the frequency of occurrence of regions with a certain percent GC within the molecule. The pairs *B-C*, *A-B*, and *A-C* are, respectively, 8, 16, and 24 percent apart. The σ value is 4 percent GC. At most, the pair *B-C* can share 32 percent of their nucleotide sequences; *A-B*, 4 percent; and *A-C*, 0.3 percent.

labeled DNA is frequently too low to detect the hybrid molecules, and that due to its high costs, delicate techniques, and slow results, analytical ultracentrifugation is not likely to become popular with microbial taxonomists. The theoretical weakness is that quantitative results cannot always be realized because small imperfections in matching or inversions of nucleotide sequences in the high-molecular DNA strands prevent complete hybridizations. With this method, Schildkraut *et al.* (1961) concluded that the DNA homology between different strains of *Escherichia coli* is essentially complete. They also demonstrated substantial homology between *Bacillus subtilis* and *B. natto* and between *Escherichia coli* and *Shigella dysenteriae.* However, the failure to hybridize between *E. coli* and *Salmonella* is an illustration of the theoretical weakness mentioned above. An unspecified degree of homology was detected between *E. coli* and *E. freundii.* In our laboratory we detected homology within each of the two genera *Acetobacter* (De Ley and Friedman, 1964) and *Xanthomonas* (Friedman and De Ley, 1965).

A second method of measuring DNA homology was developed by McCarthy and Bolton (1963) and their collaborators. In essence ^{14}C- or ^{32}P-labeled, sheared, denatured DNA from one or more reference strains is mixed with high-molecular ordinary DNA fixed in agar from the same or a number of other organisms. The ratio 100 x ^{14}C-DNA fragments bound to heterologous DNA/^{14}C-fragments bound to homologous DNA represents the percent DNA homology. This method, which is much easier and more reliable (in particular, the competitive version) than the previous one, should become quite useful. It is also more quantitative, although one might expect it to give homology values that are too high because DNA fragments bound by their matching part may still contain regions of unbound, unequal nucleotide sequence. For closely related organisms this error appears to be negligible, as was shown in our laboratory by treatment with phosphodiesterase (De Ley *et al.*, 1966). On the other hand, at the generic level DNA homology values tend to underestimate the relationship (see below). This method has already been applied to several groups of bacteria. McCarthy and Bolton (1963) showed that *Escherichia coli* DNA is 70 percent homologous with *Shigella,* some 50 percent with *Aerobacter,* 25 percent with *Klebsiella,* 14 percent with *Proteus vulgaris,* and 7 percent with *Serratia marcescens.* The ^{14}C-DNA from *Aerobacter* is some 50 percent homologous with *Escherichia, Salmonella,* and *Shigella* and to a much smaller extent with other genera of the Enterobacteriaceae. Although this family will have to be studied more thoroughly, the *Escherichia–Shigella* community emerges as a highly similar group, and it may in the future very well be reorganized within a single genus.

Extensive DNA homology determinations for taxonomic purposes are carried out in our laboratory. I will summarize briefly the conclusions reached as a result of our work so far. The genus *Pseudomonas* is a large one, extending from 58 to 70 percent GC, and the lower DNA homology boundary is about 50 percent. These appear to be the boundaries of the genus. Phenotypically aberrant cases such as *Pseudomonas iodinum, P. atlantica,* and *P. diminuta* fall outside the boundary. The low-GC organisms such as *"P." rubescens,* and *"P." pavonacea,* display less than 5 percent DNA homology with the main group and definitely have to be removed from the genus *Pseudomonas* (De Ley *et al.*, 1966).

The genus *Xanthomonas* contains 60-odd nomen species, of which about 28 were used for DNA hybridizations. It was found that all except two hybridize over 75 percent and many of them are over 90 percent homologous with a centrally located strain, *X. pelargonii.* In view of this high-DNA homology, it seemed unjustified to keep that many separate species names; the more so as this species differentiation is based almost solely on host specificity. Therefore, we proposed (De Ley *et al.*, 1966) to gather all xanthomonads within one genospecies with the epithet "campestris." Extensive numerical analysis by Lelliott (1967) has since corroborated this conclusion.

Cross-hybridizations between xanthomonads and pseudomonads revealed that the former fit within the latter. There is no genetic reason to keep a separate genus *Xanthomonas,* and all xanthomonads are merely *Pseudomonas campestris.* It should be recalled that the only reason for creating the genus *Xanthomonas* was the desire to group together all yellow, necrotizing, phytopathogenic pseudomonads, and that only phenotypic arguments were involved. Our results demonstrate that this grouping can be done correctly at the species level, not at the genus level.

Also, the family Azotobacteriaceae needs some rearrangement. According to our percent GC and DNA homology studies, this family appears to consist of five groups: peritrichous oval cells without microcysts (*Azotococcus agilis*); peritrichous, usually microcyst-forming (*Azotobacter vinelandii, A. chroococcum*, and *A. beijerinckii*); peritrichous, acidophilic, mostly tropical (*Beijerinckia*); polarly multitrichous (*Azomonas insignis* and *A. macrocytogenes*); and polarly flagellated rods (*Derxia*).

Also in the family Rhizobiaceae there are some surprises (Heberlein *et al.*, 1967). All strains of *Agrobacterium tumefaciens* and *A. radiobacter* group together with a DNA homology of over 70 percent. They should be considered as one genospecies. *A. rubi* also falls within this genospecies, supporting the view that its phenotypic species status is not justified. *A. rhizogenes* shows a greater homology with the *Rhizobium* strains than with the *tumefaciens–radiobacter–rubi* group. The agrobacteria and the peritrichous rhizobia (*Rhizobium leguminosarum* and *R. meliloti*) all have a DNA homology of over 50 percent. If one accepts the same standards as for *Pseudomonas*, they should all be gathered into one genus. The subpolarly flagellated rhizobia *R. japonicum* hybridize to the extent of only some 42 percent. Very likely they will constitute a separate genus in the future. *Chromobacterium* is as little related to the rhizobia and agrobacteria as is, for example, *Pseudomonas* or *Acetobacter;* thus, it cannot constitute one family with the former organisms, as advocated in Bergey's *Manual.* Thus, the classification of the gall-, nodule-, and rootlet-forming organisms is one genus, *Rhizobium*, with four or five species: *radiobacter* (and its tumorigenic variety *tumefaciens*), *rhizogenes, leguminosarum, meliloti,* and *japonicum* (the latter is subject to a possible future transfer to a new genus).

Ritter and Gerloff (1966) have shown that *Pasteurella* is heterogeneous, as already indicated by its percentage of GC (see Figure 3). *Pasteurella novicida* is about 85 percent homologous with *P. tularensis*, and *P. pestis* is about 85 percent homologous with *P. pseudotuberculosis*, but the two pairs are not related to each other; therefore, a division at the generic level is necessary. The former two organisms might be aptly renamed *Franciscella* and the latter *Yersinia.* Additionally, the latter genus is some 22 percent homologous with *Escherichia* (the former is not) and might be a member of the Enterobacteriaceae. To place *Yersinia* in this family would be in line with the type of fermentation and the

45 percent GC value shown by *pestis* and *pseudotuberculosis*.

The DNA homology method allowed a search for the origin of *Mycoplasma.* DNA from *Haemophilus gallinarum* did not bind with DNA from *Mycoplasma gallinarum* and *M. gallisepticum*, showing that PPLO cannot be considered as stable *L*-forms of the former organisms (Rogul, *et al.*, 1965). Likewise, lack of DNA homology between *Streptococcus* MG and *Mycoplasma pneumoniae* (the Eaton agent) showed that there is no genetic relationship between the two organisms (McGee *et al.*, 1965).

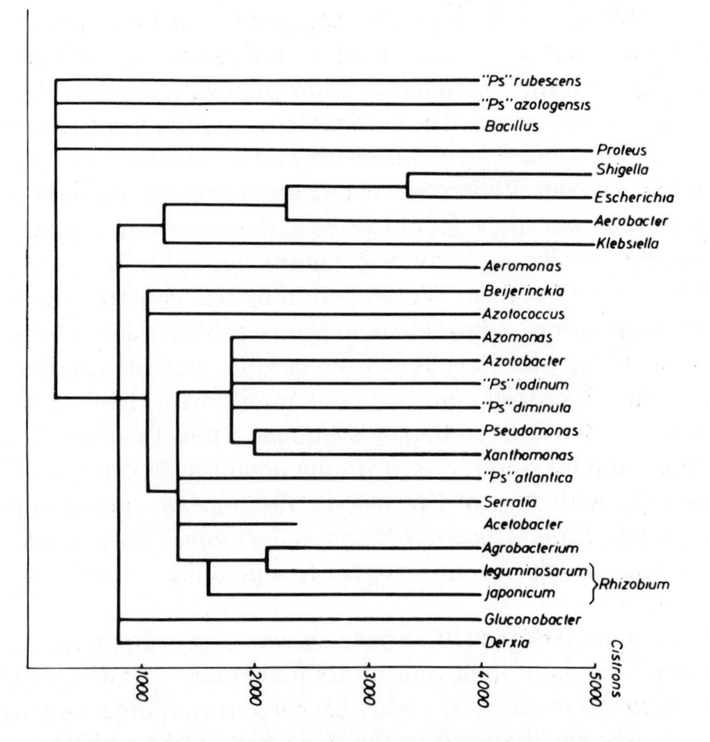

FIGURE 7 DNA homology between several bacterial genera. Data for the Enterobacteriaceae from McCarthy and Bolton (1963); all other data obtained in the author's laboratory. Not all genera have been hybridized with each of the others, the reference strains being *Bacillus subtilis, Escherichia coli, azomonas macrocytogenes, Pseudomonas putida* and *P. fluorescens, Agrobacterium tumefaciens, Rhizobium leguminosarum,* and *Acetobacter liquefaciens.* The molecular weight, expressed as cistrons, is taken from Table 1. For all other genera the molecular weight is assumed to be roughly equal to that of *Pseudomonas* (DeLey and Park, 1966).

Intergeneric hybridizations provide some further interesting insights. Our present knowledge is summarized in Figure 7. Although the homology values may be an approximation only, Figure 7 shows that there is a considerable relationship between the genera of Gram-negative bacteria, irrespective of their phenotypic divergencies. There have been practically no hybridizations carried out with Gram-positive organisms. This tends to show that many Gram-negative bacteria are evolutionarily still interrelated, in spite of the fact that they are supposed to have originated some three or four billion years ago. This may mean either that the portions common to the chromosomes of several bacteria have been little changed during evolution and have been protected and preserved by selection or that presently existing bacteria branched off more recently and are in no way representative of the original Precambrian bacterial flora.

None of the genera (except *Escherichia* and *Shigella*) hybridize by more than 50 percent. From the available data on percentage of GC and DNA homology it follows that the present classification into families and orders will have to be modified considerably. Since the bacterial genome is about 1,000 times smaller than that from plants and animals, it is questionable whether the same taxon levels for classification can be used at all.

A third method for measuring homology is DNA–RNA hybridization. RNA molecules interacting with DNA indicate phenotypic similarities, while cross-reacting DNA molecules reveal genetic similarities. When the percentage of DNA homology is compared with the percentage of numerical similarity of the same organisms (Figure 8) it is found that both values correspond very well (from 60 to 100 percent) within the limits of error. DNA homology is rarely higher than taximetric similarity, indicating that there are no, or very few, unexpressed genes in the genome. The deflection of the experimental curve from the theoretical one below 60 percent is due to the limited number of criteria in numerical analysis and to heterologous nucleotide sequences for cistrons that, phenotypically, are still similar; this is particularly true for evolutionarily remote organisms.

Genetic interrelations among mycoplasmas were studied by the DNA:RNA method. Several strains of *Mycoplasma hominis* type 1 showed a relatedness of at least 30 percent, with an average of

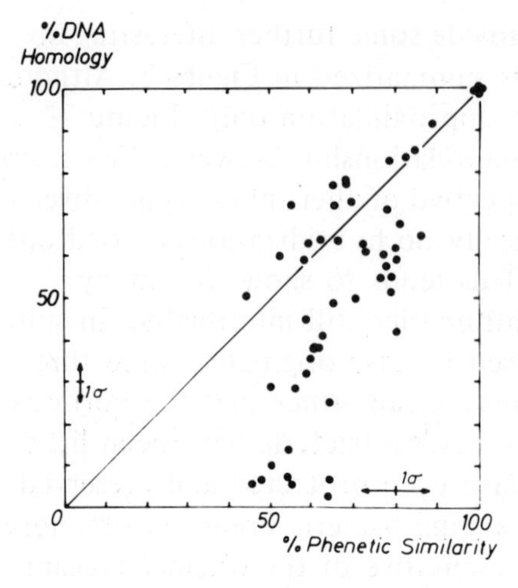

FIGURE 8 Congruence between DNA homology and phenetic similarity. The data concern strains from *Pseudomonas, Xanthomonas,* Enterobacteriaceae, *Agrobacterium, Rhizobium, Chromobacterium,* and *Bacillus.* All DNA homology data are from the author's laboratory. The phenetic data concern the same organisms, or identical groups, as published in the literature. The arrows represent roughly the standard deviation. (Modified from a work by De Ley to be published elsewhere.)

64 percent. There is practically no genetic relatedness (less than 3 percent) with *Mycoplasma hominis* type 2, *M. salivarium, M. orale, M. fermentans, M. pneumoniae, M. laidlawii,* and *Escherichia coli.* (Reich *et al.*, 1966; Somerson *et al.*, 1966). Unexpected high relatedness between the porcine *Mycoplasma hyorhinis* and two tissue-culture isolates was detected (Somerson *et al.*, 1966). The interspecies heterogeneity in general is very high. *M. salivarium, M. fermentans, M. orale* types 1 and 2, *M. pneumoniae* and *M. hominis* types 1 and 2 appear to share very few nucleotide sequences (Reich *et al.*, 1966). This is not surprising since these organisms have a small genome and their percent GC extends over a wide range.

A similar approach was followed with the streptococci (Weissman *et al.*, 1966). The Lancefield groups A and C were most interrelated (about 35 percent). Relationship with the other groups (F and H) and with *Streptococcus faecalis* was less than 10 percent. Relatedness between strains of the Lancefield group A was at least 42 percent. This closely parallels the results obtained with serological techniques. A distinct relatedness exists between *Diplococcus pneumoniae* and the Lancefield groups A and H.

REFERENCES

Belozersky, A. N., and A. S. Spirin. 1960. Chemistry of the nucleic acids of micro-organisms, p. 147–185 *In* E. Chargaff and J. N. Davidson, The nucleic acids. Vol. 3. Academic Press, New York.

Berns, K. I., and C. A. Thomas. 1965. Isolation of high molecular weight DNA from *Haemophilus influenzae.* J. Mol. Biol. 11:476–490.

Cairns, J. 1963. The chromosome of *Escherichia coli.* Cold Spring Harbor Symp. Quant. Biol. 28:43–45.

Caldwell, P. J., and C. Hinshelwood. 1950. Nucleic acid content of *Bacillus lactis aerogenes.* J. Chem. Soc. 1950:1415–1418.

De Ley, J. 1964. *Pseudomonas* and related genera. Ann. Rev. Microbiol. 18:17–46.

De Ley, J., and S. Friedman. 1964. Deoxyribonucleic acid hybrids of acetic acid bacteria. J. Bacteriol. 88:937–945.

De Ley, J., and I. W. Park. 1966. Molecular biological taxonomy of some free-living nitrogen-fixing bacteria. Antonie v. Leeuwenhoek J. Microbiol. 32:6–16.

De Ley, J., I. W. Park, R. Tijtgat, and J. Van Ermengem. 1966. DNA homology and taxonomy of *Pseudomonas* and *Xanthomonas.* J. Gen. Microbiol. 42:43–56.

De Ley, J., and A. Rassel. 1965. DNA base composition, flagellation and taxonomy of the genus *Rhizobium.* J. Gen. Microbiol. 41:85–91.

De Ley, J., and J. Schell. 1963. Deoxyribonucleic acid base composition of acetic acid bacteria. J. Gen. Microbiol. 33:243–253.

Dennis, E. S., and R. G. Wake. 1966. Autoradiography of the *Bacillus subtilis* chromosome. J. Mol. Biol. 15:435–439.

Friedman, S., and J. De Ley. 1965. "Genetic species" concept in *Xanthomonas.* J. Bacteriol. 89:95–100.

Graham, P. H. 1964. The application of computer techniques to the taxonomy of the root-nodule bacteria of legumes. J. Gen. Microbiol. 35:511-517.

Heberlein, G., J. De Ley, and R. Tijtgat. 1967. Deoxyribonucleic acid homology and taxonomy of *Agrobacterium, Rhizobium,* and *Chromobacterium.* J. Bacteriol. 94:116–124.

Hill, L. R. 1966. An index to deoxyribonucleic acid base compositions of bacterial species. J. Gen. Microbiol. 44:419–437.

Lee, K. Y., R. Wahl, and E. Barbu. 1956. Contenu en bases puriques et pyrimidiques des DNA des bactéries. Ann. Inst. Pasteur 91:212–224.

Lelliott, R. A. 1967. Taxonomy and determination of phytopathogenic Pseudomonadales. Abstr. II Internat. Conf. Phytopathogenic Bacteria, Lisbon.

Mandel, M. 1966. Deoxyribonucleic acid base composition in the genus *Pseudomonas.* J. Gen. Microbiol. 43:273–292.

Marmur, J., and P. Doty. 1962. Determination of the base composition of deoxyribonucleic acid from its thermal denaturation temperature. J. Mol. Biol. 5:109–118.

Marmur, J., S. Falkow, and M. Mandel. 1963. New approaches to bacterial taxonomy. Ann. Rev. Microbiol. 17:329–372.

Massie, H. R., and B. H. Zimm. 1965. Molecular weight of the DNA in the chromosomes of *Escherichia coli* and *Bacillus subtilis.* Proc. Nat. Acad. Sci. U.S. 54:1636–1641.

McCarthy, B. J., and E. T. Bolton. 1963. An approach to the measurement of genetic relatedness among organisms. Proc. Nat. Acad. Sci. U.S. 50:156–162.

McGee, Z. A., M. Rogul, S. Falkow, and R. G. Wittler. 1965. The relationship of *Mycoplasma pneumoniae* (Eaton agent) to *Streptococcus* MG: Application of genetic tests to determine relatedness of L-forms and PPLO to bacteria. Proc. Nat. Acad. Sci. U.S. 54:457–461.

Morowitz, H. J., M. E. Tourtelotte, W. R. Guild, E. Castro, C. Woese, and R. C. Cleverdon. 1962. The chemical composition and submicroscopic morphology of *Mycoplasma gallisepticum,* avian PPLO 5969. J. Mol. Biol. 4:93–103.

Park, I. W., and J. De Ley. 1967. Ancestral remnants in deoxyribonucleic acids from *Pseudomonas* and *Xanthomonas.* Antonie v. Leeuwenhoek J. Microbiol. 33:1–16.

Reich, P. R., N. L. Somerson, C. J. Hybner, R. M. Chanock, and S. M. Weissman. 1966. Genetic differentiation by nucleic acid homology. I. Relationships amongst *Mycoplasma* species of man. J. Bacteriol. 92:302–310.

Ritter, D. B., and R. K. Gerloff. 1966. Deoxyribonucleic acid hybridization among some species of the genus *Pasteurella.* J. Bacteriol. 92:1838–1839.

Rogul, M., Z. A. McGee, R. G. Wittler, and S. Falkow. 1965. Nucleic acid homologies of selected bacteria, L forms and *Mycoplasma* species. J. Bacteriol. 90:1200–1204.

Schildkraut, C. L., J. Marmur, and P. Doty. 1961. The formation of hybrid DNA molecules and their use in studies of DNA homologies. J. Mol. Biol. 3:595–617.

Schildkraut, C. L., J. Marmur, and P. Doty. 1962. Determination of the base composition of deoxyribonucleic acid from its buoyant density in CsCl. J. Mol. Biol. 4:430–443.

Somerson, N. L., P. R. Reich, B. E. Walls, R. M. Chanock, and S. M. Weissman. 1966. Genetic differentiation by nucleic acid homology. II. Genotypic variations within two *Mycoplasma* species. J. Bacteriol. 92:311–317.

Sueoka, N. 1961. Variation and heterogeneity of base composition of deoxyribonucleic acids; a compilation of old and new data. J. Mol. Biol. 3:31–40.

Tulecke, W., S. W. Orenski, R. Taggart, and L. Colavito. 1965. Isolation of an organism resembling *Achromobacter liquefaciens.* J. Bacteriol. 89:905–906.

Véron, M. 1965. La position taxonomique de *Vibrio et* des certaines bactéries comparables. C. R. Acad. Sci. Paris 261:5243–5246.

Weissman, S. M., P. R. Reich, N. L. Somerson, and R. M. Cole. 1966. Genetic differentiation by nucleic acid homology. IV. Relationships among Lancefield groups and serotypes of Streptococci. J. Bacteriol. 92:1372–1377.

Discussion

Manley Mandel

Professor De Ley has stated quite well the case for the inclusion of molecular data and computer-assisted correlates in the development of microbial systematics. Ravin will describe the additional weight that evidences of genetic recombination add to our attempts to deduce the degrees of relatedness among microbes. I would hasten to add my own acknowledgment to this general area of agreement that the more reliable data of different types included in our evaluations of taxonomic relations, so much the better.

Rather than appear to disagree completely with Professor De Ley's analysis of the root of the present confusion in bacterial systematics, I would add to his list of perturbations. This list would begin with the assertion that the main concerns of the microbial systematists have been utilitarian. The nomenclatural and classificational problems have been constructed from the pragmatic and empirical desiderata of identification. The imposition of this requirement for specific identification within the bounds of the Linnaean system of binomial nomenclature has led to the erection of classes, and classes of classes, whose constructions are repeatedly called into question.

Van Niel (1946) was among the first in modern times to question seriously the application of the binomial concept to the bacteria. His objections were valid two decades ago, and we may profitably ask today whether they are still tenable. There are several questions that require resolute answers. Does the species concept apply to bacteria? Or as Ravin (1963) has put it, can we define a genospecies? Do these kinds of things exist in nature so that they may be ordered into precise nomenclatural species, and these species into meaningful suprataxa? Next on my list and further complicating our attempts at classification have been the "dearth of lumpers and plethora of splitters" finding occupation in the smog of bacterial classification and often decried by the late A. T. Henrici. Unfortunately, much of this splitting and relumping has been accompanied by some poor bacteriology and errant scholarship. But all is not quite hopeless. The general assorting of individual isolates of bacteria into nomenclatural bundles and consideration regarding the relationships between these bundles have often been made with great acumen. We can, and do, subjectively recognize the over-all similarities between the individuals comprising the family Enterobacteriaceae, and molecular and genetic data and Adansonian analyses of phenotypic traits generally have confirmed these relationships (Colwell and Mandel, 1964). The genus *Bacillus* has been extensively examined by means of these new approaches (Marmur *et al.*, 1963), and these new results confirm our respect for the expertise and judgment of Nathan Smith in his assessment of the relations within the aerobic spore-forming bacilli (Smith *et al.*, 1952). And Smith had no information of GC contents, DNA homologies, or interspecific transformations; his assessments were based upon almost a lifetime of experience with the organisms. In short, there is no substitute for extensive and careful observation of a group of organisms in providing the data for considered delineation of the classes.

This returns us to theory. Can the isolates of bacteria be grouped into definitive primary and secondary classes based upon evidences of evolutionary descent? In the absence of a paleontology we shall have to rely upon molecules as documents of evolutionary history (Zuckerkandl and Pauling, 1965) and upon the extent of homology between polynucleotide sequences of increasing lengths as evidences of the degree of equisemantic contents in the genomes being compared (Marmur *et al.*, 1963).

As these homologies approach 100 percent, so then does the isology of information content and arrangement necessary for unit classification. Where genetic exchange and the opportunity for gene recombination exist, similar and complementary definitions of homology can be ascertained. The genetic exchanges have the further advantage of defining the precise regions of the genomes that are identical, near-identical, and nonidentical within the cistron being examined and of doing so with respect to the neighboring genetic material. The advantages of these measurements are obvious in those cases where adequate genetic systems are available. In the absence of such, molecular hybridization tests alone will have to do, supplementing our best information on the phenotypic expressions of the genotype.

It may seem that I am belaboring the obvious and avoiding an attempt at answering the question of whether particular genospecies of bacteria exist. The reason for my obvious reluctance resides in the apparent indeterminacy of some of the data that have been quoted. I would like to take the time to discuss some technical points. If there is, indeed, a group of individuals that can be equated with a real thing that we can term a species, we might expect these individuals to share certain properties within the narrow limits permitted by evolutionary drift. The first requirement is that the individual representatives have substantially equal genetic content, which implies: (a) equivalent amounts of DNA per haploid chromosome; (b) substantially indistinguishable mean GC content in the total DNA, with uniform distributions of molecules of equal GC content in the population of shared molecules of equal average lengths derived from the unit DNA molecule, or molecules, composing the genomes being compared; (c) a high degree of homology between the DNA molecules evidenced in hybridization trials where the lengths compared are of cistron length and longer, under conditions optimal for the formation of hydrogen-bonded lengths comparable to those found in the native molecules; and (d) that phenotypic similarities, as evidenced by particular enzymatic properties, are the consequence of the presence of proteins of substantially equal lengths and amino acid sequences. Additional properties in common may be demanded, but let us review the difficulties in obtaining the data necessary to establish the points required above.

The amount of DNA per cell is a simple matter for precise determination. In the case of nongerminating bacterial endospores, the amount per haploid cell can be determined reliably. In the case of vegetative cells, the mean number of nucleoids per cell and the mean number of replicating points and their distributions on the replicating molecules provide a degree of uncertainty in the measurements that may exceed the limits of precision demanded. The direct visualization of the lengths of complete DNA molecules as developed by Kleinschmidt and his co-workers (Kleinschmidt *et al.*, 1962) should obviate this problem, but instead it provokes a more serious one. The distribution of contour lengths in a population varies to a greater degree than does the distribution of measurements of a single molecule; and the course of this discrepancy has not yet been traced (Inman, 1967).

With regard to variations in GC content, Professor De Ley has detailed ranges of values determined for representatives of a given species. Do these representatives indeed have sufficient differences in GC content to constitute a spectrum about a central representative value? Or do experimental errors involving the techniques for measuring GC contents account for this resemblance? I hold the latter view. Undoubtedly, part of the error involved is due to the practice of comparing data generated by different techniques and in different laboratories. The remainder of the error is due to the extent of the errors involved in the determinations themselves. For example, the range of 50 to 55 percent for various strains of *Escherichia coli* is not borne out when the melting temperatures of the DNA or the buoyant densities in CsCl are compared for various authentic strains of *E. coli* (Mandel and Rownd, 1964). The variation here does not exceed that encountered when any one specimen is subjected to repeated measurement. Authentic strains of *Bacillus subtilis* likewise have indistinguishable GC contents in their DNA (the variation between 42 and 47 percent GC is in the literature, not the bacteria). Gasser and I re-examined the strains of *Bifidobacterium bifidum* found to have 57 to 64 percent GC in the DNA by chromatographic techniques, and the CsCl buoyant densities were discovered not to be significantly different (Gasser and Mandel, 1968).

In brief, where the identification of strains of a nomen species has been good and the analyses reproducible, there is no indication that the mean GC contents or the distribution range about the mean differs sufficiently between isolates (strains) to be detectable by the techniques at our disposal. Nor are we convinced that base compositional changes of a magnitude sufficient to be detected as differences in mean nucleotide composition have occurred as abrupt mutational events, despite occasional claims to the contrary.

The third technical problem to which I allude has been discussed at length recently by B. J. McCarthy in his Eli Lilly Award Lecture (McCarthy, 1967). In brief, I would say that one must be exceedingly cautious about estimating macromolecular homologies by either direct-binding or competition experiments. The lengths of the interacting nucleotide runs determine the specificity of the binding being measured. At low temperatures of annealment (for a given ionic environment), large amounts of "genetically nonspecific" interactions can and do occur. As the hybridization conditions approach an optimum, the nonspecific interactions are minimized and the formed products may display the hydrogen bonding properties of the native molecules. (This is evidenced by the elution profile of the single-stranded material from DNA membranes, hydroxylapatite, or agar gels as a function of temperature.) For example, if one measures the binding of radioactive fragments of single-stranded DNA's to immobilized high-molecular-weight, single-stranded DNA where the hybrid formation is occurring in 0.39 *M* Na^+ at different temperatures, the ratio of heterologous to homologous interactions is high at the lower temperatures and becomes minimal at a temperature between 23°C and 25°C below the Tm calculated in 0.195 *M* Na^+. This is the point at which the product elutes with the characteristic of the "well-bonded" native molecule. For DNA's of about 65 percent GC content, the temperature at which specific hybrids can be formed is closer to 70°C than to 60°C. The latter temperature is ideal for hybrid formation at this ionic strength for DNA's of the base composition of *Bacillus subtilis* or nuclear DNA of vertebrates. If rhizobial or pseudomonad DNA's, for example, are compared by hybridizations at this temperature, then a high degree of association but of false homology will be displayed with samples of DNA of heterologous sequence.

To summarize, then, before homology percentage measurements can be confidently accepted, control experiments on the nature of the hybrid products are required, and these are particularly necessary and must be more detailed when the base compositions of the two DNA's being compared differ by a few percent or more. I see no evidence that suggests that the calculations of Sueoka were incorrect: when two bacteria have DNA's that differ by 10 percent in their mean base compositions, the likelihood of their sharing "DNA molecules," of cistron length, of common nucleotide composition is very low (Sueoka, 1961). With increasing evidence for universality in the genetic code and in the processes of transcription and translation of genetic information, and in the absence of evidence for extensive conservation of "nonsense genes or DNA," we may rely upon good data for differences in percentage of GC and less than complete homology in hybrid formation as species exclusion guides in the Protista.

The fourth point concerns the phenotypic measurements commonly used in our biochemical descriptions of bacteria. Adansonian analysis, whether aided by computers or not, requires that the information fed into the analysis be accurate. The specific functions of microbes almost always are the direct expression of the presence of and activities of one or more proteins. The presence of a particular functional enzyme should not automatically be scored as a point of correspondence, any more than the absence of that enzyme activity from one of a pair of organisms in a given circumstance must indicate negative correspondence for that gene. DNA sequences and amino acid sequences in the gene product are colinear. Measurements of amino acid sequence are direct measures of nucleotide sequences in the active gene. The comparison of such pairs of sequences leads to deductions concerning the types and numbers of mutational events necessary to account for any minor differences, if any, in the protein structures. These comparisons are tedious, but they are becoming less so, and shortly they may become applicable on a routine basis. Computers may then be used fruitfully for analytical problems that have real data behind them, and the lower levels of taximetric similarities would then descend to proper levels for organisms of distant relation.

On faith, I believe that there are indeed bacterial species that exist as natural groups, and that the tools for circumscribing these species are in existence and can be applied to describe the evolutionary relations between the species so that generic and familial relations may be deduced. I do not believe that we have yet accumulated sufficient reliable data to make this delineation in more than a few isolated instances. But the molecular microbial taxonomist has at least laid to rest a reasonable number of myths and fables already known to be such by perceptive taxonomists using classical methods of observation.

REFERENCES

Colwell, R. R., and M. Mandel. 1964. Adansonian analysis and deoxyribonucleic acid base composition of some Gram-negative bacteria. J. Bacteriol. 87:1412–1422.

Gasser, F., and M. Mandel. 1968. Deoxyribonucleic acid base composition of the genus *Lactobacillus.* J. Bacteriol. 96:580–588.

Inman, R. B. 1967. Some factors affecting electron microscopic length of deoxyribonucleic acid. J. Mol. Biol. 25:209–216.

Kleinschmidt, A. K., D. Lang, D. Jacherts, and R. K. Zahn. 1962. Darstellung und Langenmessungen des gesamten Desoxyribonucleinsaure-Inhaltes von T2-Bakteriophagen. Biochim. Biophys. Acta 61:857–864.

Mandel, M., and R. Rownd. 1964. DNA base composition in the Enterobacteriaceae. An evolutionary sequence?, p. 585–597 *In* C. A. Leone [ed] Taxonomic biochemistry and serology. Ronald Press, New York.

Marmur, J., S. Falkow, and M. Mandel. 1963. New approaches to bacterial taxonomy. Ann. Rev. Microbiol. 17:329–372.

Marmur, J., E. Seaman, and J. Levine. 1963. Interspecific transformation in *Bacillus.* J. Bacteriol. 85:461–467.

McCarthy, B. J. 1967. Arrangement of base sequences in deoxyribonucleic acid. Bacteriol. Rev. 31:215–229.

Ravin, A. W. 1963. Experimental approaches to the study of bacterial phylogeny. Am. Natur. 97:307–318.

Smith, N. R., R. E. Gordon, and F. E. Clark. 1952. Aerobic spore-forming bacteria. U.S. Dept. Agr. Monogr. No. 16, 148 pp.

Sueoka, N. 1961. Variation and heterogeneity of base composition of deoxyribonucleic acids: A compilation of old and new data. J. Mol. Biol. 3:31–40.

Van Niel, C. B. 1946. The classification and natural relationships of bacteria. Cold Spring Harbor Symp. Quant. Biol. 11:285–303.

Zuckerkandl, E., and L. Pauling. 1965. Molecules as documents of evolutionary history. J. Theoret. Biol. 8:357–366.

Discussion

Arnold W. Ravin

Dr. De Ley's paper is an impressive documentation of the significance of DNA composition in schemes of microbial classification. There is little doubt that the nucleotide composition of an organism's DNA reflects, to a large extent, the genetic information for its phenotypic range. If we are at all interested in developing systems of classification that indicate the extent of genetic similarity between taxa, we ought to take into consideration the extent of homology between the DNA's of representatives of those taxa. But there are some areas in which we must be cautious.

Dr. De Ley has discussed two different methods of comparing DNA's: the comparison of over-all base compositions and the measurement of percent of hybridization. With regard to the former, one wonders about the propriety of finding satisfaction with it whenever strains that have been previously placed in the same taxon are shown to possess similar GC content, while at the same time peremptorily constructing new taxa whenever strains previously assigned to a single group prove to have different GC content. What is the proper attitude to take when strains that are similar in a large number of characters are found to differ significantly in the GC content of their DNA's? To date, there are very few such cases, and this should give us confidence in the idea that similarity of stable phenotypic characters is based upon genotypic similarity, which, in turn, is based upon similarity in nucleotide composition. However, when the exceptional situation arises, it will be worth determining the cause of the disparity between the measurement of phenotype and DNA composition before taxonomic decisions are made.

We must also exercise some caution when we consider the fact that the percent GC content of the DNA of mammals, birds, reptiles, and vascular plants varies over such a small range. This fact reveals that a very rich variety of taxa can be obtained with a very limited range of GC values. Hence, it follows that a narrow range of GC values does not necessarily imply a limited extent of evolution.

With regard to the DNA hybridization method, we should ask how well it really measures the number of identical genes or cistrons shared by two groups of organisms. The method is probably suitable for setting a maximum on genic identity; that is, as the percent hybridization between two sources of DNA declines, we can be reasonably sure as to the greatest number of genes the two sources can have in common. On the other hand, when the percent hybridization increases, we are not at all certain as to the differences that may still exist between genes that are nevertheless similar enough to pair with each other. Genic differences may exist, even beyond that of a single mutational change, yet they may be insufficient to block pairing completely. At the level of incipient speciation—i.e., at the level where evolutionary divergences begin—DNA hybridization techniques may be inadequate to detect what we wish to see, at least at the present time.

For this reason it is imperative that we not ignore the purely genetic test of homology. When properly utilized, this test can be a very powerful method for studying genic differences. The genetic test of homology consists in determining the extent to which two functionally homologous genes are capable of recognizing each other *in vivo* and undergoing recombination. This is the kind of work we have pursued in my laboratory. By means of heterospecific DNA-induced transformations, we demonstrate first that genes having homologous function in different bacterial taxospecies are capable of recognizing each other; this is shown by the replacement of a marker in the recipient gene by one in the homologous donor gene (Ravin and DeSa, 1964; Ravin and Mishra, 1965). We often find, however, that, despite this recognition, the efficiency of heterospecific transformation is relatively low compared with that of a homospecific transformation (Chen and Ravin, 1966a). Sometimes it is possible to show—as we have done in the case of pneumococcal-streptococcal transformations—that the relative inefficiency of the heterospecific transformation is due entirely to reduced pairing. By means of radioactively labeled DNA, for example, it can be shown that none of the inefficiency of heterospecific transformation is due to impeded bacterial uptake of heterospecific DNA. On the contrary, the inefficiency of heterospecific transformation is related to the amount of irreversibly bound foreign DNA that fails to produce genetically transformed recipient bacteria (Chen and Ravin, 1966a). Nor is the reduced efficiency of heterospecific transformation due to any intrinsic inefficiency of transformation by the particular donor marker being followed in the transformation process. The donor marker, after it is integrated into the foreign genome, may be just as efficient a transformer as a marker of homospecific origin (Chen and Ravin, 1966 a and b). Finally, one of the most telling pieces of evidence in this regard is that the inefficiency of the heterospecific transformation is the same in reciprocal crosses (Chen and Ravin, 1966a and unpublished). This is a result predictable, of course, from the hypothesis that difficulty in pairing is the exclusive cause of the reduced frequency of heterospecific transformation. Our explanation of these results involves the reasonable assumption that two genes having similar activities in two respective wildtype strains may, nevertheless, differ at a number of nucleotide positions.

Through extended use of genetic tests of homology we may discover some interesting features of genic evolution. For example, we may be able to observe that, in two strains under examination, the two functional homologues of a given gene are sufficiently similar that they will pair and recombine, while for another gene the two homologues have evolved so far as to make pairing and recombination impossible. We may even be able to measure the rate of evolution for a given gene in a particular series of strains or species.

Deciding where one species ends and another begins may be no easier when we have progressed further with studies of DNA structure and genetic homology. A certain arbitrariness, which is an inevitable feature of the classification by humans of organisms indifferent to their taxonomic status, will undoubtedly persist. But perhaps we shall have learned a great deal about the mechanisms that give rise to the differences upon which our systematics depends.

REFERENCES

Chen, K. C., and A. W. Ravin. 1966a. Heterospecific transformation of pneumococcus and streptococcus, I. Relative efficiency and specificity of DNA helping effect. J. Mol. Biol. 22:109–121.

Chen, K. C., and A. W. Ravin. 1966b. Heterospecific transformation of pneumococcus and streptococcus, II. Dependence of relative efficiency of marker integration on host genome. J. Mol. Biol. 22:123–134.

Ravin, A. W., and J. D. H. DeSa. 1964. Genetic linkage of mutational sites affecting similar characters in pneumococcus and streptococcus. J. Bacteriol. 87:86–96.

Ravin, A. W., and A. K. Mishra. 1965. Relative frequencies of different kinds of spontaneous and induced mutants of pneumococci and streptococci capable of growth in the presence of streptomycin. J. Bacteriol. 90:1161–1173.

Informal Discussion

CROVELLO: Dr. De Ley, when stating that numerical taxonomy covers one third to one half of the genome, had you taken into account that the characters used in the numerical study are often not independent and that they are often highly correlated? Do you think that your estimate is perhaps a high limit of percentage of the genome estimated by numerical taxonomy?

DE LEY: One can, of course, make only an estimate and not a precise prediction. The estimate can be based only on the nature of the features used. Some features might involve 20 cistrons, and others only one cistron. The average feature probably involves about 5 cistrons.

CROVELLO: So, you made an estimate of the average number of cistrons for a character and multiplied that by the number of characters used in a phenetic study?

DE LEY: That is right. I believe that is about as far as one can go.

JUAN H. HUNZIKER

Molecular Data in Plant Systematics

Of all natural systems, living matter is the one which, in the face of great transformations, preserves inscribed in its organization the largest amount of its own past history.

–Zuckerkandl and Pauling, 1965:357

INTRODUCTION

Systematic biology of the present decade is characterized by, among other things, a continuously growing emphasis on molecular systematics. Some recent important articles, reviews, and books have covered various general aspects (Alston, 1965, 1967; Alston and Turner, 1963; Boulter *et al.*, 1966; Colloque de Chemiotaxinomie, 1967; Hegnauer, 1962–1966; Leone, 1964; Sibley, 1965; and Swain, 1963, 1966). Molecular systematics based on small molecular weight compounds such as alkaloids, phenolic substances, betacyanins, terpenoids, amino and fatty acids, carbohydrates, quinones, etc., have received considerable attention and adequate treatment in these books or reviews. On the other hand, macromolecular data (except for serology) such as for proteins have not been much used in systematics of higher plants, despite their usefulness and promising future in systematics and evolutionary research. Rather than attempt to review all protein research related to plant systematics, emphasis will be placed on methods and approaches and on citing the most important works in these different lines of research, including some results on protein electrophoresis.

PROTEINS AND METHODS FOR THEIR STUDY

Zuckerkandl and Pauling (1965) have recently classified the molecules that occur in living matter into three categories.

1. *Semantides* or *semantophoretic molecules,* which carry the information of the genes or a transcript thereof. The genes are primary linear "sense-carrying" units; messenger-RNA molecules are secondary semantides, and most polypeptides are tertiary semantides.
2. *Episemantic molecules.* These are synthesized under the control of tertiary semantides. All molecules produced by enzymes in the absence of a template fall into this class. Although they do not express extensively the information carried by the semantides, they result from this information.
3. *Asemantic molecules,* which are not produced by the organism.

As pointed out by those authors, the significance of molecules to evolutionary history decreases from semantides to asemantic molecules. The latter have no value in studies of phylogenetic relationships. Since episemantic molecules are formed after the collaboration of enzymes controlled by several distinct structural genes, they may be regarded as multigenic characteristics. They merely express the information contained in the active centers of the enzymes. There is, therefore, a great loss of information as one passes from semantides to episemantic molecules. Not all polypeptides are semantides; some may be episemantic. Zuckerkandl and Pauling (1965) state:

> Because tertiary semantides (enzymes) with different primary structures can lead to the synthesis of identical episemantic molecules as long as the active enzymatic sites are similar, wrong inferences about phylogenetic relationships may be drawn from the presence of identical or similar episemantic molecules in different organisms (p. 359).

The authors suggest that the most rational, universal and informative molecular phylogeny must be based on semantophoretic molecules.

Some years ago Crick (1958:138) called attention to the importance of protein structure:

> Biologists should realize that before long we shall have a subject which might be called "protein taxonomy", the study of the amino acid sequences of the proteins of an organism and the comparison of them between species. It can be argued that these sequences are the most delicate expression possible of the phenotype of an organism and that vast amounts of evolutionary information may be hidden away within them.

Recent advances in the biochemistry of proteins and the progress made in the resolution of biophysical methods that enable the separation and characterization of proteins have introduced new concepts and successful techniques for the study of phylogenetic relationships. Proteins are very significant as systematic characters because they are almost direct gene products. They are regarded as the means for the transfer of information between the genetic code of DNA and the complicated processes of development and function of the organism. The order of amino acids of a protein is genetically determined, being—through RNA—the result of transcription (DNA–RNA) and translation processes (RNA–protein). It is probable also that the characteristic folding and cross-linking of a polypeptide chain results mainly from the primary structure.

If we assume that organisms are related to each other in proportion to the similarity of their DNA, it is valid to assume that the degree of relationship among these organisms is proportional to the similarity of their proteins. Sibley (1960, 1962, 1964, 1965), Alston (1965), and others have discussed the use of proteins as a source of phylogenetic information and its rational foundation. Zuckerkandl and Pauling (1965) have recently pointed out that in view of the "degeneracy" of the genetic code (many amino acids appearing to be coded for by more than one type of codon) it must be assumed that some information is lost in the passage from secondary (RNA) to tertiary (polypeptide) semantides. Differences in base sequence in allelic stretches of DNA might not lead to differences in amino acid sequence in the corresponding polypeptide chains.

The following methods are available for the study and comparison of protein structures: amino acid composition, fingerprint pattern of peptides, amino acid sequence, catalytic activity, serology (precipitin technique, double diffusion), electrophoresis, and chromatography. Each method has advantages and disadvantages in its application to systematic problems. When possible, a combination of these methods should be used (Jackson *et al.*, 1967). A detailed discussion of the limitations of each of these methods and approaches is beyond the scope of this paper, but a few points will be mentioned.

Amino acid sequence of specific proteins provides the most detailed information we can obtain about a protein. The painstaking studies of Margoliash and his collaborators on cytochrome *c* are good examples (Fitch and Margoliash, 1967; Margoliash and Smith, 1965; and Margoliash at this conference). This method is time-consuming, requires expensive instruments, and must be handled by a competent biochemist. Peptide fingerprinting–using protein digestion, electrophoresis, and chromatography–is usually performed on only a few proteins. The first method has the limitation, from the evolutionist's viewpoint, that it provides phylogenetic information from a very small fraction of the genome–only one or two genes in some cases. If rapid changes, or molecular stagnation, or convergence occur at a single gene, the evolutionary picture obtained would be a distorted one.

Serology has a disadvantage in that rabbits or other animals are required for obtaining the antisera. Moreover, there are variations in the reactions of different animals, or different inbred lines, to antigens. Also the length of the immunization period influences its effectiveness in separating similar antigens. As for the precipitin technique, no qualitative information is obtained. In the qualitative serological methods using solid media, it is sometimes difficult to interpret lines of precipitation objectively. There are, however, simpler methods that provide valuable information about protein systems and that can be used by the molecular systematist. Physicochemical properties of proteins are a consequence of the particular amino acid sequence that is specific to each of them. This sometimes enables the worker to separate and characterize specific proteins in an electrical field on the basis of the net electrical charge and the size and configuration of the molecule. Zone electrophoresis, especially through use of high-resolution media such as starch or polyacrylamide, gives information on protein systems (with or without catalytic activity) that can be scanned in the densitometer recording apparatus. The light-absorption data for different taxa can be appraised objectively and treated statistically, as has been done by Johnson and Hall (1965).

Of the above-mentioned methods, that of zone electrophoresis is probably the most amenable to the systematist because of its relative simplicity and reproducibility. Electrophoretic patterns of protein systems are often characteristic of each species and can provide valuable data for the experimental systematist. Even when the information provided by this method is too crude and superficial for the biochemist, the evolutionist can derive from it a broader view of the genome products of each species than he can from the amino acid sequence of a single molecule.

From the standpoint of systematics, plant protein research is undoubtedly found to be lagging when compared with the work already done in animal proteins (amino acid sequences, fingerprinting, multiple enzymes, and electrophoresis, for example). This is partly due to difficulties encountered with extraction and dissolution of plant proteins. Organ specificity of plant proteins has been pointed out by several authors analyzing leaves, roots, buds, and seeds (Kloz *et al.,* 1960; Sahulka, 1965). When making species comparisons, it is essential that proteins from the same organ at a similar stage of development be analyzed.

SEROLOGY

The principles of immunochemistry are fully discussed by Kabat and Mayer (1961). If *antigens* are injected into a rabbit or other animal, such animals become immunized and produce *antibodies* in the blood serum. If this antiserum is then extracted from the animal and placed in contact with the antigens that caused its production, both antibodies and antigens react and form a precipitate. Such a reaction is known as a *homologous reaction,* and its specificity is thought to depend on the arrangement of groups of atoms on the surfaces of both types of molecules. Molecules that are similar but not identical to the original antigens may also react with the antibodies and precipitate in what is called a *heterologous reaction* or *cross-reaction.*

For half a century or more, comparisons of the serological reactions of different groups of plants on liquid media have been made. The reactions were measured quantitatively through different methods and devices that, with time, became more accurate. However, because the medium was liquid, information could not be gathered on the quality of different proteins. This type of serological approach has been subjected to much criticism (Lester, 1965).

Some newly discovered facts raise serious doubts about the value of much of the quantitative serological work done prior to 1940. Some of the results were based on comparisons of proteins from different organs that are now known to have differences in protein. The amount of precipitate obtained with constant amounts of antiserum and increasing dilutions of antigen rises from zero to a maximum and then decreases again to zero (phenomenon of optimal proportions). In most of the early serological research, only one proportion of antigen and antibody was used, so results based on work in which this phenomenon was not taken into account lose considerable value (Alston and Turner, 1963).

In the quantitative precipitin reaction, the serological correspondence is measured in terms of the amount of precipitate obtained from a cross-reaction as compared with that of the corresponding homologous test. M. A. Johnson (1953, 1954), Baum (1954), Hammond (1955 a and b), Fairbrothers and Johnson (1961), and Fairbrothers and Boulette (1960) have used the quantitative precipitin reaction as an indicator of serological correspondence in plants of the families Magnoliaceae, Cucurbitaceae, Solanaceae, Ranunculaceae, Gramineae, and Umbelliferae. Paradoxical results of some of these works, where, in some instances, interspecific differences surpass intergeneric differences, have been pointed out by Alston and Turner (1963). The same paradox is noticed in the results of Johnson and Fairbrothers (1965), where interspecific differences between *Magnolia portoricensis* and *M. virginiana, M. kobus,* and *M. ovata* are greater than intergeneric differences of the latter with *Michelia, Manglietia,* and *Talauma.*

Even after technical advances had been made in measurement procedures, such as Boyden's method (based on the total area of the curve obtained with various antigen dilutions), Gell *et al.*, (1960) questioned the validity of the total quantitative precipitin reaction. They pointed out the serious risk of error if taxonomic conclusions are based upon measurements of the total bulk of precipitate produced when crude plant extracts containing many different antigenic proteins react with their corresponding antisera. Conclusions based on this quantitative approach are dangerous because in some cases most of the precipitate could be due to a very abundant single antigen, while in other cases several proteins in lower concentrations could be more meaningful phylogenetically. When species A, for example, yields more precipitate in a cross-reaction with B than it does with C, this may be the consequence of different amounts of a single protein that is abundant in B but scarce in C. However, C may contain three or four other proteins that are present in A but not in B, where they are represented by other non-cross-reacting antigens. A and C might be regarded as more closely related species (Gell *et al.*, 1960). This could easily happen also if A and B are rather distantly related diploids sharing a single abundant protein and C is a polyploid derivative of A, with which it shares several proteins. Due to the proteins of the other genomes, however, C would have a rather low concentration of A proteins in the extracts.

Moreover, long periods of immunization increase the amount of precipitate in cross-reactions and therefore magnify serological correspondence. On the other hand, short periods tend to reduce serological correspondence (Johnson and Fairbrothers, 1965). Several authors believe, however, that quantitative and qualitative methods are complementary and that the use of both methods increases the value of serological data in systematics (Fairbrothers, 1966).

The more antigens that can be differentiated, the more data for determining relationships will be available. It is advisable to use serological methods by which different antigen–antibody systems in the same total reaction can be distinguished. This has been made possible by the newer techniques in which gels rather than liquid media are used for precipitation (Crowle, 1961; Grabar and Burtin, 1964; Lester, 1965). Among these, the Ouchterlony double-diffusion technique uses a layer of agar gel or a film of cellulose acetate. The antiserum and the antigens are placed in separate reservoirs in the gel or in the surface of the cellulose acetate. Both reagents diffuse from the points of application at speeds determined by the physicochemical properties of the molecules. A precipitation line is formed at the places where homologous antigens and antibodies meet, and several such lines may be distinguished when a mixture of different antigen-antibody systems is present.

Another important advance in serological methodology is the immunoelectrophoretic analysis of Grabar and Williams. This method combines the separation of the macromolecules through electrophoresis and their identification and location through immunodiffusion. Protein extracts are prepared and then subjected to agar-gel electrophoresis, after which parallel or perpendicular troughs are cut into the agar between or in front of the samples and antiserum is poured in. After diffusion into the agar, corresponding antigens and antibodies meet and form precipitates in the shape of arcs. A characteristic spectrum of arcs is formed for every species or group of species.

Hawkes and Lester (1966), studying species of *Solanum*, reported that results of comparisons by the double-diffusion techniques were by no means constant and that spectra were hard to analyze, due to overlapping lines, even after absorption. This technique did not provide much information on the similarities or differences between species within series. Immunoelectrophoresis, on the other hand, gave results that were easier to analyze and provided greater resolution of the individual species and more valuable information.

As pointed out by Lester (1965), the value of immunoelectrophoresis is that it enables characterization of proteins having similar mobility but different immunological properties. Also, it makes possible the recognition of serologically similar molecules having different electrophoretic mobilities.

One of the shortcomings of immunoelectrophoresis, as it has been so far utilized, is that the electrophoretic separation is performed in a gel with poor resolution. Simpler zone polyacrylamide electrophoresis might prove in some cases to give more information because it often yields multiband spectra. After comparing results obtained with immunoelectrophoresis and polyacrylamide electrophoresis, Vaughan *et al.* (1965) concluded that the latter "has the greater resolving power and also has the added advantage that it is a quick and simple technique." Boulter *et al.*, (1966), using electrophoresis, found in at least one species of *Baptisia* a unique protein band pattern where no such difference could be detected by immunoelectrophoresis. Loeschke and Stegemann (1966 a and b) have obtained polyacrylamide electrophoretic patterns in *Solanum tuberosum* that are composed of many bands and in some cases have detected striking varietal differences in these patterns. Desborough and Peloquin (1966) have found differences among South American tuberous species of *Solanum* through use of polyacrylamide electrophoresis. This group of species could not be separated by immunoelectrophoresis or immunodiffusion (Gell *et al.,* 1960; Hawkes and Lester, 1966).

Gell *et al.* (1960) have applied double-diffusion and perpendicular immunoelectrophoresis to studies of the tuber antigens of 37 wild species of potato. Using an antiserum to the cultivated potato *Solanum tuberosum,* they recorded identical four-line spectra in the precipitation reactions of species in series Bulbocastana (IV), Polyadenia (XIV), Longipedicellata (XIII), and Demissa (XII) as well as in all the 22 South American species studied. Except for Bulbocastana all these series have rotate corollas, while all low-numbered series–such as Morelliformia (III), Bulbocastana (IV), Cardiophylla (V), and Pinnatissecta (VI)–have stellate corollas. Species belonging to series Longipedicellata and Demissa cross well with each other and with most of the South American species but not with the species in series Bulbocastana. The serological results concerning Bulbocastana did not agree with the evidence from morphology (corolla shape) and crossability; however, this was clarified later by the further results of Hawkes and Lester (1966) that placed series Bulbocastana close to Pinnatissecta.

Series Cardiophylla and Pinnatissecta were grouped together, as they produced two-line spectra. Morphologically and cytogenetically they are similar to each other but differ from the other series. Hawkes (1963) has merged both in a single series, Pinnatissecta.

Solanum morelliforme (series III, Morelliformia) produced only one precipitation line with antisera to both *S. tuberosum* and *S. ehrembergii.* This information as well as morphological and crossability data supported the idea that *S. morelliforme* is related only distantly to other species of the genus.

In general, the results showed a remarkably close agreement with those obtained from the classical taxonomic methods and with the general conclusions arrived at through cytological and genetical studies.

Recently, Hawkes and Lester (1966), using similar methods, made further contributions in regard to the genus *Solanum.* The results of comparisons by double-diffusion were by no means constant, but some general tendencies were apparent. Double-diffusion against antisera to six species showed a difference between series having stellate corollas, such as Bulbocastana and Pinnatissecta (including Cardiophylla) and series having rotate corollas, such as Longipedicellata and Demissa. This result agreed with the findings of Gell *et al.* (1960) except that *Solanum bulbocastanum* was shown to be in the former group and not in the latter. The results obtained by immunoelectrophoretic analysis of the Mexican species of tuberous *Solanum* were similar to those from double-diffusion tests but showed in greater detail the differences within the two main groups of species (Hawkes and Lester, 1966).

A special study of *S. morelliforme* and *S. clarum*—two peculiar species with some vegetative similarities but rather uncertain sectional position—emphasized the distinctness of the former from all other potatoes and indicated that the latter is more closely related to *S. bulbocastum* and *S. cardiophyllum* subsp. *ehrenbergii* than to *S. tuberosum.* These results confirm Hawkes' (1956) separation of *S. morelliforme* (previously included in series Bulbocastana) into series Morelliformia on account of its morphological characteristics. Several results indicated that *S. polyadenium* (series Polyadenia) had some of the group-specific antigens of both series Bulbocastana and Pinnatissecta on the one hand and of Longipedicellata and Demissa on the other. Therefore, this species was thought to be in some intermediate position between these two major groups of species.

The studies of Gell *et al.* (1960), Lester (1964, 1965), and Hawkes and Lester (1966) showed greater variation in the immunological reactions of the North American species than in the South American species. Also, there is greater morphological variation among the former (with about 30 species) than among the latter (with about 100 species). In a study of South American species of tuber-bearing *Solanum,* Lester (1965) found that only *S. commersoni* differed from the other species in its tuber antigens.

Lester *et al.* (1965) obtained parallel immunoelectrophoretic spectra belonging to 14 species of *Baptisia* and unexpectedly found this group of species to be homogeneous serologically. They stressed the fact that the species studied were very diverse morphologically and chemically (chromatography of phenolic compounds) and that immunoelectrophoresis, in this case, was incapable of discriminating between these species. The immunoelectrophoretic spectra of *B. pendula* and *B. leucantha* were, however, slightly different from other species. These two species are easily distinguished from most other species of *Baptisia* on morphological and chromatographic evidence, and they are closely similar to one another. It is interesting that in *Baptisia,* where secondary phenolic compounds have been so useful for the characterization of species and the detection of interspecific hybridization (see Alston, 1967, for a recent review), protein immunoelectrophoresis did not yield differences among species. In the algal genera *Chlorococcum* and *Tetracystis* the same methods have disclosed clear-cut differences between groups of species within each genus (Brown and Lester, 1965).

Fairbrothers and Johnson (1964) studied several species of Cornaceae and Nyssaceae by means of double-diffusion and the turbidimetric method (photronreflectometer). They found that the seven species of *Cornus* studied could be separated into three groups and that the results from both methods indicated the same serological groupings, which also agreed with the results based on cytological studies. The serological evidence obtained suggested a close relationship between the North American flowering dogwood (*Cornus florida*) and the temperate Asiatic flowering dogwood (*C. kousa*), which is not surprising in view of the known similarities between eastern North American species and those from temperate Asia.

Hall (1959) has shown by agar electrophoresis and immunoelectrophoresis that an allopolyploid between wheat and rye possessed most of the proteins of both parental species. One protein fraction of rye was either completely lacking or indistinguishably low in the rye-wheat extract. Kloz (1962) studied the proteins of seed-enclosed cotyledons and of hypocotyls and primary root of germinated seeds of four species of *Phaseolus.* He found that practically identical phaseolin (protein III) was present in the cotyledons of *P. vulgaris* and *P. coccineus* and absent in *P. lunatus* and *P. aureus.* A protein component was found in the hypocotyl and root of *P. vulgaris, P. coccineus,* and *P. lunatus,* but it was not found in *P. aureus.* It was concluded that *P. vulgaris* and *P. coccineus* are relatively closely related, even though they have been placed in different groups by taxonomists. However, the protein evidence agrees with crossability because it is possible to cross *P. coccineus* with *P. vulgaris.* A significant point in Kloz's results is that reserve proteins apparently possess a narrower taxonomic distribution (i.e., occur in fewer taxa) and that structural proteins of hypocotyl plus root occur in a greater number of taxa. Also, it is interesting that protein III is characteristic of American species (*P. vulgaris, P. coccineus, P. lunatus*), while both protein III and phaseolin are absent in the Asiatic *P. aureus.*

Later, Kloz *et al.* (1966) dealt with a greater number of *Phaseolus* species and found that *P. vulgaris* subsp. *vulgaris* and subsp. *aborigineus* contain an identical protein (*P. vulgaris* protein I) and an identical phaseolin. Nearest to *P. vulgaris* is *P. coccineus,* having an almost identical phaseolin fraction and small differences in the albumin and globulin fractions. *P. acutifolius* contains a somewhat different phaseolin fraction and greater deviations in the albumin and globulin fractions. *P. lunatus* and *P. aureus* are quite different in all protein characteristics studied. Fox *et al.* (1964) have studied the albumins of 17 species of Leguminosae by polyacrylamide electrophoresis and, similarly, their results suggest a close relationship between *P. vulgaris* and *P. coccineus* (their Figure 3, parts a and b, shows at least 11 homologous bands).

ELECTROPHORESIS

Electrophoresis can be defined as the migration of charged particles or molecules suspended in a liquid under the influence of an electric field. The speed of movement in the case of protein molecules results from the net electrical charge and, perhaps to a slight extent, from the distribution of the charged amino acids. The size and possibly the shape of the molecule also influence the migration speed in such media as starch or polyacrylamide gels, which are known to inhibit the migration velocities of large molecules relatively more than those of small ones. The various proteins of a plant organ can be separated because of their different velocities. Using starch or polyacrylamide gel as supporting media, it is possible to obtain a pattern characterized by the position, width, and density of the different proteins within a definite period of time. The comparison of these patterns, or spectra, after proper staining will show differences and similarities among taxa. These patterns can be qualitatively and quantitatively expressed by means of a light-absorption curve, each band resulting in a peak of definite height depending on the concentration of each protein band and its light absorption in the densitometer.

Sibley (1965) has pointed out that the limitations of electrophoresis should not be overlooked. Two proteins differing in only a single amino acid may show quite different electrophoretic behavior, or two proteins with different amino acid sequences may show identical behavior. One safeguard against erroneous interpretations due to such problems is to use electrophoretic comparisons only for protein systems such as blood serum, egg white, and seed proteins, which contain an array of many different proteins (Sibley, 1965). The complex spectra obtained are likely to be completely identical only if they are derived from organisms that are very similar genetically. If about 12 or more different protein fractions are resolved in the patterns, and these are identical, it is not likely that they result from what we could call "biophysical convergence," that is, evolutionary convergence of the biophysical properties of chemically different proteins, resulting in a similar electrophoretic pattern.

Despite the high resolution of some new media, another limitation of electrophoresis is that a single band on the gel may be composed of more than one protein (Boulter *et al.*, 1966).

We may distinguish between two kinds of electrophoretic studies: those on the protein systems of specific organs, such as tubers and seeds, and those on specific enzymes and their different molecular forms. The former, perhaps, are more important for the systematist and for the evolutionist interested in systematics above the species level and speciation processes, since they deal with whole complexes of different proteins and they may yield vast amounts of molecular data, especially if different types of protein extractions are performed. The pattern in this case is obtained through a general protein staining after electrophoresis. In the case of enzymatic studies, on the other hand, specific enzyme stains that reveal the particular catalytic activity of the enzyme are used. Recent studies on enzyme variation are extremely valuable for systematics and population and developmental genetics. For the systematist they are particularly significant for the understanding of intraspecific variation, the biochemical basis of adaptation to different environments, and other basic biological problems.

Alston and Turner (1963) have objected that electrophoresis yields only patterns, which are a cumulative expression of the protein complement, but do not provide evidence as to the structure of single proteins (see their criticism of Sibley's monumental work on electrophoretic egg-white protein patterns of 650 species of birds). It is obvious that, with the present state of knowledge, objections of the same type could be made to the molecular systematist who obtains only spot patterns of phenolic compounds or peptide fingerprints, to the morphologist working with characters without knowing the sequence of biochemical events involved in their morphogenesis, to the karyotype analyst who does not know how DNA has been redistributed in the chromosomes during evolution, to the genome analyst who does not know the physicochemical causes of chromosome synapsis and disjunction, and so forth.

There seems to be some danger in deriving phylogenetic conclusions from mobilities of single enzymes or proteins. The value of working with protein systems rather than with single proteins has been emphasized by Sibley (1965). Obviously, the higher the number of proteins of different taxa that we are comparing, the larger the portion of the genome that is being considered.

NONENZYMATIC PROTEIN PATTERNS

If protein extracts are prepared in a standard way from the same organs at a similar stage of development, and if electrophoretic conditions are kept constant, reproducible band patterns can be obtained for each population or individual (Boulter *et al.*, 1966).

There is evidence that extremely different environmental conditions have no influence on the reproducibility of results with storage proteins from mature grains, at least in regard to the presence, position, and width of the different bands of the patterns. Seed samples of *Agropyron tilcarense* and *A. attenuatum* obtained from their original habitats (2,500 m above sea level at lat. 23° S and 3,400 m above sea level at lat. 15° S, respectively) and from cultures at a different soil and at warmer environments (sea level and lat. 34° S) yielded identical electrophoretic patterns (Figure 1a–d). These results agree with the findings of Feillet (1965) on protein constitution of wheat.

It is my experience that, if electrophoretic conditions are kept uniform, these storage protein spectra are less plastic and less affected by environmental conditions than many single quantitative exomorphic traits. In species of *Agropyron* and *Hordeum,* my results indicate that seed storage proteins separated by means of polyacrylamide gel and high voltage provide band patterns that—as pointed out by Coates (1967) for the serum proteins of *Taricha* (Reptilia)—are: (a) genetically determined and not modified by environmental factors; (b) different enough that species and (in some cases) semispecific or racial populations may be distinguished; and (c) sufficiently conservative as to reflect accurately the relationships within the genus.

Desborough and Peloquin (1966), using polyacrylamide disc electrophoresis of tuber proteins, have found great differences in patterns among species of different sections of tuberous *Solanum.* They have been able to separate the South American species of tuberous *Solanum* and even groups within *S. tuberosum.* Their results and those of Loeschchke and Stegemann (1966 a and b) when compared with those of Gell *et al.* (1960), Hawkes and Lester (1966), and Lester (1965) suggest that polyacrylamide electrophoresis is a better tool than immunoelectrophoresis and immunodiffusion. In the hybrid *S. verrucosum* x *S. tuberosum* (cultivar Katahdin) the protein pattern shows bands at positions different from those in the parental species (Desborough and Peloquin, 1966, Figure 5).

Hall and Johnson have presented evidence (based on electrophoresis) that amphiploid plants have, in regard to their seed

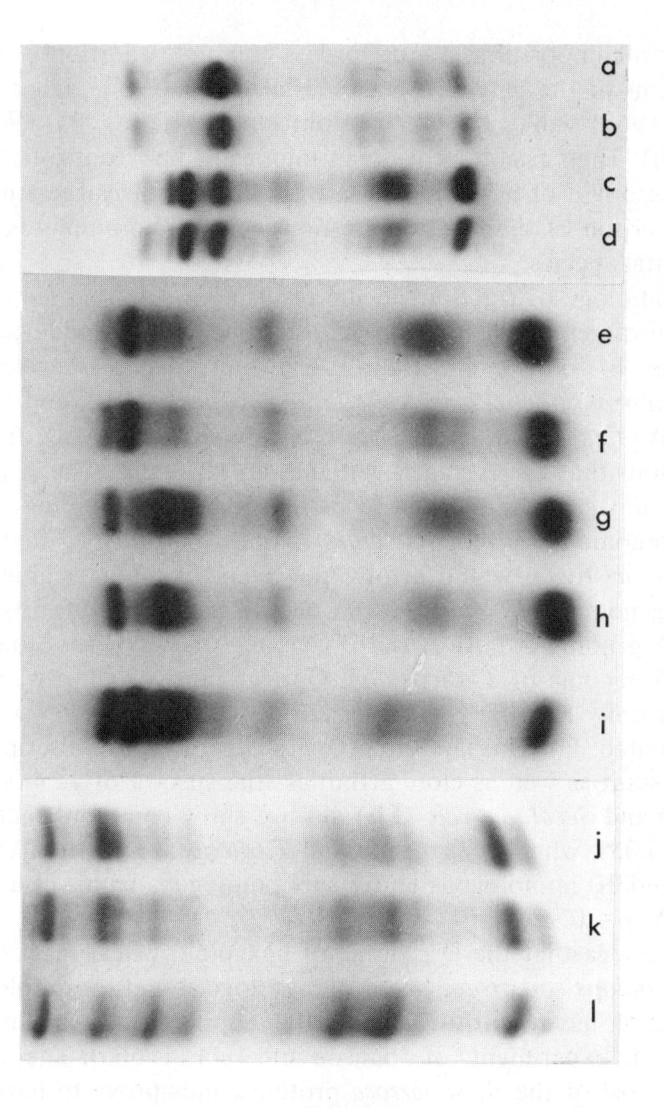

FIGURE 1 Electrophoretic patterns of several South American species of *Agropyron.* a, b = *Agropyron attenuatum:* (a) Uni, La Paz, Bolivia; (b) the same, but cultivated at Castelar (near Buenos Aires), Argentina. c, d = *Agropyron tilcarense:* (c) Tilcara, Jujuy, Argentina; (d) the same, but cultivated at Castelar. e–l = *A. scabriglume* complex; (e) San Martín, San Luis, Argentina; (f) Tafí del Valle, Tucumán, Argentina; (g) Balcarce, Buenos Aires; (h) El Carancho, La Pampa, Argentina; (i) Tilcara, Jujuy; (j) El Carancho, La Pampa; (k) a mixture of proteins from j and l; (l) Balcarce, Buenos Aires. Cathode to the right; origin near the left end. Single horizontal polyacrylamide gel slabs; a–d, e–i, j–l. (Technique as in Hunziker, 1967b.)

protein composition, a more-or-less complete addition of the proteins of the parental species (Hall, 1959, 1964; Hall and Johnson, 1962; Hall *et al.*, 1966; B Johnson and Hall, 1965, 1966 a and b). Their results provide an important new tool for the study of the origin of amphiploids—a work that involves the study and comparison of the electrophoretic spectra of amphiploids and parental species.

Homology of fractions in the resulting spectra is used as a criterion of genetic affinity among the species and among their genomes. B. Johnson and Hall (1965) found that the spectra of *Triticum monococcum* (AA), *T. dicoccum* (AABB), and hexaploid wheat (*T. aestivum,* AABBDD) confirmed the evidence from other methods that the A and B genomes are different. The A genome of *T. dicoccum* was found to be only partially homologous with the genome of *T. monococcum.* Affinity between *T. dicoccum* and *T. aestivum* would involve the A and B genomes about equally. The genome of *T. monococcum* would have more affinity with the A genome or both A and D genomes of *T. aestivum* than with the A genome of *T. dicoccum.* Optical density values were treated statistically and the total correlation value (r) between species was calculated. Protein band homologies permitted the discrimination of distant as well as close affinities—the spectra of *T. monococcum* (AA) and *Secale cereale* (EE) did not show common fractions ($r = 0.05$), whereas *T. durum* and *T. dicoccum* (both AABB) showed 10 homologous and 5 subhomologous bands in a total of 15 ($r = 0.92$).

The idea that the D genome of hexaploid wheat was contributed by *Aegilops squarrosa,* based on cytological and morphological evidence, has recently gained further support through the electrophoretic experiments of Johnson and Hall (1966a). They found that most of the *A. squarrosa* protein bands prove to have homologues in the *Triticum aestivum* spectrum. Similar results had been obtained previously by using starch gel electrophoresis of the water-soluble endosperm proteins, by Coulson and Sim (1964). They pointed out similarities between *T. durum* and *T. dicoccum* spectra, on the one hand, and *T. compactum, T. spelta, T. vulgare,* and *Aegilops squarrosa,* on the other. The curve corresponding to the last species, however, was rather distinctive.

Morphological traits and chromosomal evidence and data on DNA content suggest that *Aegilops speltoides* is the B-genome donor (Sarkar and Stebbins, 1956; Riley *et al.*, 1958; Rees and Davies, 1963). Detailed electrophoretic data, however, throw doubt upon both *A. bicornis* and *A. speltoides* as donors of the B genome (Johnson and Hall, 1966b).

As suggested by Johnson and Hall (1966b), protein electrophoresis provides valuable information for distinguishing autopolyploidy from allopolyploidy. Simple meiotic studies of polyploids might be misleading because some species of known autopolyploid origin (such as *Phleum pratense*, an autohexaploid) have races that form multivalent chromosomes in meiosis and others that behave cytologically as diploids, forming only bivalents. This is due to genetic differences related to the control of meiotic behavior (Riley and Law, 1965). Protein-band data would help to distinguish types of polyploids, since typical autopolyploid patterns should be like those of the diploid ancestor and typical allopolyploid patterns should be like the combined pattern of the diploid ancestors.

An extension of the approach used by Hall and Johnson in the study of the origin of amphiploids is the combined use of protein electrophoresis and meiotic studies of hybrids in experimental systematics, even at the diploid level. The cytogenetic approach to experimental systematics, based mainly upon the analysis of chromosome behavior in meiosis of hybrids, has several limitations. Among these, we may mention the possibility of gene interaction in the hybrids causing asynapsis or lack of pairing of the chromosomes at diakinesis or first metaphase even when these might be largely homologous. It is a well-known fact that chromosome pairing and meiotic behavior are under genetic control (Riley and Law, 1965; Feldman, 1966). The study of homology of proteins produced by the different genomes involved in a hybrid can, indeed, be very helpful in the interpretation of meiotic pairing in hybrids. Important aids in the interpretation of chromosome pairing in hybrids are the obtaining of the amphiploid through the use of colchicine and the studying of its meiosis and fertility. If pairing improves to the extent that it becomes almost normal and chiasma frequency increases, it means that low pairing in the hybrids is associated with little chromosome homology and that there is no genic interaction causing asynapsis. The comparison of the protein spectra of both parental species is an easy, fast, but indirect way for obtaining additional evidence in order to attribute low pairing to genetically induced asynapsis or lack of chromosome homology. Several examples will illustrate different situations in which protein patterns have proven useful in this connection.

High Chromosome-Pairing and High Protein-Band Homology

When tetraploid *Agropyron tilcarense* ($2n$ = 28) is crossed to sympatric northern populations of the hexaploid *A. scabriglume* complex ($2n$ = 42), the hybrid shows an average of 12.64 ± 0.11 closed bivalent chromosomes. Since 12.64 ± 0.10 closed bivalents have been found in *A. tilcarense* itself there is close homology between the two genomes of *A. tilcarense* and two of the three genomes of the hexaploid. *A. tilcarense* is probably the ancestral tetraploid progenitor of *A. scabriglume,* as suggested by morpho-

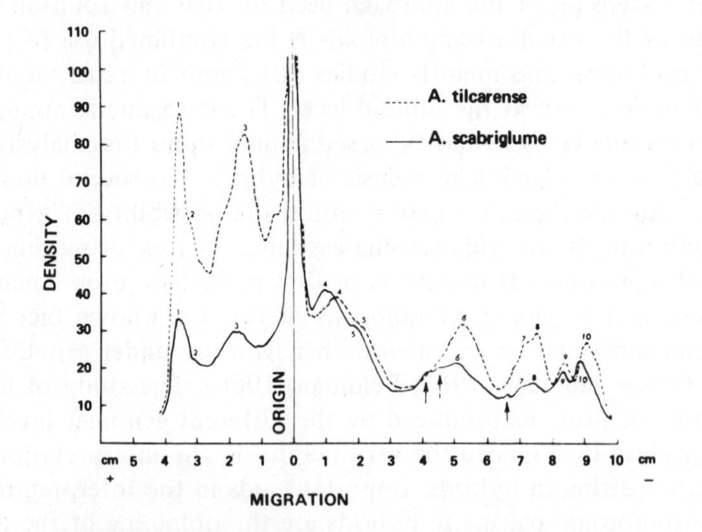

FIGURE 2 Optical density curves of water protein extracts, agar electrophoresis: *Agropyron tilcarense* ($2n$ = 28) and its hexaploid derivative *A. scabriglume* ($2n$ = 42). Assumed homologous peaks are numbered. Arrows point at peaks found exclusively in *A. scabriglume.* (From Hunziker, 1967a.)

logical, cytogenetic, and protein electrophoretic data (Hunziker, 1966, 1967a). Water extracts and 70 percent alcoholic extracts—the latter obtained from the pellet left after centrifugation of the water extract—were subjected to electrophoresis, and the results revealed that, except for a few differences, there was a remarkable homology of protein fractions (Figures 2 and 3). This is in agreement with the chromosome homology as indicated by frequency of closed bivalents (Hunziker, 1966, 1967a). Direct 70 percent alcohol extracts also revealed considerable homology (Figure 4 e and f).

Low Chromosome-Pairing and Low Protein-Band Homology

Natural crossing between South American populations of tetraploid *Hordeum jubatum* ($2n = 28$) and hexaploid *H. parodii* ($2n = 42$) is frequent. Extensive hybrid swarms detected near Balcarce, Buenos Aires, Argentina, suggest very high crossability, which has been confirmed in experimental reciprocal crosses. Both species differ in a number of morphological characteristics; and meiosis in the hybrid is highly irregular, with an average of only 1.97 ± 0.25 closed bivalents. (As in species of *Agropyron,* already mentioned, most of the chromosomes in the parental species form closed bivalents in meiosis, with at least one chiasma

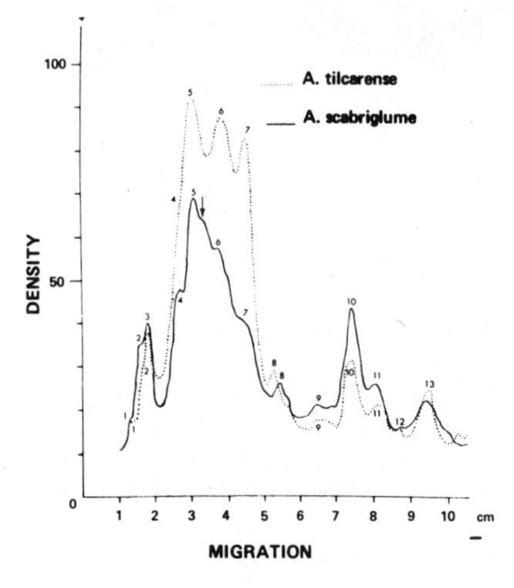

FIGURE 3 Optical density curves of 70 percent alcohol protein extracts (after previous water extraction), polyacrilamide horizontal electrophoresis: *Agropyron tilcarense* and *A. scabriglume.* Assumed homologous peaks are numbered. Arrows point at peaks found only in *A. scabriglume.* (From Hunziker, 1967a.)

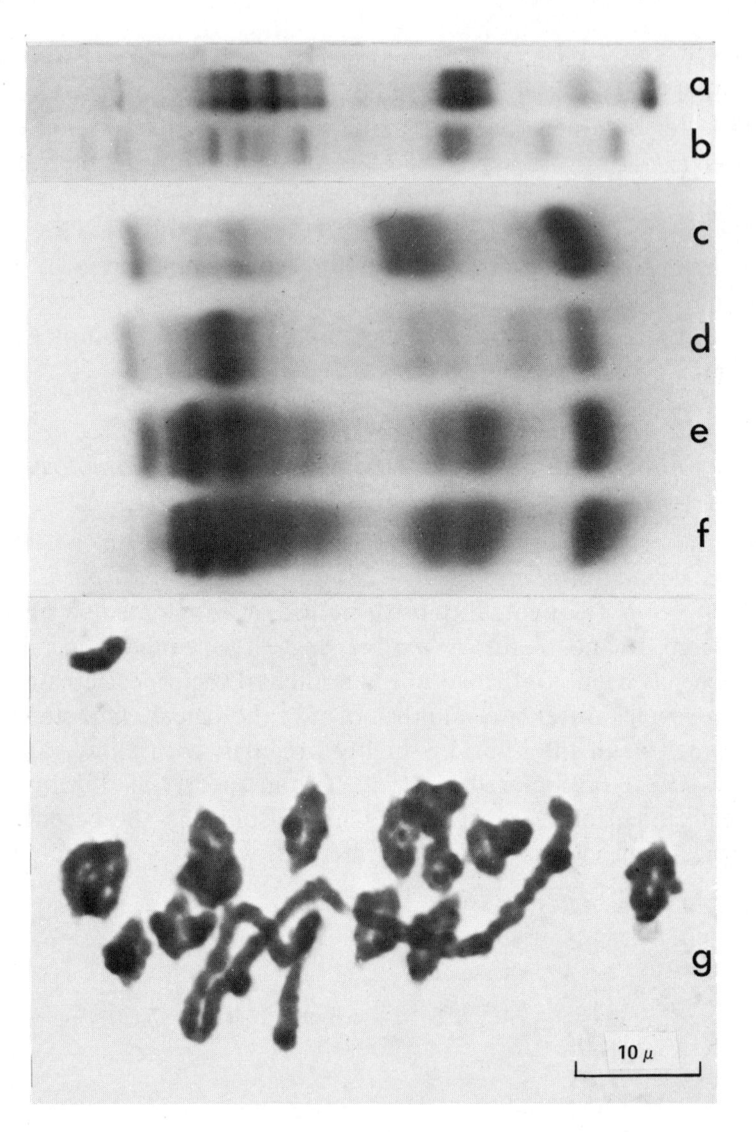

FIGURE 4 Electrophoretic patterns of South American species of *Hordeum* and *Agropyron* and meiosis in a hybrid between different geographic populations of *A. scabriglume.* (a) *Hordeum parodii,* (Balcarce, Argentina); (b) *H. jubatum* (Balcarce, Argentina); (c) *Agropyron scabrifolium* (La Colorada, Uruguay); (d) *A. attenuatum* (Uni, La Paz, Bolivia); (e) *A. tilcarense* (Tilcara, Jujuy, Argentina); (f) *A. scabriglume* (Tilcara). Cathode to the right; origin near the left end. Single polyacrylamide gel slabs: m–n, c–f. (Technique as in Hunziker, 1967b.) (g) First metaphase cell of *A. scabriglume* hybrid (Balcarce x El Carancho, plant No. 407–11), 1 XIII, 14 II, 1 I. Propiono-carmine.

at each side of the centromere.) The protein patterns so far obtained (Figure 4 a and b) have about half the total number of bands in common. Therefore, genic asynapsis causing failure of the chromosomes to pair might be considered, in this case, to be of secondary importance and perhaps could be disregarded. Both taxa would not be very closely related despite the ease for crossing (Hunziker, Itria, and Costas, unpublished data).

Several South American species of *Agropyron* also seem to illustrate this situation. [All species mentioned below are tetraploid ($2n = 28$) except *A. scabriglume,* which is hexaploid ($2n = 42$), as previously mentioned.] The meiotic behavior of the interspecific hybrids was studied, and all showed different amounts of low pairing, having low average of closed bivalents per cell: *A. attenuatium* x *A. tilcarense* (0.48), *A. tilcarense* x *A. scabrifolium* (2.52), *A. scabriglume* x *A. scabrifolium* (1.15). This low pairing and the predominant absence of homology among their protein patterns (Figure 4 c–f) suggest that the tetraploids among themselves are not closely related. The close relationship between *A. tilcarense* and the northern populations of *A. scabriglume* was discussed previously.

Gross Structural Chromosomal Differences and High Protein-Band Homology

The *Agropyron scabriglume* hexaploid complex is composed of a series of geographically isolated populations. Most of these populations are morphologically indistinguishable, but some have apparently undergone ecological differentiation and chromosome repatterning (Hunziker, 1966, 1967 a and b).

There are several situations. The populations may be chromosomally identical with similar seed protein band patterns (Tafí del Valle, San Martín, Figure 3 e and f); they may be chromosomally identical, but with somewhat different patterns (Tupungato, Balcarce); or, as in the case of El Carancho and Balcarce populations, they may show differences of at least one paracentric inversion and at least four reciprocal translocations (Figure 4g)—a chain of 13 chromosomes has been observed at first metaphase. (In most populations of *A. scabriglume* a quadrivalent is frequently observed in first metaphase, and in El Carancho itself two quadrivalents have been observed occasionally.) These differences in chromosome structure are not coupled with differences in the protein patterns, which are almost identical (Figure 3 g, h, j, k, and l). These data suggest that a similar genic material is present in both populations (at least regarding those structural genes that control the quality of about 18 protein fractions), but the occurrence of extensive chromosome repatterning has reduced fertility to about 20 percent in the hybrids (Hunziker, 1967b; Hunziker and Palacios, unpublished). The striking similarity of protein bands as well as morphological identity point out the extremely close relationship of these populations and exclude the idea of polyphyletic origin and convergence. The extensive chromosome repatterning could be explained through the action of occasional mutator genes causing rapid chromosome repatterning. Though genic contents could remain almost the same except at rupture–reunion points, some chromosomes would thereafter be partly and not wholly homologous.

ENZYME PATTERNS

Genetic differences or alterations—which change the electrophoretic mobility of enzyme molecules—can be detected through the combination of electrophoresis followed by staining procedures to demonstrate the regions of enzyme activity directly in the electrophoretic medium (zymogram method). The genetic variants detected by these methods are enzymes in which structure presumably is altered but activity is retained. In the last five years, a large and rapidly increasing number of electrophoretic variants of enzymes has been discovered. Shaw (1965) has emphasized the usefulness of the zymogram method in several aspects of genetics and biochemistry, including its suitability for mass screening a number of different enzymes in large populations.

Mutations that do not alter the catalytic activity but do change the electrophoretic mobility of enzyme molecules provide a new tool for molecular systematics and population genetics. There are different ways by which these changes in mobility might result from alterations in the charge of the protein molecule. One way is by substitutions of certain amino acids for others having a different charge as a result of a base pair substitution in the DNA chain of a structural gene. Other mechanisms that could alter the net charge of a protein are: (1) nonhomologous crossing over, resulting in deletion or duplication of a segment of DNA (Shaw, 1965); (2) once a duplication exists in the genome, unequal but homologous crossing over becomes possible and could be a source of protein variation (Smithies, 1965); (3) finally, inversion involving part of a structural gene could also produce mutant proteins (Smithies, 1965).

Changes in mobility in high-resolution media such as starch and polyacrylamide could result from alterations in size and configuration of the protein molecule. Assuming, however, that the size and shape of the enzyme have remained constant and that the enzyme is a monomer product of a single allele, the changes that can be detected through electrophoresis are amino acid substitutions in the polypeptide chain. Since most of the amino acids are neutral in charge, it has been calculated that a single substitution in the nucleotide will produce a change in net charge in 27.56 percent of the cases, which means that almost three fourths of all mutants will not be electrophoretically detectable (Shaw, 1965).

Enzymes may occur, therefore, in multiple forms, which have been named "isozymes" (Markert and Möller, 1959). As Shaw (1965:940) has pointed out:

> . . . an important question in the study of isozymes is whether multiple zones of activity in a zymogram represent "true" isozymes; that is, are they structurally similar molecules or are they quite different molecules which have catalytic activity toward the same substrate?

Shaw (1965) has discussed several ways in which genetic variants can elucidate some of the relationships between isozymes.

Schwartz (1960) studied genetic variants of an esterase in maize in which each of the homozygous forms had a single esterase band (slow or fast), whereas the heterozygote possessed both slow and fast bands plus a third band having intermediate mobility. Schwartz postulated that the enzyme was a dimer composed of two randomly associating subunits, the band with intermediate velocity representing pairs of the two different subunits (allodimer). Polymer structure of enzymes seems to be rather general, and hybrid enzymes occur in approximately half of the enzymes in which electrophoretic variants have been detected (Shaw, 1965). In the future, hybrid proteins and enzymes might prove to have fundamental importance in genetic, developmental, and evolutionary problems such as hybrid vigor, developmental homeostasis, amphiploidy, and introgression.

Shaw has recently reviewed the literature dealing with enzymes and their variation, especially in relation to frequency of polymorphism among enzyme systems. His conclusions were that "it would seem that enzymes which vary are the rule rather than the exception" (Shaw, 1965:938). In maize, Schwartz *et al.* (1965) have found seven alleles of the pH 7.5 esterase, each specifying a different isozyme.

On the basis that most studies showing enzyme polymorphisms have been made on cultivated or caged organisms, Boulter *et al.* (1966) favored the view that the selection of enzyme types would prove more effective under natural conditions. These authors maintain it is unlikely that enzyme polymorphisms will prove to be the rule. They studied L-glutamate dehydrogenase (GDH) in 12 species of *Vicia* (including *V. sativa*) and all proved to have the same characteristic pattern. Five species of *Lathyrus* gave a band pattern identical to that shown for the *Vicia* species, although *Lathyrus roseus* and *L. nissolia* had different patterns. The GDH patterns of *Pisum* and *Lens* species examined were identical to that of *Vicia sativa.* Jackson *et al.* (1967) have expressed a similar view, and they are inclined to think that the variation found in homologous enzyme molecules might be correspondingly less than the variation encountered in nonenzymatic proteins.

Contrary to the opinions of Boulter, *et al.* (1966) and Jackson *et al.* (1967), recent studies on wild populations of *Drosophila* and *Colias* (Lepidoptera) have shown remarkable polymorphisms for electrophoretic mobility at a variety of loci (Hubby and Lewontin, 1966; Lewontin and Hubby, 1966; Burns and Johnson, 1967).

An important new approach to population genetic problems on a molecular basis has been made recently (Hubby and Lewontin, 1966; Lewontin and Hubby, 1966). Studying wild *Drosophila* populations, these authors obtained estimates of the percentage of polymorphic loci and frequency of heterozygotes based on the identification of single individuals according to their electrophoretic patterns of proteins. About 39 percent of the loci in the genome of *Drosophila pseudoobscura* is estimated to be polymorphic over the whole species. The authors have estimated that the proportion of all loci in an individual genome that are in heterozygous condition ranges from 8 percent to 15 percent for different populations, with an average of 12 percent. Explanation for the maintenance of such large amounts of genic heterozygosity is not simple, according to these authors. Among other things, they postulate that heterosis could be explained partly by the presence, in some cases, of new hybrid enzymes in heterozygotes. But in those cases where no new hybrid enzymes are formed, variation in physicochemical characteristics of the same functional protein might enhance the flexibility of an organism living in a variable environment.

In *Colias euritheme*, an extraordinary polymorphism has been found for an esterase (Burns and Johnson, 1967). The populations consist almost entirely of heterozygotes formed from a large number of alleles at an autosomal locus.

Vaughan and Waite (1967a) studied the patterns of β-galactosidases, β-glucosidases, and esterases by means of starch electrophoresis on *Brassica campestris* var. *autumnalis, B. campestris* var. *rapa, B. oleracea, B. nigra* and *Sinapis alba.* The enzyme results, as well as results obtained with immunoelectrophoresis, indicate that both varieties of *B. campestris* are similar and that *Sinapis* differs considerably from the *Brassica* species and from *B. oleracea* and *B. campestris,* especially. *B. oleracea* would be closer to *B. campestris* than to *B. nigra.* More recently, the same authors (Vaughan and Waite, 1967b) studied the same enzyme systems in the natural amphiploids of *Brassica* and found evidence–partial addition of enzyme bands–to support the hypothesis that the amphiploids *B. carinata, B. juncea,* and *B. napus* (with 17, 18, and 19 pairs of chromosomes, respectively) have resulted from amphiploidy between *B. nigra, B. oleracea,* and *B. campestris* (with 8, 9, and 10 pairs of chromosomes, respectively). Immunoelectrophoretic results obtained by these authors, although somewhat limited, also support the findings of isozyme patterns.

Enzyme research in plants offers an almost virgin field to the molecular systematist and to the ecological and population geneticist. On *a priori* grounds, one would think that problems of racial and ecotypic differentiation–involving adaptation of distinct populations of the species to different environments–might be based at least partly on enzyme differences between these populations. Studies on the variation of specific enzymes and their inheritance, distribution, and frequencies in plants are badly needed, and it is hoped that more data will be available in the near future. As Alston (1967:297) recently pointed out:

> . . . intensive comparative studies of similar (and often homologous) enzymes should yield some knowledge about differences in primary structure that are directly attributable to evolutionary adaptations. Fortunately, the permissible changes (allowing the protein to retain its function at least in part) appear to be rather drastic in some proteins studied so that a surprisingly large pool of variation is available.

FINGERPRINT PEPTIDE PATTERNS

Jackson *et al.* (1967) have applied the fingerprint method (which combines electrophoresis and chromatography) to peptides separated from tryptic digests of the globulin fraction of seeds of five genera of Vicieae (*Vicia, Lathyrus, Lens, Pisum,* and *Cicer*) and found that the fingerprint patterns were very similar. Patterns obtained with *Phaseolus vulgaris* and two species of *Canavalia* (Phaseoleae, *sensu lato*) were different from those of the Vicieae. Fingerprint patterns of *Abrus precatorius* (Abreae) were different from those of *Phaseolus vulgaris* and also from those of Vicieae. Similarly, Kloz and Turkova (1963), using immunoelectrophoretic analysis, have shown that the tribe Vicieae is characterized by the presence of leguminoid and vicilinoid proteins and that these types of proteins are absent in the Phaseoleae. An electrophoretic study of the globulin fractions of species of these two tribes also showed differences (Boulter *et al.*, 1967). Finally, it is very interesting to compare all these protein results with those obtained by Bolton and collaborators by means of DNA hybridization on *Pisum sativum, Vicia villosa,* and *Phaseolus vulgaris,* which show that such hybridization between *Vicia* and *Pisum* involves about 50 percent of the DNA, and that between *Pisum* and *Phaseolus* involves about 20 percent (Boulter *et al.*, 1967).

CONCLUSIONS

Electrophoresis seems to be the simplest method and one of the most useful methods for comparing proteins of one organism with those of another. It yields data that may be easily and objectively interpreted. Results obtained by the immunoelectrophoretic and high-resolution zone electrophoresis techniques in the same groups of plants (*Brassica, Solanum,* etc.) suggest that the latter technique is more discriminating than the former and has the additional advantage of being simpler. It is likely that protein and enzyme high-resolution electrophoresis will be used more often as an analytical tool in such important evolutionary and taxonomic problems as polytypic and semispecific differentiation, cryptic speciation (sibling species), enzyme polymorphism and hybridity, the nature of polyploidy (whether autoploidy or allopolyploidy), the interpretation of chromosome pairing in meiosis of diploid or polyploid interspecific hybrids (providing additional evidence as to whether there is genic asynapsis in the hybrid), and estimations of heterozygosity in populations.

As pointed out by Hall (1964:37), protein electrophoresis "ought to be used along with the more conventional methods in determining the parental species of hybrids of unknown origin." The origin of ancient amphiploids—which, because of recently developed genetic incompatibility can no longer be synthesized by crossing their ancestral diploid species—might be elucidated by comparing their protein spectra with those of the putative parental species. This type of evidence might prove very important for establishing the origin of, and for improving, amphiploids of economic importance.

Finally, I plead for "integral systematics," but certainly I do not want to create a new synonym. There are too many synonyms in some subdisciplines of systematics already. By themselves, molecular data often might be of no more value than a traditional morphological trait. Sibley (1965:120) has recently pointed out that molecular data for systematic purposes "require a systematist who knows, appreciates and understands the other available information about the group of organisms he is studying."

Undoubtedly, molecular data are fascinating. They require more laborious and time-consuming procedures than the more conventional methods, but they should be integrated with data from all possible sources that furnish important information for systematic and evolutionary purposes. Storage seed proteins, for instance, are extracted easily, and, provided they are taken from mature seeds, they yield uniform patterns despite great environmental differences. Moreover, my electrophoretic results indicate that even when these proteins are conservative to a certain extent (as to reflect affinities within the genus), they show intraspecific, semispecific, and interspecific variations. These data are extremely valuable for the systematist when they are integrated with morphological, cytogenetic, ecological, and biogeographical evidence.

ACKNOWLEDGMENTS

My research on electrophoresis and cytogenetics, summarized in this paper, has been supported by grants from the Consejo Nacional de Investigaciones Científicas y Técnicas, the Comisión Administradora del Fondo de la Promoción de la Tecnología Agropecuaria, and the Instituto Nacional de Tecnología Agropecuaria, Argentina. The author expresses his gratitude to Professor Otto T. Solbrig, University of Michigan, and to Dr. Richard N. Lester, University of Kansas, for bibliographical help in preparing this review; to Mrs. Vilma B. de Fernández, Mrs. Amalia G. de Valesi, Mr. C. A. Naranjo, Mr. R. A. Palacios, and Miss Aída De Gregorio for technical help; and to Mr. Roger Glass for suggesting improvements in the manuscript.

REFERENCES

Alston, R. E. 1965. Comparisons of the importance of basic metabolites, secondary compounds and macromolecules in systematic studies. Lloydia 28(4):300–312.

Alston, R. E. 1967. Biochemical systematics, p. 197–305 *In* T. Dobzhansky, M. K. Hecht, and Wm. C. Steere [ed] Evolutionary biology, Vol. 1. Appleton-Century-Crofts, New York.

Alston, R. E., and B. L. Turner. 1963. Biochemical systematics. Prentice-Hall, Englewood Cliffs, New Jersey. 404 p.

Baum, W. C. 1954. Systematic serology of the family Cucurbitaceae with special reference to the genus *Cucurbita.* Serol. Mus. Bull. 13:5–8.

Boulter, D., D. A. Thurman, and E. Derbyshire. 1967. A disc electrophoretic study of globulin proteins of legume seeds with reference to their systematics. New Phytol. 66(1):27–36.

Boulter, D., D. A. Thurman, and B. L. Turner. 1966. The use of disc electrophoresis of plant proteins in systematics. Taxon 15(4):135–143.

Brown, R. M., and R. N. Lester. 1965. Comparative immunology of the algal genera *Tetracystis* and *Chlorococcum*. J. Phytol. 1(2):60–65.
Burns, J. M., and F. M. Johnson. 1967. Esterase polymorphism in natural populations of a sulfur butterfly, *Colias eurytheme*. Science 156(3771): 93–96.
Coates, M. 1967. A comparative study of the serum proteins of the species of *Taricha* and their hybrids. Evolution 21:130–140.
Colloque de Chemiotaxinomie. 1967. Organisé à Paris le 15 et 16 Oct. 1965 par. C. Mentzer. Bull. Soc. Bot. France. Mem. 1965. 186 p.
Coulson, C. B., and A. K. Sim. 1964. Proteins of various species of wheat and closely related genera and their relationship to genetical characteristics. Nature 202(4939):1305–1308.
Crick, F. H. C. 1958. On protein synthesis, p. 138–163 *In* The biological replication of macromolecules. Symp. 12, Soc. Exp. Biol. New York.
Crowle, A. J. 1961. Immunodiffusion. Academic Press, New York. 333 p.
Desborough, S., and S. J. Peloquin. 1966. Disc electrophoresis of tuber proteins from *Solanum* species and interspecific hybrids. Phytochemistry 5(4):727–733.
Fairbrothers, D. E. 1966. Comparative serological studies in plant systematics. Serol. Mus. Bull. 35:2–6.
Fairbrothers, D. E., and R. R. Boulette. 1960. Some phytoserological relationships within the Umbelliferae. Am. Inst. Biol. Sci. Bull. 10:45.
Fairbrothers, D. E., and M. A. Johnson. 1961. The precipitin reaction as an indicator of relationship in some grasses, p. 116–120 *In* Recent advances in botany. Univ. Toronto Press, Toronto.
Fairbrothers, D. E., and M. A. Johnson. 1964. Comparative serological studies within the families Cornaceae (dogwood) and Nyssaceae (sour gum), p. 305–318 *In* C. A. Leone [ed] Taxonomic biochemistry and serology. Ronald Press, New York.
Feillet, P. 1965. Contribution à l'etude des protéines de blé. Influence des facteurs génétiques, agronomiques et technologiques. Ann. Tech. Agr., 14(1):1–94.
Feldman, M. 1966. The effect of chromosomes 5B, 5D and 5A on chromosomal pairing in *Triticum aestivum*. Proc. Nat. Acad. Sci. U.S. 55(6): 1447–1453.
Fitch, W. M., and E. Margoliash. 1967. Construction of phylogenetic trees. Science 155(3760):279–284.
Fox, D. J., D. A. Thurman, and D. Boulter. 1964. Studies on the protein of seeds of the Leguminosae. I. Albumins. Phytochemistry 3:417–419.
Gell, P. G. H., J. G. Hawkes, and S. T. C. Wright. 1960. The application of immunological methods to the taxonomy of species within the genus *Solanum*. Proc. Roy. Soc. London, Ser. B 151:364–383.
Grabar, P., and P. Burtin. 1964. Immuno-electrophoretic analysis. Elsevier Publ. Co., Amsterdam, London, New York. 294 p.
Hall, O. 1959. Immuno-electrophoretic analysis of allopolyploid ryewheat and its parental species. Hereditas 45:495–504.
Hall, O. 1964. Use of proteins in determination of parental species of un-

known hybrids. Bio Science 14(4):37.

Hall, O., and B. L. Johnson. 1962. Electrophoretic analysis of the amphiploid of *Stipa viridula* x *Oryzopsis hymenoides* and its parental species. Hereditas 48:530–535.

Hall, O., B. L. Johnson, and R. Olered. 1966. Evaluation of genome relationships in wheat from their protein homologies. Proc. 2nd Int. Symp. Wheat Genetics. Hereditas (suppl.) 2:47–54.

Hammond, H. D. 1955a. A study of taxonomic relationship within the Solanaceae as revealed by the photron'er serological method. Serol. Mus. Bull. 14:3–5.

Hammond, H. D. 1955b. Systematic serological studies in Ranunculaceae. Serol. Mus. Bull. 14:1–3.

Hawkes, J. G. 1956. A revision of the tuber-bearing Solanums. Ann. Rept. Scott. Pl. Breed. Sta. 1956:38–110.

Hawkes, J. G. 1963. A revision of the tuber-bearing Solanums, 2nd. ed. Scott. Pl. Breed. Sta. Rec. 1963:76–181.

Hawkes, J. G., and R. N. Lester. 1966. Immunological studies in the tuber-bearing Solanums. II. Relationships of the North American species. Ann. Bot. 30(118):269–290.

Hegnauer, R. 1962–1966. Chemotaxonomie der pflanzen. Birkhaüser Verlag, Basel. Vols. 1–4.

Hubby, J. L., and R. C. Lewontin. 1966. A molecular approach to the study of genic heterozygosity in natural populations. I. The number of alleles at different loci in *Drosophila pseudoobscura.* Genetics 54:577–594.

Hunziker, J. H. 1966. Diferenciación cromosómica en el complejo hexaploide *Agropyron scabriglume.* Kurtziana 2:127–149.

Hunziker, J. H. 1967a. Analysis of phylogenetic affinities and differentiation in South American *Agropyron* by cytogenetics and protein electrophoresis. Ciencia e Cultura (São Paulo) 19(1):199–217.

Hunziker, J. H. 1967b. Chromosome and protein differentiation in the *Agropyron scabriglume* complex. Taxon 16:259–266.

Jackson, P., J. M. Milton, and D. Boulter. 1967. Fingerprint patterns of the globulin fraction obtained from seeds of various species of the Fabaceae. New Phytol. 66(1):47–56.

Johnson, B., and O. Hall. 1965. Analysis of phylogenetic affinities in the Triticinae by protein electrophoresis. Am. J. Bot. 52(5):506–513.

Johnson, B. L., and O. Hall. 1966a. Electrophoretic studies of species relationships in *Triticum.* Qual. Plant. Mat. Veg. 13:68.

Johnson, B. L., and O. Hall. 1966b. Electrophoretic studies of species relationships in *Triticum.* Acta Agr. Scand. Suppl. 16:222–224.

Johnson, M. A. 1953. Relationship in the Magnoliaceae as determined by the precipitin reaction. Bull. Torrey Bot. Club. 80:349–350.

Johnson, M. A. 1954. The precipitin reaction as an index of relationship in the Magnoliaceae. Serol. Mus. Bull. 13:1–5.

Johnson, M. A., and D. E. Fairbrothers. 1965. Comparison and interpretation of serological data in the Magnoliaceae. Bot. Gaz. 126(4):260–269.

Kabat, E. A., and M. M. Mayer. 1961. Experimental immunochemistry.

Charles C. Thomas, Springfield, Illinois. 905 p.
Kloz, J. 1962. An investigation of the protein characters of four *Phaseolus* species with special reference to the question of their phylogenesis. Biol. Plant. (Praha) 4(2):85–90.
Kloz, J., and V. Turkova. 1963. Legumin, vicilin and proteins similar to them in the seeds of some species of the Viciaceae family (a comparative serological study). Biol. Plant. (Praha) 5:29–40.
Kloz, J., E. Klozova, and V. Turkova. 1966. Protein characters and relationships between *Phaseolus vulgaris* ssp. *aborigineus* Burk. and related taxons of the genus *Phaseolus*. Biol. Plant. (Praha) 8(3):187–196.
Kloz, J., V. Turkova, and E. Klozova. 1960. Serological investigations of taxonic specificity of proteins in various plant organs in some taxons of the family Viciaceae. Biol. Plant. (Praha) 2:126–137.
Leone, C. A. [ed] 1964. Taxonomic biochemistry and serology. Ronald Press, New York. 728 p.
Lester, R. N. 1964. Comparative immunochemistry of the tuber-bearing species of the genus *Solanum*, p. 291–303 *In* C. A. Leone [ed] Taxonomic biochemistry and serology. Ronald Press, New York.
Lester, R. N. 1965. Immunological studies on the tuber-bearing Solanums. I. Techniques and South American species. Ann. Bot. 29(116):609–624.
Lester, R. N., R. E. Alston, and B. L. Turner. 1965. Serological studies in *Baptisia* and certain other genera of the Leguminosae. Am. J. Bot. 52:165–172.
Lewontin, R. C., and J. L. Hubby. 1966. A molecular approach to the study of genic heterozygosity in natural populations. II. Amount of variation and degree of heterozygosity in natural populations of *Drosophila pseudoobscura*. Genetics 54:595–609.
Loeschcke, V., and H. Stegemann. 1966a. Polyacrylamid-Elektrophorese zur Beurteilung von Proteinen der Kartoffel (*Solanum tuberosum* L.). Z. Naturforsch. 21b(9):879–888.
Loeschcke, V., and H. Stegemann. 1966b. Proteine der Kartoffelknollen in Abhängigkeit von sorte und virosen (polyacrylamid-elektrophorese). Phytochemistry 5(5):985–991.
Margoliash, E., and E. L. Smith. 1965. Structural and functional aspects of cytochrome *c* in relation to evolution, p. 221–242 *In* V. Bryson and H. J. Vogel [ed] Evolving genes and proteins. Academic Press, New York.
Markert, C. L., and F. Möller. 1959. Multiple forms of enzymes. Tissue, entogenic and species specific patterns. Proc. Nat. Acad. Sci. U.S. 45:753–763.
Rees, H., and W. I. C. Davies. 1963. DNA and wheat ancestry. Proc. XI Int. Congr. Genetics 1:136.
Riley, R., and C. N. Law. 1965. Genetic variation in chromosome pairing. Adv. Genetics 13:57–114.
Riley, R., J. Unrau, and V. Chapman. 1958. Evidence of the origin of the B genome of wheat. J. Hered. 49:91–98.
Sahulka, J. 1965. Electrophoretic assay of protein extracts from apple tree blossoms and leaves. Biol. Plant. (Praha) 7(3):165–168.

Sarkar, P., and G. L. Stebbins, Jr. 1956. Morphological evidence concerning the origin of the B genome in wheat. Am. J. Bot. 43:297–304.

Schwartz, D. 1960. Genetic studies on mutant enzyme in maize: Synthesis of hybrid enzymes by heterozygotes. Proc. Nat. Acad. Sci. U.S. 46:1210–1215.

Schwartz, D., L. Fuchsman, and K. H. McGrath. 1965. Allelic isozymes of the pH 7.5 esterase in maize. Genetics 52:1265–1268.

Shaw, C. R. 1965. Electrophoretic variation in enzymes. Science 149:936–943.

Sibley, C. G. 1960. The electrophoretic patterns of avian egg-white proteins as taxonomic characters. Ibis 102:215–284.

Sibley, C. G. 1962. The comparative morphology of protein molecules as data for classification. Syst. Zool. 3:108–118.

Sibley, C. G. 1964. The characteristics of specific peptides from single proteins as data for classification, p. 435–450 *In* C. A. Leone [ed] Taxonomic biochemistry and serology. Ronald Press, New York.

Sibley, C. G. 1965. Molecular systematics: New techniques applied to old problems. L'Oiseau et Rev. Française d'Ornithol. Berlioz jubilee vol. (35):112–124.

Smithies, O. 1965. Protein variations in man. Proc. XI Int. Congr. Genetics 3:897–901.

Swain, T. [ed] 1963. Chemical plant taxonomy. Academic Press, New York. 543 p.

Swain, T. [ed] 1966. Comparative phytochemistry. Academic Press, London. 360 p.

Vaughan, J. G., and A. Waite. 1967a. Comparative electrophoretic studies of the seed proteins of certain species of *Brassica* and *Sinapis.* J. Exp. Bot. 18(54):100–109.

Vaughan, J. G., and A. Waite. 1967b. Comparative electrophoretic studies of the seed proteins of certain amphidiploid species of *Brassica.* J. Exp. Bot. 18(55):269–276.

Vaughan, J. G., A. Waite, D. Boulter, and S. Waiters. 1965. Taxonomic investigation of several *Brassica* species using serology and the separation of proteins by electrophoresis on acrylamide gels. Nature 208(5011): 704–705.

Zuckerkandl, E., and L. Pauling. 1965. Molecules as documents of evolutionary history. J. Theoret. Biol. 8:357–366.

Discussion

Bert G. Brehm

Dr. Hunziker has demonstrated the significance of protein analyses with reference to genomic contributions in various amphidiploids.

The essentially additive nature of parental contributions to the chemistry of amphidiploids has been shown for other types of compounds (Smith and Abashian, 1963), but particularly with flavonoid glycosides (Smith and Levin, 1963; Stebbins *et al.*, 1963; Torres and Levin, 1964; Brehm and Ownbey, 1965; Melchert, 1966). These compounds have a relatively low molecular weight and size and are frequently considered to be secondary compounds because, to date, no essential function of the plant has been consistently correlated with their presence (Alston, 1967).

I will discuss very briefly three examples in the family Compositae in which amphidiploid ancestry has been investigated by means of comparative chemistry utilizing two-dimensional paper-chromatographic techniques. In each case, the taxa are characterized by an association or pattern of phenolic compounds. Various studies of the specific chemistry of such patterns indicate that flavonoid glycosides frequently are the most significant constituents (Alston *et al.*, 1965; McClure and Alston, 1966; Kroschewsky, 1967).

The first example is from work by Torres and Levin (1964) on the genus *Zinnia* (Compositae-Helianthoideae). Table 1 includes data on the seven taxa represented in this study: three are diploid (2*n*), three are tetraploid (4*n*), and one is an octaploid (8*n*). Since the three diploid species are represented by only two chromatographic patterns, $A_{1,3}$ for *Z. juniperifolia* and *Z. oligantha* and A_2 for *Z. acerosa,* morphological and cytological data were combined with the chromatographic data to interpret the relationships within the system. The proposed relationships are summarized as follows: (1) tetraploid *Z. acerosa* is alloploid, confirming what has been suggested previously on the basis of cytological data; (2) tetraploid *Z. citrata* originated from the combination *Z. juniperifolia* + *Z. oligantha* ($A_{1,3}$ + $A_{1,3}$); (3) *Z. acerosa* (A_2) apparently has not contributed to the genomic make-up of the tetraploid *Z. grandiflora* or the octaploid *Z. anomala.* In this genus the chromatographic patterns have provided a basis for choosing between alternative interpretations of the ancestry of certain allopolyploids when morphological and cytological data were not conclusive.

Melchert (1966) examined, by chromatographic pattern analysis, 11 of the 15 recognized taxa in the genus *Thelesperma* (Compositae-Coreopsidineae). Each species, with the exception of *T. burridgeanum* (an endemic of very limited distribution), had a very similar pattern (Table 2). The taxa are characterized by a generic pattern rather

TABLE 1 Biochemical Constituents from Chromatograms of Species of *Zinnia.* Compounds Common to All Species Are Not Included. (Adapted from Torres and Levin, 1964.)

Taxon	Chromatographic Spot Number 1	2	3	4	5	6	7	Pattern Designation	n	Presumed Genome
Z. juniperifolia	–	–	–	X	X	X	X	$A_{1,3}$	10	A_1A_1
Z. acerosa	X	X	X	–	–	–	–	A_2	10	A_2A_2
Z. oligantha	–	–	–	X	X	X	X	$A_{1,3}$	10	A_3A_3
Z. acerosa	X	X	X	X	X	X	X	$A_{1,3}$ A_2	20	$A_2A_2A_3A_3$
Z. citrea	X	X	X	X	X	X	X	$A_{1,3}$ A_2	20	$A_1A_1A_2A_2$
Z. grandiflora	–	–	–	X	X	X	X	$A_{1,3}$	21	$A_1A_1A_3A_3$
Z. anomala	–	–	–	X	X	X	X	$A_{1,3}$	42±	$(A_1A_1A_3A_3)_2$

than by individual species patterns. However, distinct biochemical differences appear between the diploid (n = 10, 11) forms of *T. simplicifolium* and the tetraploid (n = 22) forms of the same species. Although the latter were morphologically indistinguishable from the diploids, they occupy a distinct geographical area at the western edge of the species distribution. Since meiosis in the tetraploid is generally regular and only occasional associations of four chromosomes have been noted, origin of the tetraploid by the amphidiploid process seems likely. The principal chemical differences between the taxa are the ability of the tetraploid to make anthochlors (aurones or chalkones; spots 6, 14, and 16), whereas the diploid cannot, and the dissimilarity of the diploid to the over-all generic pattern. This evidence supports the interpretation that the tetraploid forms did not develop from the extant diploid but rather that the 2n and 4n forms had a common origin in the past. Apparently, the phenolic chemistry of each has evolved independently, in contrast to their common morphology.

Ownbey (1950) has shown that the tetraploid *Tragopogon mirus* (Compositae-Chicorieae) originated in the past 25 years from the

TABLE 2 Distribution of Phenolic Constituents in *Thelesperma.* [Taxa: A, "Typical" *Thelesperma* chromatographic profile characteristic of eight species: *T. filifolium, T. flavodiscum, T. curvicarpum, T. nuecense, T. megapotamicum, T. ambiguum, T. longipes, T. subnudum;* B, *T. burridgeanum;* C, *T. simplicifolium* ($n = 22$); D, *T. simplicifolium,* ($n = 10, 11$). The symbol (-) indicates major differences between the chemistry of diploid and tetraploid *T. simplicifolium;* preliminary characterization suggests these are aurones or chalkones, in contrast to the other flavonoid groups comprising the remaining pattern constituents.] (Adapted from Melchert, 1966.)

	Two-Dimensional Chromatographic Spot Number																														
Taxa	1	2	3	4	5	6	7	8	9	10	11	12	13	14	15	16	17	18	19	20	21	22	23	24	25	26	27	28	29	30	31
A	+	+	+	+	+	+	+	+	+	+	+	+	+	+	+	+	+	+	+	+	+	+									
B	+	+	+	+	+		+	+						+	+	+	+		+				+	+	+	+	+	+	+	+	+
C	+	+	+	+	+	+	+	+	+	+	+	+		+		+	+		+	+	+										
D	+	+	+	+	+	(-)		+	+					(-)	+	(-)	+		+	+											+

TABLE 3 Flavonoid Composition of Amphidiploid *Tragopogon mirus* and Related Taxa. Flavonoids Common to All Taxa Are Not Included. (Adapted from Brehm and Ownbey, 1965. Chemical identifications from Kroschewsky, 1967.)

Compound	(2*n*) *T. dubius*	(2*n*) *T. porrifolius*	(4*n*) *T. mirus*	F_1 Hybrid *dubius* x *porrifolius*
3, luteolin-7-0-monoglucoside	+	(-)	+ (-)	+ (-)
6, luteolin-6-8-di C-glycoside	+	(-)	+	+
8, quercetin-3-0-glucoside	+	+	+	+
10, 7-0-methyl luteolin-6-C-glycoside	+	(-)	+	+
13, apiginin-6-C-glucoxyloside	+	(-)	+ (-)	+
14, 7-0-methyl apiginin-6-C-glycoside	+	(-)	+	+
19, apiginin-8-C-glycoside	(-)	+	+	+

natural doubling of the sterile F_1 hybrid *T. porrifolius* x *T. dubius.* The relationship of *T. mirus* to these two species was originally postulated on the basis of morphological and cytological analyses. Proof of the origin of this amphidiploid has been obtained by resynthesis of the taxon from appropriate parental types. The flavonoid chemistry of these species (Table 3) is characterized by a regularly appearing association of C-glycosyl flavonoids based on the flavones apiginin and luteolin plus a miscellany of other flavonoids and phenolic compounds (Kroschewsky, 1967). The most pronounced differences between the flavonoid chemistry of the parental species are the absence of luteolin-7-0-monoglucoside and certain C-glycosyl compounds in *T. porrifolius* and the absence of apiginin-8-C-glycoside in *T. dubius.* The F_1 hybrids and the derived amphidiploid *T. mirus* are essentially additive for the presence of the parental constituents. However, with respect to the synthesis of luteolin-7-0-monoglucoside, both the F_1 and the tetraploid display critical populational differences. Four of the five known colonies of *T. mirus* exist in the eastern Washington region. In one of these colonies, all the sampled individuals of *T. mirus* lacked luteolin-7-0-monoglucoside, and three of the ten natural F_1 hybrids examined from the immediate environment also failed to synthesize this compound. In a comparable colony, all *T. mirus* synthesized the compound, and all F_1 hybrids of the area contained the compound as well. We interpret these results as evidence that *T. mirus* in the two colonies have been derived from distinct hybrids and represent independent origins of the same species. Cytological evidence obtained by Ownbey strongly indicates that the origin of each of the remaining colonies also was an independent event (Ownbey and McCollum, 1954). Why this species should originate independently in four areas within 30 miles of each other, within a few years of each other, and only in this region is a most intriguing question that has not yet been answered.

In comparison, the macromolecular constituents (e.g., proteins) may serve as distinctive genomic markers in tracing the ancestry of amphidiploids. Higher ploidy levels, particularly when endosperm tissue is examined, reduce the opportunity for observation of genetic variability and should provide an exceptionally stable (nonvariable) set of chemical constituents characteristic of the genome. The studies reported by Dr. Hunziker on the additive nature of endosperm storage proteins of various Gramineae allopolyploids provide direct evidence for the operation of this type of system. Much smaller molecules (e.g., flavonoids) may serve in a similar fashion, but frequently the amphidiploid taxa exhibit genetically regulated variability expressed as the presence or absence of specific parental compounds. Such variability does not reduce the utilization of these patterns as genomic markers, and it may provide additional insights into the relationships under investigation that were unsuspected on the basis of other data.

REFERENCES

Alston, R. E. 1967. Biochemical systematics, p. 197–305 *In* T. Dobzhansky, M. K. Hecht, and W. C. Steere [ed] Evolutionary biology, Vol. I. Appleton-Century-Crofts, New York.

Alston, R. E., H. Rösler, K. Naifeh, and T. J. Mabry. 1965. Hybrid compounds in natural interspecific hybrids. Proc. Nat. Acad. Sci. U.S. 54:1458–1465.

Brehm, B. G., and M. Ownbey. 1965. Variation in chromatographic patterns in the *Tragopogon dubius-pratensis-porrifolius* complex (Compositae). Am. J. Bot. 52:811–818.

Kroschewsky, J. R. 1967. Investigations of flavonoids in the genus *Tragopogon* (Compositae). Doctoral dissertation, Univ. of Texas.

McClure, J. W., and R. E. Alston. 1966. Chemotaxonomy of the Lemnaceae. Am. J. Bot. 53:849–859.

Melchert, T. E. 1966. Chemo-demes of diploid and tetraploid *Telesperma simplicifolium* (Heliantheae, Coreopsidineae). Am. J. Bot. 53:1015–1020.

Ownbey, M. 1950. Natural hybridization and amphidiploidy in the genus *Tragopogon*. Am. J. Bot. 37:487–499.

Ownbey, M., and G. D. McCollum. 1954. The chromosomes of *Tragopogon.* Rhodora 50:9–21.

Smith, H. H., and D. V. Abashian. 1963. Chromatographic investigations on the alkaloid content of *Nicotiana* species and interspecific combinations. Am. J. Bot. 50:435–447.

Smith, D. M., and D. A. Levin. 1963. A chromatographic study of reticulate evolution in the Applachian *Asplenium* complex. Am. J. Bot. 50:952–958.

Stebbins, G. L., B. L. Harvey, E. L. Cox, J. N. Rutger, G. Jelencovic, and E. Yagin. 1963. Identification of the ancestry of an amphidiploid *Viola* with the aid of paper chromatography. Am. J. Bot. 50:830–839.

Torres, A. M., and D. A. Levin. 1964. A chromatographic study of cespitose zinnias. Am. J. Bot. 51:639–643.

Discussion

Otto T. Solbrig

Biochemical systematics is the latest of a series of approaches that look at the problem of diversity and variability of organisms from the narrow point of view of a set of information that is obtained through the application of a specialized technique. Fortunately, practitioners of chromosome taxonomy, cytogenetics, and numerical taxonomy, to name just a few other approaches, have shown, mostly through their excessive enthusiasm, that there is no one way of looking at nature. As has repeatedly been stressed today and yesterday, nature refuses to accept neat categorization, no matter how clever our formulas, how obtuse or acute our dendrographic angles, and even in spite of very impressive and expensive gas chromatographs, nuclear resonance spectrographs, amino acids analyzers or high-voltage electrophoresis apparatus.

However, each approach introduces a new set of information, allowing the investigator to describe more precisely the patterns of variation of his organisms, and more importantly, to try to explain the mechanisms that brought about this variation. In this sense, biochemical systematics is in my opinion very promising. As for strict classification, on the other hand, its usefulness is indirect. I predict that biochemical systematics is going to provide very few diagnostic characters in flowering-plant taxonomy, and, although there is no doubt that chemodemes, chemovars, and chemospecies are going to be added to our constellation of categories in due time, their half-life is likely to be brief. However, a better understanding of the patterns of variation through the knowledge of molecular phenomena will lead to better biological understanding and, eventually, to a better taxonomy.

Dr. Hunziker's excellent presentation has shown how macromolecular data can be used to explore new avenues, as well as how old problems can be looked at in a new light.

The amphiploids studied by Dr. Hunziker have protein patterns that are truly additive. Although this is also the case with the storage proteins of wheat, as shown by Johnson and Hall (1956), I question whether the evidence at hand is sufficient to accept this as a universal fact. For example, working with beans, Garber and collaborators (personal communication) have found that in crosses between *Phaseolus coccineus* and *P. vulgaris* there is dominance in the esterase pattern of the F_1 hybrid, so that only the bands of *P. vulgaris* are expressed. However, in the case of leucine amino peptidase the F_1 hybrid expresses the bands of both *P. vulgaris* and *P. coccineus;* consequently, leucine amino peptidase patterns serve as a check on the cross. In the F_2 of this cross, there is segregation in the expected mendelian ratios for both enzymes, esterases still showing dominance. In chickens, Law (1967) has found dominance in the F_1 for the pattern of alkaline phosphatase and of leucine amino peptidase. In the case of the chicken, the observed dominance can be explained by hypothesizing the presence or absence of a gene controlling the attachment of sialic acid units to both leucine amino peptidase and alkaline phosphatase. To my knowledge there still is no experimental evidence for this hypothesis. In view of these cases of suppression of the expression of an enzyme, I wonder whether a similar phenomenon might not occur also, at least in certain cases, in polyploids.

The question of whether the enzyme pattern of polyploids is additive in respect to its diploid parents or whether certain loci become suppressed is of great interest from the point of view of development as well as of evolution. Although the evidence so far favors the additive idea, I think that it is still very much an open question.

Dr. Hunziker mentioned some of the areas where he thought macromolecular data would be useful for solving evolutionary problems, and I concur with him in his assessment. However, it is my feeling that in these studies an effort should be made to obtain, whenever possible, electrophoretic enzyme patterns in addition to total protein, and, if possible, from several tissues, such as leaves or flowers, in addition to storage organs. Ideally, we should try to obtain the sequence of amino acids, but this is still quite impractical.

In regard to Dr. Hunziker's results on correlation of protein patterns with chromosomal rearrangements, it is very interesting to see that, in spite of a minimum of six reciprocal translocations and two paracentric inversions, no change is observed in the protein pattern in one of his crosses within the *Agropyron scabriglume* complex. This shows very nicely, I think, how sterility can arise as a result of purely cytological phenomena. The El Carancho population presumably could be classed as an incipient sibling population. I ask Dr. Hunziker if he agrees, and if he would comment on some of these points.

REFERENCES

Johnson, B. L., and O. Hall, 1956. Analysis of phylogenetic affinities in the Triticineae by protein electrophoresis. Am. J. Bot. 52:506–513.

Law, G. R. J., 1967. Alkaline phosphatase and leucine-amino-peptidase associations in plasma of the chicken. Science 156(3778):1106–1107.

Informal Discussion

HUNZIKER: Regarding the last question about the chromosomal differences between the populations that create a barrier to gene interchange, I agree completely. However, I should have said "potential gene interchange" because at the present the populations are geographically isolated. I have discussed the taxonomic and evolutionary status of El Carancho and other populations in several recent articles (Hunziker, 1966, 1967 a and b; for citations see page 310). The fact that El Carancho and some other populations seem to have diverged enough that they deserve the status of semispecies or sibling species is the reason why I refer to this morphologically fairly homogeneous group as "*A. scabriglume* complex."

In regard to your suggestion that we should study enzyme patterns, I am not sure that this approach would prove fruitful in this case. So far, we have been working with storage proteins that, although they denote variation, are sufficiently conservative to keep some meaningful clues for the evolutionist. The striking resemblance in protein band patterns between *A. tilcarense* and its hexaploid derivatives (the northern populations of *A. scabriglume*) exemplifies this point (see Figures 2, 3, and 4 e and f, pp. 298–300). On the other hand, recent evidence on enzyme patterns in several organisms (*Drosophila, Colias*) seem to indicate an extraordinary variation at the intraspecific level. If I understood correctly, Dr. Sibley has just told me that he thought the data on hemoglobins of birds are much more conservative and more meaningful phylogenetically than are the data on enzymes.

SIBLEY: We might say that data on "hemoglobins and some enzymes" are more meaningful, but we could not make a general statement for all. The comment I really wanted to make was in relation to the botanists' tendency—which I think has grown out of their preoccupation with low-molecular-weight compounds—to fail to distinguish with sufficient clarity between the information content of low-molecular-weight compounds and the informational macromolecules, such as proteins and DNA. These two groups of compounds are not comparable, and I consider it important to distinguish between them clearly in all cases.

The low-molecular-weight compounds usually have behind them a biosynthetic series of enzymes. Mutations affecting these enzymes may produce a change in the end products of the pathway—that is, the low-molecular-weight compounds that the plant taxonomist examines. There is no simple relationship between the structure of the enzymes (the information-containing units) in this pathway and the low-molecular-weight compounds that are examined at the end of the pathway. Herein lies the reason why it is a fallacy to think that low-molecular-weight compounds can be used as taxonomic data relating to categories above the species level.

The great contributions made with materials of this kind have been in cases like the famous *Baptisia* hybridization problem where, I think we all agree, the results have been spectacular and unquestionably correct. I was delighted to read in the summary of Ralph Alston's recent paper, in the first volume of *Evolutionary Biology,* that he said—and I quote from memory—"The future belongs to the macromolecules."

BREHM: There is some recent and continuing work on the betalins, a group of low-molecular-weight compounds that have a distribution limited to certain families of flowering plants. Some systematists feel that the presence of this biosynthetically distinct group of compounds is important enough to consider those families capable of producing them as a distinct order and suggest a re-evaluation of the morphological basis for the previous taxonomic disposition. In this situation, the compounds characterize not only individual families, but also an order. I believe there is considerable evidence in plants for use of low-molecular-weight compounds at all taxonomic ranks.

SIBLEY: I would call that a possible case of circular reasoning. You may have decided the boundaries of the order from the occurrence of betacyanins. Even if you did not define the order in this fashion the correlation does not mean that low-molecular-weight compounds have a high information content. Ernest Baldwin called attention to various correlations of this kind far back in the history of comparative biochemistry. Some of these correlations are spectacular, but others are taxonomically meaningless. I criticize the botanists only in that they sometimes have been a little casual about differentiating between these two classes of molecules. In a general audience such as this, many persons might assume that all molecules are equal in their taxonomic information content. So, I am taking you gently to task and I am not questioning the existence of some interesting correlations.

CRONQUIST: The statement that the presence of betacyanins characterizes an order is true only if you assume *a priori* that this is the critical character and that all other characters must be disregarded. If you consider all of the characters available to us, you will find that there are a couple of families belonging in the same order that do not have betacyanins, as far as anyone knows. One of these families is the Caryophyllaceae, which in most respects is so typical of the order that it gives its name to the order Caryophyllales. It does happen to be true that the betacyanins, as far as we know, are restricted to a relatively small taxonomic group—a sizable order and perhaps a couple of satellite orders—so they have taxonomic significance, but to say that the betacyanins *characterize an order* is, indeed, circular reasoning.

SOLBRIG: I agree entirely with Dr. Sibley, and I was hoping to make the same point. I think there is some confusion here between the use of characters purely for classification and for knowledge of the evolution and biology of the organism. For the purpose of classification, any character is, in principle, of equal value, and I would say—from that point of view—that perhaps the proteins are worse because they are hard to get at. Technically, it is not easy. On the other hand, from the point of view of learning something about the biology of the organisms, the proteins and the enzymes as primary gene products give us a new set of information, and from them we can estimate gene frequencies and get kinds of information that were very hard to get before. Their great value lies in studies of evolution and in studies of the biology of organisms and not so much for classification or for delimiting taxa and constructing a key.

HERBERT C. DESSAUER

Molecular Data in Animal Systematics

INTRODUCTION

Florkin, (1949, p. 120) has said:

> The study of biochemical characteristics depends upon techniques which frequently are complicated, and such a study is more difficult to accomplish than direct observation of morphological characters. Nevertheless, had naturalists started from these rather than from morphological observations they would have been bound to conceive the idea of evolution of animals.

Although a late addition to the armamentarium of the systematist, the molecular approach is strengthening the foundation of natural classifications by uncovering evidence on mechanisms of evolution at the gene level; by emphasizing the dynamic rather than typological nature of the species; and by making possible quantitative, unbiased assessments of genetic relationships and rates of evolution (Bryson and Vogel, 1965; Florkin and Mason, 1960–1964; Leone, 1964).

OBTAINING THE DATA

Florkin's statement, however, not only suggested this promise of the molecular approach but also alluded to its greatest handicap, the difficulty of obtaining the evidence. Evidence is largely made up of data on physiological processes, on the proteins that make these processes possible (Figure 1), and on the nucleic acids that control the presence and determine the structure of specific proteins.

Deoxyribonucleic acid (DNA) hybridization and protein sequence offer a maximum of information on genetic relatedness. In the former technique, DNA's from different organisms are separated into single strands and hybridized. Extent of combination of heterologous strands provides, *in vitro*, a physicochemical assessment of genetic relatedness. This recent technique has great possibilities, especially in comparing degrees of diversity of total genomes (Hoyer *et al.*, 1964, 1965).

The complete amino acid sequence (Anfinsen, 1959) of a protein gives a detailed, though indirect, assessment of the primary structure of a single gene. Information is encoded in such polymers in terms of sequences of repeating units. Possible sequences are virtually infinite (Asimov, 1954); for example, the 20 varieties of amino acids can be arranged in over a billion different linear combinations in a peptide only seven residues long. With the aid of the genetic code one can translate these unique sequences into corresponding sequences of nucleotides and can express sequence differences between a pair of homologous peptides as mutation distances, the minimum number of nucleotide changes required for one polypeptide to code for another (Eck and Dayhoff, 1966; Jukes, 1966).

Many varieties of evidence on polymers of comparative value (Sibley, 1962, 1963) are obtained with simple techniques, in striking contrast to the formidable problems inherent in DNA-hybridizations and protein sequence analysis. The quantity of DNA per cell (Mirsky and Ris, 1951) and its base composition (Sueoka, 1964), crude but useful taxonomic data, are measured relatively easily with histochemical or optical techniques (Brawerman and Shapiro, 1962). "Peptide fingerprints," stained patterns of fragments of partial digests of proteins spread over sheets of filter paper by means of electrophoresis and chromatography, allow sensitive comparisons of the primary structures of proteins (Alexander and Block, 1960–1961; Canfield and Anfinsen, 1963). Electrophoresis is a most useful process for systematically comparing proteins of different organisms, even from individuals of small body size (Dessauer, 1966a; Dessauer and Fox, 1963, 1964). Electrophoresis through concentrated gels has unsurpassed resolving power (Smithies, 1959). Numerous samples may be compared on a single gel; after electrophoresis it is possible to identify on the gel many specific proteins, *in situ,* based on their composition or activities (Bergmeyer, 1965; Dessauer, 1966b). One can compare polypeptide substructures (Muller, 1960; Poulik, 1960) and perhaps test polypeptide homologies, *in vitro,* by means of hybridizations of these subunits (Manwell *et al.,* 1963, 1966; Markert, 1965; Riggs and Herner, 1962). Immunological methods are relatively simple, yet they yield quantitative assessments of structural complementarity of polymers (Boyden, 1965, 1966). The microcomplement fixation test (Reichlin *et al.,* 1964; Wasserman and Levine, 1961; Wilson *et al.,* 1964) is sensitive enough to distinguish proteins that differ by a single residue (Figure 1). Cell typing (Boyd, 1964; Cushing, 1962; Frair, 1963), gel diffusion, and immunoelectrophoresis (Crowle, 1961) offer excellent means for identifying specific antigens.

GENE STRUCTURE AND FUNCTION

MECHANISMS OF EVOLUTION AT THE MOLECULAR LEVEL

Molecular data focus attention upon mechanisms of evolution at the level of gene structure and function. Sources of variation are analyzed in terms of gains, losses, and substitutions of single nucleotides or larger segments of DNA (Stahl, 1964). Such changes are reflected in altered protein structure or synthesis (Ingram, 1965; Dixon, 1966). Duplication of a segment of DNA may allow increased production of its polypeptide product (Zuckerkandl and Pauling, 1962). Subsequent independent evolution of such duplicates appears to explain the origin of structurally related families of polypeptides, e.g., the globins of primates (Ingram, 1963). Series of proteins, functioning as catalysts in metabolic pathways (Dixon, 1966) and in serial processes such as blood clotting (Putnam, 1965), also may originate in this way. Evolution by gene loss or by a masking of gene expression may explain the absence of single enzymes or of entire metabolic pathways in organisms of specific taxa (Florkin, 1949).

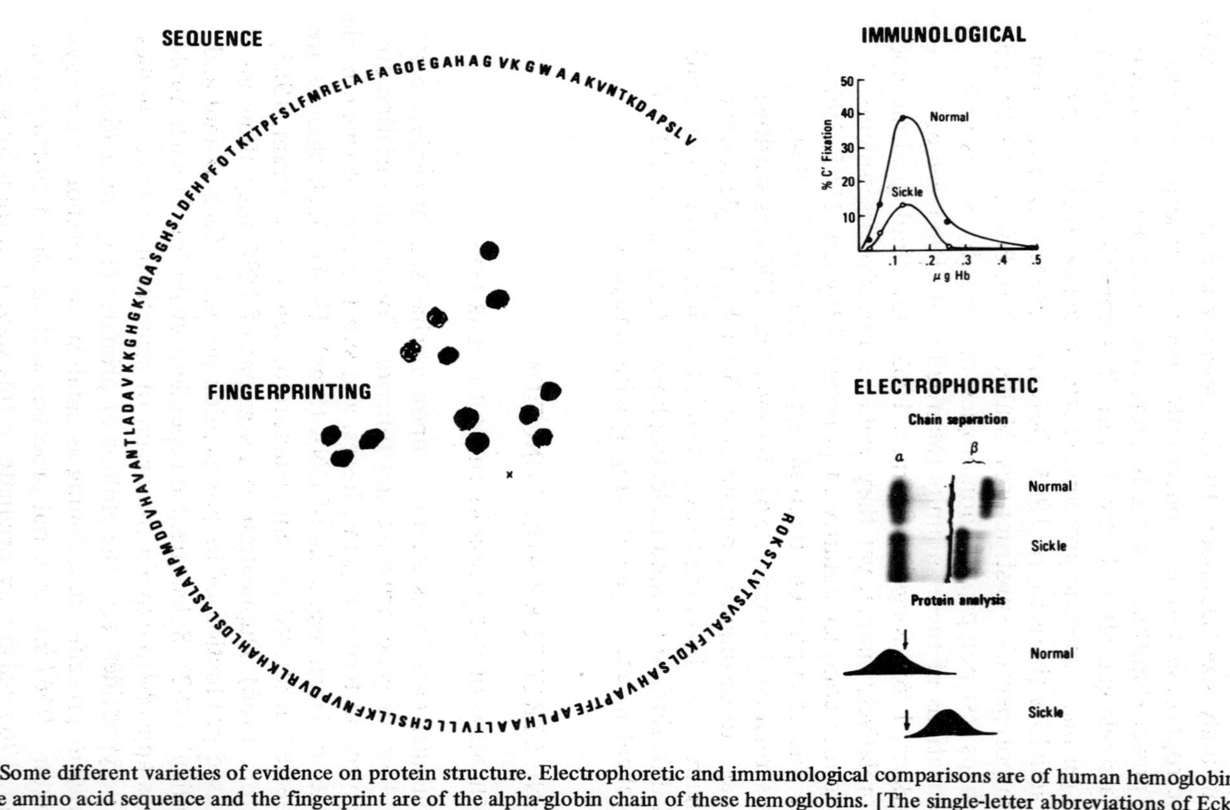

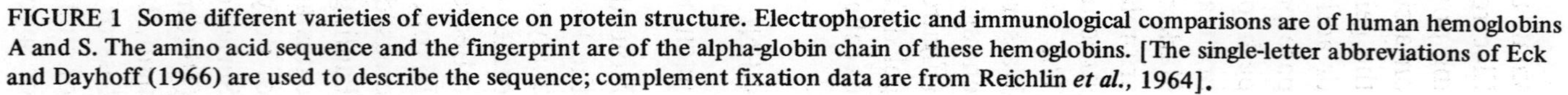
FIGURE 1 Some different varieties of evidence on protein structure. Electrophoretic and immunological comparisons are of human hemoglobins A and S. The amino acid sequence and the fingerprint are of the alpha-globin chain of these hemoglobins. [The single-letter abbreviations of Eck and Dayhoff (1966) are used to describe the sequence; complement fixation data are from Reichlin *et al.*, 1964].

MOLECULAR HOMOLOGIES

Identifying homologous molecular structures often presents difficulties (Florkin, 1964; Rutter, 1965; Wald, 1952). Sequences of polypeptides may become so varied in widely divergent organisms as to mask fundamentally similar structural patterns. An ever-recurring problem is the proper alignment of sequences of polypeptides being compared, especially when selection has led to the accumulation of large numbers of residue deletions and additions. Protein homologies cannot be made on the basis of a single property (Rose and Wilson, 1966) and without some knowledge of relationships within families of polypeptides of the organism (Dixon, 1966). This problem is illustrated by Hill and Buettner-Janusch's experience (1964) determining whether the non-alpha-chain of prosimian hemoglobin has closest homology to the gamma- or to the beta-chains of other primate hemoglobins. Proteins of very different function may prove to be distant homologues; possibilities include collagen, silk fibroin, and the keratins (Gross, 1963; Rudall, 1962; Seifter and Gallop, 1966); casein and vitellin (Dessauer and Fox, 1959); transferrin and conalbumin (Baker, 1967); and hemocyanin, erythrocuprein, and ceruloplasmin (Manwell and Baker, 1963a).

ACTIVITIES OF CONTROL GENES

Control genes probably determine variations in protein distribution and in metabolic activities that characterize development and different physiological states (Karlson, 1965; Manwell and Baker, 1966). Homologous structural genes are often active in different cell types in one organism as compared to another. Enzymes necessary for melanin synthesis, commonly present only in specialized cells of many animals, are active in great numbers of cell types in melanistic forms.

Differentiation

Certain patterns of metabolic capabilities characterize stages of fetal life; others characterize postembryonic forms (Engle and Woods, 1960; Markert, 1965; Wright, 1964; see Figure 2). Five globin peptides are synthesized by structural genes of man;

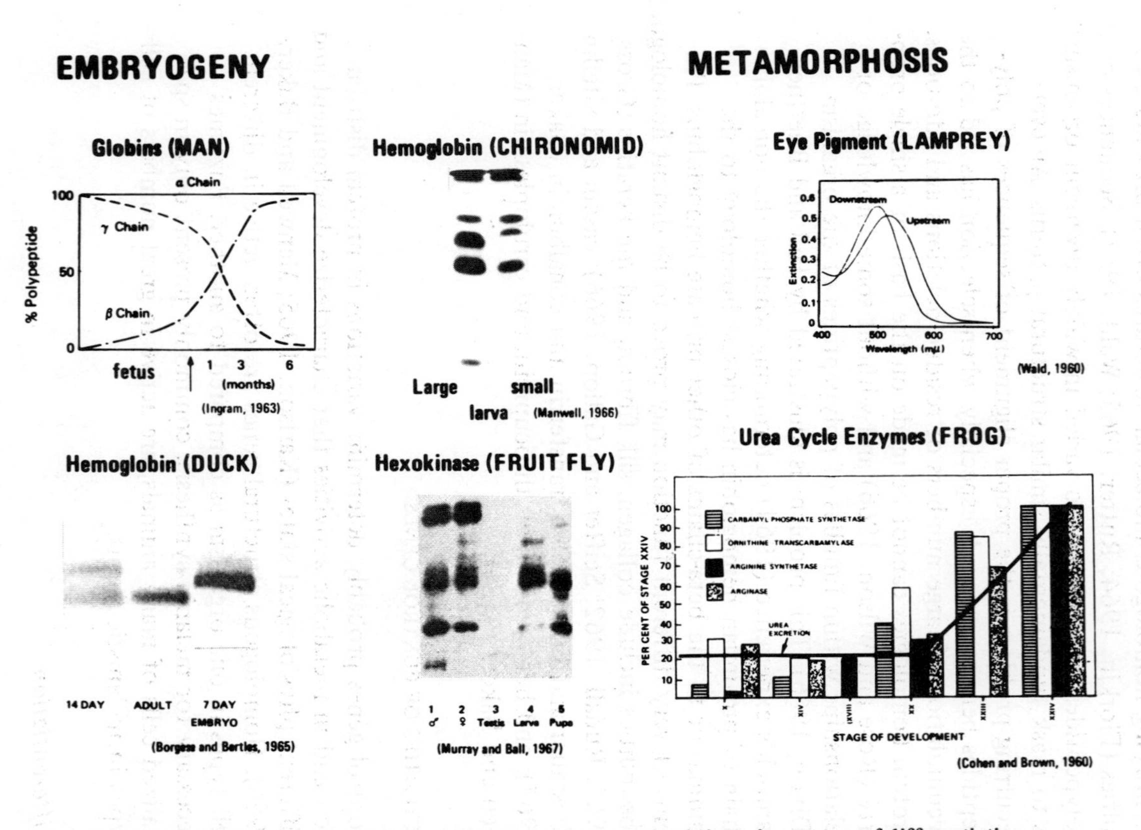

FIGURE 2 Protein and metabolic differences between animals in various stages of differentiation.

normally, gamma- and epsilon-chains are produced only by the fetus (Heckt *et al.*, 1966; Ingram, 1963). Some shifts in protein synthesis may have arisen in mammals as adaptations to placentation and the "possibilities it affords for making the maternal immunological system accessible to proteins of the developing embryo" (Goodman, 1963). Yet, similar shifts occur in many oviparous forms of highly differentiated animal life (Borgese and Bertles, 1965; Manwell, 1963). Even chironimid insects exhibit an ontogenetic sequence of hemoglobin peptides (Manwell, 1966a). In birds (Florkin, 1949) and some reptiles (Clark, 1953) urea is synthesized during embryogeny but is absent from the tissues of the adult organism (Cohen and Brown, 1960). At each postembryonic stage an animal exhibits different metabolic potentials. Remarkable changes in protein complement accompany metamorphosis in arthropods (Karlson and Sekeris, 1964; Laufer, 1964; Schneiderman and Gilbert, 1964) and vertebrates (Wald, 1952, 1960). In *Drosophila* a hexokinase, present in both sexes during early stages of development, persists only in adult males (Murray and Ball, 1967). Many proteins of amphibians, including enzymes of the urea cycle, attain functional activity at the time of metamorphosis (Bennett and Frieden, 1962; Cohen and Brown, 1960; Manwell, 1966b).

Physiology

Numerous physiological factors influence the activity of protein-synthesizing systems (Figure 3). Many shifts in protein production occur during the reproductive cycles in vertebrates, affecting synthesis of vitellins (Dessauer and Fox, 1959), oxytocinase (Page *et al.*, 1961), gonadotropins, caseins, etc. (Gorbman and Bern, 1962). The pituitary gland of *Anolis* lizards secretes melanophorotropic hormone when the animal rests on a dark background (Kleinholtz, 1938). Cold-blooded animals may not synthesize antibodies unless their body temperatures are elevated (Evans, 1963). When sheep, characterized by gene for "hemoglobin A," become anemic, a different hemoglobin appears in their blood (Boyer *et al.*, 1966).

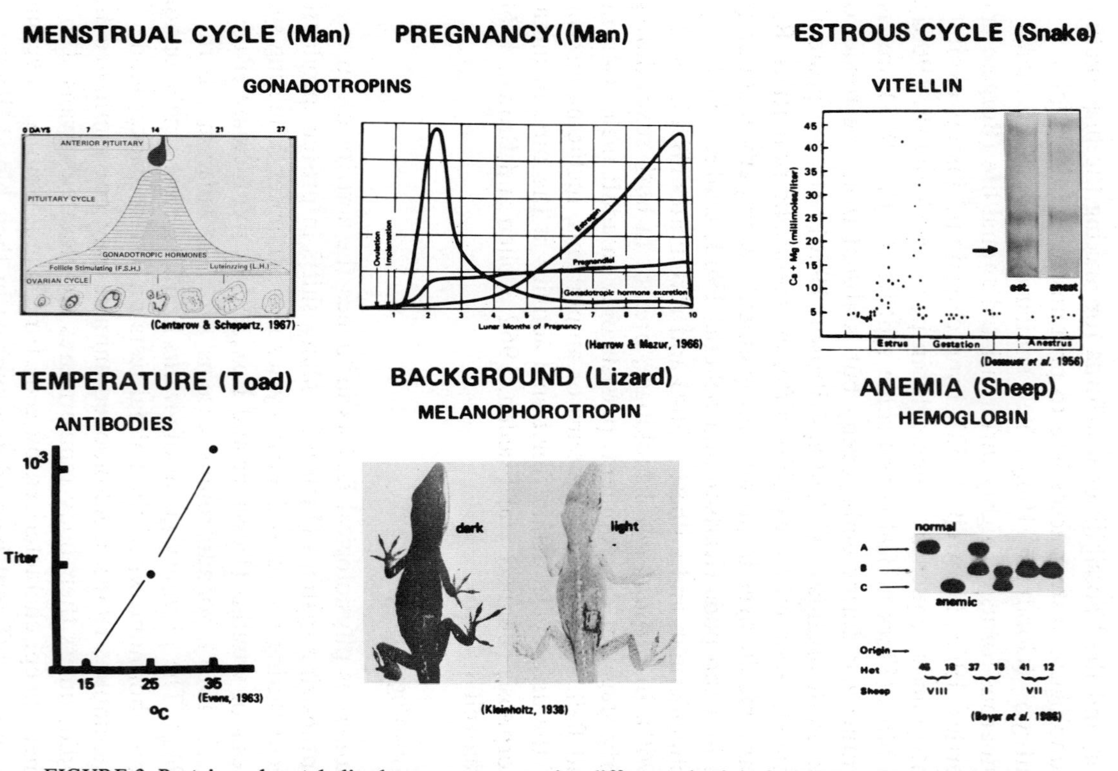

FIGURE 3 Protein and metabolic changes accompanying different physiological and environmental states.

DEFINING THE SPECIES

Molecular evidence illustrates the dynamic nature of the biological species. As the activity of the genome varies with stage of development and physiology, the systematist is forced into an awareness of the state of the organism. As individuals within a population exhibit heritable differences in protein complements, the biologist is forced to recognize the population rather than the typological nature of the species.

BIOCHEMICAL UNIQUENESS OF THE INDIVIDUAL

Variant forms of homologous proteins and other cellular antigens, probably inherited as allelomorphic genes, have been discovered in all species of animals extensively examined (Allison, 1959; Leone, 1964; Vegotsky and Fox, 1962). Structural differences between such proteins are usually small, commonly substitutions of single amino acid residues (Zuckerkandl and Pauling, 1965; however, see Boyer *et al.*, 1966). Partial polypeptide duplication (e.g., human haptoglobins; Dixon, 1966) and single residue deletions (human hemoglobin, Freiberg; Jones *et al.*, 1966) have been observed. Generally, variants are discovered either by high-resolution electrophoresis or by serological techniques.

Among human beings and other animals, possible combinations of structural variants are so great as to make each individual biochemically unique (Medawar, 1957). The extent of polymorphism of a particular protein may be very great (Figure 4). Starch-gel electrophoresis of esterases of individual sulfur butterflies, *Colias eurytheme*, indicates that populations from central Texas and from Connecticut are strikingly variable. Few wild individuals are identical in esterase (Burns and Johnson, 1967). Nine patterns of five electrophoretically distinguishable esterases were observed in livers of a small sampling of the big brown bat, *Eptesicus fuscus*, from Illinois (Manwell and Kerst, 1966). Extensive individual variation in esterases and malate dehydrogenases occurs in copepods (Manwell *et al.*, 1967). Transferrin polymorphism has been found in almost all adequately tested populations of vertebrates (Baker, 1967; Dessauer *et al.*, 1962; Goodman *et al.*, 1965; Jamieson, 1966).

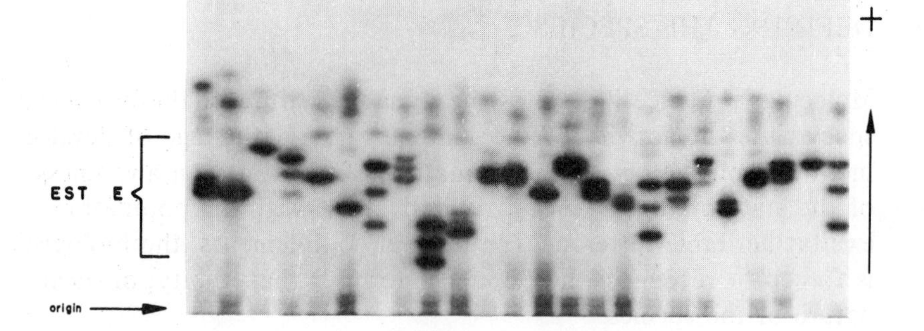

FIGURE 4 Electrophoretic patterns of esterases of individual sulfur butterflies collected from a single field (Burns and Johnson, 1967).

Some variant proteins and cellular antigens occur, but only rarely. The Lutheran blood group K is of low frequency in all populations of man (Boyd, 1964). Of 14 types of human transferrins, nine have been seen in isolated individuals only (Giblett, 1962). Most populations of men are characterized by the same plasma albumin; few exceptions have turned up despite routine clinical examination of sera of hundreds of thousands of patients (Putnam, 1965). One of the rare variants occurs with high frequency among the Naskapi Indians of Quebec and with lower frequency among other North American Indians (Melartin and Blumberg, 1966). A variant leucine aminopeptidase was found in but one snake from a population sample of 500 such animals (Dessauer, 1966a). Aberrant biochemical characteristics allowed Wright (1966) to detect an occasional aphallic individual of a population of Sardinian snails. Such rare instances emphasize the hidden resources of variation within a species.

DISTINCTNESS OF THE SPECIES

Biologists such as Mayr (1963:19) visualize a species as being made up of "groups of actually or potentially interbreeding natural populations . . . reproductively isolated from other such groups." Degree of molecular diversity may be used to advantage in systematic studies. Highly variable characters are often valuable in solving problems of population dynamics; conservative characters assist in species identifications and groupings.

Population Dynamics

Frequencies of individual proteins and tissue antigens reflect gene representation and can serve to describe populations. Subgroups of many wild and domestic species have been so identified. Boyd (1964) organizes populations of man into 13 races of five geographic groups on the basis of an extensive collection of such evidence.

Comparisons of frequencies of proteins and cellular antigens show the extent of interbreeding between individuals of adjacent populations; frequencies in different populations over the range of the species may indicate clines of gene flow. The occurrence of transferrins paralleled the patterns of geographic distribution of chimpanzees (Goodman *et al.,* 1967). Molecular evidence indicated probable paths taken by toads in populating islands of Lake Michigan (Abramoff *et al.,* 1964). Frequencies of transferrins, esterases, and other variant proteins proved more sensitive than morphological characters in gauging the extent of introgression of two subspecies of lizards (Dessauer *et al.,* 1962). On the basis of the distribution of the Diego blood group factor, Lagrisse and Wilbert (1961) postulated that at least two major migrations of mongoloids settled the New World. Blood types of finback whales in the region between Antarctica and South Africa showed that the Atlantic Ocean population intermingles with whales endemic to that sea. Because of maternal–fetal incompatibilities in blood types, matings between individuals of the two populations result in a high incidence of abortions (Fujino, 1962). Serological evidence made possible the identification of two distinct populations of sardine herrings in the Gulf of Maine and indicated the adult populations from which they originated (Sinderman, 1962). Such evidence has been useful in describing breeds of domestic animals and demonstrating their kinships (Baker and Manwell, 1962; Jamieson, 1966; Leone and Anthony, 1966).

Geographically isolated populations of a species may have unique forms of a specific protein. Jumping vipers living on the Pacific side of the mountains of Costa Rica have a different form of proteolytic enzyme in their venom than snakes on the Atlantic side (Jiminez-Porras, 1964a). Goncalves and Vieira (1950) have emphasized the necessity for preparing regional types of antisera.

Albacores of the Atlantic and Pacific Oceans have markedly different red-cell antigens, suggesting that the populations do not interbreed (Suzuki, 1962).

Intergrades and Hybrids

If populations having unique proteins renew contact and interbreed, resulting hybrids offer a rich source of genetic data. A study of such a situation allowed us to infer that transferrins are inherited as allelomorphic, autosomal genes in *Cnemidophorus* lizards (Dessauer *et al.*, 1962). Blood proteins (Fox *et al.*, 1961) and venom constituents (Wittliff, 1964) of toads from an area where two species were hybridizing served to identify rare backcross individuals and to indicate the probability of a one-directional transfer of genetic material between the species. Crenshaw (1965), using an interspecific hybrid swarm of *Pseudemys* turtles, worked out the probable mechanism of inheritance of "albumin-like" proteins and found evidence for gene exchange between turtles known to be reproductively isolated over most of their range. Analysis of serum proteins suggested that the minnow *Poecilia formosa* is a hybrid species containing haploid genomes from *P. latipinna* and *P. sphenops* (Abramoff *et al.*, 1965). Red cells of hybrid sunfish from stocked ponds contained hemoglobin with oxygen-transport properties superior to those of either parental species, an example of hybrid vigor at the molecular level (Manwell *et al.*, 1963). Extensive hybridization with *Colias philodice* over large areas of North America may contribute to the extreme variability of esterases in the sulfur butterfly, *C. eurytheme* (Burns and Johnson, 1967). Perhaps speciation through hybridization, or at least gene flow from one species to another, is more common in animals than has been expected.

Species Identifications and Grouping

Polytypic complexes of closely related, actively evolving organisms have challenged the astuteness of the systematist for years (Mayr, 1963). Certain proteins represent the type of conservative character needed to clarify relationships of such organisms. Among the West Coast garter snakes, morphological variation is very great, and few characters are available with which to group the many populations. Distribution of transferrins showed that aquatic and terrestrial groups of subspecies did not intergrade and should be considered distinct species (Dessauer *et al.*, 1962; Fox and Dessauer, 1965).

Where morphological changes accompanying speciation have been few, molecular evidence is useful in identifying sibling species. Manwell and Baker (1963b) discovered a sibling species of sea cucumber by an examination of tissue fluid proteins. The copepods *Colanus finmarchicus* and *C. helgolanchicus,* so similar that there is controversy as to whether they are true species, differed in a great number of their enzymes (Manwell *et al.*, 1967). The snakes *Bothrops picadoi* and *B. nummifera,* sympatric and of almost identical morphology, have very different but characteristic patterns of venom proteins (Jiminez-Porras, 1964a). Strains and "species" of *Entamoeba,* difficult or impossible to identify by morphological criteria, are distinguished easily by physiocochemical properties of metabolic enzymes (Montalvo and Reeves, 1967). Steroid analysis led to the correct taxonomic assignment of the Florida sponge *Antosigmella varians* (Bergmann, 1962).

Highly conservative molecular evidence often suggests affinities of species and generic groups. Electrophoresis of blood and egg-white proteins supports the opinion that geese of the genera *Anser* and *Branta* are close relatives (Baker and Hanson, 1966; Sibley, 1960). Affinities of two prosobranch molluscs, *Bulinus nyassanus* and *B. succinoides,* were placed in the *B. tropicus* complex on the basis of immunological and electrophoretic properties of their egg and digestive-gland proteins (Wright *et al.*, 1967). Relationships among the *virilis* group of *Drosophila* were estimated from data on solubility and electrophoretic properties of proteins of different forms (Hubby and Throckmorton, 1960).

The pattern of distribution of blood proteins among *Anolis* lizards of the Lesser Antilles illustrates how electrophoretic evidence can help unravel relationships of closely related, insular organisms (Gorman and Dessauer, 1965, 1966). Lactic dehydrogenases in these lizards are relatively conservative proteins. All *Anolis* of the *roquet* species group have a characteristic pattern of dehydrogenases. *Anolis* of other species groups have different patterns. Hemoglobins are of intermediate variability; they seem to vary from species to species. Transferrins are most variable; populations of near relatives, occupying different islands, have different transferrins. *Anolis aeneus* of three islands and mainland South America were classified into three named forms until the identity of their blood protein patterns substantiated the suggestion that populations had been introduced on two islands and the mainland.

Identifications of organisms on the basis of molecular characteristics are beginning to have practical value. In addition to its usefulness in forensic medicine, such evidence on man is required in tissue-transplant and biological-tolerance studies to locate individuals with similar genetic potentials (Billingham, 1966). Physicochemical properties of muscle proteins allow the detection of improperly labeled fish fillets (Lillevik and Schloemer, 1961). Proteins of blood meals of mosquitoes indicate vectors of viral and parasitic disease (Crans, 1965). Remnants of tissue may serve as material for ascertaining the species of birds involved in collision with aircraft (Baker, 1966).

RELATIONSHIPS OF HIGHER CATEGORIES

CATALOGING MOLECULAR DATA

Classifications of higher taxa, developed through years of effort by morphologists, have been effective frameworks for cataloging molecular data (Florkin and Mason, 1960-1964; Leone, 1964). The distribution of metabolic pathways and of structural variants of complex molecules such as sterols and proteins fits well into present schemes of taxonomy. As Wald (1952:338) has said, "it is all too easy to order the facts; when the facts begin to order themselves one can but listen."

Molecular data provide strong evidence for the genetic relatedness of all forms of life. Such metabolites as adenosine triphosphate, thiamine, choline and diphosphopyridine nucleotide are ubiquitous. Many metabolic pathways are similar wherever encountered. Mechanisms of information storage and of protein synthesis are fundamentally the same in all living systems (Chantrenne, 1960). Nearly all proteins are polymers of the same

18 to 20 amino acids, and the over-all composition of these proteins is similar in the simplest or most complex organisms (Vegotsky and Fox, 1962). Further, the genetic code, which determines the sequence of amino acids in proteins, essentially is universal; the same triplet code of nucleotides is recognized by bacterial, amphibian, and mammalian transfer RNA's (Marshall *et al.*, 1967).

From this basis of biochemical unity, molecular diversity developed essentially in terms of three modes of nutrition (Figure 5): absorptive bacteria and fungi, photosynthetic green plants, and ingestive animals (Whittaker, 1959). Resulting patterns of nutritional requirements, distributions of complex compounds, and structures of homologous proteins characterize major groups of organisms and have predictive value.

Procaryota are distinct in their apparent lack of sterols or a metabolic requirement for sterols (Bloch, 1965; Figure 5). Eubacteria especially have diverged significantly from other organisms. Bacterial enzymes, catalyzing the synthesis of long-chain saturated fatty acids, are very different from those of other organisms. Bacteria apparently do not use triglycerides for storing energy (Bloch, 1964). Cytochromes *c* of all major groups of organisms except bacteria interact with cytochrome oxidase of mammalian origin (Smith and Margoliash, 1964). Procaryota, fungi, and *Euglena* exhibit a fructose diphosphate aldolase different from that of higher plants and animals (Rutter, 1965; Figure 5).

In their adaptation to acquiring food by ingestion, animals lost the ability to synthesize many substances of metabolic importance—for example, the metabolic pathways leading to the synthesis of lysine (Vogel, 1965; Figure 5); but they acquired other synthetic capabilities. The basic structure of the carotenoids cannot be synthesized by animals but can be modified into pigments having specialized functions (Goodwin, 1962; Wald, 1952, 1960).

In the words of R. H. Whittaker (1959:223), "The line separating organisms evolving and differentiating . . . within limits of a single cell, from those evolving, enlarging, and differentiating with multinuclear or multinucleate organization is certainly one of the most significant. . . ." The DNA content of a haploid nucleus is roughly proportional to the number of specialized cell

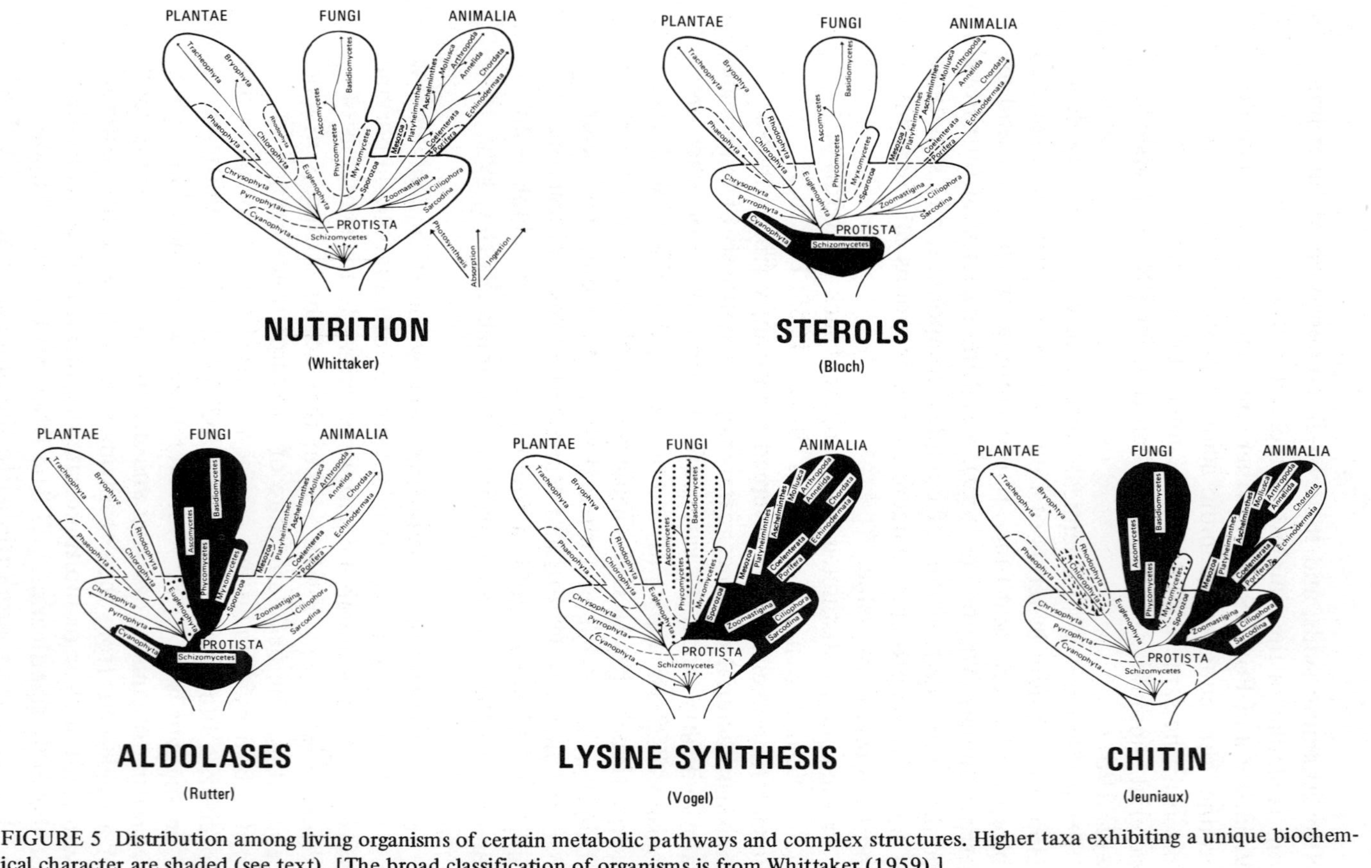

FIGURE 5 Distribution among living organisms of certain metabolic pathways and complex structures. Higher taxa exhibiting a unique biochemical character are shaded (see text). [The broad classification of organisms is from Whittaker (1959).]

types of the animal. Sneath (1964) has suggested that an organism of 100 cell types needs more than 100 times as much information as a unicellular organism. This DNA may include many replicates of specific genetic units; polyploidy explains in part the large amount of DNA present in dipnoan and amphibian nuclei (Brawerman and Shapiro, 1962).

The division of highly differentiated animals into two major lines of decent, the arthropod and the chordate, is supported by molecular data (Wald, 1952): for example, vertebrate and molluscan eyes exhibit a number of structural similarities, but lens proteins of the eyes do not exhibit immunological cross-reactions (Manski *et al.*, 1964). Among protozoa and other less highly differentiated invertebrates, the structual protein collagen and the structural polysaccharide chitin have wide distribution. In more highly differentiated animals, chitin is limited to the arthropod line, characterizing skeletal structures and appendages of annelids, molluscs, and arthropods (Jeuniaux, 1965; Figure 5). Collagen, the prime structural protein of vertebrates, occurs in virtually all classes of animals (Gross, 1963). Properties of their hemoglobins and their possession of chitin suggest that the Pogonophora, occupying a critical position with respect to this "deuterostome and protostome" divergence, are more like species of the arthropod line (Manwell *et al.*, 1966).

Specialization of highly differentiated forms also included gains and losses in metabolic capabilities. Ants acquired a number of chemical pathways adapted to offense, defense, and communications (Cavill and Robertson, 1965). Tetrapods evolved a heme enzyme system capable of detoxifying foreign compounds containing a benzene ring (Granick, 1965). Complex regulatory systems mediated by protein hormones developed in arthropods and chordates (Gorbman and Bern, 1962; Karlson and Sekeris, 1964; Schneiderman and Gilbert, 1964). Proteins homologous to pituitary hormones of vertebrates have been found in some of the Protochordatas. Vertebrates acquired enzymes capable of converting cholesterol into steroid hormones, steroid toxins (Wittliff, 1964), and bile salts. The same steroid hormones are widespread among vertebrates, and the steroid toxins are restricted largely to amphibians. Bile steroid structure, however, varies among the vertebrates and serves to distinguish specific groups. Agnatha,

Chondrichthyes, and a few genera of bony fishes and tailess amphibians synthesize only bile alcohols. Turtles, crocodiles, and some squamate reptiles have bile salts with long side chains. Most bony fish, amphibians, snakes, birds, and mammals drastically alter basic cholesterol structure, producing bile salts with short side chains. Often the bile alcohol or bile salt is unique to a particular taxon—for example, anhydroscymnol of the Chrondrichthyes and pythocholic acid of the Boidae (Haslewood, 1962).

Likewise, vertebrates have lost a number of synthetic capabilities; for example, the full complement of urea-cycle enzymes is present in cartilaginous fish, lungfish, amphibians, turtles, and mammals. The great majority of bony fish and the crocodiles, lizards, snakes, and birds, however, lack virtually all enzymes of this pathway (Cohen and Brown, 1960). Similarly, cartilaginous and bony fish and amphibians possess enzymes capable of degrading uric acid to urea; but such enzymes are absent in reptiles, birds, and most mammals (Florkin, 1949).

Physicochemical and serological properties of proteins often suggest relationships between higher taxonomic categories. Fingerprints of tryptic peptides of snakes and lizards of some families exhibit similar patterns of arginine peptides, patterns much different from those of other reptiles (Dessauer and Fox, 1963). Electrophoretic mobilities of homologous proteins of related groups often cluster together within a limited range (Dessauer, 1966a; Sibley, 1960). The unique mobility of malate dehydrogenases of hummingbirds and swifts provides further evidence that the Apodiformes, as usually defined, is a distinct and natural taxonomic unit (Kitto and Wilson, 1966). Inhibitors, activators, substrate specificities, and other kinetic properties are useful in distinguishing homologous enzymes (Kaplan, 1965; Rutter, 1965). The high temperature stability of heart LDH's of birds and squamate reptiles, for instance, distinguishes these groups from other vertebrates (Wilson *et al.*, 1964). Immunologists have acquired extensive evidence on affinities within many major groups (Boyden, 1965, 1966; Goodman, 1964; Manski *et al.*, 1964; Sarich and Wilson, 1966). Immunological correspondence confirms the wide divergence of turtles of suborders of Pleurodira and Cryptodira and the present division of Cryptodira into (1) marine, (2) softshell, and (3) freshwater and land turtles (Frair, 1964). Such physicochemical and immunological evidence has been used to construct keys to orders of amphibians and reptiles (Dessauer and Fox, 1964), birds (Sibley, 1960), and primates (Goodman, 1964).

QUANTITATIVE EVIDENCE

GENETIC RELATIONSHIPS

Molecular data can be used to obtain quantitative, unbiased estimates of genetic relationships. Taxonomic levels may be defined in terms of DNA-complementarity. About 15 percent of the DNA of mammals and birds–representatives of different classes–is similar enough to hybridize. About 35 percent of the DNA of primates will hybridize with DNA from other orders of mammals, and 95 percent of the DNA of different genera of Old World monkeys will cross-react (Hoyer *et al.*, 1965). The degree of serological correspondence has been used as a basis for defining taxonomic levels among arthropods (Leone, 1947). Solubility and electrophoretic evidence indicate that as much as 20 to 30 percent of the proteins of two species of *Drosophila* may be different (Hubby and Throckmorton, 1960).

"Mutation distances," calculated from sequence data on proteins, represent virtually direct measures of relatedness of particular homologous genes. The farther one taxon diverges from another, the greater the number of amino acid differences in their proteins and in the sequence of nucleotides of the respective structural genes. Sequence data on the cytochromes *c* exemplify the principle (Figure 6). Pig, cow, and sheep (Artiodactyla) have an identical cytochrome *c*, which differs by three residues from that of the horse (Perissodactyla) and by twelve from that of man (Primates). Progressively greater numbers of sequence differences distinguish cytochromes *c* of classes of vertebrates; vertebrates and insects; animals and fungi. Mutation distances between the cytochromes *c* alone allowed a calculation of genetic relatedness above the family level that is in remarkable agreement with currently accepted ideas (Fitch

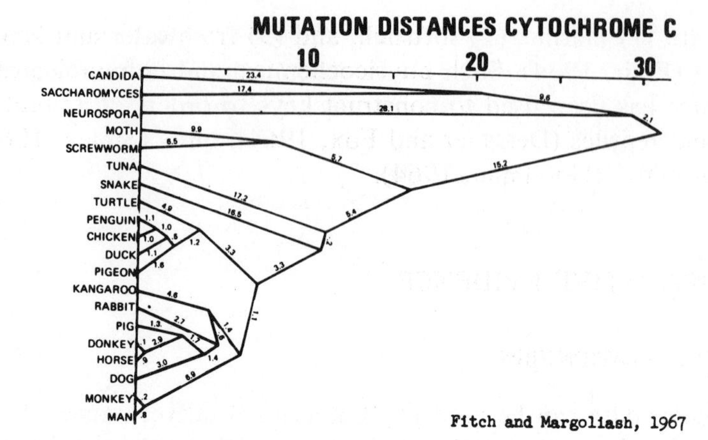

FIGURE 6 Genetic relatedness of certain living organisms based solely upon sequences of their cytochromes *C*.

and Margoliash, 1967). Hemoglobin, a more variant molecule (Zuckerkandl and Pauling, 1965), will probably be useful in establishing mutation distances between more closely related taxa.

The biologist must not overinterpret sequence data on a single polypeptide, for it represents evidence on but a single gene, certainly a minute fraction of the total genome (Bryson and Vogel, 1965:197). Recent findings of Boyer *et al.* (1966) emphasize the necessity for caution. Sequences of the two beta-chain variants of hemoglobin common in populations of sheep differ by at least seven amino acid residues, a greater difference than is found between beta-chains of camel and sheep (Eck and Dayhoff, 1966).

Man's close relationship to the anthropoid apes (especially those from Africa), his intermediate relationship to the cercopithicoids, then the ceboids, and his distant relationship to the prosimians, have been consistently confirmed by those using molecular methods (Boyden, 1958; Buettner-Janusch, 1966; Goodman, 1963). Serological data on albumins (Sarich and Wilson, 1966) and sequence studies on hemoglobins (Buettner-Janusch and Hill, 1965 a and b; Zuckerkandl and Pauling, 1962, 1965) add a quantitative meaning to these studies.

Evolutionary Rates

Molecular methods have made possible not only measures of relatedness but have increased the precision-dating of fossils (Ladd,

1959). Combining results of DNA-hybridization with evidence on the fossil record indicates that total genomes of organisms diverge exponentially with a half-life of about 100 million years. Some portions of the genome, however, apparently change more rapidly than others. As much as 80 percent of the DNA of mammals of distant relationship will not hybridize; but the remaining 20 percent is a "mammalian fraction," apparently common to all mammals. This fraction has maintained a complementary sequence of nucelotides for 200 million years. Further, the "mammalian fraction" includes a smaller "vertebrate fraction" shared with other classes of vertebrates (Hoyer *et al.*, 1964).

The rate of evolution of one protein may be different from that of another (Margoliash and Smith, 1965; Zuckerkandl and Pauling, 1965). Cytochrome *c* accumulated evolutionarily effective mutations at the rate of one amino acid residue change per 23 million years, whereas hemoglobin polypeptides changed at the rate of one residue per 7 million years. Such variations may reflect differences in the stringency of structural requirements for the two proteins. About half of the amino acid sites on cytochrome *c* may be necessary for it to perform its function. In contrast, only eight percent of the sequence of the globin peptides seems to be invariant. If rates of sequence change are calculated on the basis of variable sites, rates are more nearly equal for the two proteins. Insulin (Eck and Dayhoff, 1966), heart malate dehydrogenase (Kitto and Wilson, 1966) and actin (Carsten and Katz, 1964), like cytochrome *c*, appear to be "conservative" proteins. Myoglobin (Stockell, 1961) and gamma-globulin (Goodman, 1963) are more variant proteins. Transferrins (Baker, 1967; Dessauer *et al.*, 1962; Goodman *et al.*, 1965) and esterases (Burns and Johnson, 1967; Manwell and Kerst, 1966) seem to represent remarkably variant proteins.

Rates of evolution of a homologous protein may be rapid in one taxon and slow in another. The alpha-hemoglobin chain has a very similar sequence among most primates but has undergone a sharp structural divergence in the baboon (Buettner-Janusch and Hill, 1965b; Hill and Buettner-Janusch, 1964). Although transferrins exhibit extreme variability among most snakes, they are less variable among lizards (Dessauer *et al.*, 1962). Evolution of plasma albumin has been slower in *Aotes* than in other New World monkeys (Goodman, 1963; Sarich and Wilson, 1966). One of the lens proteins has undergone rapid independent evolution in the anthropoids (Goodman, 1963).

NATURAL SELECTION AND PROTEINS

Presumably, natural selection for mutations of adaptive value has led to the high frequency of specific proteins within a species and to species differences in protein structure (Mayr, 1964). Rarely is it obvious, however, why one protein has greater selective value than another. Selectivity of each protein must be examined in terms of its total structure, the animal in which it occurs, and the environment in which the animal lives. A structural variant of hemoglobin that causes sickling of the red cells is usually selected against by man (Ingram, 1963) but is the normal condition in deer (Kitchen *et al.,* 1964). Hemoglobin variants that oxidize readily to methemoglobin are lethal in man (Ingram, 1963) but apparently are normal constituents of the blood of many turtles (Sullivan and Riggs, 1964).

Little is known about how environmental pressures influence the selection of a protein. The maximum *temperature* likely to be encountered by an animal correlates with the heat stability of its collagen (Takahashi, see Anfinsen, 1959:215) which, in turn, depends upon the number of proline and hydroxyproline residues (Seifter and Gallop, 1966). Lactic dehydrogenases of lizards and birds—which often attain body temperatures above 40° C—denature at higher temperatures than LDH's of animals that are active at much lower temperatures (Wilson *et al.,* 1964). *Availability of oxygen* in the environment correlates with oxygen affinity and the Bohr effect of hemoglobins (Manwell, 1960). Among birds, muscles of sustained fliers contain heart-like LDH units geared to oxidation, whereas muscles of birds that move with bursts of energy have typical muscle LDH units (Kaplan, 1965). The *quality of the light* in the abysmal depths appears to have been an important selective agent for rhodopsins in deep-sea fish (Wald, 1960). Selective pressures due to *disease-producing parasites* and *toxic agents* involved a number of molecules (Blumberg, 1961). Individuals with an atypical variety of serum cholinesterase are unable to inactivate muscle relaxants during surgery;

serum esterases may have preadapted pheasants and mallard ducks to withstand concentrations of insecticides toxic to other species (Baker *et al.*, 1966).

Systematists have postulated that a gene will not remain neutral for many generations in a population, since even small mutations would be important in the fine balance of the genetic environment (Mayr, 1964). Are some mutations leading to structural changes in proteins completely neutral in respect to selection? How does one explain the evolution and maintenance of so great a series of allelomorphic proteins as that occurring in the sulfur butterfly (Burns and Johnson, 1967). From what is known of the properties of different amino acids it is difficult to understand how some substitutions can alter significantly the properties of a protein (Dixon, 1966; Zuckerkandl and Pauling, 1965). Yet organisms of recent divergence and living in very similar environments often exhibit uniquely different proteins. Anole lizards of the West Indies, presumably of the same species but occupying islands only a short distance apart, have distinct transferrins (Gorman and Dessauer, 1965, 1966). Have processes of natural selection chosen a specific transferrin for each island environment? If known substitutions for lemur hemoglobins are selectively neutral, Buettner-Janusch and Hill (1965a) believe that synchronous mutations throughout the populations or species must be postulated.

CONCLUSIONS

Molecular evidence is strengthening the idea of evolution, substantiating Florkin's confident statement. The danger now lies with those who consider that only molecular biology is worthwhile and those who imply that molecular biology can teach us nothing new about evolution. Organismic and molecular biology are not exclusive (Dobzhansky, 1964; Mayr, 1964; Simpson, 1964). To understand a species, all aspects of its structure and life history must be considered. Certainly, far greater emphasis on ecology and physiology will be necessary if we are ever to understand how processes of natural selection operate at the molecular level.

For most biologists, however, the molecular approach is kindling an enthusiasm reminiscent of the stimulus created by genetics in the 1940's. Systematists are beginning to accept molecular data as legitimate. Biochemists and biophysicists are finding that much molecular data "makes sense" only when organized according to natural groupings and analyzed in light of evolutionary theory.

This work was supported by NSF Grant No. GB-3124.

REFERENCES

Abramoff, P., R. M. Darnell, and J. S. Balsano. 1964. Serological relations of toad populations of the Lake Michigan area, p. 515–524 *In* C. A. Leone [ed] Taxonomic biochemistry and serology. Ronald Press, New York.

Abramoff, P., R. M. Darnell, and J. S. Balsano. 1965. Serological comparison of four species of fishes of the genus *Poecilia.* Am. Zool. 5:701.

Alexander, P., and R. J. Block. 1960–1961. A laboratory manual of analytical methods of protein chemistry. Pergamon Press, New York. 3 Vol.

Allison, A. C. 1959. Metabolic polymorphisms in mammals and their bearing on problems of biochemical genetics. Am. Natur. 93:5–16.

Anfinsen, C. B. 1959. The molecular basis of evolution. John Wiley & Sons, New York, 228 p.

Asimov, I. 1954. Potentialities of protein isomerism. J. Chem. Educ. 31:125–127.

Baker, C. M. A. 1966. Species, tissue, and individual specificity of low ionic strength extracts of avian muscle and other organs revealed by starch-gel electrophoresis. Can. J. Biochem. 44:853–859.

Baker, C. M. A. 1967. Molecular genetics of avian proteins. VII. Chemical and genetic polymorphism of conalbumin and transferrin in a number of species. Comp. Biochem. Physiol. 20:949–973.

Baker, C. M. A., and H. C. Hanson. 1966. Molecular genetics of avian proteins. VI. Evolutionary implications of blood proteins of eleven species of geese. Comp. Biochem. Physiol. 17:997–1006.

Baker, C. M. A., and C. Manwell. 1962. Molecular genetics of avian proteins. I. The egg white proteins of the domestic fowl. Brit. Poultry Sci. 3:161–174.

Baker, C. M. A., C. Manwell, R. F. Labisky, and J. A. Harper. 1966. Molecular genetics of avian proteins. V. Egg, blood and tissue proteins of the ring-necked pheasant, *Phasianus colchicus* L. Comp. Biochem. Physiol. 17:467–499.

Bennett, T. P., and E. Frieden. 1962. Metamorphosis and biochemical adaptation in Amphibia, p. 483–556. *In* M. Florkin and H. S. Mason [ed] Comparative biochemistry. Academic Press, New York, Vol. 2.

Bergmann, W. 1962. Sterols: Their structure and distribution, p. 103–162 *In* M. Florkin and H. S. Mason [ed] Comparative biochemistry. Academic Press, New York, Vol. 3.

Bergmeyer, H. U. 1965. Methods of enzymatic analysis. Academic Press, New York, 1064 p.
Billingham, R. E. 1966. Tissue transplantation: Scope and prospect. Science 153:266–270.
Bloch, K. 1964. Comparative aspects of lipid metabolism, p. 377–390 *In* C. A. Leone [ed] Taxonomic biochemistry and serology. Ronald Press, New York.
Bloch, K. 1965. Lipid patterns in the evolution of organisms, p. 53–65 *In* V. Bryson and H. J. Vogel [ed] Evolving genes and proteins. Academic Press, New York.
Blumberg, B. S. 1961. Inherited susceptibility to disease. Arch. Environmental Health 3:612–636.
Borgese, T. A., and J. F. Bertles. 1965. Hemoglobin heterogeneity: Embryonic hemoglobin in the duckling and its disappearance in the adult. Science 148:509–511.
Boyd, W. C. 1964. Modern ideas on race, in the light of our knowledge of blood groups and other characters with known mode of inheritance, p. 119–169 *In* C. A. Leone [ed] Taxonomic biochemistry and serology. Ronald Press, New York.
Boyden, A. A. 1958. Comparative serology: Aims, methods, and results. p. 3–24 *In* W. H. Cole [ed] Serological and biochemical comparisons of proteins. Rutgers University Press, New Brunswick, New Jersey.
Boyden, A. A. 1965. A review of the present status of systematic serology: Part I. Bull. Serol. Mus. 33:5–8.
Boyden, A. A. 1966. A review of the present status of systematic serology: Part II. Bul. Serol. Mus. 34:1–4.
Boyer, S. H., P. Hathaway, F. Pascasio, C. Orton, J. Bordley, and M. A. Naughton. 1966. Hemoglobins in sheep: Multiple differences in amino acid sequences of three beta-chains and possible origins. Science 153:1539–1543.
Brawerman, G., and H. S. Shapiro. 1962. Nucleic acids, p. 107–183 *In* M. Florkin and H. S. Mason [ed] Comparative biochemistry. Academic Press, New York, Vol. 4.
Bryson, V., and H. J. Vogel. 1965. Evolving genes and proteins. Academic Press, New York. 629 p.
Buettner-Janusch, J. 1966. Origins of man. John Wiley & Sons, New York. 674 p.
Buettner-Janusch, J., and R. L. Hill. 1965a. Evolution of hemoglobin in primates, p. 167–181 *In* V. Bryson and H. J. Vogel [ed] Evolving genes and proteins. Academic Press, New York.
Buettner-Janusch, J., and R. L. Hill. 1965b. Molecules and monkeys. Science 147:836–842.
Burns, J. M., and F. M. Johnson. 1967. Esterase polymorphism in natural populations of a sulfur butterfly, *Colias eurytheme*. Science 156:93–96.
Canfield, R. E., and C. B. Anfinsen. 1963. Concepts and experimental approaches in the determination of the primary structure of proteins, p. 311–378 *In* H. Neurath [ed] The proteins. 2nd ed., Academic Press, New York. Vol. 1.

Cantarow, A., and B. Schepartz. 1967. Biochemistry. 4th ed., W. B. Saunders Co., Philadelphia and London, 693 p.

Carsten, M. E., and A. M. Katz. 1964. Actin: A comparative study. Biochem. Biophys. Acta 90:534–541.

Cavill, G. W. K., and P. L. Robertson. 1965. Ant venoms, attractants, and repellents. Science 149:1337–1345.

Chantrenne, H. 1960. Comparative biochemistry of free energy utilization for the biosynthesis of peptides and proteins, p. 139–160 *In* M. Florkin and H. S. Mason [ed] Comparative biochemistry, Academic Press, New York, Vol. 2.

Clark, H. 1953. Metabolism of the black snake embryo. I. Nitrogen excretion. J. Exp. Biol. 30:492–501.

Cohen, P. P., and G. W. Brown, Jr. 1960. Ammonia metabolism and urea biosynthesis, p. 161–244 *In* M. Florkin and H. S. Mason [ed] Comparative biochemistry. Academic Press, New York, Vol. 2.

Crans, W. J. 1965. Host preference studies with New Jersey mosquitoes. Bull. Serol. Mus. 33:1–4.

Crenshaw, J. W. 1965. Serum protein variation in an interspecies hybrid swarm of turtles of the genus *Pseudemys*. Evolution 19:1–15.

Crowle, A. J. 1961. Immunodiffusion. Academic Press, New York, 333 p.

Cushing, J. E. [chairman] 1962. A symposium on immunogenetic concepts in marine population research. Am. Natur. 96:193–246.

Dessauer, H. C. 1966a. Taxonomic significance of electrophoretic patterns of animal sera. Bull. Serol. Mus. 34:4–8.

Dessauer, H. C. 1966b. Multiple localizations of specific proteins on starch gel electropherograms. Bull. Serol. Mus. 36:1–4.

Dessauer, H. C., and W. Fox. 1959. Changes in ovarian follicle composition with plasma levels of snakes during estrus. Am. J. Physiol. 197:360–366.

Dessauer, H. C., and W. Fox. 1963. Electrophoretic techniques in systematics, p. 128–132 *In* C. G. Sibley [chairman] Symposium on new techniques for systematics. Proc. XVI Int. Congr. Zool. 4:128–132.

Dessauer, H. C., and W. Fox. 1964. Electrophoresis in taxonomic studies illustrated by analyses of blood proteins, p. 625–647 *In* C. A. Leone [ed] Taxonomic biochemistry and serology, Ronald Press, New York.

Dessauer, H. C., W. Fox, and N. L. Gilbert. 1956. Plasma calcium magnesium and protein of vivaparous colubrid snakes during estrous cycle. Proc. Soc. Exp. Biol. Med. 92:299–301.

Dessauer, H. C., W. Fox, and Q. L. Hartwig. 1962. Comparative study of transferrins of Amphibia and Reptilia using starch-gel electrophoresis and autoradiography. Comp. Biochem. Physiol. 5:17–29.

Dessauer, H. C., W. Fox, and F. H. Pough. 1962. Starch-gel electrophoresis of transferrins, esterases and other plasma proteins of hybrids between two subspecies of whiptail lizard (Genus *Cnemidophorus*). Copeia 1962: 767–774.

Dixon, G. H. 1966. Mechanisms of protein evolution, p. 147–204 *In* P. N. Campbell and G. D. Greville [ed] Essays in biochemistry. Academic Press, New York, Vol. 2.

Dobzhansky, T. 1964. Biology, molecular and organismic. Am. Zool. 4:443–452.

Eck, R. V., and M. O. Dayhoff. 1966. Atlas of protein sequence and structure. National Biomedical Research Foundation, Silver Spring, Maryland, 213 p.

Engle, R. L., Jr., and K. R. Woods. 1960. Comparative biochemistry and embryology, p. 183–265 *In* F. W. Putnam [ed] The plasma proteins. Academic Press, New York, Vol. 2.

Evans, E. E. 1963. Antibody response in Amphibia and Reptilia. Federation Proc. 22:1132–1137.

Fitch, W. M., and E. Margoliash. 1967. Construction of phylogenetic trees. Science 155:279–284.

Florkin, M. 1949. Biochemical evolution. Academic Press, New York, 157 p.

Florkin, M. 1964. Perspectives in comparative biochemistry, p. 51–74 *In* C. A. Leone [ed] Taxonomic biochemistry and serology. Ronald Press, New York.

Florkin, M., and H. S. Mason [ed] 1960–1964. Comparative biochemistry. Academic Press, New York. 6 Vol.

Fox, W., and H. C. Dessauer. 1965. Collection of garter snakes for blood studies. Am. Phil. Soc. Year Book 1964:263–266.

Fox, W., H. C. Dessauer, and L. T. Maumus. 1961. Electrophoretic studies of blood proteins of two species of toads and their natural hybrid. Comp. Biochem. Physiol. 3:52–63.

Frair, W. 1963. Blood group studies with turtles. Science 140:1412–1414.

Frair, W. 1964. Turtle family relationships as determined by serological tests, p. 535–544 *In* C. A. Leone [ed] Taxonomic biochemistry and serology. Ronald Press, New York.

Fujino, K. 1962. Blood types of some species of antarctic whales. Am. Natur. 96:205–210.

Giblett, E. R. 1962. The plasma transferrins, p. 34–63 *In* A. G. Steinberg and A. G. Bearn [ed] Progress in medical genetics. Grune and Stratton, New York. Vol. 2.

Gonçalves, J. M., and L. G. Vieira. 1950. Estudos sôbre venenos de serpentes brasileiras. An. Acad. Brasileira Ciéncias. 22:141–149.

Goodman, M. 1963. Man's place in the phylogeny of the primates as reflected in serum proteins, p. 204–224 *In* S. L. Washburn [ed] Classification and human evolution. Viking Fund Publ. Anthropology, Chicago, Illinois.

Goodman, M. 1964. Problems of primate systematics attacked by the serological study of proteins, p. 467–486 *In* C. A. Leone [ed] Taxonomic biochemistry and serology. Ronald Press, New York.

Goodman, M., A. Kulkarni, E. Poulik, and E. Reklys. 1965. Species and geographic differences in the transferrin polymorphism of macaques. Science 147:884–886.

Goodman, M., W. G. Wisecup, H. H. Reynolds, and C. H. Kratochvil. 1967. Transferrin polymorphism and population differences in the genetic variability of chimpanzees. Science 156:98–100.

Goodwin, T. W. 1962. Carotenoids: Structure, distribution, and function,

p. 643–675 *In* M. Florkin and H. S. Mason [ed] Comparative biochemistry. Academic Press, New York, Vol. 4.

Gorbman, A., and H. A. Bern. 1962. A textbook of comparative endocrinology. John Wiley & Sons, New York, 468 p.

Gorman, G. C., and H. C. Dessauer. 1965. Hemoglobin and transferrin electrophoresis and relationships of island populations of *Anolis* lizards. Science 150:1454–1455.

Gorman, G. C., and H. C. Dessauer. 1966. The relationships of *Anolis* of the *roquet* species group (Sauria:Iguanidae). I. Electrophoretic comparison of blood proteins. Comp. Biochem. Physiol. 19:845–853.

Granick, S. 1965. Evolution of heme and chlorophyll, p. 67–88 *In* V. Bryson and H. J. Vogel [ed] Evolving genes and proteins. Academic Press, New York.

Gross, J. 1963. Comparative biochemistry of collagen, p. 307–342 *In* M. Florkin and H. S. Mason [ed] Comparative biochemistry. Academic Press, New York, Vol. 5.

Harrow, B., and A. Mazur. 1966. Textbook of biochemistry. 9th ed., W. B. Saunders Co., Philadelphia and London, 599 p.

Haslewood, G. A. D. 1962. Bile salts: structure, distribution and possible biological significance as a species character, p. 205–229 *In* M. Florkin and H. S. Mason [ed] Comparative biochemistry. Academic Press, New York, Vol. 3.

Heckt, F., A. G. Motulsky, R. J. Lemire, and T. E. Shepard. 1966. Predominance of hemoglobin Gower 1 in early human embryonic development. Science 152:91–92.

Hill, R. L., and J. Buettner-Janusch. 1964. Evolution of hemoglobin. Federation Proc. 23:1236–1242.

Hoyer, B. H., E. T. Bolton, B. J. McCarthy, and R. B. Roberts. 1965. The evolution of polynucleotides, p. 581–590 *In* V. Bryson and H. J. Vogel [ed] Evolving genes and proteins. Academic Press, New York.

Hoyer, B. H., B. J. McCarthy, and E. T. Bolton. 1964. A molecular approach in the systematics of higher organisms. Science 144:959–967.

Hubby, J. L., and L. H. Throckmorton. 1960. Protein differences in *Drosophila.* II. Comparative species genetics and evolutionary problems. Genetics 52:201–215.

Ingram, V. M. 1963. The hemoglobins in genetics and evolution. Columbia University Press, New York. 165 p.

Ingram, V. M. 1965. The synthesis of macromolecules, p. 125–171 *In* J. A. Moore [ed] Ideas in modern biology. Natural History Press, Garden City, New York.

Jamieson, A. 1966. The distribution of transferrin genes in cattle. Heredity 21:191–218.

Jeuniaux, C. 1965. Chitine et phylogénie: Application d'une méthode enzymatique de dosage de le chitine. Bull. Soc. Chimie Biol. 47:2267–2278.

Jiminez-Porras, J. M. 1964a. Intraspecific variations in composition of venom

of the jumping viper, *Bothrops nummifera.* Toxicon 2:187–195.
Jiminez-Porras, J. M. 1964b. Venom proteins of the fer-de-lance, *Bothrops atrox,* from Costa Rica. Toxicon 2:155–166.
Jones, R. T., B. Brinhall, T. H. J. Huisman, E. Kleihauer, and K. Betke. 1966. Hemoglobin Freiburg: Abnormal hemoglobin due to deletion of a single amino acid residue. Science 154:1024–1027.
Jukes, T. H. 1966. Molecules and evolution. Columbia University Press, New York, 285 p.
Kaplan, N. O. 1965. Evolution of dehydrogenases, p. 243–277 *In* V. Bryson and H. J. Vogel [ed] Evolving genes and proteins. Academic Press, New York.
Karlson, P., and C. E. Sekeris. 1964. Biochemistry of insect metamorphosis, p. 221–243 *In* M. Florkin and H. S. Mason [ed] Comparative biochemistry. Academic Press, New York, Vol. 6.
Karlson, P. 1965. Table ronde sur les manifestations hormonales liées aux méchanismes génétiques. Arch. Anat. Micro. Exp. Morph. 54:643–655.
Kitchen, H., F. W. Putnam, and W. J. Taylor. 1964. Hemoglobin polymorphism: Its relation to sickling of erythrocytes in white-tailed deer. Science 144:1237–1239.
Kitto, G. B., and A. C. Wilson. 1966. Evolution of malate dehydrogenases in birds. Science 153:1408–1410.
Kleinholtz, L. H. 1938. Studies in reptilian colour changes. II. The pituitary and adrenal glands in the regulation of the melanophores of *Anolis carolinensis.* J. Exp. Biol. 15:474–491.
Ladd, H. S. 1959. Ecology, Paleontology, and Stratigraphy. Science 129:69–78.
Largisse, M., and J. Wilbert. 1961. Absence of the Diego antigen, a genetic characteristic of early immigrants to South America. Science 134:1077–1078.
Laufer, H. 1964. Macromolecular patterns in development and evolution, p. 171–189 *In* C. A. Leone [ed] Taxonomic biochemistry and serology. Ronald Press, New York.
Leone, C. A. 1947. Systematic serology among certain insect species. Biol. Bull. 93:64–71.
Leone, C. A. 1964. Taxonomic biochemistry and serology. Ronald Press, New York, 728 p.
Leone, C. A., and R. L. Anthony. 1966. Serum esterases among registered breeds of dogs as revealed by immunoelectrophoretic comparisons. Comp. Biochem. Physiol. 18:359–368.
Lillevik, H. A., and C. L. Schloemer. 1961. Species differentiation in fish by electrophoretic analysis of skeletal muscle proteins. Science 134:2042–2043.
Manski, W., S. P. Halbert, and T. P. Auerbach. 1964. Immunochemical analysis of the phylogeny of lens proteins, p. 545–554 *In* C. A. Leone [ed] Taxonomic biochemistry and serology. Ronald Press, New York.
Manwell, C. 1960. Comparative physiology: Blood pigments. Ann. Rev. Physiol. 22:191–244.

Manwell, C. 1963. The blood proteins of cyclostomes, a study in phylogenetic and ontogenetic biochemistry, p. 372–455 *In* A. Brodal and R. Fänge [ed] The biology of myxine. Universitetsforlaget, Oslo, Norway.

Manwell, C. 1966a. Starch gel electrophoresis of the multiple haemoglobins of small and large larval *Chironomus*-a developmental haemoglobin sequence in an invertebrate. J. Embryol. Exp. Morph. 16:259–270.

Manwell, C. 1966b. Metamorphosis and gene action. I. Electrophoresis of dehydrogenases, esterases, phosphatases, hemoglobins and other soluble proteins of tadpole and adult bullfrogs. Comp. Biochem. Physiol. 17:805–823.

Manwell, C., and C. M. A. Baker. 1963a. Starch gel electrophoresis of sera from some marine arthropods: Studies on the heterogeneity of hemocyanin and on a "ceruloplasmin-like protein." Comp. Biochem. Physiol. 8:193–208.

Manwell, C., and C. M. A. Baker. 1963b. A sibling species of sea cucumber discovered by starch gel electrophoresis. Comp. Biochem. Physiol. 10:39–53.

Manwell, C., and C. M. A. Baker. 1966. Evolution of mechanisms for the management of genetic information, p. 3–15 *In* R. T. Smith, P. A. Miescher, and R. A. Good [ed] Phylogeny of immunity. University of Florida Press, Gainesville.

Manwell, C., C. M. A. Baker, P. A. Ashton, and E. D. S. Corner. 1967. Biochemical differences between *Calanus finmarchicus* and *C. helgolandicus*. J. Marine Biol. Assoc. U.K. 47:145–169.

Manwell, C., C. M. A. Baker, and T. W. Betz. 1966. Ontogeny of haemoglobin in the chicken. J. Embryol. Exp. Morph. 16:65–81.

Manwell, C., C. M. A. Baker, and W. Childers. 1963. The genetics of hemoglobin in hybrids. I. A molecular basis for hybrid vigor. Comp. Biochem. Physiol. 10:103–120.

Manwell, C., and K. V. Kerst. 1966. Possibilities of biochemical taxonomy of bats using hemoglobin, lactate dehydrogenase, esterase and other proteins. Comp. Biochem. Physiol. 17:741–754.

Manwell, C., E. C. Southward, and A. J. Southward. 1966. Preliminary studies on haemoglobin and other proteins of the Pogonophora. J. Marine Biol. Assoc. U.K. 46:115–124.

Margoliash, E., and E. L. Smith. 1965. Structural and functional aspects of cytochrome *c* in relation to evolution, p. 221–242 *In* V. Bryson and H. J. Vogel [ed] Evolving genes and proteins. Academic Press, New York.

Markert, C. L. 1965. Mechanisms of cellular differentiation. p. 229–258 *In* J. A. Moore [ed] Ideas in modern biology. Natural History Press, Garden City, New York.

Marshall, R. E., C. T. Caskey, and M. Nirenberg. 1967. Fine structure of RNA codewords recognized by bacterial, amphibian and mammalian transfer RNA. Science 155:820–826.

Mayr, E. 1963. Animal species and evolution. The Belknap Press of Harvard University, Cambridge, Massachusetts. 797 p.

Mayr, E. 1964. From molecules to organic diversity. Federation Proc. 23:1231–1235.

Medawar, P. B. 1957. The uniqueness of the individual. Basic Books, New York. 191 p.

Melartin, L., and B. S. Blumberg. 1966. Albumin Naskapi: A new variant serum albumin. Science 153:1664–1666.

Mirsky, A. E., and H. Ris. 1951. The deoxyribonucleic acid content of animal cells and its evolutionary significance. J. Gen. Physiol. 34:451–462.

Montalvo, F. E., and R. E. Reeves. 1967. Characterization of glucokinase and glucosephosphate isomerase from parasitic amebae. Federation Proc. 26:836.

Muller, C. J. 1960. Separation of the alpha- and beta-chains of globins by means of starch gel electrophoresis. Nature 186:643.

Murray, R. F., Jr., and J. A. Ball. 1967. Testis-specific and sex-associated hexokinases in *Drosophila melanogaster.* Science 156:81–82.

Page, E. W., M. A. Titus, G. Mahun, and M. B. Glendening. 1961. The origin and distribution of oxytocinase. Am. J. Obstr. Gynecol. 82:1090–1095.

Poulik, M. D. 1960. The use of urea-starch-gel electrophoresis in studies of reductive cleavage of a alpha-2-macroglobulin. Biochem. Biophys. Acta 44:390–393.

Putnam, F. W. 1965. Structure and function of the plasma proteins, p. 153–267 *In* H. Neurath [ed] The proteins. 2nd ed., Academic Press, New York, Vol. 3.

Reichlin, M., M. Hay, and L. Levine. 1964. Antibodies to human A_1 hemoglobin and their reaction with A_2, S, C, and H hemoglobins. Immunochemistry 1:21–30.

Riggs, A., and A. E. Herner. 1962. The hybridization of donkey and mouse hemoglobins. Proc. Nat. Acad. Sci. U.S. 48:1664–1670.

Rose, R. G., and A. C. Wilson. 1966. Peafowl lactate dehydrogenase: Problem of isozyme identification. Science 153:1411–1413.

Rudall, K. M. 1962. Silk and other cocoon proteins, p. 397–433 *In* M. Florkin and H. S. Mason [ed] Comparative biochemistry. Academic Press, New York, Vol. 4.

Rutter, W. J. 1965. Enzymatic homology and analogy in phylogeny, p. 279–291 *In* V. Bryson and H. J. Vogel [ed] Evolving genes and proteins. Academic Press, New York.

Sarich, V. M., and A. C. Wilson. 1966. Quantitative immunochemistry and the evolution of primate albumins:micro-complement fixation. Science 154:1563–1566.

Schneiderman, H. A., and L. I. Gilbert. 1964. Control of growth and development in insects. Science 143:325–333.

Seifter, S., and P. M. Gallop. 1966. The structure proteins, p. 153–458 *In* H. Neurath [ed] The proteins. 2nd ed., Academic Press, New York, Vol. 4.

Sibley, C. G. 1960. The electrophoretic patterns of avian egg-white proteins as taxonomic characters. Ibis 102:215–284.

Sibley, C. G. 1962. The comparative morphology of protein molecules as data for classification. Syst. Zool. 11:108–118.

Sibley, C. G. [chairman] 1963. Symposium on new techniques for systematics. Proc. XVI Int. Congr. Zool. 4:97–142.

Simpson, G. G. 1964. Organisms and molecules in evolution. Science 146:1535–1538.

Sinderman, C. J. 1962. Serology of Atlantic clupeoid fishes. Am. Natur. 96:225–231.

Smith, E. L., and E. Margoliash. 1964. Evolution of cytochrome *c*. Federation Proc. 23:1243–1247.

Smithies, O. 1959. Zone electrophoresis in starch gels and its application to studies of serum proteins. Adv. Prot. Chem. 14:65–113.

Sneath, P. H. A. 1964. Comparative biochemical genetics in bacterial taxonomy, p. 565–583 *In* C. A. Leone [ed] Comparative biochemistry and serology. Ronald Press, New York.

Stahl, F. W. 1964. The mechanics of inheritance. Prentice Hall, Englewood Cliffs, New Jersey. 171 p.

Stockell, A. 1961. Comparative studies on tryptic digests of myoglobins. J. Mol. Biol. 3:362–366.

Sueoka, N. 1964. Compositional variation and heterogeneity of the nucleic acids and protein in bacteria, p. 419–443 *In* I. C. Gunsalus and R. Y. Stanier [ed] The bacteria. Academic Press, New York, Vol. 5.

Sullivan, B., and A. Riggs. 1964. Haemoglobin reversal of oxidation and polymerization in turtle red cells. Nature 204:1098–1099.

Suzuki, A. 1962. On the blood types of yellowfin and big eye tuna. Am. Natur. 96:239–246.

Vegotsky, A., and S. W. Fox. 1962. Protein molecules: Intraspecific and interspecific variations, p. 185–244 *In* M. Florkin and H. S. Mason [ed] Comparative biochemistry. Academic Press, New York, Vol. 4.

Vogel, H. J. 1965. Lysine biosynthesis and evolution, p. 25–40 *In* V. Bryson and H. J. Vogel [ed] Evolving genes and proteins. Academic Press, New York.

Wald, G. 1952. Biochemical evolution, p. 337–376 *In* E. S. G. Barron [ed] Modern trends in physiology and biochemistry. Academic Press, New York.

Wald, G. 1960. The distribution and evolution of visual systems, p. 311–345 *In* M. Florkin and H. S. Mason [ed] Comparative biochemistry. Academic Press, New York, Vol. 1.

Wasserman, E., and L. Levine. 1961. Quantitative micro-complement fixation and its use in the study of antigenic structure by specific antigen–antibody inhibition. J. Immunol. 87:290–295.

Whittaker, R. H. 1959. On the broad classification of organisms. Quart. Rev. Biol. 34:210–226.

Wilson, A. C., N. O. Kaplan, L. Levine, A. Pesce, M. Reichlin, and W. S. Allison. 1964. Evolution of lactic dehydrogenases. Federation Proc. 23:1258–1266.

Wittliff, J. L. 1964. Venom constituents of *Bufo fowleri, Bufo valliceps,* and their natural hybrids analyzed by electrophoresis and chromatography, p. 457–464 *In* C. A. Leone [ed] Comparative biochemistry and serology. Ronald Press, New York.

Wright, B. E. 1964. The biochemistry of morphogenesis, p. 1–71 *In* M. Florkin and H. S. Mason [ed] Comparative biochemistry. Academic Press, New York, Vol. 6.

Wright, C. A. 1966. Relationships between schistosomes and their molluscan hosts in Africa. J. Helminth. 40:403–412.

Wright, C. A., J. Klein, and D. H. Eccles. 1967. Endemic species of *Bulinus* (Mollusca:Planorbidae) in Lake Malawi (Lake Nyasa). J. Zool. 151:199–209.

Zuckerkandl, E., and L. Pauling. 1962. Molecular disease, evolution, and genic heterogeneity, p. 189–225 *In* M. Kasha and B. Pullman [ed] Horizons in biochemistry. Academic Press, New York.

Zuckerkandl, E., and L. Pauling. 1965. Evolutionary divergence and convergence in proteins, p. 97–166 *In* V. Bryson and H. J. Vogel [ed] Evolving genes and proteins. Academic Press, New York.

Discussion

Emanuel Margoliash and W. M. Fitch

If we are agreed that DNA carries the majority of if not all the biological information in the organism, then it is clear that, within the limitations of present techniques, its translated representation in the amino acid sequences of proteins constitutes the most incisive molecular information from which one may hope to derive factual phylogentic relationships.

As dedicated exponents of some of the techniques discussed by Dr. Dessauer, it is perhaps appropriate for us to point out some of the very real risks involved.

The very first requirement of the utilization of amino acid sequences in deriving phylogeny is that such sequences be known. This may sound trivial. However, at this time, even of the relatively few proteins examined, many primary structures have not been fully determined. Rather, on the basis of compositions of peptides, the residues have been ordered on the basis of an assumed homology to a previously determined structure and on the assumption that any differences that appear have resulted from a minimal number of mutations. Had such a procedure been followed, for example, with the carboxyl-terminal tetrapeptide sequences of the cytochromes *c* of the pigeon, duck, and rattlesnake, we would have concluded that they were identical; whereas, in fact, these sequences are, Thr-Ala-Ala-Lys, Ala-Thr-Ala-Lys, and Lys-Thr-Ala-Ala, respectively (see Nolan and Margoliash, "Comparative Aspects of Primary Structures of Proteins." Ann. Rev. Biochem. 37:727–790, 1968).

Having made sure of the validity of the data, one must next clearly decide if the proteins to be compared are or are not homologous in the ancestral sense. This is a decision that is vital to any further elaborations and that has all too frequently been made on no statistically significant basis. It must be emphasized that, except in those cases wherein homology is overwhelmingly obvious, mere inspection or even the calculation of an average mutation value is not acceptable. To cite an example from one of the more careful examinations of data, it has been proposed that segments of the *C*-type cytochrome from a prokaryotic organism, *Pseudomonas fluorescens,* are homologous to segments of the cytochrome *c* of *Neurospora* (Cantor and Jukes, "The Repetition of Homologous Sequences in the Polypeptide Chains of Certain Cytochromes and Globins," Proc. Nat. Acad. Sci. U.S. 56:177–184, 1966.) In this case the best concordance of two sets of 15 consecutive residues requires a minimum of 15 nucleotide changes to account for the differences of the corresponding genes. The probability that such a situation can occur by chance is 0.0027 if the sequences are chosen randomly. However, the sequences compared were chosen from over 5,000 possible pairs, making quite likely the observance of an event whose expectation is 1 in 370. Thus, even though several such presumably homologous segments are presented, the authors do not provide an adequate statistical foundation for concluding that the proteins are homologous.

To develop statistical procedures that will distinguish between true homology and a random event it is necessary to calculate the probability of the random event. An approach to the problem has been initiated (Fitch, "An Improved Method of Testing for Evolutionary Homology," J. Mol. Biol. 16:9–16, 1966) in which one calculates the minimal number of single nucleotide changes required to interrelate the gene segments corresponding to two peptide segments of fixed length (say, 30 residues) from the two proteins being compared. This is computed for all possible pairs and abnormally low numbers that would indicate homology can be readily detected on a suitable probit plot. This makes it possible to determine whether any unusually low numbers merely represent the lower extreme of a Gaussian distribution and thus are not distinguishable from a random occurrence.

A further and often overlooked difficulty is the necessity to distinguish, in protein structures, between ancestral homology and evolutionary analogy. To be able to do so requires a knowledge of the minimal number of residues that must remain invariant throughout a set of homologous proteins because of critical biological requirements. With a sufficiently large set of homologous amino acid sequences, as is now available for cytochromes *c* of eukaryotic organisms, this question is amenable to a statistical approach (Fitch and Margoliash, "A Method for Estimating the Number of Invariant Amino Acid Coding Positions in a Gene Using Cytochrome *c* as a Model Case," Biochem. Genet. 1:65–71, 1967.) Clearly, only concordances over and above the minimal functional necessities can be used to deduce homology.

The most abused method of attempting to reveal homology is the indiscriminate use of so-called "deletions." For example, in comparing the 82-residue sequence of *Pseudomonas* cytochrome-551 to the 107-amino acid sequence of *Neurospora* cytochrome *c,* one need to insert 25 amino acid deletions. There are 107!/82!/52! or 10^{25} ways of aligning the former protein opposite the latter without altering the order of the amino acids in either. With so many possible combinations, a very improbably event may become a near certainty. Nevertheless, in cases in which homologies are extensive, as for the hemoglobin chains, accounting statistically for deletions does not prevent the conclusion that the proteins are ancestrally related.

Finally, it should not be overlooked that homology in itself is not sufficient to justify the use of protein primary structures to deduce phylogenetic relationships. One must also ascertain that the proteins compared are equivalent in the sense that in the common ancestor of two species these proteins were represented by a single gene. For example, the beta-chains of hemoglobins of various species are both homologous and equivalent, while the alpha-chains and the beta-chains are only homologous and not equivalent. If one were to attempt to determine phylogenetic relations by comparing the alpha-chains of some species with the beta-chains of others, one would obtain an absurd result in which the species are segregated according to whether alpha- or beta-chains were employed. This derives from speciation having occurred more recently than the gene duplication that permitted the separate evolution of the alpha- and beta-genes.

Discussion

Lynn H. Throckmorton

Previous speakers have thoroughly covered the general field of biochemical systematics. To me it is significant that Dr. Dessauer in his introduction chose to emphasize the dynamic rather than the static aspects of systematics. In the past, biochemical systematics has been very much oriented toward description. There has been very little evidence of that type of research in the discussions here, and I hope this presages a permanent shift in perspective among taxonomists interested in biochemical methods.

We can group the contributions of biochemical and molecular approaches as follows:

1. Describing and cataloging biochemical attributes is very necessary, but it is stultifying when attention is devoted to it exclusively. It cannot be omitted, but it must be considered as a pedestrian occupation to be handled with dispatch.
2. Solution of immediate practical problems is, and will remain, a most significant aspect of biochemical systematics, wherein one recognizes and seeks to solve a problem, be it one of identification, of the origin of a population, of a species, or some other group. At any rate, we have heard enough evidence to lead us to suspect that in the arsenal of biochemical technology there exists a method for resolving most of the immediate practical problems of taxonomists. Where ordinary methods fail, or have failed, to solve a particular problem, there is a high probability that biochemical methods will succeed. Every taxonomist should therefore be prepared to exploit biochemical methods when he faces problems that challenge more classical techniques.

3. To my mind, the third area is by far the most challenging and exciting of all. Dr. Dessauer implied this when he stressed a problem-oriented rather than a method-oriented outlook and when he emphasized the dynamic nature of our most pressing problems in systematics. In particular, he pointed to the contributions of biochemical methods to our understanding of the mechanism of evolution at the gene level, to our appreciation of the dynamic nature of the species, and to possibilities for achieving unbiased estimates of genic divergence and rates of evolution.

To develop this last area, I propose a series of rhetorical questions. The answers to these questions can be found through techniques that are presently available or that will be forthcoming shortly if molecular biology continues to progress at its present rate. The questions should be viewed in the following intellectual context: (1) Almost all decisions of taxonomists are probability estimates; (2) the basis for an estimate is the taxonomist's knowledge of the properties of the biological system he evaluates; (3) the more deficient his knowledge, the more defective his probability estimates, and the more fallible his judgments.

What we as theoretical and biochemical taxonomists must undertake is to define the properties of the evolutionary system so unequivocally that preconceptions and biases lose their palatability, and sound operational analytical procedures replace authoritarian convictions. There are five questions.

1. How is the gene pool structured? We can probably dismiss as fantasy Mayr's assertion of four years ago that the gene pool is integrated at the species level. More and more evidence is becoming available, and most of it suggests that strong local, or populational, differentiation is the rule rather than the exception. In many cases species may be loose aggregations of differentially integrated populations. If this is the case, molecular methods will bring it to light. The whole field of comparative population and species genetics lies open and virtually untouched; indeed, the whole field of comparative evolution is now accessible, begging for attention. Is the structure of arthropod populations the same as that of birds, or fishes, or baboons, or redwoods? Many pronouncements have been made on some of these subjects, but almost no facts are available at present.

2. How does the structure of the gene pool relate to the ecology and history of populations? How much differentiation results from chance? Is there a part, perhaps a large part, of the genome that gets carried along, mostly selectively neutral, only rarely producing genetic variants recognized by natural selection?

3. How many modes of speciation are there, and how many kinds of species are there? Is it possible, perhaps, that one or two changes in genes of control systems are sufficient to precipitate speciation? Could we prepare a model, or models, for speciation through changes in control systems, and would not these models differ sharply from models based on divergence of nearly neutral structural genes? Are there, in addition to regulators and operators, genes, or constellations of genes, that might be called speciators?

4. What relation exists between genic change and phenetic change? Is the phenotype a delusion and a snare, as some would have us believe, or is it a somewhat blurred, but nevertheless valid, document, as many of us take it to be? Is there a general relation between phenetic divergence and genetic divergence, or is the relation quite loose and uncertain?

5. What of rates of change of genes, of DNA change, at the genome level? Are the rates constant? What can we learn studying them? Are they constant per locus over time, as suggested for hemoglobin and cytochrome *C*? Are they constant over the genome as an average over time, as suggested by work with *Drosophila*? Constant rates would be almost too good to be true, but if they are, indeed, a reality we have far better indexes of time in extant forms than we have in fossils. Even if constant rates are not found, relative rates are of much interest.

Obviously, such questions can be generated at length. I have not mentioned specific adaptation; I have not raised questions regarding biochemical mechanisms involved in ecosystem integration; I have not touched on opportunities for extracting history from molecules; and I have not examined the fascinating potentiality that exists for tracing the genetics of populations indefinitely back through time. With questions like this open, I must confess that I cannot understand why so many biochemists restrict themselves to descriptive approaches, but rather than pursue this, I would like to ask two questions of the speaker: What do you consider to be the most significant contribution of new information made to systematics from biochemistry or molecular biology? Will you predict where the next most significant contribution will come from, and what would you advise a graduate student to undertake at this time?

Informal Discussion

DESSAUER: Well, as far as the graduate student is concerned, I would say he should do what he thinks is most fun.

CLARKE: I would like to express my disagreement with Dr. Throckmorton. It strikes me that the two things that show up most clearly from the recent data on molecular systematics are (1) the evidence for coadaptation of the genotype, which supports the theories of Dr. Mayr, and (2) the apparent infrequency of selectively neutral changes (the stability of amino acid sequences within species). As far as they go, these data argue for the importance of selection. There is no need to postulate new and mysterious evolutionary forces.

SELANDER: There seems to be a note of the return of mutationism here that is somewhat alarming. If we start thinking about speciators, or changes in control systems precipitating speciation, or leading to speciation, it seems we are harking back to the problem that has plagued all schemes of mutationism—that of ignoring the ecological aspects of the situation. I tried to point out in my talk that speciation is not a genetic phenomenon alone; the ecological aspect cannot be ignored. So, it is inconceivable that genetic changes themselves precipitate speciation; there must be ecological opportunity, or niche availability, and a situation where niche adaptation can develop in isolation. It is dangerous to speculate about there being unlimited routes of speciation or there being genetic changes that precipitate it.

THROCKMORTON: I think some of the dogmas you have just proposed should be stretched a bit. I am not necessarily defending the model, and, as I said, I am not going to propose one; but I do think you should try to find one. Previous mutation theories were not formulated in terms of what we now know of developmental biology or in terms of the restricted behaviors that we see in the various organisms. Let us say that there is a tendency for a particular genotype to be restricted to a particular host plant. If a change in a control system produced sterility in any crosses between this genotype and other genotypes, this might raise a genetic barrier that may not be serious for adaptation but might make two lineages completely independent genetically. As the field of developmental genetics progresses, we will have the opportunity to see what genetic control systems exist, and to ask to what extent our increased understanding of the relationship between the gene and the genetic system—within the epigenetic system, which includes ecology—shows us new ways in which dichotomies may arise in gene pools.

FARRIS: My comment, addressed to Dr. Throckmorton, has to do with maintenance of a large portion of selectively neutral features in the genome. If you deny the existence of a highly integrated genome, then it must be clear that selectively neutral factors face an increasingly high probability of passing out of the genome by random extinction. This being the case, it appears unreasonable to believe that much of the genome at any one time would be composed of selectively neutral factors, that very much of the variability found over the geographic range of a species would be due to selectively neutral factors, or that a truly selectively neutral factor would stay in a particular phyletic line for any appreciable length of time.

THROCKMORTON: I think all of these can be recognized. I was trying to point out that new biochemical data show a great amount of variation, that some tests have not been able to show selective advantage, and that the population-genetic theory—as Lewontin and Hubby pointed out in their recent paper—is not adequate for explaining the retention of the variability in the gene pool.

FARRIS: When I first commented that selectively neutral factors had a high probability of passing out by random extinction, Dr. Throckmorton responded by pointing to various linkage phenomena and epistatic phenomena that might be regarded as possible ways of keeping so-called selectively neutral factors in the population. These, however, if they are analyzed carefully, could be seen to be a kind of selective force and thus would negate the proposition that such factors were indeed selectively neutral.

GOODMAN: I think we should keep in mind Dr. Throckmorton's statement that the advances of molecular biology and the insight they should give us in studying the genetics of populations probably have not yet made their impact on the theory of population genetics Since the concept of extreme genetic variability within populations in a species has come up, it should be pointed out that, at the molecular level, a mutational difference in a protein such as transferrin probably would represent only one amino acid out of, perhaps, 900. So, the degree of genetic divergence represented by such variability is really quite small and, in itself, should not be used to contradict theories such as those Dr. Mayr has developed concerning integrated gene pools. However, I think this is still an open question.

Roundtable Discussion: Molecular Systematics –A View of the Future

SIBLEY: The impromptu discussions that follow include the views, hopes, aspirations, and expectations of those who participated in the molecular part of the conference, as well as of Dr. Morris Goodman, an invited discussant. The statements of those contributors are followed by open discussion.

BREHM: Dr. Sibley indicated that a little passion would not be out of place in presenting our viewpoints here. Being first on the program, it is difficult for me to judge how much a little passion really is; however, since fundamentally I am conservative, my passion will be expressed in two lines of poetry:

For I dipt into the future, far as human eye could see,
Saw the Vision of the world, and all the wonders that would be;

Tonight we are individually and collectively writing a biosystematic version of Tennyson's famous and perceptive "Locksley Hall." As I gaze into my crystal ball, I see that an increasingly sophisticated chemical technology will produce an increasingly detailed chemical analysis at every level of biological structure and function. However, the future of macromolecular systematics may depend more upon the establishment of a conceptual basis for the macromolecular approach than on the solution of specific problems in the phylogeny of organisms. I will discuss, as an example, only one of the many situations that might be mentioned.

The combination of cytological observations of the behavior of chromosomes during meiosis and the genetical observations of the distribution of characteristics from parents to offspring led to the concept of homology. In the traditional sense, homology implies a close biological relationship derived through the possession of a common gene pool at some time in the past, but does not necessarily imply a common functional attribute at the present time. Therefore, if two organisms possess homologous structures, they must also have shared a common ancestor. How, then, does this concept of homology apply to macromolecular systems, and particularly, to such structures as DNA, protein, and other polymers composed of a repetitive series of basic units? In a recent and provocative paper titled "Mechanisms of Protein Evolution," Gordon Dixon has provided a general interpretation. I quote him directly:

Homologous. When applied to chromosomes, as in *homologous chromosomes,* this term denotes those chromosomes that pair (or synapse) during meiosis, have the same morphology, and contain genes governing the same characteristics. It can be extended so as to imply that identical nucleotide sequences occur in the DNAs of these corresponding genes. *Homology* as applied to amino acid sequences of polypeptide chains is a less well defined term but derives from a comparison of the overall sequences. If polypeptide chains are identical to a large extent, e.g., in the case of β and δ chains of haemoglobin, some 95%, then they are clearly homologous. When the differences are greater the relationship is more equivocal, but if several blocks of amino acid sequence are identical and disposed in similar areas of the chains (in relation to the ends), then the likelihood becomes strong that the chains are homologous. (Dixon, 1966:197)

It is not implied whether functional similarity is a property of these homologous proteins.

We will consider the case of an essential enzyme obtained from yeast and monkey tissues that has 50 of its 100 amino acid residues in a common sequence. The question arises whether yeast and monkey have a common ancestor. A principal argument for homology is that the random association of the 20 possible amino acids in an identical sequence and position in unrelated proteins is such a statistically improbable event that the interpretation of homology is the most reasonable explanation of the data. It could be that the 50 sites in common represent the essential portions for a functional enzyme molecule and the 50 altered sites represent changes in less essential or nonessential sites developed since the time of the common ancestor. This is one of the simplest probable interpretations and, in that sense, will be the preferred one until it is contradicted by new evidence. However, there are alternative points of view that should be discussed.

The 50 amino acid units in common may represent two unrelated organisms that respond in a similar fashion to perform an essential function by the process of parallel evolution. In higher plants the formation of complex structural units, which are called vessels, involves many complex developmental events that must be correlated in whole files of cells in a plant stem or root. Statistically, it is improbable that such complex events would occur more than once; yet abundant and excellent evidence in extant and fossil forms indicates that vessels have developed independently in several groups of vascular plants (Bailey, 1953). It is also possible that a complex and specialized biochemical pathway might arise on several independent occasions, since purely chemical factors may severely restrict the direction of natural selection in biochemical evolution (Cánovas *et al.,* 1967). It is reasonable to suspect, then, that the great bond of chemical similarity commonly accepted as evidence for the common origin and relationships of living systems may, in part, also be an example that the efficiency of particular arrangements of molecules provides opportunities for repeated and independent selection of that arrangement. At higher levels of biological organization the concept of natural selection as a creative force in evolution has developed (Simpson, 1953). The creativeness is manifest as an opportunity to make possible what otherwise would be very improbable events. In this sense, natural selection increases order and decreases entropy, and it may be that we should view chemical events in a similar manner. These questions might be resolved through experiments directed toward solving the conceptual problems as well as the phylogenetic problems. I will suggest one such approach.

If one essential enzyme shared by two organisms shows homology, one would expect other enzymes shared by both to be homologous if they, too, had been essential to the common ancestor, because the action of natural selection ordinarily cannot be concentrated on single genes, and it may be impossible for intermediary molecules such as enzymes to be selected for or against, independently of other molecules (Simpson, 1964). Nonhomologous or analogous enzymes performing the same function would necessarily have evolved after the separation of the ancestral gene pool into different evolutionary pathways. Therefore, the function and structure of several enzymes as well as their roles in processes essential to the survival of the organism might be considered before judgments are made as to analogous or homologous relationships. In any case, this is a testable hypothesis and could yield information to determine which of the two preceding interpretations may be correct. Regardless of methodology, determination of genetic relationships using comparative molecular structure must be subjected to vigorous application of biological and evolutionary principles established on the basis of evidence obtained from various other disciplines. These applications are among the more important and challenging tasks in the future of molecular systematics.

REFERENCES

Bailey, I. W. 1953. Evolution of tracheary tissue of land plants. Am. J. Bot. 40:4–8.

Cánovas, J. L., L. N. Ornston, and R. Y. Stanier. 1967. Evolutionary significance of metabolic control systems. Science 156:1695–1699.

Dixon, G. H. 1966. Mechanisms of protein evolution. Essays Biochem. 2:147–204.

Simpson, G. G. 1953. The major features of evolution. Columbia University Press.

Simpson, G. G. 1964. Organisms and molecules in evolution. Science 146:1535–1538.

DE LEY: I have some recommendations and comments to make about microbial systematics:

1. The current practice of basing species and genus differentiation on a few phenotypic features should be stopped.
2. No new species name should be introduced unless it is accompanied by an extensive phenotypic description and comparison with related organisms.
3. For all new isolates the percent GC should be determined and included in the description.
4. The percent GC of at least a few strains of each nomenclatural species should be determined. It seems advisable to know the percent GC of most of the strains in official collections of bacteria (ATCC, NCTC, NCIB, etc.).
5. New methods for pure DNA preparation should be rapid and yield very pure DNA.
6. The percent GC data should be combined with numerical

analysis, as experience has shown this to be the most useful approach.

7. More basic research is needed on the meaning and value of DNA hybridization techniques.

8. Simple techniques for DNA hybridization are required. Such techniques should be amenable for routine use in bacteriological laboratories, and no expensive apparatus should be involved. The technique could be automated.

9. It is predicted that molecular techniques will be very useful in mycology, algology, and protozoology.

DESSAUER: Since World War II taxonomists with a molecular bent have been concerned with the development of immunological, chemical, and physical methods and with applications of these techniques in broad surveys of various taxa. The period of orientation is over. The tools are excellent and are getting better; many problems are now in focus.

During the next decade extensive collections of structural comparisons of proteins and nucleic acids will become available. These measurements are possible because of the sophisticated developments in techniques for sequence analysis. Gas chromatography should facilitate a number of the steps in the acquisition of such data; automation will eliminate much of the drudgery.

Current techniques and others under development may soon allow the biologist to determine mechanisms of protein inheritance in species that are difficult or impossible to breed in the laboratory. When cultured together under certain conditions, combinations of somatic cells—even when the cells are from different species—may bypass sexual reproduction and yield hybrid cells. High-resolution analytical techniques permit comparisons of proteins of such hybrid cells. *In vitro* hybridizations of polypeptide subunits of proteins will also be useful in homologizing polypeptides from widely divergent organisms. Studies of such subunit interactions will also advance our understanding of cell superstructures.

Molecular methods make possible the acquisition of a surprising amount of evidence on deceased or extinct forms. Isotopic and other physical measurements permit precise dating of fossils and even allow estimates of the nature of ancient environments. Priceless evidence of genetic value on long-extinct animals can be obtained from analyses on fossilized remains of the highly stable, complex molecules that survive destructive geologic processes—for example, scleroproteins. Means may be developed for obtaining molecular data using feathers, hair, and even certain chemically treated tissues preserved in the extensive collections of the great museums of the world. Certainly, museums will begin to accumulate banks of frozen tissues and will take additional steps to facilitate the work of molecular biologists. Field men will be taught techniques for collecting tissues for biochemical studies along with traditional museum procedures. Eventually, each animal collected should serve as a source of information at many levels of organization from behavior to protein sequence.

Both organismic and molecular biologists will be increasingly concerned with questions involving speciation and mechanisms of natural selection. Are some mutations leading to structural change in proteins completely neutral in respect to selection? Is gene flow between species of substantial evolutionary importance? Are "molecular rudiments" present among the proteins and nucleic acids of an organism? Can evolution involve masking of specific structural genes? How is the structure of a particular protein molded by the structural requirements of its basic function, intrareactions with its cellular environment, and factors related to the life history and ecology of the organism in which it occurs? The last question is the central one; perhaps it is the most demanding question of all.

GOODMAN: My own interest in the molecular approach to systematics was in large measure inspired by a germinal idea of George Gaylord Simpson that he presented in his famous monograph entitled "The Principles of Classification and a Classification of Mammals." Discussing the limitations of morphological data in the study of phylogeny, Simpson pointed out that a complete analysis of genotypic similarities and differences among species would provide priceless data for deducing phylogenetic relationships. Although molecular biology has not yet provided us with the tools to effect a complete reading of the genetic codes in the genomes of organisms and, thus, a thorough step-by-step comparison of genetic code homologies between species, it has provided us with the means of sampling the correspondence between genomes in different species. This is done by comparing the structural specificities of homologous proteins in the different species.

The most precise comparisons of protein homologies due to genetic code-word homologies result from amino acid sequence determinations. However, this analytic approach is extremely laborious, and the amino acid sequence data, which are limited to only a few proteins in a scattering of species, have not yet clarified the phylogeny of any taxonomic group. Eventually, however, automated methods should become commonplace for the rapid isolation of purified proteins and for the routine analysis of the amino acid sequences of the isolated proteins. Then, molecular systematists will be able to map extensively the genealogical relationships of species in terms of amino acid sequence data.

In view of the thousands of proteins coded for by a genome, a key question that must be answered is just how many different sets of homologous proteins in the various species under comparison have to be analyzed before the sampling of genetic code homologies reveals phylogenetic relationships that would match those from a complete reading of the genetic codes in the different genomes. Considering the fantastic number of permutations possible in even a single gene—the sequence of genetic coding units that specify the amino acid sequence of a polypeptide chain—my guess is that analysis of as few as three or four proteins would be sufficient to reveal the degrees of genetic relationships among the major taxonomic branches. In all probability, however, analysis of a large number of proteins will be necessary to reveal the sequence of branching among closely related species. Statistics will have to be developed to determine just how many proteins have to be so analyzed before sequencing of additional proteins becomes redundant. Furthermore, computers will be heavily employed to process the amino acid sequence data so as to construct the best phylogenetic trees of contemporary species. This development has been foreshadowed by the work of Fitch and Margoliash (Construction of Phylogenetic Trees," Science, 1967, 155:279).

In the immediate future an extensive mapping of the genealogical relationships of species is possible on an approximate basis by the use of immunological techniques. The structural correspondence between proteins measured immunologically depends on how similar proteins are in their amino acid sequences, for the antigenic sites against which the antibodies are directed are configurations shaped by the amino acid groups exposed at a protein's surface. The value of certain immunological methods, such as the immunodiffusion Ouchterlony technique, is that they allow voluminous data on a spectrum of proteins in many different species to be gathered in a relatively short time. Although these data are qualitative, Mr. Bill Moore and I have recently shown that they are well suited to statistical analysis and to computer processing. The near future should see the development of computer programs that would construct phylogenetic classifications from such data ("A Set Theoretical Approach to Immunotaxonomy: Analysis of Species Comparisons in Modified and Ouchterlony Plates," Bull. Math. Biophys., 30:279–289, 1968). Taking as a starting point the large body of immunological data already gathered on species relationships in the primates, it should also be possible to attack the question of just how many proteins have to be examined to depict accurately the phylogenetic relationships existing among contemporary species.

Experience gained in my laboratory indicates that immunological data on proteins are not quite discriminating enough to depict degrees of relationship among very closely related taxonomic groups such as races of a species or sibling species of a genus. At this level, electrophoretic methods for detecting forms of proteins due to single mutational differences can provide abundant data for determining the degrees of genetic relatedness among the population groups found in a species or genus. Thus, a problem for the near future is to develop a suitable statistical approach that will allow the integrating of different types of data on proteins—such as data gained through the immunologic and electrophoretic methods—so as to clarify the systematics of the species and populations under study.

In my own work on the primates, the molecular data have indicated that chimpanzee and gorilla should be placed in the same family as man. This is contrary to the view of the traditional taxonomists—even those who believe that gorilla, chimpanzee, and man have a more recent common ancestor than these creatures have with the orangutan—who still insist that man should be in a family all by himself and that the chimpanzee and gorilla should be classified with the orangutan in the family Pongidae. This type of disagreement is just part of the broad problem of grade classification versus clade classification. As more and more molecular data reflecting genetic relationships are gathered, the construction of clade classifications rather than grade classifications will, in my opinion, tend to be favored, since the former will not be subject to the anthropomorphic biases of the latter.

HUNZIKER: Different lines of progress seem to be evident. Some of these have already contributed important information, and they clearly are recognized as valuable tools in systematics. Undoubtedly, however, in the years to come these lines of molecular systematics will acquire a higher resolution and will yield even more detailed and more reliable results. They will be used more widely by systematists, and, surely, they will be applied to a greater number of plant groups and will furnish solutions to new problems. Among the techniques that seem to be important for their impact on systematics, genetics, and evolution are the following:

1. The application of *chromatographs* of phenolic compounds as genetic markers in problems of systematics, hybridization, introgression and amphiploidy (for example, see Alston, 1967).

2. The use of *protein electrophoresis* in problems of amphiploidy, species and racial differentiation, estimation of isozyme heterozygosity and molecular polymorphisms in the populations, and interpretation of chromosome pairing in meiotic studies of hybrids by comparison of chromosome homologies versus protein band homologies, and so forth. (Frydenberg *et al.,* 1965; Hunziker, this volume, page 280; Hubby and Lewontin, 1966; Johnson and Hall, 1965; Lewontin and Hubby, 1966).

If possible, systematists should use protein and other molecular studies in groups wherein chromosomes are either small or offer little or no evolutionary clues, and in groups such as slow-growing trees wherein genetic and cytogenetic results accumulate too slowly.

Another important future contribution of protein electrophoresis will be its usefulness in detecting natural autoploids in cases of questionable alloploid origin. In natural autoploids one would expect qualitatively identical proteins, as in the original diploids.

3. *DNA Studies.* In 1947 Kihara said: "The history of the earth is written in its layers, the history of living organisms is inscribed in the chromosomes." Since we now know that genetic information is encoded in the linear sequence of the nucleotides of DNA, we may say that the history of living organisms is inscribed in the DNA

sequence of nucleotides in genes and also in chromosomes (if there is more than a single molecule of DNA per chromosome).

The methods of DNA base composition and DNA hybridization that have given valuable information in microorganisms have not been applied successfully so far, to higher plants, but it is probable that the future will provide technical tools for these or other detailed studies of DNA. I feel tempted to predict that perhaps we are not too far from the day when phylogenetic arrangements within a genus will be constructed on the basis of comparisons furnished by computers that have been fed with incredibly detailed data on enormously long DNA-base sequences and clusters of genes, distributed along known chromosome arms. Molecular systematics then would become mathematical systematics, and the degree of relationship of two taxa—including their adaptation to different environments—perhaps could be expressed by a relative index summarizing the results of all their evolutionary history since they diverged from a common ancestor. We should realize that all the evolutionary history of the different populations composing a taxon—including mutational differences, chromosomal rearrangements, and ecological adaptations, for example—theoretically is recorded in their DNA and chromosomes. Until this stage is reached, however, partial molecular data should be added to the information from all other biological disciplines that a systematist working on a particular group must understand thoroughly, evaluate critically, and integrate fully.

REFERENCES

Alston, R. E. 1967. Biochemical systematics, p. 197-305 *In* T. Dobzhansky, M. K. Hecht, and W. C. Steere [ed] Evolutionary biology, Vol. 1. Appleton-Century Crofts, New York.

Frydenberg, O., D. Moller, G. Naevdal, and K. Sick. 1965. Haemoglobin polymorphism in Norwegian cod populations. Hereditas 53:257–271.

Hubby, J. L., and R. C. Lewontin. 1966. A molecular approach to the study of genic heterozygosity in natural populations. I. The number of alleles at different loci in *Drosophila pseudoobscura.* Genetics 54:577–594.

Johnson, B. L., and O. Hall. 1965. Analysis of phylogenetic affinities in the Triticinae by protein electrophoresis. Am. J. Bot. 52(5):506–513.

Lewontin, R. C., and J. L. Hubby. 1966. A molecular approach to the study of genic heterozygosity in natural populations. II. Amount of variation and degree of heterozygosity in natural populations of *Drosophila pseudoobscura.* Genetics 54:595–609.

MANDEL: The kinds of information that I would like to see accumulated are covered in the following outline. This treatment relates most particularly to the Protista, but most items are also relevant to higher organisms.

I. DNA
  A. Mean base composition
  B. Molecular length(s)
  C. Frequency distribution of GC contents of fragments at 20 x 10^6 Dalton and 1 x 10^6 Dalton mean molecular weights
  D. Nearest-neighbor base frequencies
  E. Isostich analysis of purine and pyrimidine runs
  F. "Satellite" components and their function

II. Nucleotide homologies (DNA–DNA : DNA–RNA)
  A. Over all (as function of molecular weight)
  B. With each ribosomal RNA component
  C. With 4S and 5S RNA components
  D. Multipoint assays of homologous regions, the question of redundancy

III. Chromosomes
  A. Karyotype analysis
  B. Genetic mapping
    1. Macrohomology and cytogenetics
    2. Microhomology and crossing-over

IV. Genetic exchange in interspecific crosses
  A. Plasmids
  B. Molecular arrangements in synapsis and exchange
  C. Compatability factors
    1. Surfaces
    2. Modification and restriction

V. Protein structure
   A. Immunological cross-reaction
   B. Active center kinetic analysis with substrate and coenzyme analogues
   C. Tertiary structure
   D. Primary sequence analysis

Such information will serve to help define (a) the species and their relations to each other; (b) the time scale and direction of evolutionary change of macromolecules when fitted to the paleobotanical scale of the diatoms and coccolithophorids; (c) the origins of the organelles (chloroplasts, mitochondria, centrioles, kinetoplasts, etc.); and (d) the nature of mechanisms of gene duplications and alterations as they may have occurred and do occur in evolution.

It may not be premature to believe that the future will bring a detailed understanding of the molecular nature of the processes involved in cellular differentiation and organismic form. In that happy time we may reflect with amusement upon the current arguments as to the relative amounts of information content available in numbers of fish scales or veins of leaves versus measurements of molecular homologies for the diverse purposes of systematics.

MARGOLIASH: To ask us to look into our crystal balls and tell what the future holds for molecular systematics is somewhat akin to asking a zoologist to predict the adult from the morphology of a fertilized ovum. The best one can hope to do at this time is to define what appears to be necessary to bring about the development of the subject, rather than to foresee the course of this development.

Assuming there is fairly unanimous agreement that proteins do represent by far the most satisfactory objects from which molecular data of systematic importance can be obtained, I make a strong plea for going the whole way—to settle for nothing less than complete primary structures for as many proteins as possible. On the one hand, the disadvantages of other approaches, such as DNA hybridization and immunological comparisons, are obvious. On the other hand, techniques for the determination of the primary structures of polypeptide chains are developing at an impressive rate, so that the unraveling of relatively long amino acid sequences is a much simpler undertaking today than was similar work with much smaller sequences even a few years ago. This will certainly be an accelerating trend in the future. Again, the enormous advantage of knowing complete primary structures needs no elaboration.

Ideally, for broad phylogenetic comparisons one would choose a protein that is as nearly ubiquitous as possible, is not too large and not too difficult to sequence, is abundant, and can be easily purified. As techniques develop, these qualifications are sure to become less and less stringent. Given enough work, the subject is quite likely to develop far beyond a current appraisal of its potential.

Since we must try to predict the future at this very early stage, I can list only a few of the techniques that have been initiated and those potential developments that appear to be approaching realization.

1. The construction of phylogenetic trees, for which the only biological information utilized is the amino acid sequences of sets of homologous proteins, and in which no other biological bias whatsoever is introduced. Using average minimal mutation distances and a purely statistical procedure, this has been done with cytochrome *c* (Fitch, W. M., and E. Margoliash, Science, 155:279–284, 1967. Construction of phylogenetic trees.) in a surprisingly satisfactory fashion, considering the minute fraction of the genome examined and the minute sample of all extant cytochromes *c* utilized.

2. Gene phylogeny as well as species phylogeny can be derived on a similar basis.

3. Such phylogenetic trees can be used to reconstruct the probable primary structures of the protein of ancestral species at various branching points. Ancestral amino acid sequences, in turn, may reveal relationships between different proteins that are not obvious in present-day structures.

4. Similar procedures are capable of detecting internal gene duplications as well as the formation of hybrid genes.

5. Statistical phylogenetic trees also lead to an estimate of the order in which mutations were fixed and of their relative location in time in various lines of descent.

6. Using a set of homologous proteins of known primary structure, one can obtain an approximation of the total number of residues that are invariant because of biological necessity. This

leads directly to a differentiation between evolutionary homology and analogy in protein structures.

7. One also can detect the existence of nonrandom mutagenic processes in evolutionary changes in protein structure. The present evidence indicates a remarkable predominance of guanine to adenine transitions in the descent of the cytochrome *c* genes and among present-day abnormal human hemoglobins.

8. There is a possibility that statistical phylogenetic trees of this type, combined with other varieties of information, will lead to the development of time scales of evolution and the estimation of the point in time at which particular species diverged.

9. One might be able to estimate how and at what times the rate of fixation of mutations into a gene type has varied during evolutionary history.

10. Finally, there may be possibilities of developing methods that would derive phylogeny according to the minimal numbers of mutations interrelating the genes for various proteins in a homologous set, rather than according to the average minimal mutation distances, as has been done so far. This would change the present phenograms to true cladograms.

There is no time to dwell on any of these possibly near-term developments. More distant vistas should be left to more vivid imaginations than mine.

The methods for extracting information concerning ancestral genes and their relationships from known amino acid sequences, to which I have referred, have been developed by Dr. Walter M. Fitch at the University of Wisconsin.

To end with a note of caution, I quote from Berzelius, who in 1842 wrote: "This easy kind of physiological chemistry is created at the writing desk and is the more dangerous the more genius goes into it." To make the quotation entirely modern, all one has to do is to change "writing desk" to "computer console."

RAVIN: I have two points to make. The first is that the genetic approach should accompany, whenever possible, whatever molecular approaches are being pursued in systematic research. Without genetic tests, one may fail to perceive the biological or populational significance of the differences in DNA, RNA, protein, or other macromolecular structures being measured. For example, a very small difference in the primary structure of two homologous polypeptides may be associated with a very great effect in the ability of the responsible structural genes to pair and recombine with each other, and the latter effect may be an extremely important one in the ultimate biological test of species differentiation. Conversely, a very great difference in the primary structure of the polypeptide may be associated with only minor influences on genic recognition and recombination.

The second point is that systematic research in the future ought to combine the talents of the molecular, the genetic, the organismic, and the population biologist. I think great progress will be made if biologists representing researches at the various levels of biological organization work either as teams or near each other as interacting groups interested in the basic biological problems of genetic diversity, population dynamics, and evolution. Not only will such an interdisciplinary effort be an efficient way of bringing to bear on a major problem the arsenal of technology and knowledge that no one person can master, it also should produce some intellectual dividends. In the increasing dialogue between the ends of the biological spectrum, we may come to realize a much larger common denominator to our efforts than we had imagined. The molecular biologist will remain conversant with the issues and problems needing solution, and he will invent or modify methods to aid in the solution. The organismic and population biologists, on the other hand, will find interested colleagues who may have either methods or concepts to contribute. The language of the systematist and ecologist should be no more esoteric to the molecular and cellular biologist than the latter's should be irrelevant to the evolutionary biologist. In fact, we will appreciate each other's work only when we see clearly how our work is connected each to the other.

SOLBRIG: At present, when the problem at hand is to establish the degree of similarity between two taxa, the practicing plant taxonomist wants to have as many unbiased criteria as possible. Morphological and anatomical characters, as well as geographical criteria, are classically employed when trying to assess relationships; but also, cytological, genetical, and chemical characters occasionally are highly useful. However, these more analytical characters usually require living material, often at a special stage of the life cycle, and thus are more difficult to obtain in terms of time and effort; also, they require special skills on the part of the investigator and special apparatuses that are not always available. So, the determination of the chromosome number of a plant for example, takes much more time and effort than the determination of the color of the flower of that same plant. This is particularly true with regard to macromolecular characters.

Although chemical characters are not without value in orthodox taxonomic studies, and, as we have just been told, they will be the thing of the future, I believe that, at present, the effort and time involved in obtaining them are justified only when the problem at hand cannot be resolved with more orthodox methods of establishing relationships. However, when we seek the reasons for a pattern of variability, or try to determine the mechanisms underlying evolutionary phenomena, then chemical characteristics promise to open up a whole new area of research and, in my opinion, will change the field of population genetics into a much more experimental one.

In effect, it is now possible to obtain in a relatively easy and quick manner (at least with plants) data on frequencies of isozymes for 20–25 enzyme systems at least, and, no doubt, in a few years there will be ways to detect a score or two more.

In addition, techniques are available for isolating and determining storage proteins from seeds and other organs. Although the relationship between enzyme and cistrons is not exactly 1:1, it is very nearly so, and single base pairs changes can sometimes be detected. Consequently, frequencies of isozymes in populations provide the best available estimate of gene frequency.

In the area of macromolecular data, it now is possible to set up biochemical experiments to test the following: degree of intrapopulational variability, and changes from year to year; effect of population size on genic frequencies; changes of gene frequencies along ecological gradients; amount of gene flow between populations; effect of breeding system on gene frequencies, particularly in situations where an organism is in the process of changing from self-incompatibility to self-compatibility; and effect of different intensities of selection on genic variability. This can be done in a quick and easy manner, in such a way that many populations can be tested. Through classical genetic methods it would take years to obtain the information that can now be obtained in a summer.

In regard to compounds of low molecular weight, it is now possible to analyze phenotypic characters (and secondary metabolites are certainly to be classed as phenotypic characters) more precisely than it is possible to analyze morphological phenotypical characters. In effect, the biosynthesis, physiology, and role of an anthocyanin, for example, are amenable to study and experimentation and therefore can be discovered. No such exact attack is possible on leaf shape, to give another example. Also compounds of low molecular weight are very fine markers in studies of hybridization and introgression, as the studies of Brehm, Smith, and the team of Alston and Turner and collaborators have shown repeatedly.

But I have a word of caution. Biochemistry, in addition to promises, has many pitfalls. There are still many areas within biochemistry that remain unresolved, and work in these areas can be very frustrating for nonbiochemists. In addition, many systematists (such as myself) have had, at best, very little biochemistry in their training, and a lot of retooling is necessary in order for them to work in this field. I conclude with a plea that we give our students good training in the principles and methods of molecular biology as well as in systematics and evolution. I am confident that a generation that is thoroughly familiar with these two areas will bring into systematics the rigor and precise thinking characteristic of physics and chemistry and thus will be able to realize the promises that the new methods and techniques are offering.

THROCKMORTON: I do not know the appropriate poetry, but there is something in literature about no man being an island unto himself. I think the same thing could be said about taxonomy. Its future, I believe, has to be considered in the light of the probable future of biology as a whole, and if we have difficulty in being prescient about the future of biology we have even more difficulty telling where taxonomy itself is going.

We can see some major trends developing, and one of the most significant of these is that biology is becoming more and more a single field. There is an implosion. A generation ago we had many disciplines that could function independently of each other; but today we have a great deal of difficulty separating some of the disciplines we consider to be major. Where, for example, are the boundaries between genetics and population genetics? Then, if you go from genetics to population genetics, where do you draw the line between that and ecology, and so on? If you go in the other direction from genetics—to developmental biology, for instance—you begin to consider the influence of the environment on regulatory systems and on development itself, and, again, you find yourself rapidly coalescing and fusing with the field of environmental biology and the general integration of an organism into its ecosystem. All of these are processes involved in the static present, so to speak, integrated with an analysis of the relationships of genes in the gene pools (population genetics).

We should inquire as to the position and obligation of taxonomy in a science that is rapidly becoming one discipline. What I see happening today is essentially a fusion of what we might call contemporary biology into one unit, and that leaves out a very large area of historical biology, which has been traditionally one of the responsibilities, if not one of the major interests, of systematics. It is unlikely that many of the other disciplines will occupy themselves with history, and for this reason, taxonomy will be required by other biologists to preoccupy itself with history. It is very interesting that the speakers tonight, almost to a man, have seemed to press the idea that systematics is concerned only with history, or with the analysis of historical relationships. This is important, and is itself a good prediction for taxonomy. However, it is also important to point out that taxonomy has many levels of study other than the long-distance phylogenetic level. The boundary at or just above the level of the species is one that none of the other disciplines is equipped to handle at the present time. The workers in other disciplines may extend their interests into this field, but consideration must be given to the nature of the system, and this can be done only in the deeper historical context. One of the points I made earlier was that we have to analyze the properties of the system from the level of the population as far as we can go back in time. Taxonomy is responsible for history and for the developing of historical methods. This is probably the one function that is unique to taxonomy. To do this we will have to form the bridge between systems biology in the ecological sense and population biology in the genetic and developmental sense.

GOODMAN: Dr. Margoliash, if after analyzing more and more species, certain ambiguities do not disappear and you still see a series of amino acids at certain points, this might be evidence that the ancestral species might have been polymorphic rather than uniform for various sites of cytochrome *c.*

MARGOLIASH: That, of course, is possible. The only thing I can say is that, so far, every time we have obtained more information, the degree of apparent polymorphism has decreased, not increased. This result is given by a purely statistical procedure with a few logical assumptions. However, I do not know how correct the assumptions really are, so there exists a latitude of possibilities.

MANDEL: In your list of the types of organisms examined you went down as far as *Neurospora* and *Saccharomyces.* There was a paucity of plants and of Protista outside of the yeasts and fungi.

MARGOLIASH: One plant has now been added, and this decreases the redundancy.

Bacteria, as far as is known, do not carry proteins homologous to cytochrome *c.* All of the *C*-type cytochromes of bacteria appear to be unrelated to the eukaryotic cytochromes *c,* and therefore cannot be compared.

RAVIN: When you take samples from different strains of a given species do you find any polymorphism at a given amino acid locus?

MARGOLIASH: So far, there has been no indication of that. We have been careful about examining odd fractions every time a preparation is made. We also have determined the sequences of the cytochrome *c* from kidney, liver, skeletal muscle, heart muscle, and brain of the hog, and we have examined the protein from about a dozen individual hearts from both horse and human and have seen no trace of polymorphism. With ordinary preparations, made from pooled tissues of numerous individuals, one might expect to observe polymorphism by the current techniques if it involves a substitution of one particular amino acid for the common one at a level of at least 10 percent. If several different variant residues occur, together making up as much as 25–35 percent of the total for any one amino acid position, the situation is likely to go unnoticed.

RAVIN: Of course, there is always the possibility that this is a peculiarity of cytochrome *c*, and that there might be differences with respect to different proteins.

MARGOLIASH: That is possible, of course. You may have seen, on that subject, the recent work of von Ehrenstein indicating polymorphism of rabbit hemoglobin alpha-chains. All I can say is that this has so far not been observed with cytochrome *c*. Much more extensive and careful work would have to be done before one could definitively state that polymorphism does or does not exist in the case of cytochrome *c*. Two different cytochromes *c* do exist in baker's yeast (iso-1 and iso-2-cytochromes *c*). These are, however, coded for by independent genes and therefore do not represent polymorphism in the sense we are discussing.

DE LEY: Dr. Margoliash, in the case of the cytochrome *c* of yeast, plants, and higher organisms, we are fortunate in knowing which side is up. Man is up; yeast is down. But suppose you carry out a similar analysis of bacterial cytochrome *c*—would you see any possibility of determining whether there is a top side and a bottom side?

MARGOLIASH: The statistical procedure used to construct this sort of phylogenetic tree does not answer this question. You automatically start with extant material at the bottom, and build backwards from it. Closely related groups would come out together, and more distantly related groups would have a common ancestor further back. There is no up or down side to such a tree with regard to extant species. The computer is not equipped to make any judgment as to whether man is superior to yeast or vice-versa.

BREHM: Dr. Margoliash, a recent paper on ferrodoxin shows, or postulates, the evolution of that enzyme by the doubling of repetitive units. Do you have any repetitive units in the model of your primitive enzyme? Also, can you postulate what the possible origin of this primitive enzyme might have been?

MARGOLIASH: I know nothing about the origin of a postulated "primitive" protein, and we have no evidence of internal duplications in either the proposed ancestral cytochrome *c* or of the protein at any point in the statistical phylogenetic tree.

In the case of bacterial ferrodoxin the duplication of the two halves of the molecule is quite apparent, but the duplications of smaller segments that have been proposed represent a hypothesis for which there is as yet no statistically valid basis.

HUNZIKER: Dr. Margoliash, have you studied the cytochrome *c* in representatives of brachytelic groups? I am referring to living "fossils"—animals or plants that have not changed (at least in their bones or in their external morphology) for millions of years.

MARGOLIASH: Nothing of that nature has been done so far, simply because most of the so-called living fossils contain extremely little cytochrome *c* and one would have to process tons of material. We would like to study the coelacanth, which is an active animal and is suitably large. Notwithstanding several attempts, we have been unable to obtain one, or even half of one. The main interest in studying the cytochrome *c* of a species that apparently has not changed morphologically over a long period of evolutionary history would be (at least at the first level) to try to decide the question of whether evolutionary changes in proteins occur only concomitantly with morphological changes. The procedure would require (1) obtaining the amino acid sequence of a protein from a so-called living fossil, (2) working out the primary structures of the homologous proteins for a large number of closely related species that have undergone morphological evolutionary change, and (3) comparing the derived ancestral sequence with that of the protein from the "living fossil." One could then tell whether the cytochrome *c* of the coelacanth, for example, is similar to the ancestral cytochrome of that same period or whether it has changed just like the cytochromes of the other related species.

SOLBRIG: I would take slight issue with the example given here of the independent origin of the vessels, comparing it with polypeptide amino acid sequences. Unfortunately, we do not know exactly what the probability is of this event, but since plants did have tracheids in all these cases and the change from a tracheid to a vessel is not complex, I think the probability is quite high that it occurred independently at least four times. We have, however, a reasonable idea of the probability of getting parallel evolution for the sequences of amino acids. When only 150 sequences are involved, the probability is so low that we might say it is impossible.

On the other hand, I question what has been said here as it applies to the practical problem of today. At present the analysis of different amino acid sequences in proteins provides us only with the phylogeny of a few molecules, the phylogeny of the cytochrome *c*, and the phylogeny of the LDH or something of that sort. How long will it take to have enough phylogenies that we can try to extrapolate to the problem of phylogenies of the organisms carrying them? We must be careful in predicting when we can do this. Perhaps in a few years it will be very easy to get amino acid sequences, but I know how hard it is to extract these. Dr. Margoliash has said that this problem exists even for cytochrome *c*. There are still some very simple problems in biochemistry that are not quite solved. I am skeptical of our getting a phylogeny of organisms (but not of getting phylogenies of a few molecules) in the near future.

MANDEL: It is possible to shortcut much of this problem with a large number of enzymes. Nothing has been said at this conference to indicate that anyone has gone back to some of the approximation techniques capitalized upon by Nathan Kaplan and his students: that if one performs the analysis of the kinetics of reaction of a series of enzyme preparations using the normal substrate and cofactors and then compares the kinetics of the reactions with those obtained with a series of substrate and coenzyme analogs, one can infer quite a bit about the similarities or dissimilarities of the active centers of the enzymes being compared. This is the other side of the coin of what the Ouchterlony gel diffusion techniques tell us about the general configuration and amino acid sequence of proteins. Together, the two techniques will at least tell you (without a total amino acid sequence) whether the proteins of your organisms have much resemblance in general configuration and in their active centers. Where it is possible to do a few good protein purifications and run the entire amino acid sequence it should be done—and undoubtedly the automated sequence analyzer will be available commercially within a year or so. We need this as a check against some of the approximation techniques, and the approximation procedures can be used to scan a large number of samples of independent origin.

GOODMAN: It is impossible (and maybe it always will be impossible) to completely decode the whole genome, but we are in a position to sample the genome. I think individual protein molecules and their homologues in other species are the starting points of the sampling. We must have some concept of how many proteins we have to examine before we feel confident that the picture will not be altered after we see an additional series of proteins. I do not expect that this minimum number of proteins will be too large.

MARGOLIASH: I want to register an objection to the approximation procedures. The amount of information one gets from relatively fewer but complete amino acid sequences is so far beyond what one can get from even a large number of so-called approximation tests that the sequences are worth the extra effort. Such effort will become less and less as the years go by. Today the work necessary to determine the amino acid sequence of a protein of some 250 residues, not previously studied from that point of view, is probably equivalent to the effort required five years ago to examine a protein one third that size. This trend is accelerating. In fact, the biochemical journals these days are being flooded with amino acid sequences. The biologist really requires that information, and I have no doubt that this flood will rise even more rapidly in years to come.

MANDEL: I hope that the biochemist who runs the sequence of a protein will at least have the right indentification on it and on the species from which it was obtained.

SIBLEY: On that highly practical and taxonomic note we might open the discussion to the floor.

SOKAL: As a very nonmolecular biologist I have been tremendously impressed by the variety of material and ideas presented here and the great potential they have for systematics. It seems, however, that of all the facts or ideas presented, none is at variance with the principles and practices of systematics based on other evidence—cytological, morphological, or whatever. I may be wrong in this, as there may have been new principles or new procedures lurking in the presentations that, as yet, I do not understand. But if, in fact, the very same principles and procedures relevant to the rest of systematics also are relevant to molecular systematics, I think we must be equally precise in stating the sort of principles under which we are working. I think that some of the participants perhaps have not been quite as precise in formulating their principles as they might have been. It may be presumptious for me to say this, but I think that by stressing this point I am really echoing or extending the remarks of Dr. Ravin.

Perhaps owing to the limited discussion of some papers yesterday, it may not have been obvious to everyone in the audience that there is a very active controversy over almost all the facts, principles, and procedures of systematics. There are not just two schools, but numerous schools contending for attention, all of which should be examined and evaluated. In this connection, however, it is important that one take care to define his ideas and operations precisely. To illustrate my point, in a moment I will cite from the speakers whose discussions on molecular systematics we have heard, but first I must mention one other consideration.

Some taxonomic ideas that have been more or less taken for granted as facts by the molecular systematists need not necessarily be facts. Initially, we were tremendously concerned about whether our findings agreed with previous classifications. When orthodox taxonomists said this was a species and this was an order, we were apt to say: "By golly, we have to come out with exactly the same finding." However, as we have become surer of what we are doing, we are no longer so concerned about whether our findings coincide with those of others, but we may very well come out with some of the same results.

Now I will cite the two examples in regard to precise definitions. If I understood him correctly, I think Dr. Goodman clearly was talking of what we now call "cladistic relationships" or what Dr. Throckmorton likes to call "genealogical relationships"; however, I learned later that basically he was talking about branching sequences. Yet, in another passage, when talking about exactly the same thing, I think, he spoke of "degree of relationship." I think Hennig and others have shown that in a branching sequence you cannot have a degree of relationship except in certain very limited cases. Therefore, it is not appropriate for one to use the term "degree of relationship" as something that is quantifiable when he is really speaking of branching relationships or branching sequences.

I now quote from the abstract of Dr. Hunziker:

> If we assume that organisms are related to each other proportionally to their genetic similarity, it is valid to assume that the degree of relationships among these organisms is proportional to the similarity of their proteins. Sibley has thoroughly discussed the use of proteins as a source of phylogenetic information and its rational foundation.

Several difficult concepts are embodied in those two sentences. To me, it is not clear what is meant by "genetic similarity" and by "degree of relationships" and it is not clear just what it is that is "proportional to the similarity of their proteins." I repeat, in order to progress it is very important that we be quite clear and precise in our definitions.

May I conclude with a request for information. As a nonmolecular biologist, I am curious as to why almost no mention—or essentially no mention—of comparative serology has been made in this large group of molecular systematists.

GOODMAN: To explain what I mean by "degree of relationship" I have submitted a diagram to illustrate the cladistic relationship, or a branching sequence. In this diagram (Figure 1) I think it is fair to say that A and B show a closer relationship to each other than either A or B shows to C. I confess that I am not attuned to the subtleties of semantics of the systematists, so this may not be what you are referring to at all.

SOKAL: If we elaborate this diagram to include Taxa D and E (Figure 2) we can make no statement about whether D and E are closer to each other than B and A. If we interpret the figure cladistically, this is certainly true, and, therefore, degree of relationship in cladistics has only a limited meaning. The only meaning that we can

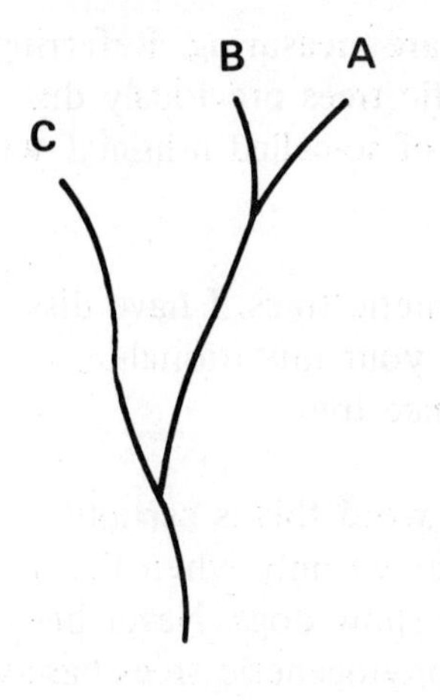

FIGURE 1 Diagram submitted by Dr. Goodman to illustrate branching sequence to explain "degree of relationship."

apply is that A and B are closer to each other than either is to C, which I think we can safely say. We can make no statement about A with respect to D and E; in phenetics we can, but in cladistics we cannot.

GOODMAN: I would say that A and B are not only closer to each other than they are to C but they are also closer to each other than they are to C, D, and E.

SOKAL: But are D and E closer to each other than B and A? When we speak of "degree of relationship" we should be able to make statements of that sort.

GOODMAN: Oh, I now see your point.

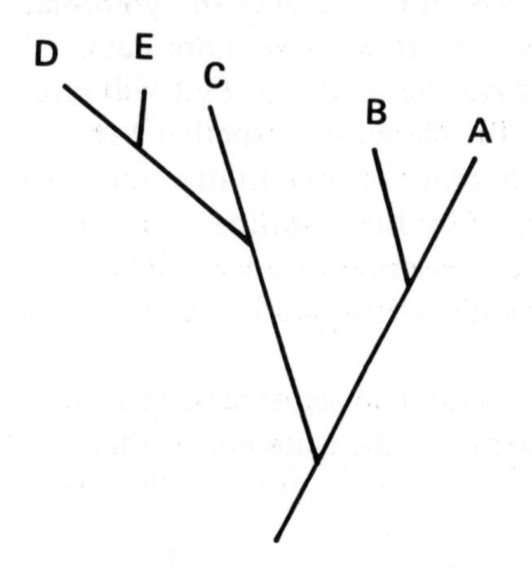

FIGURE 2 Diagram by Dr. Goodman as amended and discussed by Dr. Sokal.

MARGOLIASH: It depends on what you are measuring. Referring to a case such as the statistical phylogenetic trees previously discussed, the distances are defined in terms of so-called minimal mutation distances.

SOKAL: But your trees were, in fact, phenetic trees. I have discussed this with Fitch, and he agreed that your mutational-distance tree was actually a phenetic-distance tree.

MARGOLIASH: In the strict sense of the word this is certainly correct. Similarly, cladistic relations are known only when the actual genealogy has been recorded, as for show dogs. Nevertheless, I feel it is not fair to lump together phylogenetic trees based on approximations of the nucleotide sequences of genes, with the phenetic relations derived from phenotypic morphological characters of extremely complicated and mostly unknown genetic background. If variations in the genome, consisting primarily of changes in the nucleotide sequences of genes, are the detailed determinants of phyletic distances, then surely phylogenetic trees based on the extent of such variations are far more likely to approximate cladistic relations than a compendium of morphological characteristics. This is all the more so when the quantitation of such characteristics must necessarily be imposed by the taxonomist in a language that is unrelated to the language by which biological information is actually transmitted.

ROGERS: I welcome our molecular colleagues to the ranks of the classical taxonomists. For at least three decades of symposia we have been hearing expressions like "If we have more data. . ." and "Next year we are going to have the hardware that will give us the data." I would like to ask Dr. Margoliash whether his quantitative data are of a different order of quantitative information than, for example, those gained by the counting of petals, fish scales, or vertebrae, or by the measuring of a leaf? What is so much better about your information than any of the rest of it?

MARGOLIASH: In dealing with amino acid sequences, one has direct simple translations of segments of the genome, so that what we are examining is, in fact, the fine structure of the primary source of biological information. The other kind of quantitative data represent, genetically, extremely complex phenomena. Amino acid sequences reduce the material to the simplest situation currently available that can be analyzed in truly quantitative fashion. This is the case, for example, with the minimal mutation distances discussed earlier. These are defined as the minimal number of single nucleotide changes required to transform the gene coding for one protein to that coding for another. On such a basis one can derive a variety of quantitative conclusions similar to those listed some time ago.

SIBLEY: All numbers used other than those that Dr. Margoliash is talking about are pseudonumbers—numbers developed in the mind of the observer, not the real numbers of nature. The numbers about which Dr. Margoliash is speaking are real numbers that will be the only universal currency of information.

TOWNES: Because we are being quite logical in breaking these organisms down into their molecules to get closer to the truth, why not carry it further and break them down into atoms and count the atoms? Then we would have some real quantitative data.

FARRIS: I agree that Dr. Margoliash's data are quantitative, and in a moment I will present reasons for this. First, however, I want to comment on a few points that arise from slight differences in kinds of numerical taxonomic idealogies. The point has been raised that one cannot talk about degrees of difference on a cladogram. If the cladogram is, indeed, just a cladogram, that is true. In practice, however, all other cladograms—such as those drawn by Dr. Margoliash, those generated by maximum-parsimony computer algorithms such as Dr. Sokal's, or noncomputerized algorithms or computerized versions of algorithms such as mine and Dr. Wagner's—are, in fact, deduced on the basis of phenotypic character states; consequently, intrinsic in the very production of this most parsimonious, or most likely, tree is what can be considered as a measure of similarity or of difference along the indicated paths of evolution connecting the known data points. The amount of evolution along the paths is not equivalent to phenetic difference, but it is correlated with it somewhat. This "patristic divergence" is a number that indicates an actual amount of evolution, and it does exist on a diagram that is topologically equivalent to a cladogram.

Now further on the subject of Dr. Margoliash's procedure. There is, of course, considerable interest in numerical taxonomy in trying to find, on theoretical grounds, the best way of going about deducing—or perhaps I should say inferring—evolutionary relationships. Some theoretical work that I recently completed but have not yet published shows that, for appropriate scaling of unit characters, a cladogram of maximum parsimony is the cladogram that has the maximum probability of being true in the evolutionary sense. Because I use a computer algorithm very similar to the method developed originally by Dr. Wagner, I could develop quite easily an algorithm that would be amenable to direct use of the sort of data that Dr. Margoliash has available. In fact, the very use of his mutation distances in comparing amounts of differences between individual amino acid alternatives is equivalent to part of a maximum-likelihood procedure. The only necessary variation from this published procedure would be the substitution of a sum of absolute values of differences metric for the square root of the sum of squared differences metric. So, I am quite interested in the point made by Dr. Margoliash and others that the application of statistical techniques is important in the context of well-worked-out molecular biology and molecular systematics. I would like to point out that, for the most part, the appropriate techniques are already available.

In regard to quantitativeness, I want to state that I have also worked out a set of criteria for determining a good character and a bad character. Originally these criteria were intended for application to morphological characters, but in light of this discussion, their application to molecular biological data may also be interesting. Approximately, this is the way my study turns out: Knowledge of individual nucleotide sequences is better than almost anything else; knowledge of amino acid ratios is slightly better than knowledge of GC ratios; knowledge of ratios (of almost any kind) is substantially better than almost any knowledge of precipitin testing. And, comparing a little further, knowledge of amino acid sequences or of nucleotide sequences is extremely powerful but—and of course it must be so—knowledge of the sequences for a small quantity of the genome is not necessarily better than knowledge about a relatively large part of the genome sample—for example, that gained through classical morphological methods.

WILSON: I ask Dr. Sokal whether he equates numerical taxonomy with a specific set of hypotheses about sampling of the genome and the taking of phenetic distances or whether it encompasses something more—perhaps in methodology—than what Mr. Farris has just described.

SOKAL: That is an embarrassing question, but I will try to answer it. By way of a preamble, I would say that numerical taxonomy is a developing field. Fortunately, none of us is so old as to have become rigid in our views on this subject. There are quite a number of young, active people in this field, as you have seen. It is obvious that we think about it differently now than we did five years ago, and our ideas concerning it are continually changing. Personally, I am still prepared to change my mind on many of these ideas in the field. Eventually, after a decade or so, beliefs in this field will become rigid, as is customary, but at present ideas are still in a state of flux.

Roughly, I think we originally defined numerical taxonomy as the measurement of the phenetic similarities among organisms and the structuring of these similarities into a taxonomic system. Then more recently, as many of you know, we became interested in the other aspect of systematics—the historical or phylogenetic aspect. We also went into this aspect numerically rather than chemically because that is the way we think and work. Then I was asked whether this also was numerical taxonomy. Fortunately at that point I looked in our book and found a sentence that showed that Sneath and I had had considerable foresight. The sentence stated that numerical taxonomy would "include the drawing of phylogenetic inferences from the data by statistical or other mathematical methods to the extent to which this should prove possible." I hope and believe that the numerical approaches—be they cladistic, phenetic, or whatever—will before long result in an integrated systematics that will combine all these aspects. I would be one-sided to ignore either of these two sides of systematics. Numerical taxonomy is not meant to be so broad as to include all applications of statistics to systematics. For example, the application of geographic variations should not be considered numerical taxonomy. I hope that this is a fair answer. Mr. Farris' work clearly is numerical taxonomy, in my opinion.

WILSON: In the interests of having clear metataxonomy, would you object if we started calling it statistical, quantitative, or mathematical taxonomy so that we will not, in confusion, continue to connect it with one university?

SOKAL: I appreciate your kind reference to the University of Kansas. We did think about all these terms, and we did not loosely think up the term "numerical taxonomy." We thought about using the term "quantitative taxonomy," but a number of the chemical biologists objected because they felt that if it were called quantitative taxonomy we would not exclude biochemical taxonomy. So, "quantitative" was eliminated. We knew that statisticians would say that what we are doing is not really statistics, and we did not think so either. So, "statistical" was eliminated. We ended up by asking ourselves exactly what it was we were doing. We were working with numbers, the numerical codes that we were using to describe characters. So, "numerical taxonomy" came out as the solution.

As you know, other people have used other names for it, and the printable ones I can repeat: "taxometrics" was really very good, except that I was not the one who thought of it; and there was "taximetrics," which was not quite as good.

What you are referring to, I think, is numerical phenetics. Is it that you wish to distinguish numerical phenetics from other kinds of numerical taxonomy?

WILSON: Yes. I want to disassociate from it a particular set of hypotheses.

SOKAL: Perhaps then, the term "numerical phenetics" would be a fair way to distinguish it from numerical taxonomy, which is, perhaps, a much broader field. All right?

ROGERS: I thank Dr. Sokal for getting in that bit on that "taximetrics," which evolved, you know, from "taxometrics."

We all would like to have the word that would clear up the whole picture, but clearly the term "numerical taxonomy" suggests only a piece of the totality of elements involved in taxonomy–classification, ecology, and all the other elements that we have discussed and must concern ourselves with as taxonomists.

SIBLEY: This panel was discussing the molecular approach as a method of obtaining or discovering data. The numerical approaches are methods of analyzing data, however they may be discovered. We should not be engaged in a debate on these two approaches as they are not matters for choice. The one can be utilized to analyze the other.

TOWNES: I think that a statement I made a few minutes ago should be clarified. We learn something about an organism by analyzing its chemical constituents, but we must remember that the organization of these constituents is also important. To illustrate, we can consider the present building as a whole, and we will learn something, as we would by considering a whole organism. We consider the bricks equivalent to the molecules, from which we can learn something. We consider the plumbing, the chairs, and other furnishings and learn something from all of that. But actually, as we reduce the building to smaller and smaller bits, it becomes less distinctive as a building. I think that is somewhat true of chemistry. It teaches us something, but in studying the organism too closely we miss something important about its organization. Behavior was mentioned. There must be a molecular basis for behavior, but I am not sure that a complete reading of a DNA molecule will enable us to predict the behavior of an organism. Although those are important phyletic data and cannot be overlooked, we should remember that breaking down an organism into ever smaller units will not give us the complete picture.

GOODMAN: It is a misconception if it is thought we are claiming here that molecular systematics is the answer to everything. The particular point you have raised has much to do with grades of organization. The type of data that was emphasized, and particularly that presented by Dr. Margoliash, does not tell us, at this stage, anything about grades of organization; thus it would not be particularly useful in grade classifications. The unique value of these amino sequence data–if they could be extended to enough polypeptide chains and their homologues in a variety of organisms–is that they are at the particular level of the organization of living systems that will reveal the genealogical relationships of these systems better than data from any other level. But this information from the right kind of molecular data is very specific; it is not telling you about the whole organism, how it is organized, how it functions at different levels, and so on. By all means, we need this other kind of information too, and we are not claiming that molecular data of the type discussed will provide that kind of information.

SOLBRIG: I have a comment to make regarding the question "Why not go on to the atom?" We are not just analyzing the organisms chemically. There is genetic information in the DNA molecule; it is a blueprint that tells the organism what it is going to be. The genotype obviously is going to interact with the environment to produce the final phenotype, but all information for the development is there, and that is what we are after. We are not after some base ratio or some amount of amino acid or how many molecules of carbon there are in the plant, because such data alone would be meaningless; it is the blueprint we are after. I think it is most important that this difference be understood.

THROCKMORTON: The last question I asked really was directed to this. It is a question of to what extent, if we knew the DNA base sequence, we would have a body of real information. Then we have the question, when that information is read out and an organism is produced in the environment, and then we assay the information in the organism, to what extent is there a one-to-one correlation between the end product and the base sequence. Now that is one question that I think in part is what you are asking. Then we have the further question of going from that body of information to a classification, and I wanted to follow up and ask Dr. Dessauer this question–to what extent the panel–he and the rest of the panel–thought that molecular methods would give an assessment of similarity that is for all practical purposes equivalent to an assessment of phenetic similarities, *à la* the phenetic taxonomists. Would molecular information really be a different kind of information, i.e., cladistic information? And, going beyond that, will the molecular systematists have fulfilled their obligation if they simply produce the data, perhaps nothing more than a dendrogram, and dump them in the laps of the rest of the taxonomists and say, "O.K. There they are. You do what you want to with them"? Or is it in part the responsibility of people like us, and others elsewhere, to grapple with the issues that are being raised here? You have the information; how do you convert it into a classification? Now before I go farther, am I going around the subject you raise or is this intimately related to the question?

TOWNES: I questioned whether an analysis of a subdivision of an organism is the best way of understanding the entire organization. I think such an analysis would give some information but other information would be lost by the dissecting.

THROCKMORTON: Pardon me for interrupting, but you see there have been methods suggested for getting DNA sequence comparisons between two organisms, and if it then were possible to assess the total phenotypic relationships between these organisms, we could ask what the relationship is between these comparisons. The question I'm specifying is: "Is there a way of assessing the relationship between the information in the genome and the information in the total organism so that we can get an objective answer to your question?" You are suggesting that there is more information in the organism than there is in the DNA, and I think I agree with you. However, I would go further and say that biochemists get for us not only a readout of basic information in the genome but can derive information from the method of readout, and such information may also provide an objective answer as to whether your assertion is correct.

TOWNES: Suppose we agree, theoretically, that the information is in the genome; but analysis of the genome may not be the most proficient way of getting the information we want.

As brought out by the panel itself, we are planning great things here, but we are planning them without a realization of what the plant and animal kingdons are like. We are in an air-conditioned building and no insects are flying around, but outside there may be thousands of insects, and among them may be a dozen, or a hundred, new species that no one has ever collected. For instance,

I work on a single family containing about 50,000 species, but you talk about the frog, the turtle, the fish, and three species of plants. Certain theoretical concepts and understandings can be developed from this kind of analysis, but the real taxonomic problem is probably far removed from your experience. Many of the species are not even represented in any museum, and to talk about getting a specimen three millimeters long and reading out its genome is just nonsense.

SIBLEY: Those of us on this platform are not unaware of the complexities of some groups of organisms or of the difficulties of classical taxonomic procedures. However, I think it is important that your original question about reduction to the level of atomic structure be approached from a point different from the one of information content.

The problem here is that you would reach a point in reductionism, in terms of structure, at which you destroy all the information that was present. This point is reached approximately at the molecular level. The level of the molecule is the lowest common denominator for information in biological systems.

If a protein chain is a translation of a gene and reflects approximately a one-to-one relationship to that gene, all that is needed to destroy the information content of that protein is to divide it up into its constituent amino acids, break every peptide bond. These are molecules—a long way from atoms—yet you have destroyed the information content just as surely as if you had cut up an English sentence into its constituent letters. In other words, it is not a matter of getting more information the deeper you go, because you will destroy your information after you reach a certain point. The biological unit is the molecule; below that we have nothing. That is the answer to your question of whether we should break the organism down further.

BESCHEL: There is something about the molecule that I would comment on. If I take a few cells off my tongue I have not destroyed that organism, and it is still present. I think each level of the hierarchic organization has its own pattern of low variance and thus its own predictive value; consequently, each level can be studied from multivariate approaches, and it is convenient to bring these multivariate procedures together, whether we use simple or complicated ordination procedures.

I personally am concerned, however, that molecular biology not only is getting a considerable number of grants but also is going into a blind alley.

The following passages from Fabre's *The Life of the Fly* may be a little strong, but I think they are quite appropriate (J. H. Fabre, *The Life of The Fly,* transl. De Mattos; Hodder and Stoughton, London: p. 14):

> I make my observations under the blue sky to the song of the cicadas; you subject cell and protoplasm to chemical tests, I study instinct in its loftiest manifestations; you pry into death, I pry into life. And why should I not complete my thought: the boars have muddied the clear stream; natural history, youth's glorious study, has, by dint of cellular improvements, become a hateful and repulsive thing. Well, if I write for men of learning, for philosophers, who, one day, will try to some extent to unravel the tough problem of instinct, I write also, I write above all things for the young. I want to make them love the natural history which you make them hate. . . .

RAVIN: I would no more want to deny to the man who wants to go into the field the pleasure of the spectacle of nature, the pleasure of enjoying the frolic of the bees and the birds, than I would want the ecologist or the population biologist to deny to the molecular biologist the real fun that he gets (not by prying into death) by prying into things that are meaningful and vital to him.

I deplore this kind of discussion with its polarization of attitudes in which the population biologist sees nothing in molecular biology but a threat, in which he sees the men who represent the new wave as wanting to take over biology. You know as well as I that your methods will not be replaced because they are perfectly good ways of getting very relevant information about biological phenomena. But we are claiming that we have good ways too. We have to coexist, so let us coexist peacefully.

I urge that we have a dialogue, but we cannot have a dialogue if you insist that we are saying that ours is the only way of getting any kind of important information. When you charge us with making such a claim, some of us are silly enough to defend it sometimes. Then we are really stupid, and you can get people to say that they know the total information in an organism when they know the primary structures of its proteins. In our right minds, when we are not pressed to the wall, we know that that is not true.

We can know the amino acid sequences in a lot of proteins and still not know many things about the living cell. Protein molecules interact with each other, and the way in which they interact is influenced by their structure. But how they will interact depends upon a number of other things: whether other proteins are present in the cell; the intra- and extracellular environments, which in turn may be dependent upon what other kinds of cells are present. In other words, we need to have information not only about the molecular level of organization, but also about the supramolecular level, the organellar level, the cellular level, and so on, up to the community level, but none of us can study all of these levels at the same time with even a moderate degree of sophistication.

Let us talk to each other in a meaningful way and work together; then we will have some real systematics to talk about in the future.

CRONQUIST: I wanted to present the same views, but Dr. Ravin has expressed them so much better than I can that I defer to his statement.

CROVELLO: My first question involves the catholic currency that Dr. Sibley talked about with respect to DNA sequences, readouts and so forth. If certain parts of an enzyme are considered active sites and others are thought to be passive, shouldn't this information be taken in account when for phylogenetic purposes we compare the DNA base sequences from which this enzyme was constructed? That is, should we consider each nucleotide in a sequence coding for a certain enzyme as equal in estimating phyletic relationships, or should nucleotides from passive sites, for example, be considered more (or less) important? This is essential information because if one can tolerate a certain number of mutations at passive sites and still retain enzyme activity, who is to know how often and in what directions such mutations have occurred? Yet this is required knowledge when DNA sequences are used to construct accurately the phylogeny of the organisms under study. But before this can be answered, two pieees of information are required. Can you tell me if the base sequence at an active site for a certain reaction must be *exactly* the same in different organisms producing this active site? Also, can biochemists, knowing the sequence of DNA that codes for a certain enzyme, indicate what part of the DNA sequence codes for the resulting active site on the protein and what parts code for passive sites? Unless this sort of information is available, it seems that whether one should give different importance to active or passive sites is an academic question.

SIBLEY: We were not discussing active sites but the problem of protein structure. My only reason for talking about a common currency was to note that the idea that the genetic code is universal seems to be accepted.

MARGOLIASH: As far as its translation into a polypeptide chain is concerned, the information content of the gene is equivalent in any portion of the gene. That the synthesized polypeptide chain will eventually fold and form an active site consisting of various segments that have come together in the appropriate spatial configuration has little, if anything, to do directly with the situation, as far as I can see, except when we are trying to distinguish between analogy and homology. When comparing enzymes, obviously you cannot take the primary structures of the active sites as evidence for homology, because they may very well have evolved in a convergent manner from entirely different origins. Excellent examples of such secondarily acquired similarities can be found among the different classes of proteases that have an active serine in the enzymic site.

CROVELLO: My second question, directed to Dr. Margoliash, concerns the assumption that his method of producing a dendrogram involves parsimony. On what basis is this assumption accepted, other than that it is operational, simple, and sometimes seems to be elegant?

MARGOLIASH: I know at present of no other basis on which such calculations can be made. Whether the results are only sometimes elegant remains to be seen.

GOODMAN: I think the question you raise is the sort of thing Dr. Throckmorton would put his finger on with respect to trying to go from the sequence of amino acids to other levels of biological organization. This is an issue separate from the one regarding what amino acid sequence data can tell you about genealogical relationships. As I said before, we are not claiming that the level of organization represented by amino acid sequence data provides all kinds of information, but we do think it is a unique sort of level to get information on genealogy.

SIBLEY: One of the advantages of the approach of examining protein structure is that it is simple. I think this point continues to be missed only because the techniques are novel and unfamiliar to many. The impression is gained that they are complex. Although the techniques are complex to a degree, the information, once available, is far simpler, for instance, than gross morphological data. The techniques are not in the same range of complexity. The gross morphological comparisons are incredibly complex, and that is what makes taxonomy so difficult.

HOWDEN: With the vast numbers of organisms with which many of us, particularly entomologists, have to deal, and with all the methods that supposedly are assisting systematics, there is one thing often not considered—the time element. For a number of years I have tried to keep up with genetics. It has been very helpful in theory, but rearing the insects has been nearly impossible in many cases. Although genetics has been an invaluable tool for the taxonomist, we have found no solution to the problems that arise from the long life cycles of some insects. In terms of time, we do not live so long. Then along comes numerical taxonomy, which I find very useful in many ways. However, I do not need to run any statistics to tell the difference between a mouse and an elephant. In many cases I can do a visual analysis five times as fast as a statistical one for 95 percent of the species I am examining; and on perhaps 2 to 3 percent I find statistical analyses useful. So, again, the tool is occasionally useful to the working systematist, but it is also more time-consuming. This is the point I am raising about molecular biology. I ask in all seriousness, are any conceivable chemical methods on the molecular level going to be able to cover the million or more organisms that we are worrying with before they evolve into something else? This is the problem.

SIBLEY: In my work, we deal with something more than a thousand species of birds, and we do not find that too difficult. Ours are not the elegant techniques of Dr. Margoliash, but we are excited and interested in his data because they are the first really hard taxonomic data in existence. They are the first ones that give the promise (whether or not the promise is fulfilled) of being able to provide us with something other than the basis for an opinion. They provide us with the basis for proof. We have only morphological data of exactly the same caliber as the other morphological data; it is just the morphology of molecules.

Your problem is a matter of logistics, dealing with a million insects. Of course you deal with far fewer than a million insects. All the entomologists in the world are not dealing with a million insects. For various levels of problems and for various numbers of species, certain of these molecular techniques can deal with large numbers of species and add to the body of data already available. We are not talking about proving anything.

HOWDEN: Can you take something the size of an insect and get the information you want from closely allied species? How long would it take to analyze, for instance, the 8,000 species I have been trying to cover in a family that is equal to the birds of the world? Using chemical analysis at the molecular basis, how long would it take to analyze the relationships of 8,000 species of insects, with many specimens 3 mm long?

SIBLEY: You could get plenty of material from an insect much smaller than that for some kinds of analyses. The number you would have to examine to get the answers to your problem is something you would have to determine, but the amount of material required would be infinitesimal compared with a 3-mm insect.

SOKAL: Although personally I do not necessarily subscribe to this view, I feel that in response to Dr. Howden's comment and to Dr. Townes' earlier comment, an answer different from Dr. Sibley's should be given to this question, which might be called Ehrlich's heresy. The question might seriously be asked if it is really necessary that we know the cladistics of phylogeny of every single species of the two million species in the biologic world. Is it not really enough to have the type of analysis that Dr. Margoliash has shown us for the orders of insects and for representatives of a few of the important families? Do we really have to know all the cladistics and every last bit of information about every living organism in the world? Or is it better that we study a few groups intensively in order to learn certain principles?

While I have the floor, I will mention that I did not get an answer to my previous question on comparative serology. I know someone wanted to give me the answer, but no one did.

GOODMAN: I think I came closest to answering it by referring to our extensive immunological study of primate systematics. The term comparative serology certainly applies to this study. The immunological approach allows for comparisons of a great many species and a spectrum of proteins in these species in a much, much shorter time period than the approach of amino acid sequencing. By using the immunological approach, we can gather a great deal of data on various species of primates while there is still time. For example, the orangutan is about to disappear, and the gorilla may be in danger of disappearing. So far, to my knowledge, there are not any amino sequence data, except perhaps on hemoglobins, that compare gorilla and orangutan to other primates. Yet there are already considerable immunological data on serum proteins that do so.

SOLBRIG: It seems that all the discussion here has been concerned with relationships of one sort or another and with phylogenies. I want to emphasize what I said before and what Dr. Throckmorton said—that we have a powerful set of techniques by which we can analyze population phenomena. The mathematical population geneticist has not always been able to test his ideas experimentally because at present, with the classical genetical techniques, it takes too long and thus is impractical. Now I think we have a technique by which we will be able to understand, or at least attempt to understand, certain phenomena. As Dr. Sibley said, you can obtain quite a number of data. I know of techniques by which you can easily analyze about a thousand plants in a week for particular enzyme patterns and in this way obtain reliable estimates of gene frequency.

MARGOLIASH: I want to mention one of the difficulties I think exists with immunological work. When one studies the antigenic properties of a set of proteins, one is only looking at a minute fraction of the over-all protein structure. In one case, for example, two proteins, human and *Macaca mulatta* cytochromes *c*, differ by a single residue only out of the 104 in the chain and show about a 100 percent difference in their reaction to antiserum made to human cytochrome *c*. This is because the single residue substitution happens to yield a particularly strong immunogenic determinant in the human protein. The kangaroo protein, which also happens to have the same residue as human cytochrome *c*, would, on this basis, be judged to be closer to the human than the monkey protein. Thus, it would appear that in using immunological data we really are sampling—in a peculiar and very particular nonrandom way—a small fraction of the total primary structure. The danger of using immunological criteria is, therefore, greater the smaller the number of antigenic determinants. When the proteins to be compared are large and carry numerous antigenic determinants, the chances of error are correspondingly less. Such sources of error should not, however, be overlooked or underestimated.

CLARKE: Perhaps we have missed an important point. Dr. Margoliash has presented a phylogenetic tree based on what is essentially one gene. I wonder if someone would comment on the remarkable similarity between that phylogenetic tree and the one arrived at in more conventional ways. It seems to me that every single amino acid in the protein must be of selective importance, because the amino acid sequences of proteins within one species normally remain constant. If this is so, the fact that phylogenetic trees resemble each other must mean that all the genes in the organism are interacting very strongly. This, in fact, argues very forcibly in favor of a coadapted genotype.

MARGOLIASH: To discuss the question you have raised would open a Pandora's box of conflicting opinions, so I will make only a few comments. The question of whether every amino acid is necessarily of selective importance is too complicated for me to discuss in any detail. The direct evidence, such as we have it today, seems to indicate that the majority of amino acid substitutions have no detectable functional significance, and I do not know what to make of it.

The reason why cytochrome *c* gives a phylogenetic tree that looks like one a zoologist would accept must be that in this case, at least, the evolutionary variations of a single gene do, in fact, provide, by and large, a statistically valid expression of the evolutionary variations undergone by the species as a whole. However, cytochrome *c* appears to be particularly conservative, and, therefore, the tree is satisfactory with species that are relatively far apart. Species that are too closely related are likely to show either no amino acid variations or too few to yield the correct relationships. For example, the pig, sheep, and cow have identical cytochromes *c,* and this can hardly be taken as good evidence that they are a single species. To derive, on this basis, the relationships of closely related species one would need to examine a protein that has varied relatively rapidly in the course of evolution, as for example, the fibrinopeptides. Naturally, the larger the number of different sets of homologous proteins that are dissected in this way, the more accurate the derived relations are likely to be. What is truly remarkable is that even with a single protein one can already obtain a roughly acceptable statement of some phylogenetic relations, without injecting any biological bias whatsoever into the calculation, other than that provided directly by the amino acid sequences.

CLARKE: I would not expect a conservative protein to discriminate between species. Hemoglobin is less conservative, but a phylogenetic tree based on hemoglobins still shows a general correspondence to trees based on conventional characters. The conservatism, or otherwise, of a protein may determine the fineness of the correspondence, but it does not explain its origin. The conservatism itself must be the product of selection.

BREHM: In regard to the phylogenetic tree, like Dr. Margoliash, I think it is one that any zoologist would accept. However, we are referring only to a limited portion of his phylogenetic tree. The portions of the model that extend to the inclusion of yeasts and other organisms do not resemble a phylogenetic tree that would be generally accepted.

TOWNES: It seems that all taxonomists have one difficulty in common. They start with a preconceived notion and examine one character after another until they find a set of characters that coincides with that notion. I am afraid that the biochemists sometimes have a similar difficulty. They seem to have grown up with an idea that certain mammals are more closely related to each other than mammals are to fish. They find a chemical that shows that relationship and is likely to illustrate it. If they get a chemical that shows some different relationship they are likely to revise their technique or select a different chemical. Is this considered scientific proof?

SIBLEY: Please, please, do not call proteins "chemicals." Chemicals are something chemists work with; proteins are something biologists work with. The protein is an entirely different class of organism.

Perhaps you underestimate how much experience with actual organisms most of us have had. Some of the remarks indicate that you might consider us biochemists. I certainly am not. I am a birdwatcher, and some of the others here lay no claim to being even biochemically oriented. We are taxonomists who have found a new technique that works, and we are applying that technique to problems we discovered long before we discovered proteins.

I think it is time that we bring this interesting session to a close. After being quite uncertain as to whether this type of session was a good idea, I am delighted with the way it turned out. The discussions that developed here have been most illuminating, but any attempt to summarize would be hopeless.

GRANT*: The recent emphasis on biochemical systematics in biology brings to light a new role for the herbarium. In our studies in the genus *Lotus,* we have obtained fluorescent spot patterns by means of thin-layer chromatography from leaves of herbarium specimens up to 90 years old. It is most likely that greater use will be made of the herbarium in the future by nonsystematists. For example, it might be expected that biochemists and geneticists whose primary training has not been in systematics will want to consult with taxonomists and obtain minute samples of

*Comment submitted after the roundtable discussion.

material of different taxa from herbarium specimens for biochemical analyses. At the same time, since a large number of specimens may be analyzed biochemically in a relatively short period, the proper identification of herbarium specimens cannot be overemphasized, and this responsibility lies with the taxonomist. Likewise, reference to herbarium specimens in publications should be made by the biochemical systematist. Perhaps a new means of reference to herbarium specimens may have to be devised, or agreed upon, for biochemical systematic papers. This new role for the herbarium should make it possible for curators to obtain greater financial support for staff, facilities, and technical assistance.

WALTER J. BOCK

Comparative Morphology in Systematics

INTRODUCTION

Comparative morphology has had a long and unique relationship to systematic studies ever since their simultaneous origins in the early days of scientific inquiry. Comparative anatomy has always contributed and continues to contribute the great bulk of evidence for systematic investigations of the supergeneric categories. It provides much of the needed evidence for formulating general concepts of systematics, phylogeny, and evolution at these higher taxonomic levels; for example, most of the principles of comparative biology have been drafted on the basis of morphological data. Also, such data provide the link by which fossil material can be analyzed, thereby permitting the incorporation of the essential dimension of time into systematic studies. Yet the basic tenets and facts of comparative morphology are poorly understood by most taxonomists who use morphological information in their systematic investigations.

Few students are trained as comparative morphologists as compared with the number of systematists utilizing morphological data. But this is not a recent development. Even in the golden era of classical comparative anatomy, morphology was studied more as a guide to classification than as morphology *per se*. Moreover, it remained a comparative descriptive study of morphological form, closer to a purely geometrical science than to a biological science.

Sharp gaps developed between comparative vertebrate anatomy on the one hand and physiology, embryology, and human anatomy on the other, most aspects of the developmental and functional causal bases of morphological structures being investigated in the latter disciplines. There was little exchange of information and ideas between comparative morphology and related areas. Consequently, growth of the conceptual basis for comparative morphology was stifled, and the field was characterized by naive notions to the effect that "anyone can compare" and "morphological study requires only the ability to observe." The near-total eclipse of comparative morphology after 1900 was inevitable. I do not intend to lament the past decline of morphology or comment further on the factors responsible for it; rather, I will discuss the work of the past decade that was responsible for a renewed interest in morphology (see Davis, 1958).

Recent morphological studies are characterized by two important attributes. First, much of the work is directed toward the clarification of morphological questions and does not primarily seek systematic conclusions, although the morphological results still have pertinent taxonomic implications. Second, many new ideas are advanced and tested; these include utilization of information and insight from other biological disciplines, development of new techniques for functional studies, and re-evaluation of many basic theoretical tenets of comparative morphology. The maturation of these new concepts and approaches is creating a morphology that differs sharply from classical comparative anatomy. The emerging synthesis is a broad-based discipline—which may be called "evolutionary morphology"—built upon traditional comparative morphology and evolutionary principles.

Essential to evolutionary morphology is a comparative study of the forms, functions, and biological roles of anatomical structures, and the interaction of these structures with environmental factors. It includes observations of organisms living normally in their natural environment, analyses of the exact interactions between the organisms and their environment, and the study of all other pertinent ecological features. It includes the study of fossil as well as recent organisms; exactly the same methods of study are applied to both. All aspects of evolutionary morphology must be based upon the general principles and mechanisms of organic evolution.

Thus, evolutionary morphology is a comparative study of the biology of morphological features in accordance with the principles of evolutionary theory. Evolutionary morphology is simply comparative anatomy catching up with the "New Systematics."

The foundations of evolutionary morphology are very broad—as they well need be—because the general goal of this endeavor is the elucidation of the evolutionary history of morphological structures and of plant and animal groups.

In this paper, I outline some of the theoretical and practical concepts being developed within evolutionary morphology and illustrate how they may be applied to taxonomic problems. The historical background and scope of the paper are restricted to comparative vertebrate morphology, and examples are limited to vertebrates, mainly birds; yet, I believe that the conclusions are broadly valid for all groups of plants and animals. I make no distinction between morphology and anatomy as in plant anatomy and plant morphology—all structural features are included under the same heading. Moreover, I do not distinguish between the definition of morphology and anatomy, as does Simpson (1959: 287; 1961:70); rather, I follow the common usage in treating these terms as strict synonyms.

The term "systematics," is used only in the sense of conventional phylogenetic systematics of the higher categories—generic level and higher (Simpson, 1961; Mayr, 1965). I do not make many direct references to paleontological problems, but I would like to emphasize that an extremely close link exists between morphological and paleontological studies. Fossils provide the paleontologist only with the observable structural details of their morphology (skeleton) and their (relative) position in time. Fossils do not furnish direct information as to their relationships to other fossil and recent organisms or their positions in a phyletic lineage. Conclusions in regard to this type of information can be reached only after the specimens are studied through use of comparative methods such as those discussed in this paper. Moreover, phylogenies drawn by paleontologists are dendrograms or inferred phylogenies, as are those of the neontologists. The paleontologist knows only the position of fossils in geologic time; any lines of affinity (=phylogeny) drawn between these fossils are inferences, no matter how good the fossil record may be.

HOMOLOGY

Comparative anatomy has always been based on the concept of homology, an idea that has survived radical shifts in the underlying philosophies of morphological studies. Coupled with it is the notion that the same name should be given only to homologous features in different organisms. The fact that this is not always possible, and sometimes not even desirable, does not detract from the importance of this policy.

Homology as a basic concept of comparative studies in biology has meaning only if it is founded upon the fact and consequences of organic evolution. Hence, the only meaningful definition of homology is one based on evolution—a phylogenetic definition of homology. Ghiselin (1966 a and b) and Bock (1963a) have pointed out that the definition of the term "homology" must be clearly separated from the methods by which features in different organisms are judged to be homologous. Further, they emphasized that a definition of homology based upon phylogeny is not circular (see also Hull, 1967). Ghiselin (1966a:128–129) pointed out that homology is not an intrinsic property of a feature, such as mass or color, but a relationship depending upon the existence of corresponding features in other organisms. The definition of homology that I advocate is the generally accepted one (Bock, 1963a; Ghiselin, 1966a) and may be stated as: "A feature (or condition of a feature) in one organism is homologous to a feature (or condition of a feature) in another organism if the two features (or conditions) can be traced phylogenetically to the same feature or condition in the immediate common ancestor of both organisms." This definition may be recast, if one prefers, in the opposite but absolutely equivalent way by stating that: "A feature . . . is homologous . . . to a feature . . . if the two features (or conditions) stem phylogenetically from the same feature or condition in the immediate common ancestor of these organisms."

Homology can be applied to any attribute of organisms—morphological features, developmental sequences, behavioral displays, functional properties—as long as the definition applies to it. Nonhomology, the opposite of homology, applies to features or conditions in two or more organisms that cannot be traced back to the same feature or condition in the immediate common ancestor of the organisms. I now advocate the use of the term "nonhomology" instead of "analogy"–which was recommended in an earlier paper (Bock, 1963a:269)–because of the continued ambiguity and multiple use of the latter term.

Statements about homologous features should always be put in the form of the following examples: "The wing of birds is homologous to the wing of bats as the forelimb of vertebrates" or, "The pectoral flipper of whales and the pectoral fin of sharks are homologous as vertebrate limbs." A phrase stating the conditions of homology must always be included; this "conditional phrase" will be discussed in more detail. Statements such as "The arm of the gorilla is homologous to the arm of the chimpanzee" or "The quadrate of birds is homologous to the incus of mammals" are meaningless. Simply to say that two features are homologous or nonhomologous conveys no information.

No mention of resemblance or of similarity in ontogenetic development appears in the definition of homology. Contrary to common opinion, the concepts of homology and nonhomology have nothing to do with the similarity of features; they are associated only with common origin versus noncommon origin. Degree of resemblance and common origin are quite distinct problems of phylogenetic study and must be kept separated. Moreover, homologous features need not possess a similar ontogenetic development.

The methods by which homologous features are recognized must be in agreement with the general principles of evolution and phylogeny, but these methods must not, of course, be based upon earlier conclusions of the phylogeny or relationships of the organisms under study. Any methods for recognizing homologies that depend upon earlier conclusions about the phylogeny of organisms should be discarded. Corresponding features in different members of a monophyletic taxon or of a particular phyletic lineage are homologous by definition, and features can, of course, be labeled as homologous on this basis. But such a procedure is redundant as it does not provide any new independent phylogenetical information. Features considered to be homologous on this basis must not be cited later as additional evidence for the phylogenetical relationship of the organisms. A practicing systematist must be aware of this problem and must know which homologies have been established upon independent study and which have been established upon the accepted phylogeny of the taxon. However, the establishing of homologies on the basis of known phylogenies does not, in itself, indicate circular reasoning (see Ghiselin, this volume, page 45). Hence, one of Remane's "major criteria for homology," (1956:58) that of connection through intermediate forms, and all of his "helping criteria" are redundant because they depend upon earlier conclusions about the phylogeny (relationships) of the organisms and hence must not be employed if one wishes to establish independently based homologies. If any homologies based upon these criteria are used to further strengthen arguments for relationships between the organisms, then the argument will be directly circular. Remane's major criterion of connection through intermediate forms is redundant if such intermediate forms are considered to be intermediate systematic forms (= related organisms). But it is valid if the intermediate forms are intermediate morphological conditions or intermediate developmental sequences. Generally accepted criteria used to recognize homologous features include morphological similarity, position in the body, relationship to other features, similar ontogenetic development, and so forth. None of these criteria is infallible, and conclusions on homologies can never be proven with absolute certainty. Some criteria–for example, relationship to other features–depend upon previous conclusions on the homology of these other features, and this may compound earlier erroneous decisions.

A serious theoretical and methodological problem stems from the following phrase in the definition of homology: "the same feature in the immediate common ancestor." Considerable vagueness exists in the degree of precision with which the immediate common ancestor must be identified (whether it is an ancestral species or a higher taxonomic category) and with which the similarity in the feature of the ancestral and descendent forms must be described. In an earlier paper (Bock, 1963a) it is shown that homology is a relative concept corresponding to the relative nature of monophyly (Simpson, 1961) and that a gray zone exists between homologous and nonhomologous features. Basically, this problem is one of *resolving power* of the available methods for recognizing homology; it may be solved by modifying the definition of homology (Bock, 1963a:272–282) or by considering the consequences of differential resolving power of methods for recognizing homology, as is done in this paper. Results of the two approaches are the same.

The resolving power of methods for recognizing homologues is closely associated with the degree of uniformity of the organisms being examined. The greater the uniformity, the less the resolving powers of these methods become. Groups that, at the present time, are heterogeneous were much more uniform at the time of their origin or shortly thereafter (before major adaptive radiation of the group had occurred). If structures must be traced back to the more uniform ancestral group, then the resolving power of the methods for recognizing homologies decreases. Moreover, the "dot" representing the ancestral form in diagrams accompanying discussions of homologies or phylogenies actually may represent a family or order of animals, and not an ancestral species as is often assumed. This is demonstrated clearly in the following examples in which I am interested only in establishing independent homologies, not in recognizing redundant homologies.

Many marine birds possess a salt-secreting nasal gland lying on the supraorbital rims (Bock, 1958, 1963a). The ontogenetic development of the glands and rims follows a similar course in birds possessing varied adult conditions (Figure 1). The size of the gland is directly correlated with the salinity of the environment and will adapt physiologically to changes in salinity. As the glands increase in size, they exert more pressure on the bony supraorbital rims, causing them to deossify—another physiological adaptation. If several freshwater species of plovers had salt-water descendents, then all the salt-water forms would have large nasal glands and deossified supraorbital rims (Figure 2). A study of the supraorbital rims in only the salt-water species would lead to the conclusion that the deossified condition was homologous in these forms. This would have been the only conclusion possible if the several freshwater species in the example were extinct and not available for study. Only with knowledge of the phylogeny of these birds can it be ascertained that the deossified condition of the supraorbital rims is not strictly homologous (called "pseudohomologous" in Bock, 1958); but knowledge of the presumed phylogeny of the group is inadmissible evidence for recognizing homology of a feature found in that group.

The several conditions of the palatine process of the premaxilla in

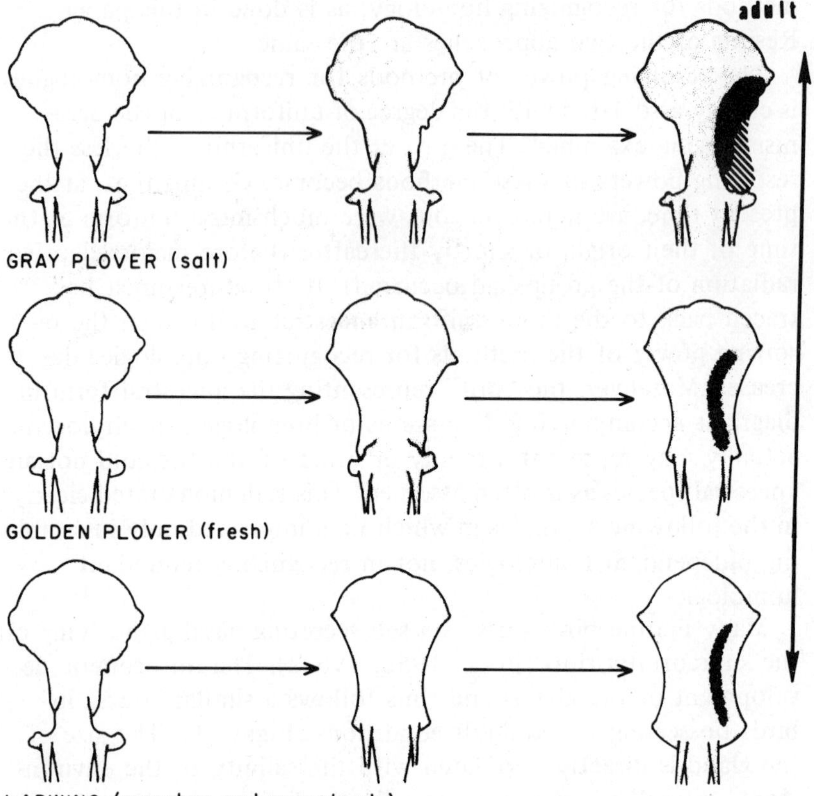

FIGURE 1 Simplified scheme showing ontogeny of the supraorbital rims of plovers found on salt water, freshwater, and grasslands. Approximate size of the nasal gland is indicated by the shaded area in the adult stage. Note the similar starting points and sequences in development. Vertical arrow indicates morphological change in the adult brought about by physiological adaptation to a greater (upward) or lesser (downward) amount of salt in the environment. (From Bock, 1963a.)

passerine birds (Figure 3) show similar embryological developments (Bock, 1960b, 1963a). The several conditions are found in different subgroups of the Ploceidae and Fringillidae (*senso lato*), as shown in the accompanying dendrogram (Figure 4). Again, if the palatine process were studied to ascertain whether the lateral flange condition or the free condition were homologous in the birds having either condition, the only possible conclusion would be that each condition is indeed homologous. No study methods exist that would show the

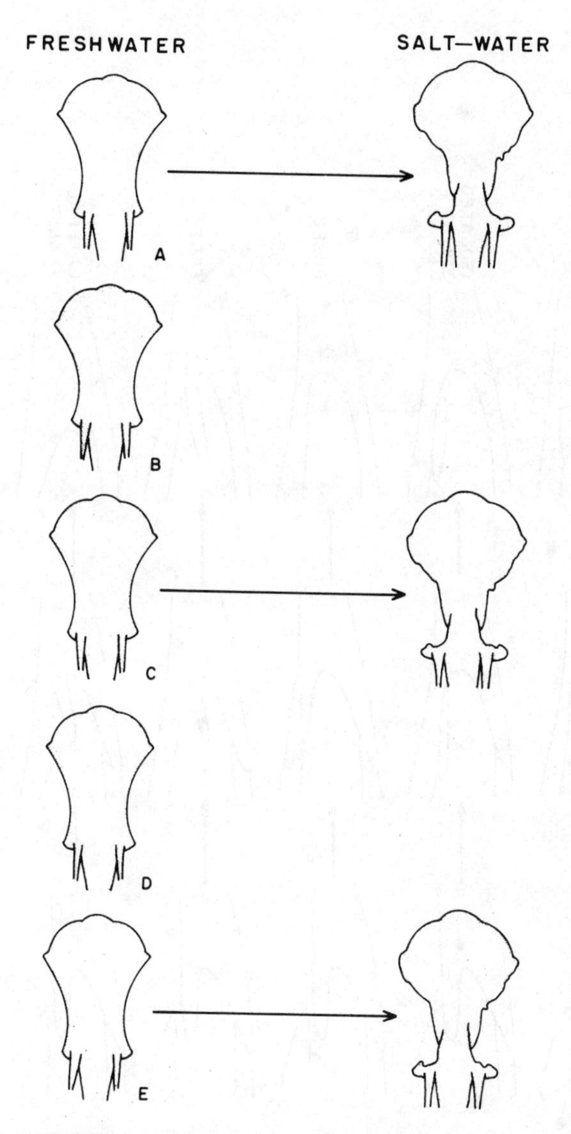

FIGURE 2 Dendrogram of a hypothetical evolution of the salt-water condition in three congeneric species of plovers, The morphologically identical condition in the three descendent salt-water species would be pseudohomologous. If all the fresh-water species had been extinct, we could have concluded only that the condition of the supraorbital rims in the three salt-water forms was strictly homologous. (From Bock, 1963a.)

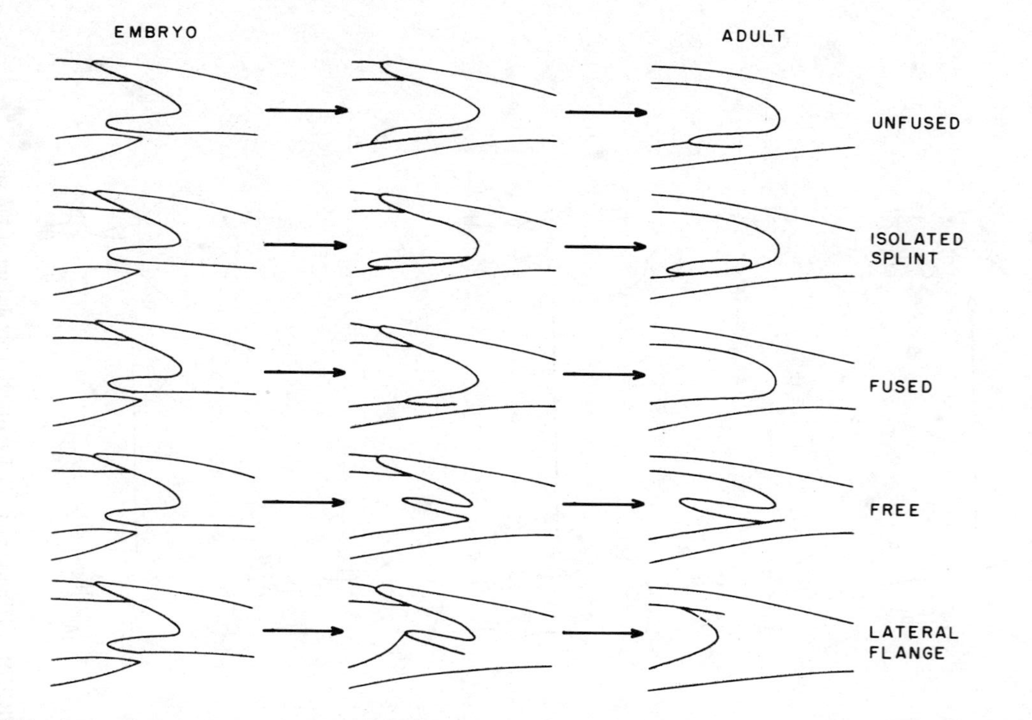

FIGURE 3 Simplified scheme of the ontogeny of the several conditions of the palatine process of the premaxilla in the Passeres. Note the similarity of the earliest stages and the relatively similar development until the last stage. The relative ease by which one condition could evolve from another–for example, the fused or the free condition from the unfused condition–can be appreciated readily after comparing the developmental sequences. (From Bock, 1963a.)

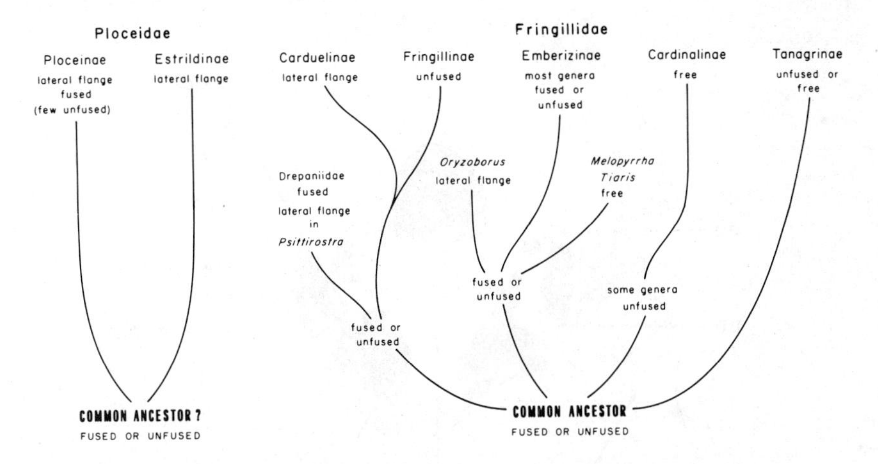

FIGURE 4 Dendrogram showing a possible phylogeny of the palatine process of the premaxilla in the Fringillidae (s.1.) and the apparently unrelated Ploceidae. The lateral flange condition in the Ploceidae is nonhomologous to that in the Fringillidae, although most difficult to prove by study of the flange alone; but the lateral flange in the Carduelinae, *Psittirostra,* and *Oryzoborus* is pseudohomologous. Nevertheless, if all finches lacking the lateral flange should become extinct, the distinction between the homologous, pseudohomologous, and nonhomologous conditions of the lateral flange would become obscure. (From Bock, 1963a.)

lateral flange to be homologous in the members of the Carduelinae but not homologous in the Ploceidae, Carduelinae, *Psittirostra,* and *Oryzoborus.* Only by introducing the supposed phylogeny of these groups is it possible to show that the lateral flange condition is not strictly homologous in some of the forms possessing it.

A similar case exists in the secondary articulation (Figure 5) that forms an accessory brace for the mandible (Bock, 1960a; 1963a) in a number of avian orders, including the Charadriiformes (Figure 6). Absence of the articulation is the most probable ancestral condition. If one studied only the structures comprising the secondary articulation in the Charadriiformes, the only possible conclusion would be that the secondary articulation is homologous in the forms possessing it. And if only those forms possessing the articulation existed today, no conclusion other than strict homology could be reached. But when the phylogeny of the Charadriiformes is considered, it is clear that the articulation probably is not homologous in all charadriiform birds possessing it. Even after the secondary articulation has been studied carefully in all birds possessing it and the

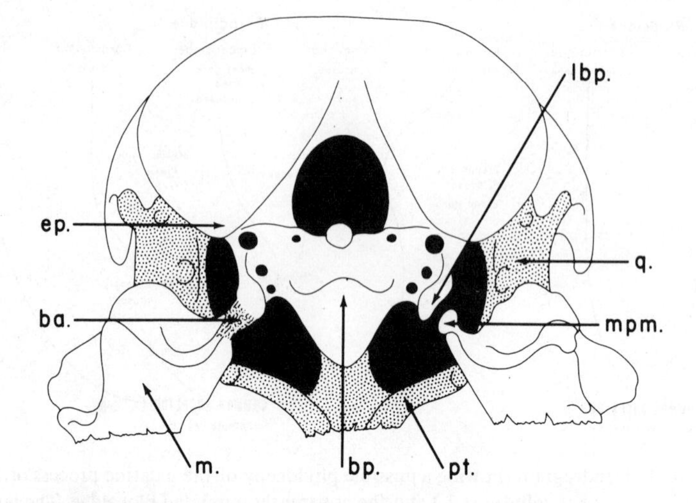

FIGURE 5 The skull of a skimmer (*Rynchops*) seen from the posteroventral side to show the basitemporal articulation (ba.) on the left side of the skull (rough lines). This articulation is formed by the medial process of the mandible (mpm.) abutting against the lateral process of the basitemporal plate (lbp.). (From Bock, 1960.)

known evidence of phylogeny has been introduced, no definite decision can be reached on its exact homology.

As a last example, the nature of the foot (arrangement of toes), bill, and tail feathers in the ivory-billed woodpeckers (Figure 7) is considered (Bock and Miller, 1959; Bock, 1963a). Whether these structures are studied separately or together, the most feasible conclusion would be that the condition of each feature found in the genera *Chrysocolaptes, Blythipicus,* and *Campephilus* is homologous. Yet when the phylogeny (based upon the color pattern of the plumage) of these woodpeckers is examined, the strict nonhomology of the features is clear.

Conclusions can be drawn clearly from these examples. Analysis of the features alone allows only the conclusion that each feature is homologous in the forms under consideration. The strict nonhomology is revealed only after the phylogeny of the forms (based upon other evidence) has been introduced.

It is invalid to conclude on the basis of the above examples that homologies cannot be established without knowledge of the phylogeny of the group. After all, the evidence of the presumed phylogeny introduced into each argument was established upon an

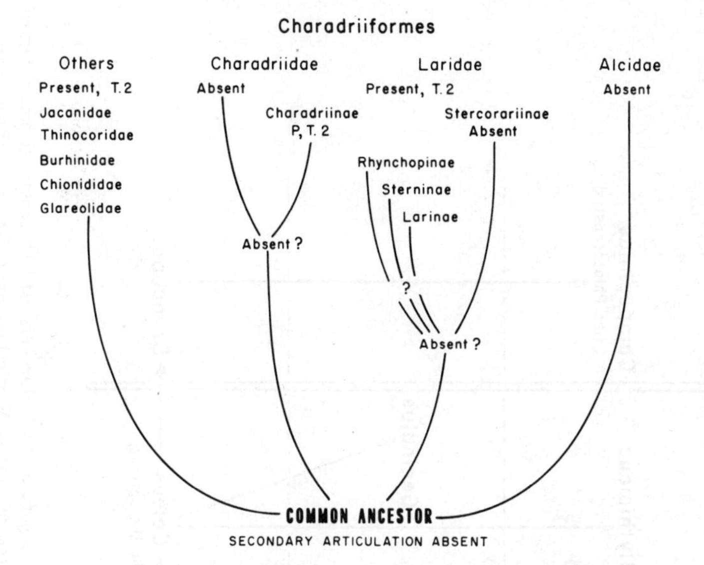

FIGURE 6 Simplified dendrogram showing a possible phylogeny of the basitemporal articulation of the mandible in the Charadriiformes. (The forms grouped under "others" constitute an artificial assemblage.) This articulation was probably absent in the common ancestor of the living forms, hence its presence in the Lariidae, Charadriinae, and other groups most likely is pseudohomologous. The symbol T.2 refers to the particular condition of the articulation which, in this case, involves the ventral edge of the lateral basitemporal process. (From Bock, 1963a.)

evaluation of *other* homologous features that usually were not mentioned; and it is possible that the phylogeny is wrong, which might invalidate the particular argument. A conclusion that could be reached is that all working methods available for ascertaining homologies have relatively low resolving power; hence, it would not be possible to establish precise homologies (i.e., distinguish between true homologies and pseudohomologies) by the use of those methods. However, since such evidence is inadmissible for ascertaining homologies, it cannot be concluded that the features are nonhomologous; they must be treated as homologous or pseudohomologous. If all extant forms had deossified supraorbital rims or a secondary articulation, it would be impossible to distinguish between true homology and pseudohomology. Pseudohomology is associated with morphologically uniform groups, but even present-day heterogeneous groups were quite uniform at the

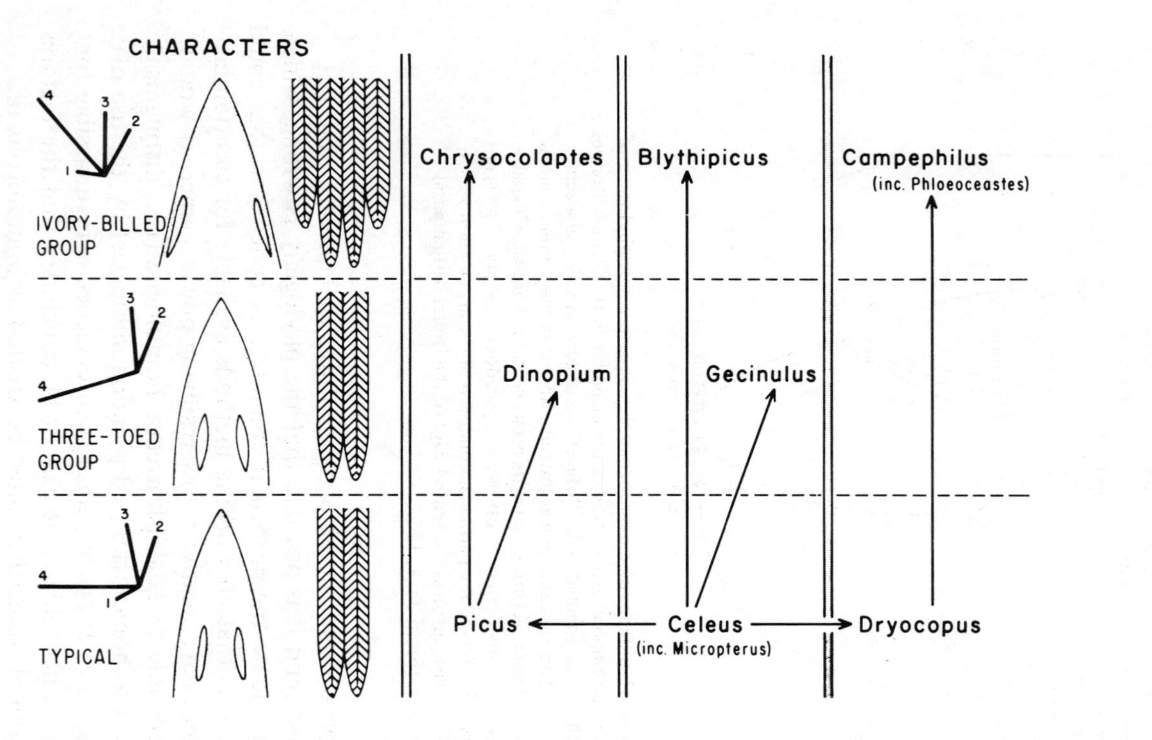

FIGURE 7 Simplified dendrogram showing the probable phylogeny of the ivory-billed genera of woodpeckers. At left: Diagnostic characters of each group. Horizontal zones: Grouping of genera on basis of tail-foot-bill structure (grade groups). Vertical columns: Grouping of genera on basis of similarity of color patterns and indication of true phyletic lines and relationships. The similar conditions of foot, tail, and bill in the ivory-billed genera of woodpeckers are pseudohomologous. (From Bock, 1963a.)

time of their origin, and many features regarded as being homologous really fall into the pseudohomologous category. A gray area exists between strict homology and strict nonhomology, and many features in the gray area must be regarded as homologous because the resolving power of our working methods does not allow a more precise answer. Hence, the demonstration that one or a few features in several organisms are homologous usually is not a sufficient basis on which to deduce phylogenetic relationships; these features may actually be pseudohomologous and not provide evidence for a monophyletic relationship of the group of organisms. The homologies of many features must be pieced together before a solid basis for phylogenetic speculation is reached.

The sequence of phylogenetic study is simple, but it deserves to be restated briefly. First, features in a series of organisms are studied and decisions about their homologies are reached upon the basis of appropriate comparative methods that exclude previous information on the possible phylogeny of the organisms. Then phylogenetic decisions about groups of organisms are based upon previously established homologies. This sequence for establishing homologies of features for phylogenies of organisms has nothing to do with the definitions of homology and phylogeny. Although particular phylogenies are based upon homologies, the definition of phylogeny is not given in terms of homology (Ghiselin, 1966 a and b). A hierarchical series of homologies can be constructed by asking more and more precise statements about the features; that is, by making the conditional phrase describing the homology more and more restricted and by testing whether the features are still homologous. Once this is completed, a hierarchy of relationships between the organisms (based upon the hierarchy of the homologies) can be established.

Classification must be based upon established homologous features, and herein lie the strength and weaknesses (perhaps one should say pitfalls) of comparative morphology because of the wealth of available information published over the past 100 years.

Older works are generally excellent descriptively, but one must know the foundation upon which the comparisons and conclusions rest. Many of the ideas in those works are no longer acceptable, and a worker of today should not cite conclusions from older morphological papers without knowing their bases. Although regrettable, utilization of the available morphological information is neither simple nor obvious. There are no easy rules for using morphological information in systematic studies. Unfortunately, errors in the interpretation of comparative morphological data are all too easy to make.

In every case, the reasons given by the earlier worker for concluding that features in the several organisms are homologous must be investigated. Often this is an easy task, but occasionally the homologies must be re-established, and one must always check whether the same anatomical name really connotes homologous features or conditions in the different organisms. Often it does not, and this can easily lead the investigator astray.

An example that illustrates this point nicely is the os prominens in hawks and owls (Bock and McEvey, in press). The os prominens is an enlarged sesamoid bone in the wrist associated with the tendon of the M. tensor patagii longus (Figure 8). A small sesamoid bone is found in this tendon in many other groups of birds. Careful reading of the early literature leaves the impression that the os prominens is homologous in hawks and owls and that it provides evidence for relationships between these birds. Moreover, the

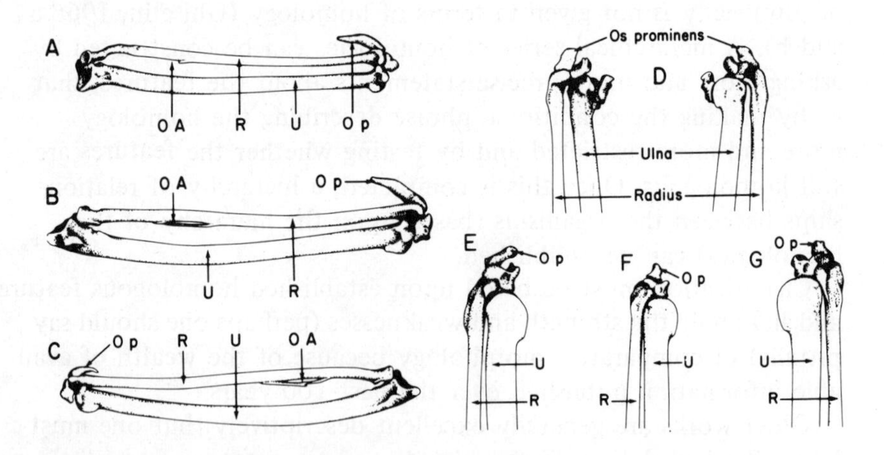

FIGURE 8 The os prominens (Op) of the radius (R) in several genera of owls (A, B, and C) and hawks (D, E, F and G). Note differences in shape of this bone and its relationship to the radius. The osseous arch (OA) of the radius is shown in the figures of owls' wing bones. (From Bock and McEvey, in press.)

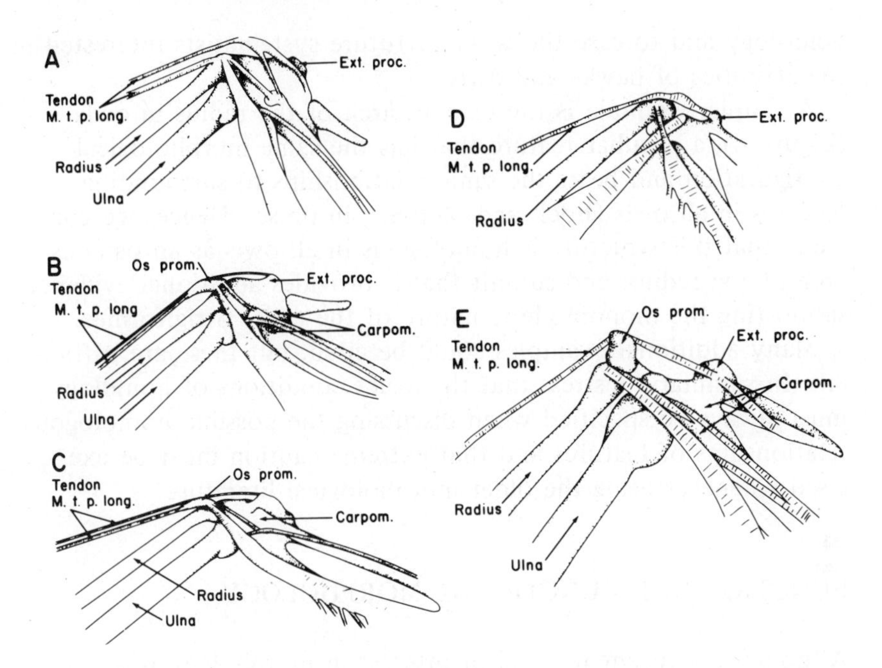

FIGURE 9 Relationship between the os prominens and the tendon of the M. tensor patagii longus in the wrist of several genera of owls (A, *Tyto;* B, *Ninox;* C, *Asio*) and hawks (D, *Falco;* E, *Buteo*). (From Bock and McEvey, in press.)

absence of this bone in barn owls and falcons appears to lend additional support to the suggestions by some morphologists and other systematists regarding the close affinities of these birds. A restudy of this bone revealed that its shape differs considerably in hawks and owls and that its relationship to the tendon of the M. tensor patagii longus (Figure 9) also differs considerably in the two groups. Hence, it was concluded (Bock and McEvey, in press) that this heterotopic bone is homologous in hawks and owls only as a sesamoid in the tendon of the M. tensor patagii longus. This sesamoid is found in many birds and could be considered homologous as a sesamoid in the tendon of the M. tensor patagii longus wherever it is found. However, this heterotopic bone is not homologous in hawks and owls as an enlarged sesamoid in the tendon of the M. tensor patagii longus, and as such it provides no evidence for relationship between hawks and owls. The bone should be given separate names in the two groups to emphasize the nonhomology and to ease the work of future systematists interested in the affinities of hawks and owls.

A simpler example is the osseous arch of the radius in owls (Figure 8), a peculiar feature that has the same morphological configuration and bears the same relationships to surrounding features in all owls (Bock and McEvey, in press). Hence, we conclude that this structure is homologous in all owls as an osseous arch of the radius, and submit that it provides additional evidence supporting the monophyletic nature of the order Strigiformes.

Many additional examples could be cited, but these are sufficient. In summary, I stress that the exact conditions of homology must always be specified when discussing the possible homologous relationships of features and that extreme caution must be exercised whenever using the older morphological literature.

FUNCTION AND FUNCTIONAL MORPHOLOGY

Although the recent renewal of interest in morphology was heralded by work in functional morphology, considerable vagueness still accompanies the use of the central term "function." Indeed, usage is so varied that it is often impossible to know exactly what is meant. A statement such as "The function of a structure can be determined from its morphological form" may be correct or incorrect, depending upon the author's choice of one of the two common definitions of function. Likewise, the statement "Change in form precedes change in function during the evolution of a feature" could be correct, incorrect, or quite meaningless, depending upon the author's usage of the same term. It is impossible to know just what is covered by the term "functional morphology." I am quite sure that my understanding of this branch of morphological inquiry differs considerably from that of many other functional morphologists. One of the consequences of this vagueness is a plethora of morphological disciplines, such as functional morphology, biological morphology, ecological morphology, and the like, each with its advocates and all overlapping rather broadly.

The term "function" is being used for (1) action or operation of a morphological feature and (2) the use made by the organism of a feature while it is living naturally in its normal environment. Occasionally an author uses both in the same paper. These meanings are so contradictory that continued dual usage is intolerable. In an attempt to resolve this problem, Bock and von Wahlert (1965) advocated a system of terms relating to morphological features and their interaction with the environment and proposed formal definitions for each of these terms. A clear distinction was made between a feature's function and its biological role.

The definition of function (Bock and von Wahlert, 1965:p. 274) is:

> In any sentence describing a feature of an organism, its functions would be that class of predicates which include all physical and chemical properties arising from its form (i.e., its material composition and arrangement thereof) including all properties arising from increasing levels of organization, provided that these predicates do not mention any reference to the environment of the organism.

Modifications in form would result in changes in function. Functional anatomy would be those studies carried out in the laboratory in which the properties of the features are ascertained with the help of a series of testing devices. Thus, one might determine the force developed by a muscle at different relative lengths (the tension–length curve of a muscle) or ascertain how rapidly a muscle shortens with different loads placed upon it (the force–velocity curve); or one might study the movements of the skeletal elements of both jaws in the kinetic skull of a bird (Bock, 1964) or of a snake (Frazzetta, 1966); or one might examine the relationships between external forces placed upon an avian jaw and the shape of the jaw with the help of free-body diagrams (Bock, 1966). In none of these cases is any mention made of the natural environment of the organism or the use made of the feature in the life of the organism.

The definition of biological role (Bock and von Wahlert, 1965: 278):

> In any sentence describing a feature of an organism, the biological roles would be that class of predicates which includes all actions or uses of the faculties (the form–function complexes) of the feature by the organism in the course of its life history, provided that these predicates include reference to the environment of the organism.

Thus, one would have to observe the organism while it is living normally under natural conditions and have to observe the organism's actual use of its morphological features. In this area there is overlapping of morphology, behavior, and ecology. Hence, knowing the functional abilities of the locomotor apparatus in rabbits, one would have to see how the animal uses this apparatus in escaping from predators, whether the rabbit runs rapidly in a straight line or resorts to quick turns and reversals in which high acceleration is required, and so forth; or one would have to observe exactly how a warbler catches insects as well as identify the species of insect that constitute its food, or one would have to see what seeds are taken by a finch and exactly how it holds these seeds in the bill while they are being shelled. It is obvious that deductions about the biological roles of features—which must be known before the adaptive significance can be evaluated—cannot be based with any degree of certainty upon a study of the form and function of the feature alone.

The large mucus-secreting salivary glands of the gray jays provide a good example (Bock, 1961). Only the genus *Perisoreus* in the Corvidae possesses large mucous glands as well developed as those in woodpeckers. *Perisoreus* is the only corvid genus confined to the northern coniferous forests. It was suggested (Bock, 1961) that the mucus coats the tongue so that the bird can probe into crevices for food when the ground is covered with snow. This deduction, which was based upon known facts about the feeding methods of woodpeckers, has a serious defect—it is wrong. Dow (1965) showed that the mucus serves as a glue to bind particles of food into small boli that are cemented onto the branches of trees. The gray jays store food by this method during the winter and return to these stores in periods of inclement weather. Not only was this biological role difficult to guess on the basis of the information available at the time of my study, but I doubt that any editor would have accepted such a story.

Some of the most difficult problems in deducing biological roles come from paleontology. The hollow crests in the hadrosaurian dinosaurs still pose problems in spite of Ostrom's fine study (1964). It is still entirely feasible that these hollow crests are resonating chambers—the different calls being species-specific and perhaps associated with reproductive behavior—although it is doubtful that this idea can ever be verified or rejected. The sail in pelycosaurs may be a heat-regulating device, but this is neither clear-cut nor proven conclusively. Similar problems must be faced in the attempt to deduce the biological roles of many features, especially of those in fossil forms not having similar living counterparts.

Work in functional morphology has been hampered by a lack of comprehension of the pertinent problems, by a lack of knowledge of approaches by which these problems can be solved, and by a sadly insufficient foundation of experimental study. Most functional observations are still deductions based upon the observed morphological form. This is a valid and necessary procedure—the only one possible in many living forms and in all fossil forms—but frequently it suffers from an unsound deductive base which often is unnecessary, as can be seen from the following examples.

The shape of the bill in different avian groups is known to be correlated with feeding habits and, presumably, with the particular set of external forces acting upon it. Yet none of the earlier analyses was convincing, and as a consequence, the bill could not be used in taxonomic studies of the higher categories of birds. Yet, many (but not all) aspects of bill shape can be understood by a consideration of the kinetic mechanism and the application of the method of free-body diagrams (Bock, 1966).

In Figure 10 the upper jaw of a crow is shown with the forces acting upon it and the necessary equations describing the torques and linear forces when the structure is under static conditions. These equations indicate that, for a constant muscle force, the force exerted by the bill will increase as an object is held farther back in the bill; and the force at the nasal-frontal hinge will increase in magnitude and modify its vector toward the y-axis. The bill of the crow is not well suited for exerting large biting or probing forces.

Finches and other birds that crush seeds in their bills have decurved bills (Figure 11). The angled tomium places the two torque-producing forces in opposition to one another so that their component forces tend to cancel one another and hence reduce the resulting force at the nasal-frontal hinge. More specialized finches have a more angled tomium, which results in even less force at the nasal-frontal hinge.

Woodpeckers have straight bills, and they experience large forces at the tips (Figure 12). Again the two torque-producing

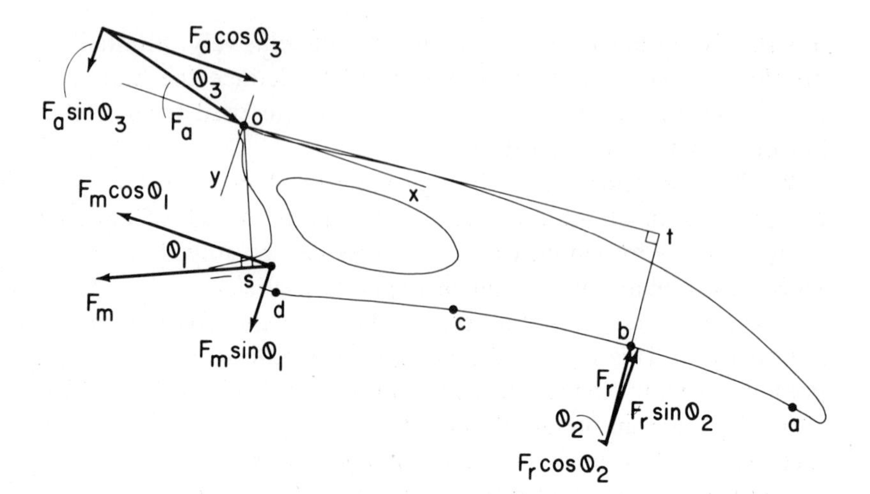

$$\Sigma M_o = F_m(os) - F_r(ot) = 0$$

$$\Sigma F_x = -F_m \cos \Theta_1 - F_r \cos \Theta_2 + F_a \cos \Theta_3 = 0$$

$$\Sigma F_y = -F_m \sin \Theta_1 + F_r \sin \Theta_2 - F_a \sin \Theta_3 = 0$$

FIGURE 10 Free-body diagram of the forces acting on the upper jaw of a crow under static conditions. The equations describe the sum of the moments and the sums of the linear forces. Each of the external forces–muscle force, F^m; resistance force, F^r; and articular force, F^a–is decomposed into its rectilinear components according to the *x-y* axes established at the center of rotation (*o*). All of these components act on or from the point of application on the bill (shown by the heavy dots) although, for clarity, some components were drawn from the tail of the force arrow. As the object is held at varying points along the bill from *a* to *d*, the same muscle force would produce a larger resistance force and a larger and more vertically directed articular force. (Modified from Bock, 1966.)

forces are in opposition and tend to cancel one another. More specialized woodpeckers have a flatter, straighter bill in which the vector of the force at the tip of the bill is brought closer to the vector of the muscle force, thereby reducing the force at the nasal-frontal hinge. The latter force is a tensile force, not a compression force as is commonly believed. Such an analysis may be applied to the varied bill shape in many groups of birds, permitting greater insight into the adaptive significance of bill shape and

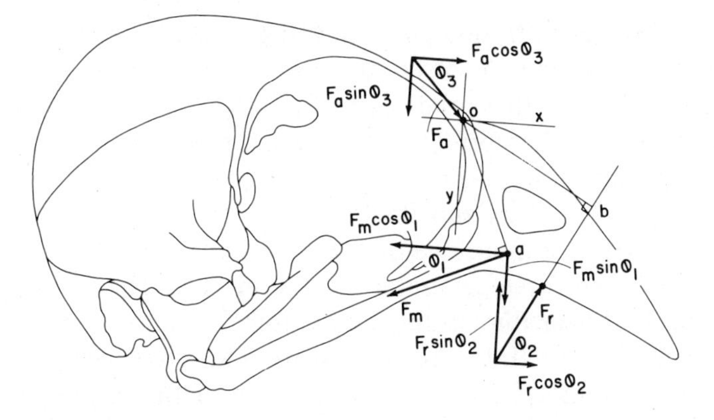

FIGURE 11 Free-body diagram of the forces acting on the upper jaw of a cardinal under static system. Explanation of forces and analysis as for crow, in Figure 10. (Modified from Bock, 1966.)

possibly reintroducing bill shape as a useful taxonomic feature.

Comparative functional analyses of vertebrate skeletal muscles are of utmost importance in morphological-systematic investigations because the bulk of these studies deal with the skeletal-muscular system. Morphologists have tried to reduce morphological parameters of muscles into a single index which is usually the weight or volume or, in more recent years, the physiological cross-sectional area of the muscle. The indices are used without

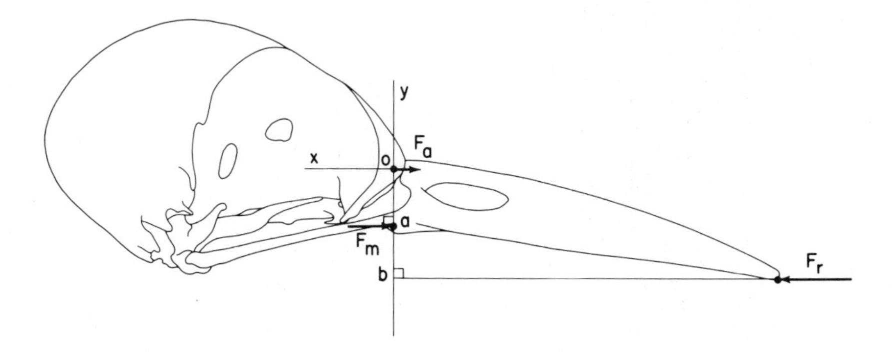

FIGURE 12 Free-body diagram of forces acting on the upper jaw of a woodpecker under static conditions. The forces were oriented along the x-axis for convenience. Explanation of forces and analysis as for crow, in Figure 10. (Modified from Bock, 1966.)

inquiring into the physiological meaning of the morphological parameters of weight or of cross-sectional area and without determining whether these indices really indicate what they are believed to; yet, the correlations between many morphological factors and physiological factors have been well known for many years (e.g., Gans and Bock, 1965).

The weight of a muscle is of little use as it definitely is not correlated with the force generated by the muscle. The over-all size of a muscle (linear dimensions and volume) is important because the muscle must fit into the framework and space available in the body. The morphological cross section of the muscle is not correlated with any functional property; however, the physiological cross section—the cross-sectional area formed by a plane cutting each muscle fiber transversely—is equivalent to the number of muscle fibers and, hence, to the absolute force developed by the muscle (Figure 13). But force development is not all that a muscle can do. The length of the muscle fibers, not the length of the muscle, is correlated with the distance of shortening (and stretching); the longer the fibers, the greater is the absolute shortening (Figures 13 and 14). Both the number and length of the fibers are correlated with the speed of shortening and the

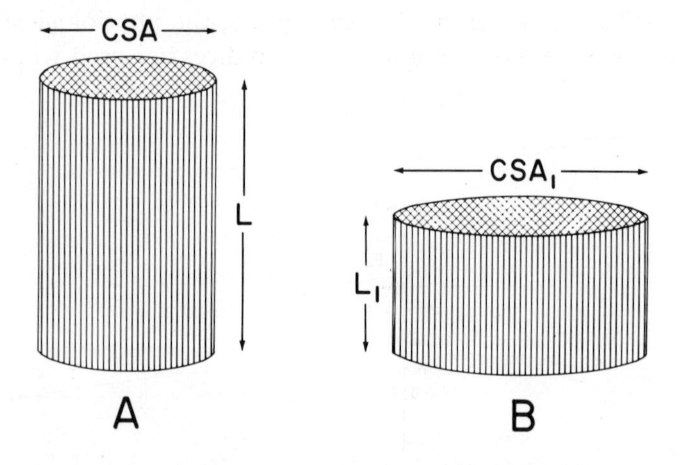

FIGURE 13 Schematic drawing of two parallel-fibered muscles of equal volume but unequal in length and cross-sectional area. The shorter muscle, B, can develop more force but can shorten a smaller absolute distance than the longer muscle, A.

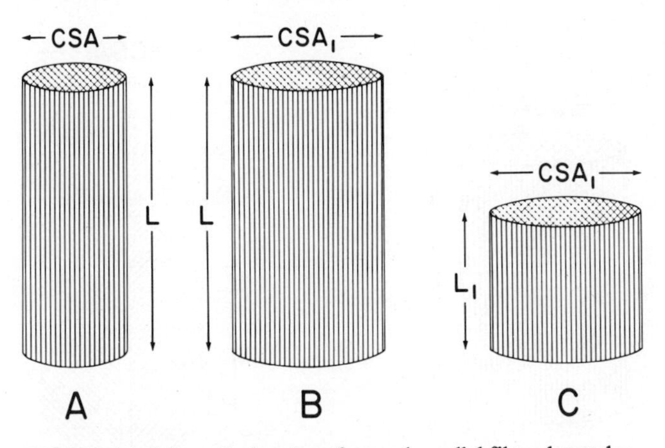

FIGURE 14 Schematic drawing of several parallel-fibered muscles. Muscles A and B are of equal length and can shorten the same distance, but B can develop more force. Muscles B and C can develop equal force, but B can shorten more than C.

amount of force development after the muscle has shortened. For any fixed volume of a muscle (Figure 15) it is clear that as the force (number of fibers) increases, the amount of possible shortening (length of fibers) decreases; both desirable properties cannot increase together without an increase in muscle size. Pinnation is a simple mechanism whereby many more, shorter fibers can be packed into a muscle of reasonable dimensions (Figure 15); a pinnate muscle would develop more force but would shorten less than a comparable parallel-fibered muscle.

Few comparative studies of vertebrate muscle systems include any recognition of these morphological–physiological parameters. The pertinent morphological measurements are not collected, and those that are gathered, usually of weight or volume, are almost useless. This situation is doubly sad because sufficient information is available on which to reach meaningful conclusions in comparative functional studies of muscular systems, which are an absolute necessity for evolutionary and systematic studies.

Considerable information is available from other biological disciplines for the formulation of meaningful, functional conclusions for most morphological systems used in vertebrate classification. The morphologist must seek out and make greater use of such data.

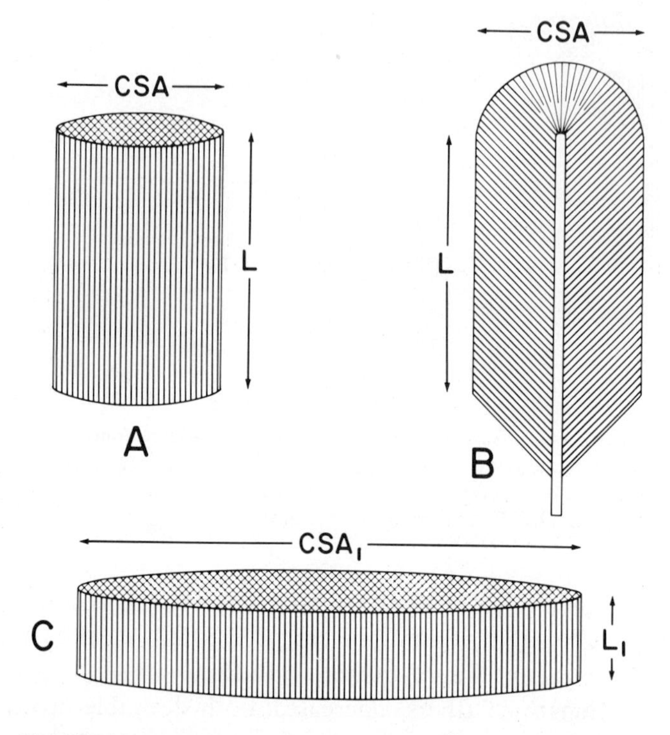

FIGURE 15 Schematic drawing of a parallel-fibered muscle, A, a pinnate muscle, B (of the same volume as A), and a parallel-fibered muscle, C (of the same fiber properties as B). The pinnate muscle has more fibers and can develop much more force than the parallel-fibered muscle, but it has shorter fibers and can shorten less. The pinnate muscle is equivalent to the short, broad, parallel-fibered muscle, but its fibers are arranged in a more "convenient" shape.

At present a plague of erroneous and vague functional statements bedevils morphological work; this is the result of the acknowledged importance of functional studies and the inadequate training of most morphologists in functional studies. In any developing field many mistakes will be made–I have contributed my share–but the extent of erroneous or useless functional statements has grown so great that future advances in the field may be hampered seriously. Functional morphologists will be faced with the arduous but essential task of correcting these errors before they can undertake new topics. Because functional analyses are so valuable for all anatomical and systematic work, morphologists have the responsibility to understand the basis of any functional conclusion offered. Often it may be better to say nothing than to contribute further to the existing confusion.

One should not avoid functional analyses just because they are inherently difficult and dangerous; functional morphology in the broadest sense has contributed enormously to evolutionary and systematic studies. The inclusion of a functional analysis, even a simple and very incomplete one, often can lead to the solution of a difficult systematic problem. The relationships between the ratite birds (ostriches and allies) are a case in point.

Little agreement existed between ornithologists and certain morphologists on the affinities between the extant flightless ratites. Most ornithologists and some anatomists concluded that these birds constituted several independent lines, largely because of their disjunct distribution. Other anatomists believed the ratites to be monophyletic, but did not present a convincing argument. Moreover, a few anatomists reached the further conclusion that the ratites evolved from the reptiles completely independently of the origin of the flying birds–a conclusion completely unacceptable to ornithologists. In a reanalysis of the ratite skull (Bock, 1963b) through use of features known for at least 50 years, but also including a simple functional consideration of the individual features and of the whole skull, it was possible to formulate a coherent argument. The complex of features comprised of the palate, basipterygoid articulation, large zygomatic process, continuous orbital and nasal septum, and gap in the lateral nasal bar are all associated with a peculiar and unique type of rhynchokinetic skull (see Bock, 1964) that all ratites share, in spite of wide divergence in feeding habits. For example, the woodcock and the kiwi probe into the ground for earthworms and are closely convergent in skull structure; but the woodcock skull is a clear modification of the charadriiform skull, and the kiwi skull is an obvious modification of the ratite skull. Hence, it was concluded that the ratites constituted a monophyletic group that became flightless after reaching the limits of their distribution; this conclusion is supported by the studies of Meise (1963), Sibley (1960; 1965, in part), and Parkes and Clark (1966).

ADAPTATION AND PARADAPTATION

The increased attention given by morphologists to functional studies has contributed greatly to the comprehension of biological adaptation as a theoretical concept and to the recognition of particular adaptations in anatomical features. Various methods for comparing adaptations in different organisms have been advocated. One suggestion for measuring and comparing the degree of adaptation is to determine the amount of energy required by an organism to maintain successfully its synergeal relationship with the environment; the less energy required, the better the degree of adaptation (Bock and von Wahlert, 1965). With a clearer understanding of adaptation, it has been possible to inquire into the old controversy of the role of adaptive features in systematics; namely, whether adaptive features do or do not possess value as taxonomic features (Bock, 1967). Both possibilities have been advocated, but consensus favors the possibility that adaptive features are useless as taxonomic characters and the obvious converse that valuable taxonomic characters are nonadaptive. Such statements often are not clearly expressed, and the converse statement may be tacitly assumed; but the implication is always that adaptiveness and taxonomic usefulness are conflicting properties of characters.

This problem is rather meaningless, because, on theoretical grounds, all existing features are adaptive. At least, it may be argued that all features (not differences between features) used in the classification of animals are adaptive. In an informal survey of features used in avian classification, I found none that are not clearly adaptive. Obviously, at least some useful taxonomic characters must exist. A dilemma therefore exists between the belief that adaptive features are useless as taxonomic characters and the demonstration that all taxonomic characters are adaptive, a dilemma that allows only the conclusion that no useful taxonomic characters exist, and, consequently, that further attempts to establish classifications are futile. This conclusion can and must be rejected at once as absurd; it serves only to indicate the existence of flaws in the argument upon which it is based.

This situation has resulted from an incomplete analysis of the evolutionary mechanisms by which features originate and change and from an artificial and overwhelming emphasis upon natural selection. I would advocate here the following dual hypothesis: that all features used in classification are adaptive, and that adaptive features may be extremely useful taxonomic characters. Adaptiveness in itself does not negate the taxonomic value of a character; the value depends upon considerations quite apart from the simple one of whether a feature is adaptive (Bock, 1967).

Support for this dual hypothesis is available from the consideration of *all* evolutionary mechanisms by which features originate and change. A clear distinction must be made between (a) those evolutionary mechanisms associated with the origin of new features and with the appearance of modifications in their later evolution (e.g., with the formation of all types of genetical variation that give rise to the phenotypical variation involved in the origin of new features and in their later modifications) and (b) natural selection, which is that phase of the interaction between the environment and the organism resulting in differential survival and reproduction of genetical material.

The consequences of both sets of evolutionary mechanisms upon the observed aspects of taxonomic features must be distinguished clearly and analyzed separately. Only after this is done will it be possible to assess their taxonomic value.

Adaptation is associated only with the evolutionary mechanism of natural selection. By definition, features that are favored and maintained by selection are adaptive. Features that are rejected by selection are nonadaptive and are conspicuously absent. Hence, those aspects or properties of features responsible for the features being favored by selection would be the adaptive aspects of the features.

Selection can operate only according to rather fixed interactions between the organism and its environment. Selection and, hence, adaptation are the design aspect of evolution in the sense of Mayr (1962), who presents a lucid analysis of the design and accidental factors of evolution and clarifies the apparent dilemma.

Selection can establish limits on the range of acceptable features. All features within this range will be retained by selection, those outside these limits will be rejected. (These limits are not sharp boundaries but broad zones in which acceptance of a feature by selection is based upon a varying probability.) Usually, selection can accept a number of possible features ("adaptive answers") offered to it, in which case selection is said to have wide limits. When it accepts only one or a few restricted answers, selection is considered to have narrow limits. Although it can establish limits on the range of acceptable features, selection cannot predetermine the exact properties of the features exposed to it. Selection cannot reject a feature lying within the acceptable limits simply because it is not the theoretically best possible one or because it may prove to be detrimental at a later time. The several features (adaptive answers) lying within the limits of a particular selection force (see, for example, Bock, 1959; Bock and Miller, 1959) differ morphologically. But selection did not have any role in the generation of these morphological differences; they must be explained on the basis of other evolutionary principles.

It is important to realize that aspects of a feature are not solely adaptive—that is, adaptiveness is not the only evolutionary property of features. And natural selection is not the sole evolutionary mechanism controlling the evolution of features and determining their taxonomic value.

The origin of all features, be they adaptive or nonadaptive, and the appearance of their later modifications lie outside the control of natural selection. The origin of these features—for example, the basis for the phenotypical variation to be acted upon by selection—lies under the control of a different set of evolutionary mechanisms and phenomena such as (a) mutations, recombinations of all sorts, gene flow, and other chance-based genetical processes that generate the genotypical variation underlying the phenotypical variation; (b) the nature of the pre-existing features of the ancestral group; (c) the geographical and ecological location of the ancestral group; and (d) the timing of events, such as which group is first to acquire a new feature and thus be able to exploit first a new adaptive zone (for discussion see Mayr, 1960). Only the first of these could be regarded as a true mechanism; the others can be grouped together under the heading of "the evolutionary situation" (von Wahlert, 1965). The common and significant property of all these factors is that they are chance-based (stochastic) with respect to the demands of selection, to future evolution of the feature, and to the future selection forces that will act upon the feature. These factors constitute the accidental aspect of evolutionary change in the sense of Mayr (1962).

Those aspects of a feature that are dependent upon, result from, or are under the control of these chance-based evolutionary factors may be termed "paradaptive" (from "para" and "adaptive"), meaning "besides adaptive" in the sense that such aspects are not dependent upon selection and hence cannot be judged on a scale of adaptive to nonadaptive (Bock, 1967:7). Paradaptive properties of a feature are either adaptive or nonadaptive, according to whether they are accepted or rejected by selection. Nonadaptive paradaptations would disappear quickly and not be available for study and for use as taxonomic features.

The essential attribute of paradaptive aspects of features is that their occurrence is chance-based; thus, the chance that a particular paradaptation will appear (and be exposed to selection) depends upon its probability of occurrence. This probability is based upon a series of complex factors (genetical mechanisms and aspects of the particular evolutionary situation) and can be ascertained with difficulty, if at all. In many cases, an approximation of the probability may be made.

The relationship between paradaptive and adaptive is clearly shown in the heterodactyl foot of trogons (Bock and Miller, 1959). In these birds the second toe is paradaptive because it happened to reverse to the rear of the foot. The second toe is adaptive because it opposes the remaining anterior toes and had been accepted by selection forces for a perching foot. A series of similar examples is shown by the different types of climbing feet possessed by various groups of birds (Bock and Miller, 1959). In each case, the particular arrangement of toes in a climbing bird is dependent largely upon the toe arrangement in the perching foot of the ancestral group.

Comparisons may be classified (Figure 16) as horizontal (between members of different phyletic lines) and vertical (between members of the same phyletic line). Adaptive differences are associated more with differences in vertical comparisons (Figure 17); paradaptive differences are associated more with differences in horizontal comparisons, and they form the basis for multiple pathways of evolution (Bock, 1959).

Essentially, classification is the distinction between monophyletic (vertically based) groups of organisms, and as such it is the distinction between groups of organisms possessing different paradaptive properties of taxonomic characters. Paradaptive properties of features, being associated with the origin of features, will also be associated

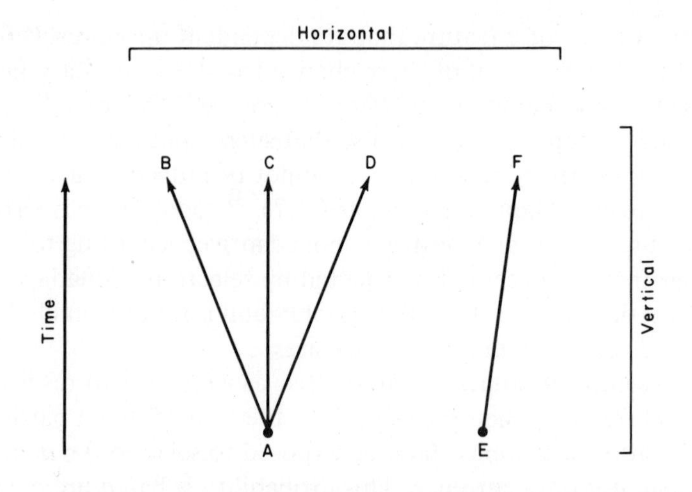

FIGURE 16 Schematic diagram showing the difference between horizontal and vertical comparisons. Vertical comparisons are between members of the same phyletic lineage, as between A and B, or A and C, or A and D, or E and F. Horizontal comparisons are between members of different phyletic lines, as between B, C, D, and F, or A and E, or B, C, D, and E, or A and F, regardless of whether the forms being compared are at the same time level. (From Bock, 1967.)

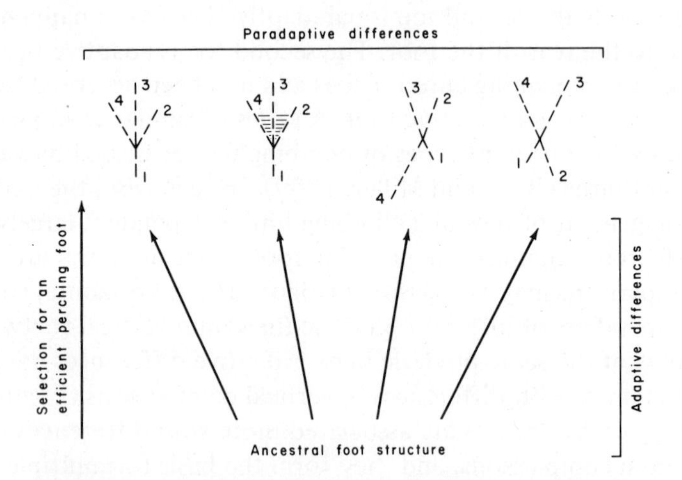

FIGURE 17 Schematic diagram showing pattern of multiple pathways of evolution of perching feet in (from left) anisodactyl, syndactyl, zygodactyl, and heterodactyl. The evolution of the four different arrangements of the toes from the ancestral condition was under the control of the same selection force for a more effective perching foot. Differences observed in vertical comparisons are adaptive; those in horizontal comparisons are paradaptive.

with the origin of taxonomic groups. Thus, a study of paradaptations would provide a good guide to the existence and limits of groups of organisms. (Many paradaptations also possess value as diagnostic or key characters whether they have value as indicators of relationships or not.)

If paradaptive properties of taxonomic characters determine the taxonomic value of such characters, the question arises whether all paradaptive properties have the same taxonomic value and, if not, what factors influence the taxonomic value of paradaptations. Obviously, paradaptations vary in their taxonomic usefulness because all features possess paradaptive aspects and all features certainly are not of equal taxonomic value. One of the significant differences among various paradaptations is the probability of their occurrence; this difference is of paramount importance in determining their taxonomic value. Hence, the probability of unique occurrence of a particular paradaptation in the evolutionary history of a group of organisms would vary from very low to very high. Those paradaptations with a high probability of unique occurrence would have great taxonomic value; those with a low probability would have little taxonomic value. The taxonomic level at which particular paradaptations have taxonomic value cannot be given by estimating the probability of their unique occurrence. Decision on the categorical level of a taxon depends partly upon the hierarchy of homologues, but it depends to a greater extent upon the "distinctiveness" of the group and the accepted scheme for expressing such distinctiveness. The width of the limits imposed by selection has an important bearing upon the taxonomic value of paradaptations. Generally, when selection has very narrow limits it is not possible to estimate the probability of unique occurrence (Bock, 1967:11–13).

The claim that paradaptations with high probability for unique origin* have great taxonomic value is neither novel nor even very useful without instructions on how such paradaptations can be distinguished from those with low probability. No simple instructions can be offered at this time. The most feasible method for

*It is at this point where most erudite (and usually obvious) statements on taxonomic procedure, including the present one, bog down. That convergent characters must be deleted before attempting systematic analyses, or that only homologous features can be used in classification, or that only features with a high probability of unique origin have great taxonomic value, cannot be disputed; however, rarely are practical and accurate instructions offered by those expressing such beliefs. One is reminded of the suggestion offered by the learned elder mouse that a bell be tied about the neck of the cat.

recognizing adaptive and paradaptive properties is by careful and detailed functional and biological-morphological studies. In this way, the adaptive aspects of the feature can be ascertained; then the paradaptive aspects can be deduced, and the probabilities for their unique occurrence can be estimated. Since work along these lines has barely started, only a few rough suggestions can be offered.

The arrangements of the toes for perching feet in birds appear to be restricted to the anisodactyl, syndactyl, heterodactyl, and zygodactyl types (Bock and Miller, 1959). If the ancestral condition of three anterior toes and a short, elevated posterior hallux is considered, then the probability that any of these four paradaptive toe arrangements will arise only once is about 0.25. These probabilities certainly vary, and with the possible exception of the probability for the heterodactyl foot, they are almost certainly less than 0.25. Hence, the arrangement of the toes is a feature with little taxonomic value. This low taxonomic value does not depend upon the fact that the zygodactyl foot apparently arose independently in nine groups of birds or that the heterodactyl foot apparently arose only once, but rather upon an independent evaluation of the chances of multiple independent origins of the feature. Although the arrangement of the toes has little taxonomic value, other anatomical features associated with toe arrangement may have more value. Whenever a toe is reversed, certain modifications must occur in the distal tarsal condyles for efficient reversal of tendon pull. The detailed paradaptive aspects of these condylar modifications may be such that the probability of their having a unique origin is very high. Therefore, whereas the zygodactyl arrangement of the toes of the Pici, Psittaci, and Cuculidae has little taxonomic value, the detailed structure of the distal tarsal condyles may have much value.

The osseous arch of the radius is a low arch on the inner side of the bone at the level of the nutrient foramen (Bock and McEvey, in press). There are no connections with the surrounding muscles or ligaments that indicate any functional restrictions to the location and shape of the arch. I regard this feature as a paradaptation with a high probability of unique origin, and hence, it has much taxonomic value.

In general, more complex structures possess paradaptive properties with a higher probability for unique occurrence and, hence, would have a greater taxonomic value than simpler structures–a conclusion that should not come as a surprise to systematists working with the higher categories. Moreover, features that are acted upon by selection forces with wide limits would possess greater taxonomic value than those acted upon by selection forces with narrow limits. Whether paradaptations are adaptive is of no real importance for their taxonomic value; presumably all existing taxonomic characters possess paradaptive aspects that also are adaptive.

The above analysis is not novel; at best, it formalizes existing procedure, and in so doing serves to focus attention upon the problem areas. Moreover, establishing taxonomic value on the basis of probability for the unique occurrence of paradaptations is, basically, what most systematists have implied under the notion of taxonomic weight of characters. The only difference is that invalid reasons, such as consistency within a species or uniformity within a group of organisms, were often cited as the basis for assigning taxonomic weight.

A combination of the method of estimating the probability for the unique origin of paradaptations and Wilson's consistency test (Wilson, 1965) may result in a powerful phylogenetic technique. Wilson's test is completely sound within the assumptions and limits he has set upon it. The major limitation is in choosing the unique and unreversed character states in the initial hypotheses to be tested; herein lies the advantage of the method for estimating probabilities for unique origins of paradaptations, as it provides an approach by which more precise initial hypotheses may be formulated. The above suggestion for using the estimated probability for the unique occurrence of paradaptations to estimate taxonomic value lacked a procedure for testing the results; this deficiency is covered by Wilson's consistency test. I reiterate Wilson's repeated warnings (1965, 1967) that the consistency test can be used only to prove the incorrectness of a particular cladogram and cannot prove the correctness of any cladogram.

CONCLUSIONS

Two separate methods are available by which considerable systematic information may be obtained from studies of morphological features. One method involves the formation of increasingly precise conditional phrases in hypotheses about homologous features and the test of these hypotheses. The other method involves estimating the probability for the unique occurrence of particular paradaptations. Unfortunately, exact procedures do not exist for either method, and it is doubtful that completely accurate and consistent procedures ever will exist. These methods represent only a fragment of the ideas being tested in current morphological work.

The emergence of evolutionary morphology is establishing a more sophisticated theoretical foundation for systematic study of the higher categories with the clear realization that these studies are not simply a comparison of the similarities of the groups under question. Earlier notions such as "anyone can compare" are no longer tenable with the highly rigorous training for morphological study that is becoming so necessary. With the available wealth of comparative information, the ease of storing material, the only available direct key to fossils and the essential element of time, and the great impetus being generated by the emergence of evolutionary morphology, it may be predicted that morphology will long remain a major cornerstone of theoretical and practical studies of biological classification.

ACKNOWLEDGMENTS

I thank Dr. H. Morioka for reading the manuscript and offering many helpful comments and criticisms and Mrs. Frances Jewel for preparing the illustrations. Earlier studies, from which many of the examples were taken, were made during the tenure of several pre- and postdoctoral fellowships and under research grants from the National Science Foundation.

The preparation of this review was supported by National Science Foundation Grant NSF-GH-3802.

REFERENCES

Bock, W. J. 1958. A generic review of the plovers (Charadriinae, Aves). Bull. Mus. Comp. Zool. 118:27–97.

Bock, W. J. 1959. Preadaptation and multiple evolutionary pathways. Evolution 13:194–211.

Bock, W. J. 1960a. Secondary articulation of the avian mandible. Auk 77:19–55.

Bock, W. J. 1960b. The palatine process of the premaxilla in the Passeres. Bull. Mus. Comp. Zool. 122:361–488.

Bock, W. J. 1961. Salivary glands in the gray jays (*Perisoreus*). Auk 78:355–365.

Bock, W. J. 1963a. Evolution and phylogeny in morphologically uniform groups. Am. Natur. 97:265–285.

Bock, W. J. 1963b. The cranial evidence for ratite affinities. Proc. XIII Internat. Ornithol. Congr. 1963:39–54.

Bock, W. J. 1964. Kinetics of the avian skull. J. Morph. 114:1–42.

Bock, W. J. 1966. An approach to the functional analysis of bill shape. Auk 83:10–51.

Bock, W. J. 1967. The use of adaptive characters in avian classification. Proc. XIV Internat. Ornithol. Congr. 1967:1–4.

Bock, W. J., and W. deW. Miller. 1959. The scansorial foot of woodpeckers, with comments on the evolution of perching and climbing feet in birds. Am. Mus. Novit. 1931. 45 p.

Bock, W. J., and G. von Wahlert. 1965. Adaptation and the form-function complex. Evolution 19:269–299.

Davis, D. D. 1958. The proper goal of comparative anatomy. Proc. Cent. and Bicent. Congr. Biology, Singapore 1958:44–50.

Dow, D. D. 1965. The role of saliva in food storage by the gray jay. Auk 82:139–154.

Frazzetta, T. H. 1966. Studies on the morphology and function of the skull in the Boidae (Serpentes). Part II. J. Morph. 118:217–295.

Gans, C., and W. J. Bock. 1965. The functional significance of muscle architecture—a theoretical analysis. Ergebn. Anat. Entwick. 38:115–142.

Ghiselin, M. T. 1966a. An application of the theory of definitions to systematic principles. Syst. Zool. 15:127–130.

Ghiselin, M. T. 1966b. On phychologism in the logic of taxonomic controversies. Syst. Zool. 15:207–215.

Hull, D. L. 1967. Certainty and circularity in evolutionary taxonomy. Evolution 21:174–189.

Mayr, E. 1960. The emergence of evolutionary novelties, p. 349–380 *In* S. Tax [ed] The evolution of life. University of Chicago Press, Chicago, Illinois.

Mayr, E. 1962. Accident or design, the paradox of evolution, p. 1–14 *In* G. W. Leeper [ed] The evolution of living organisms. Melbourne University Press, Victoria, Australia.

Mayr, E. 1965. Classification and phylogeny. Am. Zool. 5:165–174.

Meise, W. 1963. Verhalten der Straussartigen Vögel und Monophylie der Ratite. Proc. XIII Internat. Ornithol. Congr. 1963:115–125.

Ostrom, J. H. 1964. A reconsideration of the paleoecology of hadrosaurian dinosaurs. Am. J. Sci. 262:975–997.

Parkes, K. C., and G. A. Clark, Jr. 1966. An additional character linking ratites and tinamous and an interpretation of their monophyly. Condor 65:459–471.
Remane, A. 1956. Die Grundlagen des natürlichen Systems, der vergleichenden Anatomie und der Phylogenetik. Akademische Verlagsgesellschaft, Leipzig. 364 p.
Sibley, C. G. 1960. The electrophoretic patterns of avian egg-white proteins as taxonomic characters. Ibis 102:215–284.
Sibley, C. G. 1965. Molecular systematics: New techniques applied to old problems. L'Oiseau 35:112–124.
Simpson, G. G. 1959. Anatomy and morphology: Classification and evolution: 1859 and 1959. Proc. Am. Phil. Soc. 103:286–306.
Simpson, G. G. 1961. Principles of animal taxonomy. Columbia University Press, New York. 247 p.
Wahlert, G. von. 1965. The role of ecological factors in the origin of higher levels of organization. Syst. Zool. 14:288–300.
Wilson, E. O. 1965. A consistency test for phylogenies based upon contemporaneous species. Syst. Zool. 14:214–220.
Wilson, E. O. 1967. The validity of the "consistency test" for phylogenetic hypotheses. Syst. Zool. 16:104.

Discussion

William L. Stern

Participants in this conference surely will agree that a botanist discussing a paper by a zoologist is at a selective disadvantage. Nevertheless, I hope you will bear with me while I make a few observations and pose a few questions, for many of Dr. Bock's remarks are applicable to plant morphology.

In examining an abstract of Dr. Bock's paper and some of his published works, I was struck by the differences between the terminology and the analytic mechanisms employed by the plant morphologist-anatomist working with the higher vascular plants (angiosperms) and those used by the animal morphologist-anatomist working with vertebrates. I think some of the more obvious differences are related not so much to the action of inherently different kinds of evolutionary mechanisms in plants and in animals but to the difficulty of relating the origin and development of plant features to the selective forces of nature; to the differences between what is generally understood as "anatomy" by botanists and by zoologists; to the still vague origins of the higher vascular plants, the angiosperms, in time; to the vaster number of kinds of higher plants as compared with the total number of kinds of vertebrates (fishes, amphibians, reptiles, mammals, and birds); and to the basic morphological-anatomical homogeneity of the higher vascular plants as compared with the vertebrates.

Being vertebrates ourselves, it is relatively easy for us to relate morphological change in other vertebrates to adaptation brought on by selective forces in the environment. Furthermore, as was emphasized by Dr. Sibley, higher animals, by and large, are mobile, whereas adult higher plants are sessile. Motility in animals is related to food-getting and reproduction, and there is corresponding adaptation of structure in the performance of these functions. An example is the prehensile tongue and massive leg muscles in certain amphibians that are easily seen as adaptations to the capture of rapidly moving insects; these have a selective advantage in a particular environment. True enough, we may ascribe a selective advantage to the development of thick cuticles and stomatal crypts in leaves of plants existing in areas of high winds and low soil moisture, but what is the selective advantage of separate versus fused petals, simple versus compound leaves, or unilacunar versus multilacunar nodes? And, more important, are these features adaptive in any way, allowing their possessors to exist in a given environment? The questions become even sharper when we recognize that plant species showing each condition may exist side by side in the same mesophytic forest niche. If there are indeed similar underlying evolutionary mechanisms acting upon all organisms, we may assume these plant modifications to be adaptive, but the selective advantage of the examples given above is obscure, at least to me.

Botanical anatomy concerns cell and tissue structure; zoological anatomy concerns organ, muscle, and bone structure, if I understand correctly. I think morphology in both sciences refers to the grosser aspects of structure; and, at least in higher plants, our taxonomy usually is founded upon these nonmicroscopic features. There are excellent, reliable, and evolutionarily sound anatomical features in plants upon which the larger phases of phylogenetic systems have been founded, some of which are verifiable through the fossil record (e.g., the origin and development of the vessel element).

The point, or points, of origin—depending upon whether one believes in the monophyletic or polyphyletic origin of the angiosperms—of the flowering plants are still unknown, largely because there is no adequate fossil record. Successive ancestral groups of plants have been discarded over the years, and the cycadeoids, Caytoniales, and other extinct plant taxa have been dismissed as origins for the angiosperms. Along with this, it is still a question of which of the two groups of flowering plants—monocots or dicots—or even *if* one of these two groups—antedates the other; if they are lineal descendants of each other, as was argued by nineteenth-century botanists; or if they are of common ancestry.

Probably these are well in excess of one quarter million angiosperms, and it is doubtful that we will ever know all the evolutionary mechanisms that brought them to their present form, their relationships, and their phylogeny. Although the distinctions among the classes of vertebrates appear sharp (barring transitional forms), the basic distinctions among the flowering plants are few, except for those relatively superficial distinctions we use to subdivide the group into orders and lesser taxa.

But perhaps we are not comparing coordinate taxa when we measure angiosperms against vertebrates, for in some systems of plant classification the angiosperms are treated merely as a subclass of the seed-bearing plants (spermatophytes). Nevertheless, I think the comparison becomes valid when we appreciate that we are comparing the most advanced animals (vertebrates) against the most advanced plants (angiosperms). How the taxonomist treats these groups of higher organisms is irrelevant to this discussion.

According to Dr. Bock, in zoology the year 1900 virtually sounded the death knell of comparative morphology. In botany, on the contrary, the turn of the century marked a shift from the typological morphology carried out in Europe, particularly in Germany, to the dynamic—or "biological" or "evolutionary" (to use Dr. Bock's terminology)—morphology pursued in England and, more importantly at the time, in the United States. A school of evolutionary morphology dedicated to the exposition and explanation of morphology as a keystone of plant systematics was established and vigorously pursued at Harvard University by E. C. Jeffrey, E. W. Sinnott, A. J. Eames, I. W. Bailey, and their students. Their lucid delineations of the evolutionary pathways in the phylogenetic development of plant cells and tissues contributed to an understanding of the systematics of higher plants that was not based on circuitous reasoning and that stood by itself. The origin and evolution of the vessel element as a guide to an understanding of higher plant systematics was propounded independently of existing taxonomic systems of the time. The recent death of Professor Bailey closed this halcyon era in plant morphology-anatomy at Harvard.

In this day it is all well and good to belittle the descriptive morphologists of the nineteenth century but, at least in the botanical world, the magnificent preparations and subsequent observations and interpretations of such scientists as Hofmeister, Strasburger, De Bary, Goebel, and others are marvels of perfection. The bases for their studies are as valid today as they were 70 or 80 years ago. The change has been that present interpretation is based on more complete materials, newer technologies, greater intercommunication among biologists, and, concomitantly, greater insight. These men were shrewd observers, and no one could say of them then—nor can we say of them now—that they chose their calling because "anyone can study morphology" or "anyone can compare." Where is there a plant morphologist-anatomist today who has not embarked on a study only to find, in searching the literature, that some German botanist had already probed the same area? Surely we owe those early morphologists a great debt, and their work is not to be disparaged, even today .

We are cautioned by Dr. Bock that it "is erroneous for current workers to cite conclusions from older literature without knowing their bases." Agreed, but we are told that "Although regrettable, the use of available morphological information is not a simple or obvious matter." Dr. Bock exhorts us to explore functional morphology through experimentation to help reach more meaningful conclusions. One cannot but agree with this plea. On the one hand, however, he tells us to tread with care in using findings of the older morphologists, and on the other hand he tells us that "Considerable information for the formulation of functional conclusions is available from other biological disciplines; morphologists must make greater use of these data."

I submit that (1) plant morphologists today use all kinds of ancillary data in drawing their conclusions, as they have for many years, and (2) what is being done today in other related biological disciplines is, *per se,* no more accurate or valid or less subject to interpretation than the work of our predecessors.

My final point: We must be ever on guard in morphological studies, as well as in other biological disciplines, not to base generalizations on the study of a single or only a few taxa. Had the first plant anatomists come upon the xylem of *Drimys* (or *Tetracentron, Trochodendron, Zygogynum, Bubbia, Sarcandra,* etc.) without surveying the wood anatomy of the flowering plants *in extenso* they might well have concluded that angiosperms lacked vessels. This, of course, is an absurd exaggeration, but I chose it as an example to make the point. Perhaps not so farfetched is the plant anatomist who characterizes the xylem of the plant family Gesneriaceae (African violet family) by examining only the wood of *Besleria,* which lacks vascular rays. The wood of other gesneriads possesses vascular rays.

Comparative morphology was, is, and probably always will be one of the important and critical bases of systematic studies. Dr. Bock has elaborated upon this salient point and has shown us some of the pitfalls to be encountered through a blind reliance upon this single discipline, uninterpreted in the light of modern evolutionary biology.

Discussion

David B. Wake

My comments are limited to the section on adaptation and paradaptation. I find the discussion of adaptation to be confusing because of imprecise use of words and apparent circular reasoning. For example, Bock states that all features existing for long periods of time, or used in the classification of animals, are adaptive. He follows this premise with the statement that in a survey he could find no characters used in avian classification that were not clearly adaptive. If the same definition of adaptation applies to the two sentences, the second is tautological; yet it is presented as support for the premise. Throughout the discussion, one is unable to determine what definition is adopted at a given moment. Bock strongly implies that he views adaptation as state of being, a viewpoint that I vigorously reject, but he may be attempting to make a point essential to the development of his argument. Certainly if every feature that exists is adaptive, nothing else can be used in classification, and discussion of the usefulness of adaptive characters in classification is reduced to the level of absurdity, as Bock correctly states. To me, however, the absurdity occurs at the point at which adaptation is essentially equated with state of being. In my view, features that increase the reproductive potential of organisms are adaptive; if they do not do so, they simply exist. Certainly, we have sufficient information from such fields as developmental biology and genetics to indicate that nonadaptive (using my definition) features are maintained in populations by such phenomena as canalization, and it appears that Bock has attempted to avoid biological facts by directing attention to the semantic arguments.

I am equally unhappy with the discussion of paradaptation, which appears to me to be an attempt to add yet another name to what has long been recognized as the opportunistic nature of evolutionary processes. Bock groups various factors, such as mutation and recombination, features of the ancestral group, and timing, as "chance-based" evolutionary mechanisms and phenomena, and he states that these give rise to paradaptations. These factors are important in determining what change will or can occur, but they are hardly evolutionary mechanisms. Placing emphasis on such factors, rather than on the results of selective processes, seems strikingly close to mutationism. To me, mutation and recombination are sources of raw material on which evolutionary mechanisms act, and to place emphasis on opportunism of occurrence rather than selection seems a step backwards. However, the main point is that while Bock suggests that the paradaptive properties of characters determine the taxonomic usefulness of the various characters, he presents neither a rigorous nor even an operational definition of paradaptation. If paradaptations cannot be consistently and objectively identified, they cannot be used. When Bock uses the word "paradaptation," one could as well substitute "character" or even "thing." As it stands, the concept of paradaptation is highly subjective and cannot be used in building classifications or in other systematic work.

Features are said to be paradaptive and, at the same time, adaptive or nonadaptive, relative to different selection forces. This would seem to place too much emphasis on isolated parts of the organism and not enough on the whole organism, including its full ontogeny and its populational and environmental relationships. However, I think that Bock's object in this paper is to make a plea for more careful character analysis with close attention paid to the origin and meaning of various morphological features. I certainly support him in this.

In my view, one ought to be very broadly comparative within groups—to study all members of the group being analyzed and all aspects of their morphology, as well as utilizing ontogenetic and developmental information—rather than emphasizing single functional units. My work on lower vertebrates indicates to me that comparative morphologists must develop an awareness of the developmental state of species at maturity. This is particularly crucial in lower vertebrates where paedomorphic and gerontomorphic modes of evolution are so prevalent.

Finally, I suggest that classifications be built on the basis of total available information, as we have heard again and again at this conference. Thus, when considering morphology, we should consider all parts and all stages of development. We must, as morphologists, remember that it is populations, not parts, of organisms that evolve. The parts are important, of course, and I consider careful and objective character analysis to be an important task of the comparative morphologist, and logical use of the derived information the most important task of the taxonomist. I prefer to build classifications on the basis of high correlation of specialized or derived (and adaptive, in my sense of the term) character states, which carry information concerning change and community of descent. By adopting rigorous methodological approaches and applying consistency tests to the results of the analysis of large bodies of data from different systems, problems resulting from convergence can now be readily surmounted. The most important role of comparative morphology to the taxonomist of the future will be in the area of character analysis, an activity that lies at the base of all taxonomic work and that has been approached too often in only a superficial manner in the past. It is at this point that the morphologist, with his functional, ontogenetic, and comparative approaches, can make his most meaningful contribution to taxonomy.

SOKAL: I would like to make several brief comments about Dr. Bock's talk.

1. I am disappointed, as I had hoped to hear an operational definition of homology. I am not yet convinced that such a definition is impossible. However, there is nothing in Dr. Bock's application of the concept of homology that differs from the conventional unsatisfactory approach.

2. I defer to Dr. Hull's professional judgment as a philosopher that reasoning about homology is not formally circular; yet, I continue to lack confidence in the unwarranted conclusions on morphology, based on taxonomy, which in turn lead to taxonomic judgments.

3. The statement by Dr. Bock that the os prominens evolved independently in hawks and owls is no different from the types of conclusions that we have seen in the past. It would seem to me that an approach based on the theory of correspondences would be a far more promising one for general morphology.

4. For the purpose of taxonomy, functional analysis is no different from other morphological studies. However, it clearly is not practical in the large number of insect groups having many thousands of species with millions of characters.

5. I must take exception to the term "evolutionary morphology." Nowadays it is fashionable to add the word "evolutionary" or "populational" to our subject of study, but there is really nothing more evolutionary in Dr. Bock's approach than in the method of comparative morphology that we have known so far.

FARRIS: When you first gave your own definition of homology, Dr. Bock, you emphasized that there should be no relationship between the definition of the term and the criteria used to find out whether a particular system met the definition. I agree with this wholeheartedly, in principle, but—and here I am relying in part on my reading of your 1963 paper in the *American Naturalist*—when you go further and speak about what the feature in the common ancestor must be in order for two features in two derived forms to be homologous, your argument seems to have a different basis. Your argument then apparently rests primarily on the consideration that since under such-and-such a circumstance we would not really be able to tell whether two features are homologous, if we define the term in the strictest sense, then, we may as well go ahead and define homology in some looser sense so that we will be able to use ordinary morphological criteria the way we want to. So, in the first part of your discussion of homology you argue against operational considerations in definitions; and in the second part of your discussion of homology you are, in fact—if not in desire—using operational criteria in your way of deciding what the definition of homology should be.

I think that in criticizing Simpson's definition of homology you have rather overextended your ideas. Simpson's definition can be stated in an entirely equivalent way—purely phylogenetically—as follows: "A feature or a condition of a feature in two derived organisms is homologous if at every point along the phyletic line connecting the two organisms that feature or condition of feature also occurs." The word "resemblance" occurs nowhere in the definition; yet, "resemblance" or "similarity" obviously has something to do with it. If the condition or the feature occurs at every point along the phyletic line, then, even by the rather restrictive definition given by Ghiselin, at every point along the phyletic line the organisms involved are similar in that respect.

In regard to the concept of paradaptation, it is not entirely clear to me what a chance-based evolutionary mechanism is.

You said something about there being four possible ways for a toe to develop to provide a perching foot on a bird, and that the probability that any one of the four would arise if a bird happened to need a perching foot is one fourth, and that the probability of unique occurrence of a kind of perching foot is low. Now, I have done some little research on a directly probabilistic approach to inferring evolution. The simple existence of four possible kinds of perching feet does not, in itself, give the probability of unique occurrence of these various kinds of feet, since the probability of occurrence of a kind of foot depends not only on the probability that it will occur in some particular phyletic line but also on the probability distributions of different kinds of phyletic lines with what you might refer to as preadaptative or paradaptive tendencies to develop these kinds of feet. In general, you would have no advance information of this sort available and consequently could not set, *a priori*, probability distribution on the unique occurrence of kinds of morphological structures.

Furthermore, the belief that a morphological structure is paradaptive depends, as you said, upon the assumption of chance-based evolutionary mechanisms. But exactly when is a structure that you see considered to have a chance-based origin? Clearly, if you see that selection for such-and-such a function can allow only a certain structure, you say that the origin of the structure is not chance-based. On the other hand, suppose you see a structure and are unable immediately to decide selection and could admit one or more possibilities. In such a situation I probably would feel that selection was operating quite normally anyway, and that I just am not able to understand it. However, your approach seems to be that if you are not able immediately to find the direct selective forces involved in the origin of some particular structure, you assume that the part you do not understand must have been achieved by random process. This is to underestimate the efficacy of natural selection.

Although paradaptation might be defined meaningfully in the sense, for example, that one phyletic line, due to the structure it now has, is more likely to evolve in one way in response to some selective force than is another phyletic line that currently looks like something else, such an evolvement cannot be regarded purely as a chance evolutionary process, even from the standpoint of natural selection, since differences—both current and past—between the phyletic lines are due to the long selective histories of the lines.

BOCK: Although Simpson's definition of homology is slightly different from mine, I don't think that the two are in any substantial disagreement. Moreover, your statement of Simpson's definition is closer to my definition than his as I exclude all notion of resemblance from my definition (above) while Simpson defines homology (1961: 78) as: "... resemblance due to inheritance from connon ancestry." I agree that resemblance is involved in homology as one of the major ways of recognizing homologous features, which brings us to your statement that I use operational criteria in deciding what the definition of homology should be. This is not so at all. In my discussion, I distinguish sharply between definition of homology and recognition of objects to which this term may be applied (recognition of actual homologous features). My methods for recognizing homologous features differ little from many operational definitions of homology, and I would be surprised if they differed more.

To be sure, the probability of each type of perching foot is not 0.25, and the factors affecting this probability are more than the number of possible types of perching foot; this estimate implied only a low probability. Indeed it may not be possible to go beyond statements that the probability for the unique origin of a certain paradaptation is high, medium, or low until our knowledge of evolutionary morphology is significantly improved over present levels. However, the origin of a particular structure is always chance-based, even when the limits of selection are very narrow. In such cases selection will favor only a certain structure, but the origin of that structure is still chance-based. I would expect that the origin of these features would be very rare because of the required close correlation between the phenotypical variants and the limits of selection. The notion of paradaptation does not in any way under-estimate the efficacy of natural selection, rather it calls attention to the other and all-too-often ignored factors of evolutionary change.

MURRAY J. LITTLEJOHN

The Systematic Significance of Isolating Mechanisms

Since speciation (divergent evolution) in biparental organisms is initially achieved through the development of adequate reproductive isolation, the understanding of this process is clearly of basic evolutionary importance (Stebbins, 1958); it is second only to the understanding of those mechanisms that enable a genetic lineage to persist through space and time (adaptive evolution). Thus, the essential and primary step in the speciation process in such organisms will be the development of those devices that restrict exchange of genetic information between sympatric species (isolating mechanisms) to a level below the critical point where natural selection can no longer maintain the specific distinctness (Ehrman, 1962). Mayr (1963) feels that isolating mechanisms are perhaps the most important of the characteristics possessed by a species.

Bigelow (1965) considers that speciation is complete at this stage, but clearly the process is fully completed only when the products of divergent evolution can coexist efficiently in a broadly sympatric state. This would require ecological compatibility as well as reproductive isolation. Mayr discussed this argument in some detail when considering the requirements for successful speciation:

> Each species is an independent genetic system, which has the properties of being reproductively isolated from and ecologically compatible with other sympatric species. Speciation means the acquisition of these properties (Mayr, 1963:546).

Thus, we really should consider speciation from two points of view: (1) the legal-nomenclatural requirements for a decision on taxonomic status, which will be fulfilled by isolational criteria alone; and (2) the evolutionary dynamics of the process, which involve both isolational and ecological criteria. Both types of consideration are very important. Decisions as to the stages of speciation are of considerable intrinsic interest, and all species, even if cryptic because of human sensory limitations, must be recognized. The recognition of these basic taxonomic units might be through the morphological and molecular consequences of reduced gene flow and differential ecological adaptation; or better, through those factors directly responsible for limiting genetic transfer (isolating mechanisms), for these clearly are more fundamental and meaningful in lower-category taxonomy. Most of the following discussion is directed toward animal speciation, but it should apply equally well to many plant systems.

THE CLASSIFICATION AND ORIGIN OF ISOLATING MECHANISMS

It is appropriate to examine the different kinds of isolating mechanisms in terms of their efficiency and possible origins. The scheme presented in Table 1 (based on Robson and Richards, 1936; Dobzhansky, 1951; Perdeck, 1958; Littlejohn, 1959; Mayr, 1963; Wilson, 1965; Stebbins, 1966; and others) should allow a fairly rapid assessment of the situation.

An important point about this classification is that premating isolating mechanisms are economical of gametes and hence are more efficient than postmating isolating mechanisms (Littlejohn, 1959). In this context, mating is defined as the liberation of gametes or the modification of gametes so that they are no longer available for a second attempt. The higher up the scale (Table 1) the interaction breaks down, the more efficient the isolating mechanism, for efficiency can also be measured in terms of time, energy, and so forth (Sibley, 1961). The prezygotic and postzygotic dichotomy of Wilson (1965) and Stebbins (1966) comes after gamete release; hence, it is not directly comparable in terms of reproductive efficiency.

The real significance of the premating-postmating subdivision is that natural selection can operate only on the former, as was clearly

TABLE 1 A Classification of Reproductive Isolating Mechanisms

---

1. Reduction of contact[a]
   (a) Temporal
   (b) Ecological
2. Reduction of mating frequency[a]
   (c) Ethological
   (d) Morphological

PREMATING

POSTMATING

3. Reduction of zygote formation[b]
   (e) Gametic and reproductive tract incompatibility

PREZYGOTIC

POSTZYGOTIC

4. Reduction of hybrid survival[b]
   (f) Hybrid inviability
5. Reduction of gene flow through hybrids[b]
   (g) Hybrid ethological isolation[c]
   (h) Hybrid sterility
   (i) Hybrid breakdown

---

[a] The "bars to crossing" of Muller (1942); considered "superficial" by Bigelow (1965).

[b] Leads to "incapacitation of hybrids" (Muller, 1942); are "absolute" according to Bigelow (1965).

[c] Category suggested by Perdeck (1958) and new to most general classifications but alluded to by several authors. Because of intermediate nature of signals (releasers) and associated response patterns in opposite sex, hybrids (in competition with the pure types), are unable to secure mates from parental species.

pointed out by Mecham (1961). Thus, the classification also provides the basis for any discussions on the origin of reproductive isolation and, hence, on speciation in biparental organisms.

There are two basic ways in which reproductive isolation can arise, and the complete isolating mechanism complex operating between two closely related (cognate) species may have developed as a result of contributions from both sources:

1. *Incidental action* (Darwin, Muller). Isolating mechanisms arise as purely incidental products of other adaptive processes in allopatric populations and not for their isolating effect as such.

2. *Direct action* (Wallace, Fisher, Dobzhansky). Isolating mechanisms are established as a result of the direct action of natural selection for the isolating effect. This can apply only to premating mechanisms (Mecham, 1961), and the process is generally termed reinforcement (Blair, 1955a; Sibley, 1957). Grant (1966) has suggested the term "Wallace Effect" for this evolutionary mechanism, which makes up one component of character displacement (Brown and Wilson, 1956), the other being sympatric ecological divergence.

Usually, for two cognate populations, the incidental mechanisms are considered in the context of allopatry, and the direct mechanisms are considered in the context of sympatry. But such restriction is not necessary, as the evolution of isolating mechanisms may be considered under the alternative conditions, directly in allopatry and incidentally in sympatry, as shown below.

3. *Differential reproductive environments.* Two disjunct, allopatric cognate populations may experience different sets of sympatric species with which each interacts; as a consequence, premating isolating mechanism complexes become differentially modified through the direct action of selection for increased reproductive efficiency. If these two isolates should become sympatric, they may already be efficiently isolated reproductively at the premating level. This process is summarized diagrammatically in Figure 1. Admittedly, the *potential* isolation between the cognates is *secondary* (hence, incidental in this context), but its origin would have been functional and not simply fortuitous. A very important aspect of this process is that there is no need for the prior development of postmating isolation, and the species could coexist solely through the operation of premating isolating mechanisms. This idea has been developed for the "sound environments" of soniferous animals (Perdeck, 1958; Littlejohn, 1959, 1965; Marler, 1960; Alexander, 1962b; Bossert, 1963; Walker, 1964). Failure to consider this process when discussing the allopatric origins of isolating mechanisms

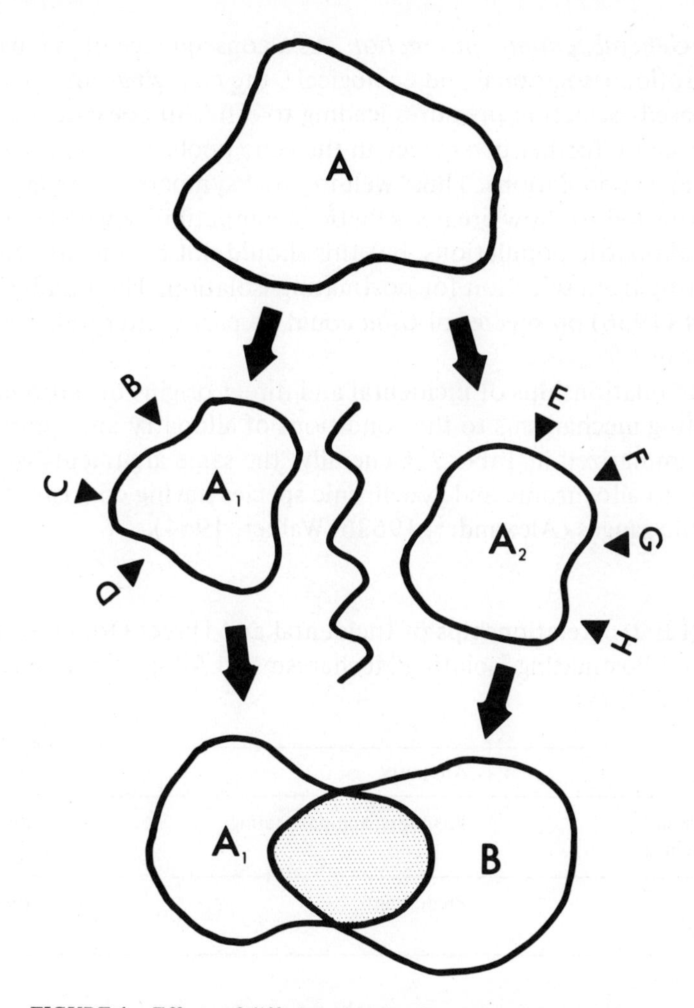

FIGURE 1 Effects of differing reproductive environments on the allopatric but directly selected origin of premating isolation. The parental population, A, is geographically isolated (wavy vertical line) into two disjunct populations, A_1 and A_2. Each of these interacts with a different set of sympatric species–A_1 with B, C, D; A_2 with E, F, G, H–and, as a consequence, the potential premating isolating mechanism complexes are differentially modified. When the geographic barrier is removed and the ranges are extended, the populations can become sympatric and can coexist as distinct species, A_1 and B.

means that earlier examples of supposedly incidental origin should be reinvestigated.

4. *General genomic interaction.* As a consequence of sympatric interaction (isolational and ecological), the changing–and perhaps increased–selection pressures leading to efficient coexistence also could cause further divergence in the gene pools of two previously allopatric populations. Thus, well-isolated sympatric populations may be expected to show greater genetic incompatibility when compared with allopatric populations, but this should not be interpreted as resulting from selection for postmating isolation. The findings of Grant (1966) on species of *Gilia* could be partly interpreted in this way.

The relationships of incidental and direct origins of reproductive isolating mechanisms to the conditions of allopatry and sympatry are summarized in Table 2. Generally, the same arguments would apply to allochronic and synchronic species having coexistent geographic ranges (Alexander, 1962b; Walker, 1964).

TABLE 2 Relationships of Incidental and Direct Origins of Premating and Postmating Isolating Mechanisms to Allopatric and Sympatric Conditions

	Allopatry	Sympatry
Incidental origin	Premating and postmating	Postmating
Direct origin	Premating	Premating

GENERAL CHARACTERISTICS OF ISOLATING MECHANISMS

In the past decade there have been several general reviews (e.g., Marler, 1957; Sibley, 1957, 1961; Blair, 1958a, 1962, 1964; Stebbins, 1958; Hubbs, 1961; Mecham, 1961; Alexander, 1962 a and b; Ehrman, 1962, 1964; Grant, 1963, 1966; Mayr, 1963; Walker, 1964) and numerous specific papers (some of which are listed in the reference section of this paper) on the operation and origin of reproductive isolation. From these reviews and papers can be drawn a number of conclusions on which there is fairly general agreement: (1) Reproductive isolating mechanisms are the most important characteristics of sympatric biparental species, and (2) they have a polygenic basis; (3) there is no correlation between morphological divergence and reproductive isolation (except where the structures are concerned with this function); (4) there is no genetic correlation between premating and postmating isolation; (5) complete isolation generally results from the additive action of several isolating mechanisms, but in higher animals ethological isolation is far more important than other mechanisms; (6) effective postmating isolation is not a general characteristic of sympatric species; (7) reproductive isolation need not be absolute, but it must be sufficient to limit gene flow below some critical level where selection can handle the input.

The point often overlooked when considering the origin of reproductive isolation is the distinction between premating and postmating isolating mechanisms (Volpe, 1955; Moore, 1957; Grant, 1966). This aspect was discussed above.

The main area of contention appears to concern the relative importance of reinforcement (direct selection) in accounting for the origin of reproductive isolation. The following arguments are advanced in support of this process:

1. Since natural selection is normally invoked to explain the process of adaptation, and premating isolating mechanisms are clearly adaptive, why make exception for these critical specific characters?

2. That the process certainly occurs has been amply demonstrated in experimental populations of *Drosophila;* for example, Koopman (1950) and Kessler (1966), through a program of direct selection, were able to strengthen ethological isolation between *D. pseudoobscura* and *D. persimilis.* Wallace (1954) and Knight *et al.* (1956) demonstrated that homogamic mating preference could be increased in mutant strains of *D. melanogaster.* However, ethological isolation can also arise incidentally in selected and inbred lines of *Drosophila* (Koref-Santibanez and Waddington, 1958; Thoday and Gibson, 1962; Ehrman, 1965).

3. There is a substantial amount of circumstantial evidence to support the hypothesis that ethological isolation is stronger in sympatric than in allopatric populations and species (Dobzhansky and Koller, 1938; Blair, 1955a; Alexander, 1962 a and b; Hubbs and Delco, 1962; Walker, 1964; Ehrman, 1965; Littlejohn, 1965).

4. An excellent theoretical and quantitative model for reinforcing selection has been advanced by Bossert (1963), and discussed by Wilson (1965), in which a number of postulates are set up and related to amounts of gene flow. This model predicts a rapid action of reinforcing selection, much of the divergence being achieved after three to five generations. This provides an excellent basis for the design of experiments with quasinatural field populations.

5. The earlier discussion on the influence of differing reproductive environments gives a reasonable explanation for the allopatric origin of some components of premating isolation.

6. Displacement of a premating isolating mechanism should not be expected in overlapping pairs of species in which the allopatric populations appear already to have effective premating isolation (on the basis of differences observed in the sympatric populations), or where the allopatric samples were taken from areas close to the overlap zone (with no allowance made for historical range change effects). Michaud (1964) and Ball and Jameson (1966) probably failed to find indications of reinforcement in anuran mating-call structure for these reasons. In addition, however, Ball and Jameson did not give due consideration to pulse-repetition rate—a call component already shown to be critical in hylid discrimination (Littlejohn *et al.*, 1960; Littlejohn, 1960; Michaud, 1962).

SYMPATRIC INTERACTIONS

If a genetic revolution (*sensu* Mayr, 1963) is to occur, then surely one of the most likely situations in which it would appear would be when two previously allopatric, incompletely speciated populations first come into contact. For under these conditions their status as species would be tested properly, and their isolational and ecological interactions would be strongest. The nature of sympatry (from contact to broad overlap) may have considerable bearing on whether directly selected, divergent evolution will occur and allow speciation to proceed. Levels of genetic input (through interbreeding with adjacent allopatric individuals of the same lineage, migration, and mutation) would have to be more than counteracted by *selective elimination.*

We will now consider the extreme cases for sympatry in two cognate populations having effective postmating isolation (e.g., hybrid sterility), but having incomplete premating isolation or ecological compatibility, or both. These situations are represented diagrammatically in Figure 2. In the case of contact sympatry, the genetic input would be much greater than the selective elimination from the extremely limited sympatry. Divergence would be highly unlikely, and the only result would be an evolutionary stalemate insofar as this particular strategy is concerned. In the other situation, where there is a broad overlap of geographic ranges, the selective elimination could more than compensate for the relatively smaller amounts of genetic input, and reinforcement would be more probable. If an objective taxonomic decision is to be made, the outcome of intermediate situations would require more precise estimates of the rates of genetic input and elimination and the application of a predictive model similar to that proposed by Bossert (1963).

The relatively narrow hybrid zones developed between the European crows *Corvus cornix* and *C. corone* (Meise, 1928) and between

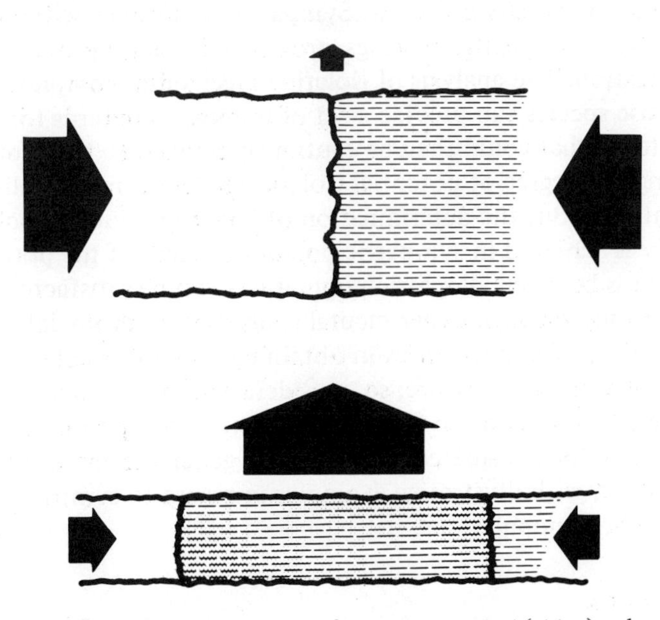

FIGURE 2 Two extreme types of sympatry: contact (at top) and overlapping. Horizontal arrows represent the relative amounts of genetic input; vertical arrows, the relative amounts of selective elimination. (See text for further explanation.)

the Australian frogs *Crinia insignifera* and *C. pseudinsignifera* (Littlejohn, 1959) provide possible examples of situations in which speciation has been retarded because of excessive genetic input (swamping). The extensive and linear overlap in geographic ranges of the Australian tree frogs *Hyla ewingi* and *H. verreauxi* and the indications of pronounced mating-call divergence in the sympatric populations of each species while calls of allopatric populations are almost indistinguishable (Littlejohn, 1965) may represent a situation in which selective elimination has been greater than genetic input. Even so, the effects reach their greatest expression in the extreme sympatric populations and are not particularly evident in the calls of those populations in "shallow" sympatry.

THE ASSESSMENT OF REPRODUCTIVE ISOLATION

In making an assessment of reproductive isolation, two questions may be asked. How effective are the isolating mechanisms? How is the isolation actually achieved? Sympatric occurrence without hybridization or interspecific matings provides the natural answer to the first question. The analysis of isolating mechanism complexes in sympatric species can provide a set of minimal standards for efficient coexistence that could then be cautiously applied to the problem of deciding the degree of potential isolation between related allopatric populations. But the determination of how reproductive isolation actually is achieved in sympatric populations and of the potential effectiveness between allopatric populations can be satisfactorily carried out only through experimental analysis in both the laboratory and the field. The difficulties in obtaining such information are largely of a practical nature, so consideration of developed techniques and the progress made so far is appropriate at this point. The methodology will be considered first in rather general terms and then in more detail, with illustrative examples in regard to sympatric species and allopatric populations.

OBSERVATION

This involves the objective and quantitative analysis of factors presumed to operate as premating isolating mechanisms and the determination of frequency of natural heterospecific matings and hybridization. Useful circumstantial evidence can be obtained in this way, and in most cases such evidence is the only kind available.

LABORATORY EXPERIMENTS

Basic data on postmating isolation can be provided by controlled artificial fertilization and the careful rearing of hybrids (if produced) to maturity for backcrossing (if the hybrids survive). Whereas negative results (inviable or sterile hybrids) are absolute, positive results (fertile hybrids) are inconclusive; consequently, attention must be directed to possible premating isolating mechanisms.

Experimental analysis of premating isolation has been largely restricted to ethological isolation, which can be tested effectively by a variety of discrimination trials. The design of such tests depends on whether the presence (or absence) of isolation alone or the underlying mechanism is to be determined. The neurophysiological investigation of sensory receptor characteristics also can provide information about peripheral discrimination and filtering (Frishkopf and Goldstein, 1963; Sachs, 1964; Schmidt, 1964), while more general reactions—such as the galvanic skin response (Strother, 1962; Weiss and Strother, 1965) and the evoked vocal response (Capranica, 1965) of Anura—may provide clues about central mechanisms of discrimination.

The previously mentioned laboratory selection studies on *Drosophila* have provided the only direct data on the evolution of ethological isolation, but the underlying mechanisms of isolation have not been determined.

FIELD EXPERIMENTS

For the study of postmating isolation, it is possible to produce viable, fertile hybrids in a controlled laboratory environment, but it is their relative survival under natural or near-natural conditions and in association with parental species that can provide meaningful information about hybrid success. This problem can be resolved only by producing quantities of hybrids, releasing them into quasi-natural environments, and then studying their survival in relation to that of the parental species. Twitty (1961, 1964, 1966) has shown the great potential of such experiments.

For factors determining premating isolation, artificially sympatric populations may be established with stocks from allopatric areas and their interactions followed through time as suggested by Bossert (1963) and Blair (1964) and as already initiated in newts by Davis and Twitty (1964). The effects of modified releasers that operate as key ethological isolating mechanisms in otherwise natural populations can also provide valuable data on reproductive isolation (Smith, 1966).

ISOLATING MECHANISMS IN SYMPATRIC SPECIES

POSTMATING ISOLATION

At present the picture is a variable one, and, apparently, effective isolation of the postmating type may or may not be present (Perdeck, 1958; Stebbins, 1958; Alexander, 1962a; Ehrman, 1962; Blair, 1964; Twitty, 1964; Walker, 1964). But this generalization is based largely on laboratory-reared hybrids, and the real test depends on studies of their survival (and that of the F_2 or backcross progeny) in the field, as carried out by Twitty (1961, 1964, 1966) with newts (*Taricha*). In sympatric species, reproductive isolation seldom, if ever, depends on postmating mechanisms. ". . . it seems that premating factors are generally so well developed that it is unusual to find a case [in anurans] where postmating isolation functions to any significant degree, although it may often have the potential of doing so" (Mecham, 1961:48). While the presence of postmating isolation would make the speciation virtually absolute, there is no reason to suggest that species cannot coexist over very long periods purely through the action of efficient premating isolation (Perdeck, 1958; Twitty, 1964).

PREMATING ISOLATION

Field and laboratory analyses of premating isolation in closely related species indicate that, although there may be several partly effective mechanisms with additive effects, there is generally one principal factor (which, in animals, is usually ethological isolation) and, in turn, only one particular component of behavior providing the absolute specificity, thus reducing the isolation to a simple releaser-response system (Perdeck, 1958; Davis and Twitty, 1964; Littlejohn, 1965; Lloyd, 1966; Smith, 1966).

The mating-call appears to be a major premating isolating mechanism in anuran amphibians (Blair, 1964), and calls of a number of congeneric sympatric species groups have been analyzed and compared (e.g., Blair, 1956, 1958b; Littlejohn, 1959; Littlejohn and Main, 1959; Fouquette, 1960; Barrio, 1964). In many cases the signals are strikingly distinct, differing in several components; only an intensive program of call synthesis and discrimination tests will enable the determination of the critical information-bearing components. In other situations the calls of closely related sympatric species are very similar, differing mainly in a single component—often the pulse-repetition rate. Thus, the specificity must reside in this characteristic, and these situations appear to be more attractive for initial experimental analysis. In such cases, the pulse rates differ by a factor of about two or more (Tables 3 and 4), and there is no overlap in the ranges of variation; rather, there is a distinct gap between the converging extremes (Littlejohn, 1965).

A similar situation exists in the calling songs of crickets (Tables 5 and 6). In general, the differences in pulse rate are not as great as in anurans, but, again, there is no overlap in the ranges of variation (Walker, 1964). Where the pulse rates are similar, the calls may differ qualitatively or quantitatively in that there is an additional characteristic—note repetition rate. The effectiveness of pulse rates in determining specificity of female response to male calling songs in tree crickets (*Oecanthus*) has been worked out in detail by Walker (1957) through use of natural and synthetic signals.

In his studies on flash communication in fireflies of the genus *Photinus,* Lloyd (1966) showed by the use of artificial signals that the most distinctive features of flashes by males of sympatric species pairs—such as pulse duration, pulse interval, and pulse number—were used by females to discriminate. He also demonstrated that the female's delay-time in answering is critical. In general, the quantitative differences between signals of these species pairs were of the order of 2 to 4.

In analyzing premating reproductive isolation in four species of Arctic gulls (*Larus*) that are sympatric in various combinations, Smith (1966), by modifying eye-ring color was able to determine the effect of eye contrast against the white heads of the gulls. He found this ethological factor to be the major one on which reproductive isolation depended, being involved both in the initiation (female discrimination) and maintenance (male discrimination) of homospecific

TABLE 3 Comparisons of Pulse Rates in Mating Calls of Sympatric Congeneric Species of Anurans

Species	Environmental Temperature (°C)	Pulse Rate (pulses/sec)	Approximate Pulse Ratio	Comments and Reference
Hyla chrysoscelis [a]	18	39	2:1	From calls recorded in a sympatric chorus and used by Littlejohn *et al.* (1960) for discrimination trials.
H. versicolor		20		
Hyla verreauxi	10	138	2:1	Mean values for western sympatric samples (Littlejohn, 1965).
H. ewingi		61		
Neobatrachus centralis	21	35	2:1	From two individuals recorded in sympatric chorus 7 miles south of Ouyen, Victoria, Australia (Littlejohn, unpublished).
N. pictus		18		
Scaphiopus bombifrons	18	40.8–55.5	2:1–3:1	Recorded in a sympatric chorus (Blair, 1955b).
S. hammondi		17.7–19.0		

[a] Referred to as "fast triller" by Littlejohn *et al.* (1960).

TABLE 4 Mating Call Characteristics (Means and Ranges in Approximate Figures) of Four Species of *Pseudacris* at Water Temperatures around 16°C. [Based on Data from Crenshaw and Blair (1959) and Michaud (1964); nomenclature of Schwartz (1957)]

Taxon	Pulse Rate (pulses/sec)	Dominant Frequency (cycles/sec)	Call Duration (seconds)
P. clarki	60 (47–75)	3,100 (2,520–3,900)	0.28 (0.18–0.36)
P. t. triseriata	12 (10–15)	3,200 (2,700–3,850)	1.08 (0.70–1.40)
P. t. feriarum	43 (37–50)	2,752 (2,150–3,000)	0.62 (0.37–0.91)
P. nigrita	11 (9–13)	3,212 (2,950–3,500)	0.82 (0.45–1.05)

TABLE 5 Characteristics of Calling Songs of Two Pairs of Sympatric Species of Ground Crickets (genus *Nemobius*) at about 26 °C. *N. melodius* and *N. carolinus* Are Sibling Species; *N. confusus* and *N. maculatus* Are of Different Subgenera. [Data from Alexander (1967)]

Species	Pulse Rate (pulse/sec)	Carrier Frequency (cycles/sec)	Note-Repetition Rate (notes/sec)
N. melodius	34–39	5,650–6,150	–
N. carolinus	≈75	≈5,800	–[a]
N. confusus	60	6,200	1
N. maculatus	48	6,000	6

[a] Partial envelope modulation at 6 to 12 per second.

TABLE 6 Characteristics of Calling Songs of Sympatric Tree Crickets (genus *Oecanthus*) at 23–25 °C. [Data from Walker (1957)]

Habitat	Species	Pulse Rate (pulses/sec)	Carrier Frequency (cycles/sec)
Weedy Fields	*O. quadripunctatus*	38	3,600
	O. argentinus	44	3,500
	O. nigricornis	64	3,700
Deciduous Trees	*O. niveus* [a]	50	2,600
	O. anguistipennis	53	2,600
	O. exclamations	80	2,600

[a] Note-repetition rate, 2.7 notes per second.

pairs. Heterospecific pairs could be readily established by changing eye-ring colors by the application of paint.

THE STATUS OF ALLOPATRIC POPULATIONS

POSTMATING ISOLATION

An assessment of postmating isolation may be made through natural or forced mating, or by artificial fertilization. If the experimental cross fails (despite the use of good, controlled experimental techniques), the populations are clearly, in the absence of linking intermediates, specifically distinct. If laboratory-raised hybrids (or their subsequent F_2 or backcross progeny) are fertile, the only way an unequivocal answer can be obtained is through following their survival under near-natural field conditions. In this way Twitty (1961, 1964, 1966) achieved considerable success with disjunct allopatric species of newts (*Taricha rivularis* and *T. torosa*) in which there was no apparent reduction in the success of the hybrids or their subsequent progeny.

Blair (1962) has discussed examples of the handling of disjunct anuran populations at different levels of divergence. *In vitro* crossing of apparently continuously distributed and conspecific populations has sometimes revealed high levels of genetic incompatibility, thus raising interesting and important problems in speciation (Moore, 1946). In other cases, where the distributions were discontinuous, new species have been recognized (Moore, 1954).

PREMATING ISOLATION

The characteristics of presumed potential mechanisms of premating isolation may be compared with those of related sympatric species. If such characteristics are of the same order of difference, their effectiveness may be presumed adequate, and taxonomic decisions may be made, but with caution (Littlejohn and Martin, 1966). However, the only satisfactory way to measure potential ethological isolation is through experimental analysis using discrimination tests, for these provide direct, objective evidence rather than circumstantial evidence.

Blair and Howard (1944) performed what has almost become a classical study of potential ethological isolation between allopatric stocks of deermice of the *Peromyscus maniculatus–P. polionotus* complex. They employed a multiple-nest-box discrimination system, in which two taxa were tested together for pairing frequencies, and they were able to show that very strong sexual isolation existed between *P. maniculatus blandus* and *P. polionotus leucocephalus,* and strong isolation between *P. m. blandus* and *P. p. albifrons.* Hybrids (*blandus–leucocephalus* and *blandus–albifrons*) were also found to be sexually isolated from the parent *leucocephalus* or *albifrons,* but this isolation was less effective than that between the pure, parental stocks. The particular behavioral factors involved in the isolation were not determined.

Godfrey (1958) made a detailed investigation of reproductive isolation in four races of bank voles of the *Clethrionomys glareolus* complex found on the Scottish mainland (*britannicus*) and three west-coast islands; Rassay (*erica*), Mull (*alstoni*), and Skomer (*skomeriensis*). While trials in which males were simultaneously offered estrous females in equal but excessive numbers of their own and another population indicated selective intrapopulational insemination ($P < 0.03$), Godfrey decided to use a more objective technique. Male discrimination of odors produced by estrous females then was tested in a two-choice Y-olfactometer using combinations of the various disjunct populations as well as some hybrids. He found in the combinations of races tested that the males of each race of *Clethrionomys* approached a female of their own kind in preference to an alternative. Hybrids were discriminated against, but did not themselves discriminate significantly between hybrid and parental types.

In attempting to assess hybrid inviability and breakdown, Godfrey found that matings between races produced more frequent and larger litters, showing that hybrid embryos survived better in the uterus than did the young produced by intrarace matings. The hybrids also had a better chance, once born, of reaching weaning, but this vigor was lost soon after weaning, and from then on they were less viable. When mated with one another, hybrids produced more frequent litters than did their parental types when mated intraracially. But the F_2 hybrids and backcross progeny had an even lower chance of survival than the F_1 hybrids.

Blair and Littlejohn (1960) used a two-choice discrimination apparatus to test the potential isolating value of the slightly differentiated mating calls of two closely related, disjunct allopatric species of chorus frogs, *Pseudacris streckeri* and *P. ornata,* on *P. streckeri* females. Although the dominant frequencies of the representative test calls differed by only about 500 cycles per second (being very similar in other respects), the females strongly discriminated against the *P. ornata* calls and moved towards the homospecific signals.

Three species of chorus frogs of the *Pseudacris triseriata* complex have an interesting distribution pattern in the southern United States. One wide-ranging taxon, *P. triseriata,* is sympatric with *P. clarki* in the western part of its range, and with *P. nigrita* in the East (Mecham, 1961). Mating calls of the western sympatric pair have been described by Michaud (1964), and those of the eastern pair by Crenshaw and Blair (1959). Geographic distribution and details of call structure are summarized in Figure 3 and Table 4. It can be seen that the call structure of the extreme populations of *P. triseriata* (as *P. t. triseriata* in the West and *P. t. feriarum* in the East) differ markedly in pulse rates; they are slow in the range of the fast-pulsed calls of *P. clarki* and fast in the range of the slow-pulsed calls of *P. nigrita.* If these relationships and distributions are correct, then the extreme call types of *P. triseriata* are as different as the calls of the

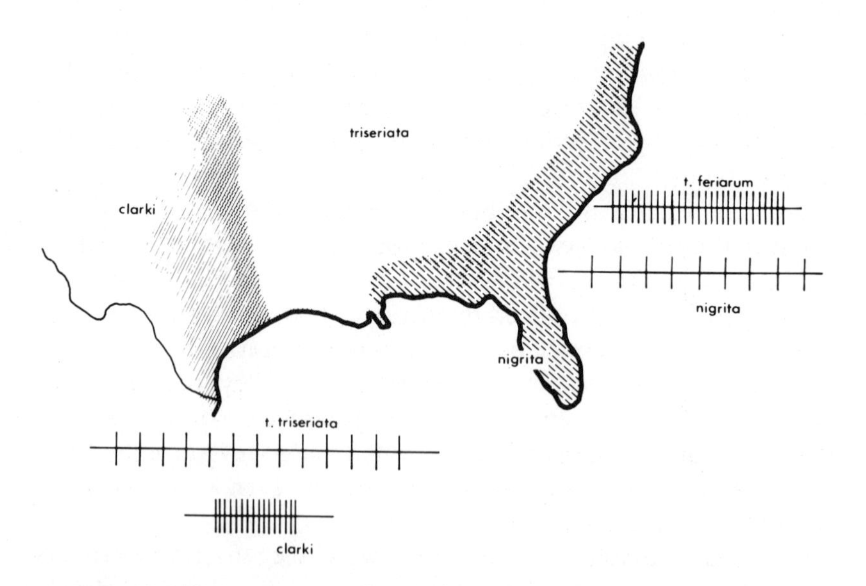

FIGURE 3 Geographic ranges (based on Mecham, 1961) and approximate mating-call durations and pulse rates (from Table 4, this paper) of three species of chorus frogs (genus *Pseudacris*) in southern United States.

sympatric populations. In addition, calls of western *P. triseriata* are very similar to those of eastern *P. nigrita.*

Littlejohn (1960) tested the discriminatory ability of western sympatric females of *P. triseriata* and found that they discriminated against calls of their presumed conspecific eastern counterpart (*P. t. feriarum*), but were unable to distinguish between western *P. triseriata* calls and eastern *P. nigrita* calls. Published results of all discrimination trials carried out on the complex are summarized in Table 7.

Ideally, stocks from two disjunct allopatric populations under consideration should be placed together in a suitable natural environment and their interactions followed over several generations (Davis and Twitty, 1964; Blair, 1964).

TABLE 7 Results of Call-Discrimination Trials in Chorus Frogs (genus *Pseudacris*). Data from Littlejohn (1960) and Michaud (1962); Nomenclature Based on Schwartz (1957). In These Laboratory Experiments, Sexually Reactive Female Frogs Were Placed in a Rectangular Enclosure and Offered the Choice of Two Sound Stimuli—the Recorded Mating Call of a Male of the Same Taxon and That of Another Taxon—Played through Two Small Loudspeakers, One at Each End of the Enclosure. A *Contact* Was Scored if a Frog Approached or Touched One of the Loudspeakers. [See Littlejohn and Michaud (1959) for a full description of the apparatus and technique.]

Female (number tested)	Male Mating Call	Type of Contact [a] 1	2	3	4	Total Contacts
P. clarki	*P. clarki*	5	6	15	13 [b]	39
(4)	*P. t. triseriata* [c]	1	1	3	0	5
P. t. triseriata [c]	*P. t. triseriata* [c]	1	6	17	5 [b]	29
(6)	*P. clarki*	0	2	5	0	7
P. t. triseriata	*P. t. triseriata*	2	0	12	8	22
(4)	*P. t. feriarum*	0	1	0	0	1
P. t. triseriata	*P. t. triseriata*	1	1	3	6	11
(3)	*P. nigrita*	0	0	4	6	10

[a] Arranged in order of presumed increasing intensity of response; see Littlejohn (1960).
[b] Contact types 4 and 5 of Michaud (1962) combined.
[c] Referred to as *P. nigrita* by Michaud (1962).

DETECTION OF CRYPTIC SPECIES

Detailed examination of isolating mechanisms often reveals discontinuities that reflect heterogeneity within a conventionally recognized single "species"; and this in turn leads to the detection of one or several sibling or cryptic species (*sensu* Walker, 1964; those not initially recognized by traditional visual taxonomic procedures). These cryptic species usually cease being "morphologically indistinguishable" after being subjected to detailed structural analysis. It is now becoming apparent that cryptic species are quite common in those groups using nonvisual sensory modes for ethological isolation, and numerous examples are known from relatively well-worked taxa (Alexander, 1962 a and b; Blair, 1962, 1964; Mayr, 1963; Walker, 1964).

ISOLATING MECHANISMS AND PHYLOGENY

One may ask whether the study of isolating mechanisms is likely to be of any assistance in the construction of phylogenies. Since premating isolating mechanisms are the most distinctive characteristics of closely related sympatric species, it would at first seem highly inappropriate to use them in establishing affinities. Marler (1957) has pointed out the dangers of using specific releasers in phylogenetic studies, but Alexander (1957) considers that, even so, calling songs of closely related orthopterans often have the same basic structure and hence are of phyletic value. Mating calls of anurans have also been used in this regard (Blair, 1962; Littlejohn, 1959), but it is clear that the conclusions should be supported by other kinds of evidence.

Because postmating isolation can arise only incidentally (Mecham, 1961) and appears to have a polygenic basis, the degree of developmental incompatibility may provide one of the best measures of the over-all degree of genetic differentiation (Blair, 1962; Hubbs and Drewry, 1959). Such information would thus be of considerable value in establishing levels of divergence and relationship, particularly within a genus.

REFERENCES

Alexander, R. D. 1957. The song relationships of four species of ground crickets (Orthoptera: Gryllidae: *Nemobius*). Ohio J. Sci. 57:153–163.

Alexander, R. D. 1962a. The role of behavioral study in cricket classification. Syst. Zool. 11:53–72.

Alexander, R. D. 1962b. Evolutionary change in cricket acoustical communication. Evolution 16:443–467.

Ball, R. W., and D. L. Jameson. 1966. Premating isolating mechanisms in sympatric and allopatric *Hyla regilla* and *Hyla californiae*. Evolution 20:533–551.

Barrio, A. 1964. Especies crípticas del género *Pleurodema* que conviven en una misma area, identificadas por el canto nupcial (Anura, Leptodactylidae). Physis 24:471–489.

Bigelow, R. S. 1965. Hybrid zones and reproductive isolation. Evolution 19:449–458.

Blair, W. F. 1955a. Mating call and stage of speciation in the *Microhyla olivacea–M. carolinensis* complex. Evolution 9:469–480.

Blair, W. F. 1955b. Differentiation of mating call in spadefoots, genus *Scaphiopus*. Texas J. Sci. 7:183–188.

Blair, W. F. 1956. Call difference as an isolation mechanism in Southwestern toads (genus *Bufo*). Texas J. Sci. 8:87–106.

Blair, W. F. 1958a. Mating call in the speciation of anuran amphibians. Am. Natur. 92:27–51.

Blair, W. F. 1958b. Call difference as an isolation mechanism in Florida species of hylid frogs. Quart. J. Florida Acad. Sci. 21:32–48.

Blair, W. F. 1962. Non-morphological data in anuran classification. Syst. Zool. 11:72–84.

Blair, W. F. 1964. Isolating mechanisms and interspecies interactions in anuran amphibians. Quart. Rev. Biol. 39:334–344.

Blair, W. F., and W. E. Howard. 1944. Experimental evidence of sexual isolation between three forms of mice of the cenospecies *Peromyscus maniculatus*. Contrib. Lab. Vert. Biol. Univ. Michigan 26:1–19.

Blair, W. F., and M. J. Littlejohn. 1960. Stage of speciation of two allopatric populations of chorus frogs (*Pseudacris*). Evolution 14:82–87.

Bossert, W. H. 1963. Simulation of character displacement in animals. PhD thesis, Harvard University, Cambridge, Mass.

Brown, W. L., and E. O. Wilson. 1956. Character displacement. Syst. Zool. 5:49–64.

Capranica, R. R. 1965. The evoked vocal response of the bullfrog. MIT Res. Monog. 33. 110 p.

Crenshaw, J. W., and W. F. Blair. 1959. Relationships in the *Pseudacris nigrita* complex in southwestern Georgia. Copeia 1959(3):215–222.

Davis, W. C., and V. C. Twitty. 1964. Courtship behavior and reproductive isolation in the species of *Taricha* (Amphibia, Caudata). Copeia 1964(4):601–610.

Dobzhansky, T. 1951. Genetics and the origin of species. 3rd ed., Columbia University Press, New York. 364 p.

Dobzhansky, T., and P. C. Koller. 1938. An experimental study of sexual isolation in *Drosophila.* Biol. Zentr. 58:589–607.

Ehrman, L. 1962. Hybrid sterility as an isolating mechanism in the genus *Drosophila.* Quart. Rev. Biol. 37:279–302.

Ehrman, L. 1964. Courtship and mating behavior as a reproductive isolating mechanism in *Drosophila.* Am. Zool. 4:147–153.

Ehrman, L. 1965. Direct observation of sexual isolation between allopatric and between sympatric strains of the different *Drosophila paulistorum* races. Evolution 19:459–464.

Fouquette, M. J. 1960. Isolating mechanisms in three sympatric treefrogs in the Canal Zone. Evolution 14:484–497.

Frishkopf, L. S., and M. H. Goldstein. 1963. Responses to acoustic stimuli from single units in the eighth nerve of the bullfrog. J. Acoust. Soc. Am. 35:1219–1228.

Godfrey, J. 1958. The origin of sexual isolation between bank voles. Proc. Roy. Phys. Soc. Edinburgh 27:47–55.

Grant, V., 1963. The origin of adaptations. Columbia University Press, New York. 606 p.

Grant, V. 1966. The selective origin of incompatibility barriers in the plant genus *Gilia.* Am. Natur. 100:99–118.

Hubbs, C. L. 1961. Isolating mechanisms in the speciation of fishes, p. 5–23 *In* W. F. Blair [ed] Vertebrate speciation. University of Texas Press, Austin.

Hubbs, C. L., and E. A. Delco. 1962. Courtship preferences of *Gambusia affinis* associated with the sympatry of parental populations. Copeia 1962(2):396–400.

Hubbs, C. L., and G. E. Drewry. 1959. Survival of F_1 hybrids between cyprinodont fishes, with a discussion of the correlation between hybridization and phylogenetic relationship. Inst. Marine Sci. 6:81–91.

Kessler, S. 1966. Selection for and against ethological isolation between *Drosophila pseudoobscura* and *Drosophila persimilis.* Evolution 20:634–645.

Knight, G. R., A. Robertson, and C. H. Waddington. 1956. Selection for sexual isolation within a species. Evolution 10:14–22.

Koopman, K. F. 1950. Natural selection for reproductive isolation between *Drosophila pseudoobscura* and *Drosophila persimilis.* Evolution 4:135–148.

Koref-Santibanez, S., and C. H. Waddington. 1958. The origin of isolation between different lines within a species. Evolution 12:485–493.

Littlejohn, M. J. 1959. Call differentiation in a complex of seven species of *Crinia* (Anura, Leptodactylidae). Evolution 13:452–468.

Littlejohn, M. J. 1960. Call discrimination and potential reproductive isolation in *Pseudacris triseriata* females from Oklahoma. Copeia 1960(4):370–371.

Littlejohn, M. J. 1965. Premating isolation in the *Hyla ewingi* complex (Anura:Hylidae). Evolution 19:234–243.

Littlejohn, M. J., M. J. Fouquette, and C. Johnson. 1960. Call discrimination by female frogs of the *Hyla versicolor* complex. Copeia 1960(1):47–49.

Littlejohn, M. J., and A. R. Main. 1959. Call structure in two genera of Australian burrowing frogs. Copeia 1959(3):266–270.

Littlejohn, M. J., and A. A. Martin. 1966. A new species of *Crinia* (Anura: Leptodactylidae) from South Australia. Copeia 1965(3):319–324.

Littlejohn, M. J., and T. C. Michaud. 1959. Mating call discrimination by females of Strecker's chorus frog (*Pseudacris Streckeri*). Texas J. Sci. 11:86–92.

Lloyd, J. E. 1966. Studies on the flash communication system in *Photinus* fireflies. Misc. Pub. Mus. Zool. Univ. Michigan. 130. 95 p.

Marler, P. 1957. Specific distinctiveness in the communication signals of birds. Behaviour 11:13–39.

Marler, P. 1960. Bird songs and mate selection, p. 348–367 *In* W. E. Lanyon and W. N. Tavolga [ed] Animal sounds and communication. American Institute of Biological Sciences Pub. 7.

Mayr, E. 1963. Animal species and evolution. Belknap Press of Harvard University Press, Cambridge, Massachusetts. 797 p.

Mecham, J. S. 1961. Isolating mechanisms in anuran amphibians, p. 24–61 *In* W. F. Blair [ed] Vertebrate speciation. University of Texas Press, Austin.

Meise, W. 1928. Die verbreitung der Aaskrähe (Formenkreis *Corvus corone* L.). J. Ornithol. 76:1–203.

Michaud, T. C. 1962. Call discrimination by females of the chorus frogs, *Pseudacris clarki* and *Pseudacris nigrita.* Copeia 1962(1):213–215.

Michaud, T. C. 1964. Vocal variation in two species of chorus frogs, *Pseudacris nigrita* and *Pseudacris clarki,* in Texas. Evolution 18:498–506.

Moore, J. A. 1946. Incipient intraspecific isolating mechanisms in *Rana pipiens.* Genetics 31:304–326.

Moore, J. A. 1954. Geographic and genetic isolation in Australian Amphibia. Am. Natur. 88:65–74.

Moore, J. A. 1957. An embryologist's view of the species concept, p. 325–338 *In* E. Mayr [ed] The species problem. American Association for the Advancement of Science. Pub. 50.

Muller, H. J. 1942. Isolating mechanisms, evolution and temperature. Biol. Symp. 6:71–125.

Perdeck, A. C. 1958. The isolating value of specific song patterns in two sibling species of grasshoppers (*Chorthippus brunneus* Thunb. and *C. biguttulus* L.). Behaviour 12:1–75.

Robson, G. C., and O. W. Richards. 1936. The variation of animals in nature. Longmans, Green and Co., London. 425 p.

Sachs, M. B. 1964. Responses to acoustic stimuli from single units in the eighth nerve of the green frog. J. Acoust. Soc. Am. 36:1956–1958.

Schmidt, R. S. 1964. Hearing and responses to calls in anurans. Behaviour 23:280–293.

Schwartz, A. 1957. Chorus frogs (*Pseudacris nigrita* Le Conte) in South Carolina. Am. Mus. Novit. 1838:1–12.

Sibley, C. G. 1957. The evolutionary and taxonomic significance of sexual dimorphism and hybridization in birds. Condor 59:166–191.

Sibley, C. G. 1961. Hybridization and isolating mechanisms, p. 69–88 *In* W. F. Blair [ed] Vertebrate speciation. University of Texas Press, Austin.

Smith, N. G. 1966. Evolution in some Arctic gulls (*Larus*): An experimental study of isolating mechanisms. Am. Ornithol. Union Ornithol. Monogr. 4:1–99.

Stebbins, G. L. 1958. The inviability, weakness, and sterility of interspecific hybrids. Adv. Genet. 9:147–215.

Stebbins, G. L. 1966. Processes of organic evolution. Prentice-Hall, Englewood Cliffs, New Jersey. 191 p.

Strother, W. F. 1962. Hearing in frogs. J. Auditory Res. 2:279–286.

Thoday, J. M., and J. B. Gibson. 1962. Isolation by disruptive selection. Nature 193:1164–1166.

Twitty, V. C. 1961. Second-generation hybrids of the species of *Taricha.* Proc. Nat. Acad. Sci. U.S. 47:1461–1486.

Twitty, V. C. 1964. Fertility of *Taricha* species-hybrids and viability of their offspring. Proc. Nat. Acad. Sci. U.S. 51:156–161.

Twitty, V. C. 1966. Of scientists and salamanders. W. H. Freeman, San Francisco and London. 178 p.

Volpe, E. P. 1955. Intensity of reproductive isolation between sympatric and allopatric populations of *Bufo americanus* and *Bufo fowleri.* Am. Natur. 89:303–317.

Walker, T. J. 1957. Specificity in the response of female tree crickets (Orthoptera, Gryllidae, Oecanthinae) to calling songs of the males. Ann. Entomol. Soc. Am. 50:626–636.

Walker, T. J. 1964. Cryptic species among sound-producing ensiferan Orthoptera (Gryllidae and Tettigoniidae). Quart. Rev. Biol. 39:345–355.

Wallace, B. 1954. Genetic divergence of isolated populations of *Drosophila melanogaster.* Proc. IX Int. Congr. Genet., Caryologia 6(Suppl.):761–764.

Weiss, B. A., and W. F. Strother. 1965. Hearing in the green treefrog (*Hyla cinerea cinerea*). J. Auditory Res. 5:297–305.

Wilson, E. O. 1965. The challenge from related species, p. 7–27 *In* H. G. Baker, and G. L. Stebbins [ed] The genetics of colonizing species. Academic Press, New York.

Discussion

W. Frank Blair

It is difficult to add anything to Dr. Littlejohn's thorough discussion of the systematic significance of isolating mechanisms. His concepts and mine are so similar that I find no major point of disagreement that could lead to a good argument.

I believe, however, that one aspect of isolating mechanisms deserves emphasis stronger than that given it by Dr. Littlejohn. I refer to the concept that systems of premating isolating mechanisms operative at any particular place and time appear to be delicately adjusted combinations of various mechanisms that individually would be effective only incompletely. This being the case, it follows that such systems–in equilibrium with the parameters of the local ecosystem–must have come into existence through selection on the component parts to produce these delicately balanced combinations of mechanisms.

The delicacy of balance of such systems is indicated by the ease with which interspecific hybridization may be brought about by a major environmental change, such as the building of a fish hatchery (in the cases of *Bufo woodhousei* × *B. valliceps; Hyla cinerea* × *H. gratiosa*) or general human exploitation of the ecosystem (in the cases of *B. woodhousei* × *B. americanus; Gastrophryne olivacea* × *G. carolinensis*). None of these or other examples of interspecific hybridization has been followed over a long period of years to determine whether the system is coming back into balance. I suspect that this is the reason why the rather extensive hybridization between *B. woodhousei* and *B. americanus,* for example, has failed to obliterate the rather distinct differences separating these sympatric species. One of the most interesting and potentially significant projects I can think of would be to follow selected examples of any one of these hybridizing pairs through a considerable number of generations.

The kinds of complexes of isolating mechanisms to which I refer are exemplified by the mechanisms that have evolved where *B. woodhousei* occurs with various other species (as elucidated by the work of A. P. Blair, W. A. Thornton, E. P. Volpe, and others, and by my own work). Three examples are well known to me from first-hand experience. In all of them, difference in mating call (referred to by Dr. Littlejohn) provides the presumably paramount isolating mechanism, although in some anurans and, in fact, in some species of *Bufo,* the mating call has been lost or is vestigial; and if there is a paramount isolating mechanism in these animals it is wholly unknown. The three examples I will discuss concern *B. woodhousei* with (1) *B. americanus;* (2) *B. microscaphus;* and (3) *B. valliceps.*

1. *B. woodhousei* in broad sympatry with *B. americanus* over much of the eastern United States. I know this sympatric pair best in eastern Oklahoma, where there is considerable temporal separation but also an overlapping of breeding seasons, with *B. americanus* tending to breed earlier and at colder temperatures than *B. woodhousei.* Males of the former species usually call—and breeding occurs—along the small headwater creeks; males of the latter species tend to call from the shores of large rivers or from floodplain rainpools. On the floodplain of a creek, pure choruses of the two species may occur only a few hundred feet apart and within easy hearing distance. The mating calls differ greatly in duration and rate, although the basic structure is quite similar. They differ more under sympatry than under allopatry, as I have suggested in an earlier publication. Mating calls of hybrid males are intermediate in character between those of the parental species.

2. *B. woodhousei* in sympatry with *B. microscaphus* in southwestern Utah. Here again, *B. woodhousei* breeds along the larger streams and in floodplain pools. *B. microscaphus,* like *B. americanus,* breeds along small, tributary streams, but it also breeds in impoundments along these streams. Differences in the mating call of the two species occur in both rate and duration, but they are greatest in the rate. In this arid region, where the breeding season of both species is independent of rainfall, there seems to be no sharply definable temporal isolation of the two species. As in the first example, the mating calls of the hybrids are intermediate between those of the parental species.

3. *B. woodhousei* in sympatry with *B. valliceps* in central Texas. Here, *B. woodhousei* is the earlier breeder and is tolerant of colder temperatures. There tends to be separation of breeding choruses except in disturbed situations, but the basis for this separation is elusive. The calls are very different in structure as well as in rate, and the calls of hybrids are very deficient in comparison with the intermediate, but forceful, calls of hybrids between members of the other pairs, which involve closely related species. In the case of *B. woodhousei* and *B. valliceps,* the postmating isolating mechanism of genetic incompatibility is almost completely effective; however, in the two earlier examples, which involve members of the same species group, viability and fertility of the hybrids are reduced only moderately.

The interspecific hybridization in all three of these examples has been attributed to environmental disturbance by man and the consequent disturbance of delicately balanced systems of isolating mechanisms.

From a purely taxonomic viewpoint, hybridizing populations cannot be allocated as to stage of speciation without intensive field investigations of the dynamics of the situation. As Dr. Littlejohn has stated so well, the spectrum of possibilities ranges from breakdown of isolating mechanisms to reinforcement of incompletely effective components of the isolating-mechanism complex. Questions concerning relationships of such populations cannot be answered in the museum; they must be answered in terms of the relationships of the living individuals of the respective populations with one another in the field.

Discussion

Eviatar Nevo

I will confine my comments to the problem of the origin of premating isolating mechanisms.

Basically, I accept Dr. Littlejohn's illuminating summary of the processes that generate isolating mechanisms. Both incidental and direct factors may be involved; and the contention, as I see it, is quantitative rather than qualitative. Dr. Littlejohn presented the case of reinforcement in establishing premating isolating mechanisms. I propose to reinforce the contributions of incidental factors to this process.

I will illustrate several operational propositions by the example of the cricket frogs, genus *Acris.* This case of supposed reinforcement (Blair, 1958) was restudied during 1965 and 1966 in collaboration with Dr. R. R. Capranica and Dr. W. H. Bossert, in regard to the variation and significance of the mating call. Although reinforcement of the mating call in sympatry may be involved in this case, in our study it was found that processes incidental to adaptive differentiation in body size in allopatry are the main factors contributing to call variation.

1. The main task ahead is to quantify the various categories in Dr. Littlejohn's scheme summarizing the ways in which isolating mechanisms arise. Quantification should start intraspecifically within populations of each partner of a species pair. Knowledge of geographic variation of the isolating mechanisms studied is indispensable for an assessment of their origin. It is highly probable that ethological factors, like anuran mating calls, will vary clinally along ecological gradients as incidental to adaptive differentiation in body size. I strongly suspect that widely ranging species will display increasing reproductive isolation with distance, as demonstrated by our work in *Acris,* and by the work of Patterson and Stone (1952) in *Drosophila.*

2. A multidirectional approach is advisable in the study of the origin of isolating mechanisms. After the complex of isolating mechanisms is clarified, a principal factor should be sought. The anuran mating call provides a perfect illustration. All the techniques outlined by Dr. Littlejohn should be employed first intraspecifically and later interspecifically. The effectiveness of the call as an isolating mechanism should be studied through female discrimination tests in the field, supplemented by neurophysiological tests in the laboratory. The testing of females in the field, rather than in laboratory tanks would avoid technical pitfalls and permit a populational approach. Synthetic calls may help to pinpoint the call parameter(s) by which females discriminate among males. The genetical component of the call may be deciphered by the conditioning of tadpoles and froglets in the laboratory to calls of different populations. Finally, artificial sympatry (Bossert, 1963; Blair, 1964) may provide the decisive test of the effectiveness of the call as an isolating mechanism.

3. The kinds of isolating mechanisms and their sequence of appearance and effectiveness vary within and between groups. Awbrey (1965) experimentally substantiated that the anuran mating call ranges from highly effective to noneffective as an isolating mechanism in different species. Alternative mechanisms operate whenever the call is ineffective, and vice versa. Hence, predictive models of the mating call as an isolating mechanism are possible only if direct female discrimination tests provide matrices for the model. I will illustrate the application of the above propositions by citing some of the results of our work in *Acris.*

The cricket frogs, *Acris crepitans* and *A. gryllus* are currently recognized as closely related sibling species of terrestrial hylids. *A. crepitans* ranges widely over the central and eastern United States, whereas *A. gryllus* is restricted to Florida and the lowlands from eastern Louisiana to southeastern Virginia. Both share a broad overlap zone in the southeastern United States, but there is no distinct interbreeding despite interfertility (Mecham, 1964). Interfertility up to F_1 has been established for widely separated populations of *A. crepitans* (Nevo, unpublished observations). Since both species have the same breeding season, and there is no spatial separation where they coexist, Mecham (1964) suggested that mating-call discrimination by females is the critical isolating mechanism involved. Earlier, Blair (1958) indicated on evidence then available that call differences are distinct in sympatry but are slight in allopatry, suggesting reinforcement.

Our preliminary results indicate that body size, call parameters, female frequency sensitivities, and female sexual response vary geographically between allopatric populations of *A. crepitans.* To assess the geographic variation in body size, three collecting transects were made. These transects comprised 119 localities in which 3,251 males were sampled. Body size of males range from 22 mm in humid Alabama (55 in. of rainfall) to 27.5 mm in arid western Texas (15 in. of rainfall). The drier the region, the larger the males, a condition reflecting adaptive differentiation.

Next, mating calls of 393 males were tape-recorded in 46 localities. Nine populations were singled out for preliminary call analysis. Both spectral and temporal patterns of the call vary as a function of male body size. The small Alabama males of *A. crepitans* have high spectral peaks (dominant frequencies) of 4,092 cps, a high click rate of 3.58 per second, and a short call duration of 12 seconds. Contrariwise, the males of western Texas, which are larger, have lower spectral peaks of 3,027 cps, a lower click rate of 2.05 per second, and a longer call of 21 seconds. The two extremes are connected by clinal intermediates. Sympatric *A. gryllus* in Alabama is 22.1 mm long, has a spectral peak of 3,593 cps, a click rate of 3.06 per second, and a call duration of 12.3 seconds. Thus intraspecific call variation of allopatric populations of *A. crepitans* is greater than *A. crepitans*–*A. gryllus* differences in sympatry. The fine temporal pattern of the call is also subject to geographic variation. "Clicking" with only slight audible pulsing characterizes western and central populations of *A. crepitans,* whereas "rattling" due to audible pulsing increases gradually eastward both in allopatric and sympatric populations of *A. crepitans.* The call of *A. gryllus* is click-like in both sympatry and allopatry.

We next tested discrimination by 70 females of *A. crepitans* (from two populations, one sympatric, the other allopatric) of calls of *A. crepitans* males from six allopatric populations. The rate of sexual response of females of *A. crepitans* from Georgia decreased with distance westward. The response of the Georgia females to males of Georgia was 1.0; to those of Alabama 0.67; of Louisiana 0.17; of eastern Texas 0.11; of central Texas 0.00; and of western Texas 0.07. Their response to males of sympatric *A. gryllus* was 0.11, greater than those of the allopatric *A. crepitans* of Texas. A crude estimate of the preference probability distribution in Georgia females, with the unrealistic assumption that spectral peak is the only component of discrimination, gives a mean of 4,000 cps with a standard deviation of 300 cps.

Neurophysiological tests conducted by Capranica and Frishkopf (1966) revealed different frequency sensitivities in females from different populations of *A. crepitans.* These sensitivities are well matched to the spectral distribution of energy in the mating call of the respective males. Electronically generated synthetic calls are being prepared to pinpoint the parameter(s) by which females discriminate male calls.

The variations in body size and mating calls of *A. gryllus* are distinctly less than those of *A. crepitans* due to the former's ecologically more limited range. Slight clinal phenomena that seem to exist in *A. gryllus* are being analyzed. It appears that maximal values of *A. crepitans* and minimal values of *A. gryllus* coexist in sympatry, thus exaggerating the interspecific genotypic differences, which comprise incidental and reinforcement components. Though reinforcement cannot be excluded in this case, it would seem that its relative contribution is small compared with the effects of incidental factors due to adaptive differentiation of body size.

In summary: (1) Incidental and direct origins of ethological isolating mechanisms are not mutually exclusive. (2) Since isolating mechanisms differ within and between groups, the assessment of their respective roles depends on analysis of each specific case;

such analysis should aim at quantitative intraspecific and interspecific differences by a multidirectional approach. (3) *Acris crepitans* illustrates a case in which mating-call differentiation and consequent reproductive isolation are largely incidental products of adaptive differentiation of body size in allopatry. (4) Populations of *A. crepitans* in the extreme western and eastern United States presumably could stand the test of artificial sympatry due to their distinct call differences; this hypothesis could be tested in natural or seminatural environments (Bossert, 1963; Blair, 1964).

REFERENCES

Awbrey, F. 1965. An experimental investigation of effectiveness of anuran mating calls as isolating mechanisms. Dissertation, Department of Zoology, University of Texas, Austin.

Blair, W. F. 1958. Mating call in the speciation of anuran amphibians. Am. Natur. 92(862):27–51.

Blair, W. F. 1964. Evolution at populational and interpopulational levels. Isolating mechanisms and interspecific interactions in anuran amphibians. Quart. Rev. Biol. 39(4):333–344.

Bossert, W. H. 1963. Simulation of character displacement in animals. Dissertation, Division of Engineering and Applied Mathematics, Harvard University, Cambridge, Massachusetts.

Capranica, R. R., and L. S. Frishkopf. 1966. Responses of auditory units in the medulla of the cricket frog. J. Acoust. Soc. Am. 40(5):1263.

Mecham, J. S. 1964. Ecological and genetic relationships of the cricket frogs, genus *Acris* in Alabama. Herpetologica 20(2):84–91.

Patterson, J. T., and W. S. Stone. 1952. Evolution in the genus *Drosophila*. Macmillan, New York.

Discussion

William Bossert

NOTE This discussion was submitted following the conference.

There has been a great deal of discussion here of phylogeny and evolutionary time scales. I would therefore like to reinforce the idea that the reproductive isolating mechanisms among closely related sympatric species can be of more than static discriminatory value. For such species it is possible to introduce a dynamic character to these mechanisms that could sometimes be of value in reconstructing a phylogeny of the group, or at least in placing some limiting time scale on certain evolutionary events.

To be more specific, it can be shown that given a number of assumptions and in the absence of counterselective pressure the rate of reduction in error in selecting a conspecific mate is related largely to the degree of error existing between several species. Most importantly, the rate of reduction is fairly independent of complexity of the mating behavior, relative densities of the various species, and so forth. With this relationship it is possible to reconstruct the pattern of reinforcement of differences in the mating behavior and, particularly, to obtain a limit on the time the species have been sympatric. That is, given the relation governing the rate of reduction in mating error, one can find that time at which the error must have been 50 percent, or mating behavior identical, to account for the current state of the system. It is tempting to use this time as an estimate of the time elapsed from initial contact of the species. Because there usually are difficulties in making assumptions concerning the degree of overlap of ranges through time in cases where sympatry is not complete and the degree of isolation already achieved at time of contact, it is usually inappropriate to use this value as anything more than a limit.

To give an example based on Professor Littlejohn's excellent data on the calls of Australian *Crinia,* I have estimated that *C. parinsignifera* and *C. sloanei* could not have been distinct sympatric species for more than about several tens of thousands of years. *C. signifera* and the *sloanei-parinsignifera* group could not have been distinct sympatric species for more than a little over one million years.

While perhaps not of completely general applicability, I feel this technique could yield meaningful phylogenies, particularly with regard to groups formed through repeated invasions of closed regions.

Informal Discussion

RAVEN: My comments will present a different point of view. If there was ever any doubt about the concept of isolating mechanisms, their crucial evolutionary role, and their systematic usefulness in certain groups of organisms, Dr. Littlejohn's excellent presentation and the related commentaries by Dr. Blair and Dr. Nevo should have dispelled it. They have shown clearly that there is a definite relationship between the basically morphological-geographical units recognized in taxonomic classifications and have shown the reproductive discontinuities existing between them. The sympatric maintenance of differentiated populations, for example, often is an excellent taxonomic criterion.

Despite all this, however, it is not legitimate to regard the isolating mechanisms themselves as an absolute criterion for a species or any other taxonomic category. In practice, we first recognize a discontinuous pattern of variation in nature and then search for genetic or other factors that explain the discontinuities; but the existence of isolating mechanisms does not mean, automatically, that distinctive units exist that would be desirable to recognize taxonomically. This depends entirely upon the pattern of variation exhibited by the group in question and the standards considered appropriate in reflecting the particular pattern taxonomically. In some groups, such as the amphibians, stress is placed on the ethological factors; and ethological differences between populations are often reflected at the species level in formal taxonomy. In other groups, stress is placed on other types of isolation, or purely on the morphological discontinuities that separate series of populations.

Categories such as "species" are best left as units that summarize many kinds of information about the organisms being classified. They should not, in general, be converted into the units of a special classification that stresses only one aspect of evolutionary strategy. To do so would lead to the unfortunate conclusion that all species are, in this respect at least, equivalent. Of course, every student of evolution "knows better." The processes of evolution are so diverse that they obviously do not lead to the production of similar units in all groups of organisms, yet all of these groups must be treated taxonomically, using the same terminology for the categories of classification. Unfortunately, the general scientific public is not so well educated about these matters, and even in the scientific literature we sometimes encounter the notion that all species are equivalent.

Regardless of the criteria used to delimit taxa at any rank, the diversity of situations is so great that the taxonomy cannot convey in a direct form the information on which taxa are based. The fact that some unknown series of populations is called a species tells us only that it is thought to be relatively similar to other species of the same genus but different from them in one or more respects. To discover what is actually known about this series of populations, including what is known about its reproductive isolation, one must turn to the original literature. Regardless of which criteria are used for delimiting species, this will necessarily remain true, even though some knowledge of the criteria employed by taxonomists in particular groups may tell us more.

To propose a universal definition of the category "species" based upon reproductive isolation is to confuse our recognition of discrete units in nature with our perception of the processes involved in the formation of these units. In my opinion, nothing is to be gained by creating such confusion, and probably a great deal is to be lost. Important evolutionary phenomena such as reproductive isolation should be studied in terms of adequate measures of the divergence between populations. They should not be studied in terms of taxonomic units or parataxonomic terms (such as "speciation"), which inevitably involve some degree of distortion and compromise in their formation and thus very often serve to conceal rather than illuminate the actual facts in a particular evolutionary study.

LITTLEJOHN: I would go along with you about reproductive isolation not necessarily being the primary criterion for a general definition of a species, if one is possible. You have not, however, left us anything with which to explain the origin of discontinuity and diversity of life.

RAVEN: It is obvious that reproductive isolation is the basis of discontinuity between the units that we recognize, but we recognize the units and then we look for the reasons for the reproductive discontinuity. I think this is an important difference.

LITTLEJOHN: Many of the species or taxa with which we deal were first recognized on the basis of rather ephemeral ethological isolating mechanisms; we found the isolating mechanism first and then found the species. When we consider uniparental or unisexual species—or populations, clones, groups, aggregations, or whatever they are—they appear to be somewhat discontinuously distributed. Could you suggest how this discontinuity is maintained in asexual or uniparental forms?

RAVEN: I think the trouble lies in the confusion between the processes of evolution, the genetics of population, and the criteria we use for the recognition of particular taxonomic categories. All of these studies are perfectly legitimate, but they should not be tied in with the units of taxonomy which must, by the very existence of assorted kinds of genetic systems, be arbitrary.

GOTTLIEB: I enjoyed your excellent discussion of reproductive isolating barriers among sympatric animal species. Your statement that postmating barriers are not important for them is not true for plants. Among closely related annual plant species, postmating barriers are very common and often take the form of chromosomal structural differences that do not prevent the formation of hybrids but do cause their sterility. Genetically determined barriers that act in the style (i.e., before the engagement of the female gametes) are apparently rare. Self-compatibility and autogamy are widespread among annuals, and since they reduce gene flow, it would be interesting to know if the lack of prezygotic barriers is related to their presence.

Among perennial plant genera such as *Quercus, Pinus, Ceanothus,* and *Arctostaphylos,* the reproductive isolating barriers are not of a genetic sort. Rather, they usually depend on ecological differences or pollinator preferences. Differences in flowering times are probably one of the few common premating barriers operative between sympatric plant species.

The absence of genetically regulated premating barriers in plants has made possible occasional hybridizations and presumably has been extremely important in the evolution of the flowering plants.

RICHARD D. ALEXANDER

Comparative Animal Behavior and Systematics

Behavior is probably the most diverse aspect of the animal phenotype—at least, as William Morton Wheeler (1905) put it, "in the field of possible observation." On this basis alone, behavior should be fascinating to the systematists because they are always looking for characters. Furthermore, among biologists, systematists are, more than any other group, the real students of diversity. Comparison is their chief method of exploration, and the comparative method, of course, depends upon and thrives upon diversity.

On the other hand, to some extent the diversity of behavior results from its being, in general, more directly and probably more complexly related to the genotype than to any other aspect of the phenotype. This particular feature discourages the systematists. They are not interested in getting involved with phenotypic variations that might be due solely to variations in the developmental environment. After all, morphology is troublesome enough in that regard.

Behavior has some other special features. In general, it is more strongly selected—or perhaps I should say more directly selected—than morphology or physiology. By this I mean that in any representation of the chains of cause-effect relationships between gene action and selective action in animals, behavioral characteristics nearly always would be placed directly next to selective action.*

* A botanist asked me abruptly in a phone conversation recently, "What *is* animal behavior, anyhow?" I tried to answer him unhesitatingly, and my reply came out: "Behavior is what animals have interposed between natural selection and the other (morphological and physiological) aspects of their phenotypes." Even with an indefinite amount of reflection, I think it might be difficult to improve on the emphasis in that definition.

The systematist's concern with adaptation should prevent him from passing this off too lightly. On the other hand, behavior is often difficult to document or to communicate to others. As Dr. Wagner stressed in his paper, repeatability is the essence of science, and to many taxonomists this traditionally has meant that morphology alone is sacred. Very little behavior is evidenced by preserved specimens or fossils.

BEHAVIOR AND MAN'S EVOLUTION

The facts I have outlined above suggest some of the problems and possibilities in using behavior to understand the history of life. I think one of the best illustrations of these problems and possibilities comes from the evolution of man himself. We surely would all agree that the most important thing we could possibly discover about man's transition from the nonhuman state to the human state would be how he behaved during that period—the details of what he did and how he lived while he was evolving into a man. We know positively that he did make the transition from ape to man. What we do not know is precisely *how* he did it. By that I mean we do not know what the selective forces were, and, for example, why such forces seem to have been relatively strong and unidirectional for a while—at least in regard to changes in size of the brain case—and then to have slacked off, perhaps rather abruptly, some tens of thousands of years ago. We speak (vaguely, I think) of tools and communication, and of growing food and fighting off predators, but the truth is we still have no really good notion how and why men with bigger brains once outreproduced those with smaller brains and then stopped doing so. A wide range of possibilities still exists, and the answers could very well turn out to be more startling than most of us might suppose. As one example, we do not really know what kinds of predators, if any, might have been involved in the steady increase in man's brain size, and, as much as we may dislike the idea, I believe the possibility still exists that man himself is the only one that could have done the job.

Perhaps I can explain what I mean, and demonstrate some of our ignorance about man's evolution, by posing a question. Intraspecific competition, in connection with natural selection, may be said to occur in three possible forms. Sometimes different individuals simply compete indirectly, without direct interactions, for whatever food, mates, shelter, or other commodities may be in short supply. In other cases, some kinds of individuals may partially or completely exclude others from the best sources of food, mates, and shelter through territoriality of one sort or another. There is another possibility, less often recognized. Superior individuals might sometimes actually pursue and destroy competitors, or potential competitors, thus removing them and their descendants from the possibility of competing. Such a superior individual might, in addition to removing competition, actually derive direct benefit from the slaughter, through cannibalism. Which of these three kinds of intraspecific competition operated during the evolution of humans from nonhuman primates, and how significant was each? The question has certainly not been answered; I do not think it has even been clearly posed before. Yet the different possibilities could scarcely fail to produce widely different attitudes among men trying to understand themselves and their behavior through knowledge of history. [Since submission of this manuscript the ideas involved here have been discussed and extended in a book review coauthored by D. W. Tinkle (Bioscience 18:245–248).]

Sometimes I have thought that to understand the selective action that made a nonhuman primate into a man could be the most important question in all of biology. It could change man's attitude toward nearly everything he does or tries to do—in education, politics, religion, and all the rest—for it could tell him more precisely what he is, and therefore why, in one sense, he persists in doing some of the things he does, and why he still fails to accomplish some of the things he seems to want to do. Any adult who has tried to explain to a child the pre-eminence of things sexual in so much of human affairs (as well as in the lives of other organisms) without using natural selection in his explanation surely will understand what I mean. To use another example, it is possible that we should be taking the history of selective action upon man much more directly into account in our attempts to deal with overpopulation and its consequences.

In other words, we cannot learn how man became a man, and therefore, in a sense, what a man really is, without knowing some things about the history of his behavior. Yet, it seems that the only thing we can do about this problem is to dig and scrape around at a few fossils that reflect his morphology and represent a few indirect traces of his behavior.

THE COMPARATIVE METHOD IN BEHAVIOR

It *seems* as though this is all we can do; but my theme here is that such an idea about evolution is false. I suggest that we can find out how man's behavior evolved and the kinds of selective action that were involved. More fossils will help, of course, but we can do it without fossils if we have to; in any case, the most important advances in understanding man's history may not come from fossil evidence, and I consider it unlikely that satisfactory progress will come from the efforts of humanists who are not simultaneously first-rate evolutionary biologists. I believe that we will make the significant advances in this area in the same way that we eventually would have arrived confidently at the conclusion—even without the help of a single fossil—that man and the other living primates have diverged from common ancestors. We would have done this, of course, through extensive, intensive, and perceptive comparative study over a period of time long enough for us to have developed—on the side, from direct observation and experimentation—an understanding of the steps and the mechanics of the process of evolution.

It should be clear by now that I am not arguing simply about the role of behavior as a tool for taxonomists. I want to argue instead for the establishment of a reasonable relationship between those biologists interested primarily in behavior and those interested primarily in systematics in the broadest sense—a relationship that will result in the kind of reverberating feedback between these fields that both need, and have needed, for a long time. I think the key to this relationship—perhaps the only key—lies in applying the comparative method to behavior on a much wider scale than has been the case. I realize that I am one small voice in a long line of people carrying this particular argument to the zoologists. But I do think the point has not yet been properly made.

To some zoologists—though perhaps not to those here—to argue for a rejuvenation of comparative study must sound a little old-fashioned. Nowadays biologists are calling for precise, quantitative results and for more and more experimentation. Comparative study and the broad-scale, observational-descriptive work that undergirds it are often viewed as outdated, trivial pursuits. The need for more experimental work, however, and the possibility of more precise experimentation do not reduce the need for good, evolutionarily oriented, comparative investigations. Rather, though it may surprise some biologists, the need for comparative study is thereby increased, for it is a central role of comparison to tell us which experiments to do, and which ones to do first.

In his recent book on adaptation and natural selection, Williams (1966a) argued that systematists never will prosecute the study of adaptation the way it ought to be prosecuted. All of us will agree that there is a lot of shortsighted, narrow-minded systematic work going on but, contrary to Williams' argument, I believe that the methods of systematists represent a great potential contribution to the study of adaptation, beginning at the point where we find ourselves today. And I refer specifically to the comparative study of behavior, which Williams himself employed effectively in his book. Comparative study is the stock-in-trade of the systematist. It has never been the stock-in-trade of any other group of biologists in a very extensive, persistent, or pertinent fashion—least of all, perhaps, the behaviorists.

One of my favorite psychologists argued recently that molecularly oriented biologists are on the wrong track when they believe they can predict everything of significance about the biological world through a knowledge of structure and function at molecular and submolecular levels. He noted that, while theoretically this may be possible, it is unreasonable or impractical unless one knows beforehand what it is that he must be able to predict. I suggest that the same criticism can be leveled at many people studying behavior. They expect to be able to predict from precise, quantitative, laboratory experimentation without having any idea of the complexity, the variety, or even the nature of the things they will have to predict.

Zoologists left behavior largely to the psychologists, long past the time of knowing that psychologists in general do not answer the kinds of questions that zoologists must have answered. And systematists, in turn, have left zoological studies of behavior to the experimental zoologists, despite the fact that certain questions about behavior that are of importance to everyone are not going to be answered for a very long time using the methods generally conceded to experimental biology.

There is nothing mysterious about the comparative method. Yet I am convinced that many systematists and other biologists who use it all the time scarcely know what they are accomplishing with it, are not sufficiently prepared to explain and defend its problem-solving value, and, in any case, could not give a clear exposition of its usefulness to systematics or to biology in general.

THE COMPARATIVE METHOD AND SPECIATION

I will cite an example from a field familiar to this audience—the study of speciation, which I rank as one of the three general problem areas of chief concern to evolutionists, the other two being adaptation and phylogeny.

I am sure that everyone in this audience believes he has a good idea how speciation usually occurs, at least in sexually reproducing, gonochoristic or dioecious organisms. But how many are prepared to list and defend, as of this moment, the specific points of evidence that allow us to argue convincingly on the question of how speciation *usually* or *generally* occurs?

One thing is certain: None of us would get very far if he were asked to rely solely upon experimental studies or upon direct observation of complete speciation processes, witnessed from beginning to end.

Instead, we rely, as Darwin did, almost entirely upon information derived from the comparative study of a vast number of fragments of the speciation process. A bit of this one, a bit of that one, and the whole taken collectively, give us a composite picture that we can construct into a process from which we can predict rather precisely what must happen in any given individual case.

Of course, the picture we construct (in oversimplified form) is that speciation in bisexual organisms usually occurs when populations become geographically separated and undergo divergence through divergent selection and differential mutations until they are sufficiently different to make hybridization either impossible or sufficiently disadvantageous that amalgamation is impossible. The evidence from comparative study that gives us this picture can be summarized, I believe, in five statements.

1. Practically all species are geographically fragmented. In other words, geographic fragmentation occurs on a wide scale and is likely to permit much speciation.

2. Taken collectively, the geographic fragments show every possible degree of divergence—from scarcely measurable up to what seems to be complete speciation. So, geographic isolation does lead in a great many cases to divergence of apparently the right sort.

3. Most cognate pairs or groups of species have a particular kind of geographic relationship: either they are allopatric or their geographic ranges are narrowly overlapping. This suggests that they were geographically separated in the recent past. [Murray Littlejohn pointed out to me recently that use of the term "cognate species" for species believed to share an exclusive common ancestor (most closely related species, or species representing last forks in the phylogenetic tree) eliminates the confusion in the dual meaning of sibling species. Henceforth, I will use the term "sibling species" to mean simply species that are especially difficult to distinguish by conventional means.]

4. Cognate species sometimes are more divergent in the area where they overlap, suggesting that the contact occurred there following geographic separation.

5. Pairs and groups of species that are not related—for example, a pair of bird species and a pair of insect species—often overlap in the same regions, suggesting a common geographic barrier that caused all of them to speciate. Often the probable barrier can be postulated with considerable confidence.

I predict—and I have some personal experience upon which to base the prediction—that no alternative to this process of geographic speciation will be accepted widely among biologists unless and until it can be documented in the same fashion—that is, until comparative study can establish sufficient replications of the individual steps in the postulated process to indicate the likelihood that it has gone all the way in one or more cases. In a recent paper (Alexander, 1968) I have tried to present such evidence for speciation by accidental seasonal separation of adults, postulated by Alexander and Bigelow (1960) to have occurred in certain crickets.

I believe it is time we stopped concerning ourselves with more theories, and ever more elaborate theories, about how sympatric speciation *might* or *could* occur. Such theories are, by now, almost a dime a dozen and can be dreamed up even by beginning biology students. The real question is the likelihood of their occurrence, and that question can be answered only if we go into the field and accumulate the kind of comparative information that alone will tell us whether, and to what extent, any particular postulated process occurs.

There is an additional point to be made about speciation and the kind of evidence from comparative study that I have just described. Many investigators seem not to realize that the list of facts I gave also represents a set of "criteria" against which one may test whether any particular case of speciation is likely to have occurred as a result of geographic isolation. To take the extreme example, if none of the five statements I have just given seems to apply to, or coincide in any way with, the status of some particular pair of species, then I suggest that the investigator not only has an excellent reason for taking a closer look but also that he has no right to assume that speciation in that case occurred as a result of geographic isolation *without* taking a closer look.

Ernst Mayr has said, and I appreciate the implication, that speciation is the most important single event in evolution. I have just argued that essentially everything we know about speciation has been learned from the classical kind of comparative study. Also, I have suggested that information from broad-scale—even though relatively shallow—comparisons not only can enable us to predict with high confidence concerning specific cases, but also can provide criteria by which to test the significance of specific information about individual cases. This, I believe, is one of the best kinds of documentation of the power and usefulness of the comparative method in biology.

Incidentally, the kinds of evidence I have just been describing are those whose significance and validity are denied—on a much wider scale than most people realize, I am afraid—by antievolutionists and, further, whose significance is often downgraded and misunderstood not only by physical scientists but by many experimental biologists. Yet, we rely almost wholly upon information from such comparative studies for a wide variety of our concepts in evolutionary biology. It behooves us to understand this method thoroughly and to be able to use and defend it.

BEHAVIOR AND REPRODUCTIVE ISOLATION

An approach similar to that used in the analysis of speciation, one that concerns behavior and has been of great usefulness to alpha taxonomy in a few groups, involves the study of reproductive isolating mechanisms. Dr. Littlejohn has discussed this topic extensively on this program, and I agree with essentially everything he said; so I will attempt to make my comments complementary to his. Reproductive isolation, however, is so clearly the best-understood liaison between behavioral and systematic work that I will go to some trouble to express certain opinions that do not seem to jibe with much of the published—and evidently influential—literature and to describe some of the arguments underlying these opinions.

Although reproductive isolation is a relatively young topic of study, it has been discussed so extensively that one would suppose that our ideas concerning it would be fairly well crystallized. Unfortunately, this is not the case. One point of confusion, I believe, is that two quite different things commonly are considered under this topic without being adequately distinguished. These are (1) those differences that, initially, make it disadvantageous or impossible for two populations newly in secondary contact to hybridize or merge and (2) those differences that, in situations of long-established sympatry and synchrony, enable two species to live together with a minimum of deleterious sexual interaction. Failure to make this distinction at the proper times and in the proper ways seems largely responsible for the somewhat clouded discussions—to which Dr. Littlejohn alluded—as to whether reproductive isolating mechanisms are, as one writer has put it several times, "an incidental by-product of the genetic divergence of isolated populations or the result of natural selection."

In some ways it is appropriate to concern oneself first with phenomena in the second of these two categories—those species differences that prevent or reduce sexually significant encounters between species that have been breeding together for a long time. This approach focuses attention on both major questions concerning reproductive isolating mechanisms: (1) their specific identity and nature, and (2) their origins. Both questions, in my opinion, are being approached in awkward fashion by many investigators.

As with speciation, we can study reproductive isolating mechanisms either experimentally or by comparison of situations known only fragmentarily. Experimental studies are actually few and far between. Hopefully, they will increase in the future, for they can be carried out with greater success than can experimental studies of speciation. Presently, I think all the good analyses of the actual reproductive isolating mechanisms between pairs of species, in animals at least, can probably be counted on one's fingers. I say this in full awareness that some authors have been telling us that the literature on reproductive isolation is massive—so massive as almost to defy review. This is not true. There is indeed a great deal of published information on courtship and mating behavior, and this is what we are told is information on reproductive isolating mechanisms. But most of this information cannot be applied easily to questions about reproductive isolation. This is one of the ways in which the study of animal behavior is currently out of focus; and it would not be so if systematists were more involved in it.

One cannot go into the field and simply describe what he observes in the courtship and mating behavior of a species independent of where it lives, where and when it mates, with whom it lives, and to whom it seems most closely related, and expect to discover very much of significance to anyone interested in reproductive isolation.

To illustrate this point, I will use the example given us by the extensive and elegant work of Tinbergen (1953, 1960) on gull behavior. While Tinbergen has provided much fine information on displays associated with courtship and mating and has posed some questions and speculated about probable isolating mechanisms, I believe that he fails entirely to comment on possible species differences in eye-ring color. Yet, as a result of extensive field study, Neal Smith (1966) has presented data to show that merely changing eye-ring colors among species that are sympatric is enough to break up pairs already formed or to cause pair bonds between individuals belonging to different species, which apparently otherwise does not happen in the areas where he studied them. Smith and Tinbergen did not study exactly the same group of gull species, but I suggest that anyone wishing to account for reproductive isolation in Tinbergen's species now would want to examine eye-ring differences; and so would anyone wishing to use reproductive isolation to explain species distinctiveness in the displays of Tinbergen's gulls.

Some of the interspecific variations Tinbergen has described may have been reproductive isolators once but are not any longer. Or they may be involved in one of the other two possible functions of what we call courtship behavior—either the selection of superior or more-compatible mates within the species or the synchronization of behavioral and physiological events between the male and female in connection with parenthood. Both functions are more likely to be prominent in animals such as gulls, which have long-term pair bonds, or strict monogamy in some cases, and complex parental behavior. Mere species specificity does not itself mean isolating mechanism.

The chief point I want to make is simply that a tremendously important species difference had evidently been overlooked because reproductive isolating mechanisms, as such, had never been investigated among gulls.

I will dwell a moment on the succession of questions Neal Smith asked about reproductive isolation among gulls, for I think his model is a good one for any of us to use when attempting to investigate specific cases. Here is the succession of questions he asked: (1) To what extent do the different species overlap geographically? (2) To what extent do they overlap ecologically? (3) To what extent do they overlap temporarily (seasonally)? (4) To what extent do they interact (behaviorally) where they do breed together? (5) What is the significance of any morphological differences among them? and (6) What is the significance of their genetic differences for hybridization and hybrids?

Of course, this is just the old familiar list of possible isolating mechanisms; but it is the sequence that is important. Anyone who does not ask these questions in this general order will not know whether he is studying isolating mechanisms among his species even if he does prove, for example, that genitalic differences or gametic incompatibility prevent or partially prevent hybridization when sexually responsive individuals are brought together. If the chance of mating has never occurred in the field, such differences may arise without having had an opportunity to function in reproductive isolation. Under such circumstances these differences are neither isolating mechanisms nor isolating differences. They are just differences.

Many authors behave as though they think that any differences they find between species breeding in the same general area at about the same general time are functional isolating differences or, even, evolved "mechanisms." In conjunction with this line of reasoning, it has become popular in recent years to speak (often glibly, in my opinion) of "chains of partially effective reproductive isolating mechanisms." This casual approach misses the important point that some differences between species may never have been involved in their inability to interbreed or merge, or even in their living together without reproductive interference or competition. To use an extreme example, this is like saying that genitalic differences are reproductive isolating mechanisms between the blue jay and the white oak, which happen to be sympatric, synchronic species that do not interbreed with each other. To use equally, but perhaps less obviously, ridiculous examples, it is like saying that genitalic differences are reproductive isolating mechanisms between two species of *Drosophila* that have always mated in different habitats, or between two species of cicadas that have never emerged as adults in the same year, or between two species of mammals that have never attempted cross-copulation.

A paper by Clark *et al.* (1954) on mating behavior in xiphophorine fishes has been referred to as a classic example of the study of reproductive isolation. But these authors did not investigate the interactions of the species of concern in the field. If the species never interact sexually there, then Clark and her co-workers may have been studying differences, but not isolating differences, and not isolating mechanisms in the sense of evolved isolating differences selected in the context of isolation.

There has been much discussion on the question of why, if selection works as I have just outlined, so many species that have never lived together have perfectly good premating isolating differences already developed. The argument has been presented—evidently very effectively, judging from published references to this topic—that differences in premating behavior between species living together usually arise in contexts other than that of reproductive isolation, and that these differences function only incidentally in reproductive isolation.

I believe that this argument (which sometimes seems to derive from a belief that sterility usually occurs before establishment of secondary contact between populations destined to remain separate*) ignores the likelihood that, as reproductive isolation

*I believe this idea to be false, and that, instead, intersterility is rare between members of the same species groups. This hypothesis appears to be supported by all of the information available on hybridization: Blair (1963) for *Bufo;* Alexander (1967) for Gryllidae; Miller (1960) for American freshwater and marine fishes; and Gray (1954, 1958) for mammals and birds. Nearly every intensive effort at hybridization seems to reveal widespread interfertility among congeneric species.

in the sense of minimal wastage of time and energy causes a focus on a few specific aspects of premating behavior (such as calls in crickets, frogs, and birds, or odor in moths, or vision in butterflies), shifts in these characteristics in the context of reproductive isolation will be going on continuously. The result is that a species may be changed in a way that incidentally results in isolation from more than just the species causing the selective effect.

A large proportion of species falling into this category must shift their most important premating isolators a little almost every time any change occurs in the complement of species with which they live. Two unrelated species, after all, may have confusingly similar signals. I suspect, therefore, that many of what we might call "incidental" isolating differences are the direct result of selection for isolation between (1) one or both of the two involved species and (2) additional species with which one or both of them formerly lived. If so, we would expect to find that species in groups that have come to rely chiefly upon one or two kinds of isolating differences (such as calls) more likely would be different in those characteristics upon first meeting than would species in groups that rely upon several kinds of differences (e.g., chemicals, vision, host specificity) in different subgroups. On the other hand, if reproductive isolating differences ordinarily arise in other contexts, differences between these two kinds of groups should not be so obvious.

If all this is true, one should expect to find in acoustical insects and anurans: (1) few cases of identical pair-forming signals among allopatric or allochronic species—I know of only five or six cases among the approximately 1,000 known calling signals of insect species (Alexander, 1967); and (2) few cases of character displacement—I know of only two probable (or possible) cases among the same 1,000 insect species (Alexander, 1967).

The next pertinent comparison, obviously, would be between groups like the calling insects or anurans and other groups in which one particular kind of signal or behavioral unit is not universally involved in reproductive isolation. Unfortunately, the information needed to make such a comparison is not readily available.

THE COMPARATIVE METHOD AND REPRODUCTIVE ISOLATION

I have been talking chiefly about experimental studies and about detailed observations on individual cases. How is the comparative method used in studying reproductive isolation, and what are its special values?

Murray Littlejohn has introduced this topic, and he and Frank Blair, in particular, have illustrated through their studies on the calls of anurans, the usefulness to taxonomists of the comparative approach. As Dr. Littlejohn has indicated, a most striking parallel can be drawn between the results of studies on the calls of anurans and various insects (specifically crickets, katydids, and cicadas)—and, I might add, the results of studies by H. S. Barber (1951) and James E. Lloyd (1966, other papers) on fireflies. I do not believe there is a single finding on anurans that does not have a close parallel in these insect groups, and I do not believe that any results on anurans, or insects, conflict with any results on the other group. However, I want to emphasize one specific point. There are now experimental demonstrations that call differences between sympatric, synchronic, closely related species are sufficient to enable both the males and females to distinguish their own conspecifics; at least one demonstration exists for anurans (see Littlejohn, this volume, page 471) and one for each major insect group in which calls are prominent in breeding behavior (see Alexander, 1967). For a long time, however, there were no such demonstrations at all, but we knew even then—or I should say we were highly confident—that the calls do indeed function in reproductive isolation, and we proceeded successfully and accurately on this basis. Our evidence, like that used in understanding speciation, was derived from broad-scale comparisons. It can be summarized in the following group of statements, which to some extent parallel my earlier statements regarding speciation.

1. The calling (or pair-forming) signals of species that breed at the same times and in the same places are almost never identical (the exceptions are newly established situations). This fact—based on comparison of nearly 1,000 insect species alone, including essentially all crickets, katydids, and cicadas in North America and many grasshoppers and fireflies there—suggests that, in these groups, no two species breeding together are exempt from selective action on reproductive isolating mechanisms until their calling or pair-forming signals are specifically distinctive. This, I believe, is a critical bit of evidence, for it indicates that no one can effectively study reproductive isolation in any group without being specific about whether the species involved breed together and, if so, for how long. I would

point out that many studies on *Drosophila* mating behavior, even those supposedly dealing with reproductive isolation, either are vague about geographic, ecological, seasonal, and daily overlaps in breeding or do not mention them at all. No wonder it sometimes seems easiest to behave as though the origin of reproductive isolating mechanisms only incidentally has anything to do with living together!

2. Calling signals of species that breed in different places, or at different times in the same places, sometimes are the same. This fact, based on six known cases in insects–four cases of geographic isolation and two of seasonal isolation (Alexander, 1967)–makes the previous statement even more significant.

3. Calling signals of closely related species that overlap narrowly occasionally differ more in the region of overlap than elsewhere, suggesting reinforcement of differences owing to competitive interaction. Two cases have been suggested in North American crickets (Alexander, 1967).

4. Calling signals represent the earliest unit in sexually significant encounters between males and females. From an *a priori* viewpoint, therefore, these signals are the most efficient possible part of the sexual encounter for the function of reproductive isolation.

5. Calling signals are more species-distinctive than any other aspect of the mating sequence, and there is a progressive loss of species distinctiveness as one considers events that occur later and later in the mating sequence. This statement is based on our knowledge of call distinctiveness in all known (several hundred) insect species with pair-forming calls and on a study of courtship, genitalic structure, and mating behavior in some 10 subfamilies, 22 genera, and 50 species of crickets (Alexander and Otte, 1967).

Call differences are behavioral differences, and reproductive isolating mechanisms in established situations must be behavioral nearly all the time, even if the behavior involved is associated with locating the habitat or host to which mating activity is restricted, or with being active only at certain times of the day, as in some fireflies. Behavioral differences, if available to selection, will always be more efficient isolators, in terms of conserving time and energy, because they operate before morphological or physiological differences. The only exception seems to be differences in seasonal life history that effectively keep the adults of two species from interacting. Differences in habitat or daily times of breeding generally involve behavioral differences, and allopatry is rarely evolved as a result of species interactions. Partially or completely effective morphological, physiological, or late-operating behavioral differences, I suggest, will always be replaced by behavior as functional isolators as selection continues between species that remain sympatric and synchronic. This suggestion indicates that no one interested in reproductive isolation can avoid studying behavior, and I believe that no one interested in species and speciation can avoid studying reproductive isolation.

Last year a writer who was using almost exactly the same title as I am said there is no valid argument that behavior should replace morphology as the main tool of alpha-taxonomy in distinguishing species. But it has already done so for groups containing, collectively, somewhere between 25 and 50 thousand species (Anura, Ensifera, Caelifera, Auchenorrhyncha, Lampyridae), and in the case of acoustical and visual signals, it has proved to be of enormous (I would say, unparalleled) value not only in distinguishing species but also in locating and collecting specimens and in tracing geographic and ecological distributions and seasonal life histories. This approach is, of course, not applicable to all kinds of organisms, for reproductive isolating mechanisms of certain sorts may be very difficult to identify and measure. Further, this method does not help us with forms that have never lived together. But the advent of new techniques and instruments suggests that anyone serious about alpha-taxonomy in any group of organisms cannot afford to assume that his organisms are taxonomically inaccessible from this approach. After all, 15 years ago we could not study sounds objectively, and only five years ago we had no instruments to record the subtleties of firefly flashes.

THE PROBLEM OF INSTINCT

So far, I have said nothing about what undoubtedly has been the knottiest problem in the study of animal behavior, and the one responsible more than any other, I suppose, for slowing the advance of comparative study of behavior. If we call this the "problem of instinct," most people have a good idea what is meant. It would be more descriptive, however, to term it the problem of the extent and nature of hereditary influences in behavioral variations, both between species and among the individuals of each species.

Adaptation is a result of selective action on alternative genetic phenomena. Therefore, it is critical for my topic to determine which behavioral variations correlate with genetic variations. Few people challenge the idea that certain species differences, such as frog and insect calls, firefly flashes, or other behavioral characteristics identified as reproductive isolating mechanisms in any kinds of animals, have genetic bases. And, we know from hybridization experiments that insect and anuran call differences do indeed have genetic bases. In fact, results from crossing experiments on crickets and frogs probably are cited more frequently in reviews concerning transmissibility of behavioral variations than are any experiments with other kinds of animals.

The systematist wants to know more about this. He wants to know whether he can be sure that he is not examining some behavioral difference that has nothing to do with hereditary differences. Some systematists and other biologists have gotten involved in long, bitter, and futile arguments about whether heredity or environment has greater influence in determining the characteristics of particular behavior patterns.

Concerning this topic, we are pursued now by a whole string of admonishments: "To ask how much a given aspect of behavior depends upon genetic factors and how much upon environmental factors is like asking how much of the area of a field depends upon its length and how much upon its width"; "Nothing is inherited but the genotype and a little cytoplasm"; "Heredity is particulate, but development is unitary"; "Instead of speaking of this or that trait as genetic or environmental, the correct way is to ask yourself which, and the extent to which, differences in characters are due to environment on the one hand and to heredity on the other."

Konishi (1966) has recently written a paper that, I think, clarifies some issues involved in this problem. He points out that, as one of our shortcomings, we have acted as though it is always true that, in behavior, stereotypy = species specificity = inheritance = central coordination = spontaneity = self-differentiation. These factors are not strictly correlated and, as with learning, what has been called "instinctive" behavior really is not a single phenomenon, and it should not be treated as if it were.

But not all these issues are of great or immediate concern to the systematist or evolutionary biologist interested in behavior. What is of concern is predictability. And it is very likely that significant increases in predictability, in many cases, can be attained sooner by insightful, properly directed, broad-scale (even superficial) comparisons than by detailed studies of development of specific patterns of behavior in individual animals or species. The comparative anatomists, as many ethologists have emphasized, have already shown this to be true. We systematists seem to have allowed ourselves to be overly concerned about precisely how individual patterns of behavior develop. We do not know a great deal about the development of morphology in a wide variety of animals; but we do know a very great deal about speciation, adaptation, and phylogenetic history—all of which knowledge was gained directly, almost solely, from comparisons of those very features of anatomy whose development we still do not understand.

When we will have carried out broad-scale comparative studies of behavior similar to those available in anatomy, and when we begin to acquire the glimmers of understanding that will come from predictiveness based on such studies, then those investigators concerned chiefly with the developmental bases of phenotypic differences will, indeed, have something to think about and work with. Because the question then would concern *how much* genetic variation is involved, a considerably sharper focus should be provided for the investigations of many biologists now skeptical that broad-scale comparisons can be made in the absence of extensive information on developmental pathways and stimuli for particular behavioral units.

This remark may raise some eyebrows, but I suggest that behavioral variations that at first glance appear useful to systematists—particularly to those working at and above the species level—rarely lack correlation with specific genetic variations. For example, is anyone here in a position to describe a species difference in behavior—any species difference in behavior—that he has cause to suspect does not have a genetic basis?* Further, and of great importance, the extent and nature of correlations between behavioral variations and genetic variations—or their absence—is predictable to a large extent.

*Alexander and Bigelow (1960) have given a possible example. Males of *Gryllus veletis* generally are much more aggressive than those of *G. pennsylvanicus.* They also occur more sparsely, and the difference can be erased, or even reversed, if males of *G. veletis* are crowded in the laboratory and males of *G. pennsylvanicus* are isolated.

One aspect of such predictability can be exemplified by cricket calls. Examination of cricket biology soon reveals that in most temperate species only the eggs pass the winter, and that the auditory organs are not functional until maturation or near-maturation. With this information alone we can predict confidently that (at least usually) selection favors insulation from influences by environmental sounds in the establishment of the pattern of the call (R. D. Alexander, "Arthropods" *in* T. Sebeok, *Animal Communication,* to be published by Indiana University Press), for there can be no appropriate sounds available to copy.

On the other hand, even a limited knowledge of passerine-bird biology allows the reverse prediction: that most young birds probably have evolved specific ways of being influenced by their parents' song patterns. There are at least two reasons: the overlap of young and adults in each generation, and an apparent premium on individuality in song pattern; the latter is associated with the presence of specialized parental behavior and tendencies toward monogamy and is promoted by having part of the pattern learned.

In precocious birds both the critical periods of song learning and the imprinting of following behavior are predictable on the same general basis. Even the indiscriminateness of suitable stimuli for imprinting of following behavior is predictable, for the situation is such that unsuitable stimuli are not likely to be available, and selection, therefore, will have no chance to focus on a restricted group of stimuli. Likewise, we would predict that different populations of birds within a given species should sometimes have song differences that lack genetic bases, as is the case with human languages.

The psychologists who chastised ethologists for erecting dichotomies with regard to learned and unlearned behavior were right, for many ethologists had their dichotomies out of focus. But this argument became a source of confusion rather than clarification when it took the form of rejecting all implications of important dichotomies in the way behavior patterns develop. An important dichotomy can be identified in the examples I have just given: Does the selection favor the use of a given stimulus (sound, for example) in the establishment of a pattern in the same modality as the stimulus or does it specifically favor insulation from all stimuli in that particular modality? This is a dichotomy as to direction of selection, and it leads to extreme differences in certain relationships between genetic phenomena and behavioral characteristics. We identify it and discover its significance by studying adaptation and natural selection in relation to behavioral development.

I suggest that selection acting consistently on any kind of behavioral variation, regardless of its original basis, will usually result in the presence, ultimately, of genetic variation that relates directly to the behavioral variation. This would mean that the more ancient a behavioral difference, the more likely it is to have some genetic basis. By this I do not mean to imply any special kind of selection, I simply mean that selection will work on both genetic and nongenetic variations, but evolution will occur only when genetically based variations become available.

No broad-scale attempt has been made to study adaptation in behavioral terms by the kind of comparison and prediction that I have just described. Yet, if what I have argued is true, such attempts would be fruitful, even those dealing with the behavior of man, of all organisms the most "labile" in the functioning of his phenotype.

I will use a simple example cited by Williams (1966a), who notes that the females of many kinds of animals usually are described as being more "coy" or discriminating or reluctant in copulation than the males (or one could turn it around and say that the males are more "aggressive" in courtship), and he notes that this is predictable because in each copulation or fertilization the female invests a greater proportion of her total reproductive potential than the male invests of his. If this argument is correct, then, as Williams points out, the situation should be reversed in parental animals in which the male is solely responsible for the zygotes, or more involved in parental behavior. Such reversals have been reported in pipefishes in the genus *Syngnathus,* in which the males carry the fertilized eggs (Fiedler, 1954), though not in all such fish (Breder and Rosen, 1966; Straughan, 1960), and also in such birds, as some tinamous and phalaropes, in which the males incubate the eggs and protect the young (Bent, 1927; Tinbergen, 1935; Höhn, 1967).

Similar reversals as to which sex behaves territorially, fights off intruding individuals, and courts more aggressively have been reported in the ornate tinamou (Pearson and Pearson, 1955), red phalarope, northern phalarope, and Wilson's phalarope (Tinbergen, 1935; Höhn, 1967; Bent, 1927). Polyandry is more likely to be prominent in such animals, and strict polygyny ought to be rare, although both polygamy (or promiscuity on the part of both sexes) and monogamy have been reported (Lancaster, 1964; Höhn, 1967). Polygyny, on the other hand, is prominent among species in which the females carry most or all of the parental responsibility, and polyandry is almost nonexistent. Some of the disagreements in the literature (e.g., see Höhn, 1967) may result from differences in sex ratios among demes studied by different investigators. In some cases, what happens when sex ratios are locally or temporarily uneven may be important in understanding how selection has operated.

The relationship between reproductive effort and proportion of reproductive potential involved in any circumstance or event can be extended to include not only the proportion of eggs or sperm used per copulation but also the proportion of the breeding season used per clutch or pregnancy and the proportion of the total probable reproductive life involved in each season, as Dr. Tinkle demonstrated on this program. Such considerations of proportions must include also the likelihood of changes in reproductive possibility—such as improvements through learning about one's mate or about the food and predators in one's territory—and the likelihood of improvement in weather conditions. Williams (1966b) and Lack (1966) have pointed out that this means that longer juvenile lives will correlate roughly with longer reproductive lives, and that clutch sizes will increase with age. We should expect, especially in long-lived, monogamous animals with specialized parental behavior, that selection continually will maximize the slope of a line depicting the increasing reproductive ability of individuals and pairs.

Since man's plasticity in behavior seems for a long time to have been a major reason for our reluctance to discuss the general problem of behavior in relation to heredity and, therefore, a major reason for the reluctance of systematists and other biologists to use behavior in comparative work, it is appropriate that I conclude by referring to the possibility of heredity in an example of variation in man's behavior. I will use the previously mentioned theory of female "coyness," or difference between male and female, and suggest that what we frequently and sometimes jokingly refer to as the "double standard" in man's sexual behavior is, in part, a reflection of differences in selective action on male and female behavior during man's evolutionary history.

In general, in both polygynous and monogamous animals with specialized parental behavior selection should favor females that promote monogamy and should favor males that promote polygyny. Even in evolutionary lines in which monogamy is never actually realized, tendencies toward it in females would be favored consistently if the male's cooperation in any way promoted the female's reproductive success. Likewise, even in a monogamous line polygynous tendencies in males often would be favored because in a species in which the female is responsible for the fertilized eggs a male is much more likely to benefit from, shall we say, "stealing" copulations with his neighbors' females than is the female who indulges in the same kind of behavior. Tendencies toward polyandry in man are evidently rare, but tendencies toward polygyny are not nearly so rare.

Is it reasonable to argue that there likely are no genetic correlates underlying even subtle intraspecific differences of this sort in an organism as plastic as man, when selection on man's breeding system has probably been consistent in the ways I have described all through man's evolutionary history? I think not.

CONCLUDING REMARKS

I have dealt in this paper with a few points that I believe will be useful in making the analysis of behavior more important in systematic work than it has been in the past, in searching for both similarities and differences among organisms. To bring these two fields into closer cooperation, I believe we need, chiefly, to be (1) more aware of the role of the comparative method in biology and in behavioral analysis, (2) more thoughtful in our searches for behavioral variations likely to be correlated with genetic differences, and (3) as systematists, more cognizant than we have been of the significance of studying adaptation directly, both by experimentation and by comparison.

ACKNOWLEDGMENTS

I wish to thank Daniel Otte, Ann Pace, and Mary Jane West, graduate students at the University of Michigan, for assistance in developing the ideas presented here and for critical examination of the manuscript at various stages.

REFERENCES

Alexander, R. D. 1967. Acoustical communication in arthropods. Ann. Rev. Ent. 12:495–526.

Alexander, R. D. 1968. Life cycle origins, speciation, and related phenomena in crickets (Orthoptera: Gryllidae). Quart. Rev. Biol. 43(1):1–41.

Alexander, R. D., and R. S. Bigelow. 1960. Allochronic speciation in field crickets, and a new species, *Acheta veletis.* Evolution 14(3):334–346.

Alexander, R. D., and D. Otte. 1967. The evolution of genitalia and mating behavior in crickets (Gryllidae) and other Orthoptera. Univ. Michigan Misc. Pub. 133:1–62.

Barber, H. S. 1951. North American fireflies of the genus *Photinus.* Smithsonian Inst. Misc. Coll. 117:1–58.

Bent, A. C. 1927. Life histories of North American shore birds, Order Limicolae. I. U.S. Nat. Mus. Bull. 142.420 p.

Blair, W. F. 1963. Evolutionary relationships of North American toads of the genus *Bufo:* A progress report. Evolution 17(1):1–16.

Breder, C. M., and D. E. Rosen. 1966. Modes of reproduction in fishes. Natural History Press, Garden City, New York. 941 p.

Clark, E., L. R. Aronson, and M. Gordon. 1954. Mating behavior patterns in two sympatric species of xiphophorin fishes: Their inheritance and significance in sexual isolation. Bull. Am. Mus. Nat. Hist. 103:135–226.

Fiedler, K. 1954. Vergleichende Verhaltensstudien an Seehadeln, Schlangennadeln und Seepferdchen (Syngnathidae). Zeit. Tierpsychol. 11(3):358–416.

Gray, A. P. 1954. Mammalian hybrids: A check-list with bibliography. Commonwealth Bur. Anim. Breed. Genet. Edinburgh, Tech. Comm. 10. 144 p.

Gray, A. P. 1958. Bird hybrids: A check-list with bibliography. Commonwealth Bur. Anim. Breed. Genet. Edinburgh, Tech. Comm. 13. 390 p.

Höhn, E. O. 1967. Observations on the breeding biology of Wilson's phalarope (*Steganopus tricolor*) in central Alberta. Auk 84(2):220–244.

Konishi, M. 1966. The attributes of instinct. Behaviour 27(3–4):316–328.

Lack, D. 1966. Population studies of birds. Clarendon Press, Oxford. 341 p.

Lancaster, D. A. 1964. Biology of the brushland tinamou, *Nothoprocta cinerascens.* Bull. Am. Mus. Nat. Hist. 127 (6):271–314.

Lloyd, J. E. 1966. Studies on the flash communication system in *Photinus* fireflies. Univ. Michigan Mus. Zool. Misc. Pub. 130:1–95.

Miller, R. R. 1960. Records of natural hybrids among American freshwater and marine fishes. (Mimeographed.)

Pearson, A. K., and O. P. Pearson. 1955. Natural history and breeding behavior of the tinamou, *Nothoprocta ornata.* Auk 72(2):113–127.

Smith, N. G. 1966. Evolution of some Arctic gulls (*Larus*): An experimental study of isolating mechanisms. Am. Ornithol. Union Ornithol. Monogr. 4. 99 p.

Straughan, R. P. L. 1960. 100 seahorses spawn. Aquarium J. 31(6):302–308; 325–326.

Tinbergen, N. 1935. Field observations of East Greenland birds. I. The behavior of the red-necked phalarope (*Phalaropus lobatus* L.) in spring. Ardea 24(1-2):1-42.

Tinbergen, N. 1953. The herring gull's world. A study of the social behaviour of birds. Collins, London. 255 p.

Tinbergen, N. 1960. Comparative studies of the behavior of gulls (Laridae): A progress report. Behaviour 15(1-2):1-70.

Wheeler, W. M. 1905. Ethology and the mutation theory. Science 21(536): 535-540.

Williams, G. C. 1966a. Adaptation and natural selection. A critique of some current evolutionary thought. Princeton University Press, Princeton, New Jersey. 307 p.

Williams, G. C. 1966b. Natural selection, the costs of reproduction, and a refinement of Lack's principle. Am. Natur. 100(916):687-690.

Discussion

Paul A. Johnsgard

Because of its implication in achieving reproductive isolation or reduction of interspecific competition, behavioral diversity of taxonomic significance most commonly occurs at the species level, whereas morphological divergence of taxonomic significance tends to appear progressively at increasingly higher taxonomic levels. There are at least two reasons for this. First, selection for behavioral differences having ecological significance—differences affecting habitat selection and food selection—is most strongly evident among closely related, sympatric species. Even where morphological differences of ecological significance occur at the species level, they are usually associated with behavioral differences related to niche specialization. Second, selection for behavioral differences that achieve ethological isolation is most intense between closely related, sympatric species, and often this is not reflected in measurable morphological differences.

Alternately, although behavioral diversity also may occur at higher levels, in contrast to many morphological traits it becomes progressively more difficult to find significant ethological traits that unequivocally characterize and distinguish genera, families, and orders, at least in larger polytypic groups. This situation seems to reflect the fact that, as Dr. Alexander points out, behavioral adaptations are usually the species' first line of defense against changing selection pressures, whereas many morphological adaptations, once perfected, may become widespread and remain essentially constant throughout a large group of related animals, thus providing the basic generic, familial, and ordinal characters so dear to the hearts of morphologists.

Therefore, the alpha-taxonomic function of *distinguishing species* is often better served by behavior than by morphology, particularly in dealing with groups of sibling species where the morphologist must admit defeat. Dr. Littlejohn and Dr. Alexander have mentioned several examples.

For the alternative function of alpha-taxonomy, that of *association* of related taxa, behavioral criteria have much the same utility and limitations as do morphological traits. Both are frequently subjected to divergent and convergent evolution under ecological sources of natural selection; thus, both run the risk of causing misassociation of unrelated but ecologically similar forms. However, the multiplicity of behavioral characters usually available often reduces the dangers of such errors of association.

I will mention two examples involving birds to illustrate this last point. Jürgen Nicolai (1964) has recently proven that the African widow birds (Viduinae) are more closely related to the true weavers (Ploceinae) than they are to the estrildine finches that they socially parasitize and whose young resemble their own, particularly in juvenile plumages and gape markings, to an amazing degree. Nicolai found that in innate song elements, courtship behavior, and other behavioral traits the widow birds clearly have evolutionary affinities with the weavers, even though as a result of their host specificity the male widow bird used learned elements of its estrildine host species' song to attract female widow birds, when it later breeds, and thus has actually borrowed one of its host's isolating mechanisms. In this case, prior predictions of the type Dr. Alexander mentions concerning the probable learned versus innate aspects of sexual behavior would go astray, providing, as it were, the exception to the exception that proves the rule.

As a second example, I mention the white-backed duck (*Thalassornis leuconotus*) which, since it was first described in 1838, has been regarded as an aberrant relative of the stiff-tailed ducks (Oxyurinae), largely on the basis of its short wings, posteriorly placed feet, and other diving adaptations. Behaviorally it differs from the stiff-tailed ducks in that both sexes have identical whistling voices and strongly monogamous pair bonds, and both participate in nest defense, incubation, and brood care. Additionally, the precopulatory and postcopulatory behavior of white-backed ducks is essentially identical to the highly distinctive corresponding behavior of whistling ducks (Dendrocygninae). Accordingly, I have suggested (Johnsgard, 1967) that the genus be transferred to the whistling duck group. Supporting evidence for this suggestion has come from the work of Dr. Janet Kear (1967) who found, on the basis of audiospectrographic analysis, that the distress calls of newly hatched white-backed ducks are very different from those of typical stiff-tails but practically identical to those of whistling ducks. She has further found that such distress calls—although they often cannot be distinguished by humans—can be audiospectrographically shown to exhibit generic and tribal affinities in a large number of cases. In this special situation, where the calls cannot be learned from the adults, are not concerned with reproductive isolation, and show little if any ecological adaptation, we have a case comparable to that of many morphological traits: Similarities between closely related species often are too close to be of discriminative value; but increasing degrees of vocal differences occur at higher levels, providing data of possible value in either association or discrimination.

As for the beta-level of taxonomy, i.e., the erection of phylogenies, behavioral traits probably are generally less valuable than morphological ones. This partly reflects the fact that, unlike morphology, behavior leaves no fossils; thus, there is no index to the relative degrees of evolutionary specialization of individual traits. Rather, one must compare and evaluate the behavioral adaptations of contemporaneously existing forms. At best, this is a dangerous procedure, and perhaps it is even more difficult to accomplish with behavior than with morphology. Also, because of the dynamic nature of the role of behavior in any species' adaptations, I am not certain that such distinctions as "primitive" and "advanced" traits normally can be made confidently.

With respect to Dr. Alexander's last point concerning the biological (and, by implication, taxonomic) significance of monogamous versus polygamous or promiscuous sexual associations, and his provocative suggestion relative to the human condition, I found this interesting food for thought and cannot resist commenting on it. I believe that, in mammals, true monogamy largely is restricted to groups in which there exists a biological need for the male to remain with the female—to help protect the family, or, as in the case of various carnivores, to provide food for the dependent female and young.

I would suggest that the probable protohominid situation may be exemplified by that of various nonhuman primates, which seems to represent the best of all possible worlds. There we may observe the presence of a multi-individual troop with several sexually active males and a variety of females that, as they individually come into estrus, become available to the most reproductively active males. The dependent females and young, in turn, benefit from the protection gained by the presence of the numerous adult males, which typically defend the troop in concert.

When considering the frequency of polygamous mating systems in various human societies, the typical patriarchal defense of the family, and the tendency of sexually mature males to form defensive groups for protecting their collective families (the state), all of these seem to reflect basic primate tendencies. I hope that the currently active comparative study of primate behavior not only will clarify the ecological adaptations and phylogenetic relationships among the nonhuman primates but also might help to resolve more accurately the biological and taxonomic status of *Homo sapiens.*

REFERENCES

Kear, J. 1967. Notes on the eggs and downy young of *Thalassornis leuconotus.* Ostrich 38:227–229.

Johnsgard, P. 1967. Observations on the behavior and relationships of the white-backed duck and the stiff-tailed ducks. Wildfowl Trust Ann. Rep. 18:98–107.

Nicolai, J. 1964. Der Brutparasitismus der Viduinae als ethologisches Problem: Prägungs phanomene als Faktoren der Rassen- und Artbildung. Zeit. f. Tierpsychol. 21:129–204.

Discussion

Peter H. Raven

In thinking how the notion of behavior could be applied to plants, and considering Dr. Alexander's excellent paper, I made several observations.

The connection between the genotype of an angiosperm and its spectrum of animal visitors is even more indirect and less precise than is the connection between the genotype of an animal and its behavior. For this reason, evolutionary shifts in the pollination regime of an angiosperm usually involve changes from one major class of pollinators to another—as from bee pollination to bird or hawkmoth pollination. Shifts within a pollination class, as suggested, for example, by the sympatric occurrence of two closely related plant species pollinated by different species of bee, are very rare. Thus, there is in angiosperms no subtle control of premating behavior comparable to that found in many groups of higher animals, such as those we have heard discussed.

In consequence of this, the so-called barriers to hybridization in plants most often are expressed as hybrid sterility. Prezygotic mechanisms have a much more limited scope and importance than in many groups of higher animals, although some, of course, particularly ones concerning habitat differentiation, are well known.

No known genetic mechanism can *increase* the sterility of hybrids in situations where organisms are hybridizing. Moreover, as we have seen, plants do not develop efficient prezygotic isolating mechanisms as readily, as precisely, or in as many ways as some groups of animals. From these facts follow three important observations about the pattern of variation in plants.

1. There is no well-documented case of character displacement known in plants, although evidence to be presented by D. A. Levin ("Natural Selection for Reproductive Isolation in *Phlox,*" in press) may constitute the first. The control of pollination systems by many groups of plants is too imprecise to allow for character displacement. In addition, the "way of life" of higher plants is monotonously uniform, and there is little opportunity for character displacement on this basis. Indeed, the higher plants as a whole recall the phenomenon of "allopatric exclusion" discussed by Dr. Selander (this volume, page 213) as characteristic of certain groups of higher animals.

2. As Dr. Ornduff has stressed in his paper, hybridization between series of populations that genetically are well-differentiated is almost a dominant theme of the adaptive system in plants. If the term "species" is to have any utility whatever in plants, many of these differentiated units must be called species.

3. The development of hybrid sterility between populations of plants is best viewed as an incidental aspect of their general evolutionary divergence. Of course, two populations that have become intersterile may coexist, and this is the most likely reason for the greater interfertility of allopatric species sometimes observed—such species might merge if they came together. When a group of plants has strong genetic isolating mechanisms separating the units recognized as species, a comprehensive study almost inevitably reveals similar, or in some cases greater, differentiation *within* the units called species. The converse is also true; if intraspecific hybrids are fully fertile, interspecific ones often are also. Thus, the so-called biological species concept has neither operational validity nor conceptual usefulness in plants, where I urge its abandonment in favor of detailed population studies with no *a priori* judgments about the nature of the units to be found (for example, see the paper by Lewis, this volume, page 523). Such studies should consider, of course, the entire gamut of biological features, including those fundamental ones stressed by the proponents of the biological species concept.

HARLAN LEWIS

Comparative Cytology in Systematics

The significance of comparative cytology in systematics depends on what we mean by cytology, the taxonomic level with which we are concerned, and our concept of systematics. When cytology is mentioned in relation to systematics, most of us probably think of chromosomes, and I suspect the organizers of this conference had chromosomes in mind when they decided to include a discussion of comparative cytology. Consequently, I will use cytology in this paper to mean chromosomes and their various attributes, and I will attempt to evaluate the significance of these attributes in making decisions at various taxonomic levels.

Chromosomes are singled out for special consideration because they not only have characteristics of their own, but also they determine most of the other characteristics of an individual, including its genetic interaction with other individuals. Chromosomes are an integral part of the genetic system; they affect the rate of gene exchange between populations and determine not only the nature of genetic recombination, but whether it occurs at all. Structural differentiation of the chromosomes results in immediate genetic discontinuity between the genotypes concerned, whether those genotypes are genetically differentiated or not.

In evaluating the significance of comparative cytology in systematics, gene exchange should be distinguished from gene recombination. Although the two phenomena are closely interrelated, the rate and the amount of each are determined by different factors.

The rate of gene exchange depends on the frequency of hybridization and on the fertility of the hybrids, whereas the amount of gene exchange, given a rate above zero, is determined primarily by natural selection. The rate of recombination, on the other hand, is determined by the number of chromosomes and the frequency of crossing-over, which is represented cytologically by chiasma frequency. The amount of recombination depends on the location of crossing-over, which is limited by the structural homology of the chromosomes. The fate of the recombinants, omitting the factor of chance, is determined by natural selection, which in turn determines the amount of gene exchange, unless, of course, the rate of gene exchange is zero.

Direct measurement of the effect of chromosomal traits on gene exchange and gene recombination is limited to organisms that can be hybridized, because only by genetic experiments can the effect be measured. Furthermore, with very few exceptions, the only possibility of approaching precision in determining structural homology of chromosomes or genomes is during the early stages of meiosis in a hybrid. With the information gained from hybridization and extensive genetic experiments with a relatively few organisms, we are able to extrapolate with varying degrees of confidence to situations in which hybridization is impractical; therein lies the special value of comparative cytology in systematics.

Because the special significance of cytological data lies in their usefulness as indicators of genetic interaction and hence of genetic relationship, they lose their special significance whenever genetic relationship is more readily or more accurately indicated by other data. If, for example, phenotypic differences are such as to preclude genetic interaction of any sort (e.g., between mice and men), cytological characters have no special significance relative to other traits and may be totally irrelevant. For example, the observation that both *Geranium macrorrhizum* and *Homo sapiens* have 46 chromosomes is certainly irrelevant. At the opposite extreme, if one knows the nature of the genetic interaction between groups of individuals through genetic experiment, cytological traits become superfluous as indicators of this interaction. In other words, comparative cytology has special significance in systematics only among organisms that have not been subjected to genetic experiment but that might be expected to hybridize. Beyond this, chromosomal traits are useful in systematics only to the extent that one can reasonably conclude that the observed characteristics reflect common ancestry rather than convergence. Such a conclusion can be reached only on the basis of correlation with other phenotypic traits. Obviously, therefore, cytological traits so evaluated cannot possibly have greater significance than the phenotypic traits used to evaluate them.

Cytological observations may be useful at genetic or higher levels, for we know of instances in which cytological observations have greatly reinforced taxonomic conclusions based on other evidence, or in which cytological observations have caused systematists to re-evaluate existing classifications; but in all these instances, cytological observations are useful only when they complement other phenotypic data. This means that the cytological observations are merely additional traits without special significance in systematics. Therefore, the remainder of this paper will be confined to levels of relationship where observations of chromosome number, morphology, structure, and behavior may have special significance, notably in distinguishing phenotypically similar populations that are conspecific from those that are not. This implies, of course, that we know what a species is.

Chromosome number is the easiest cytological trait to score, and in most organisms it is the only cytological observation available to us for evaluation in systematics. For this reason, we should examine carefully the use and the usefulness of chromosome number. Unlike most other chromosomal traits, the number can be determined from several stages of the mitotic and meiotic cycles, and the observations generally are consistent from cell to cell (especially after the observer has convinced himself of what the number is). Assuming that one has a good technique for the preparation of the material, and that dividing nuclei can be found, and that one can count, it should not be difficult to determine chromosome number. Nevertheless, many of the older records, on further study, have been found to be unreliable, in most cases because the preparations were poor.

In the case of human chromosomes, new techniques, as we all know, made the difference. Organisms vary tremendously with respect to the ease with which reliable chromosome numbers can be determined, even with adequate techniques, and very high numbers always pose difficulties. One should not worry too much about the accuracy with which high numbers are determined since organisms having them generally are polyploid and are often notably variable in chromosome number, presumably because genetic redundancy prevents the variation from having deleterious phenotypic effects. Some organisms, notably plants such as *Claytonia virginica* (Portulacaceae) even show chromosomal variability down to the diploid level. This species, for example, does not seem to care what its chromosome number is as long as it is 12 or more (up to about 191). (This is discussed in a paper by W. H. Lewis, "Cytocatalytic Evolution in Plants," to be published in *Botanical Review.*) I would argue that if an organism does not take its chromosome number seriously there is no reason why the systematist should.

Variation in chromosome number sometimes occurs among interfertile members of the same breeding population. Such variation may have evolutionary significance, but it has no taxonomic significance, and the systematist should treat it just as he would other intrapopulation variations, that is, he should record it along with any geographical, ecological, or other correlations noted. By taxonomic significance of a cytological trait I mean its relevance to classification based on the conventional scheme in general use by biologists.

When comparing chromosome numbers between populations, the systematist may find they are consistently the same, in which case the observation provides no evidence of relationship beyond that which can be inferred from phenotypic similarity. If he finds a consistent difference in number, however, it may have special taxonomic significance because we know that hybrids between individuals from populations differing in chromosome number generally, although not invariably, have low fertility and may be sterile. Since rate of gene exchange for a given frequency of hybridization is determined by the fertility of the hybrids, if fertility is low the rate of gene exchange will be reduced correspondingly. We also know that a difference in chromosome number at the diploid or haploid level is usually associated with chromosome rearrangement and that structural rearrangement indicates genetic discontinuity, the extent of which is a function of the nature and the number of the rearrangements. In the absence of evidence to the contrary, the systematist evaluating a difference in chromosome number at the diploid or haploid level reasonably may conclude that it signifies genetic discontinuity as well as a low rate of gene exchange.

When the inferred genetic discontinuity is accompanied by consistent (although not necessarily conspicuous) phenotypic differences, the systematist can formally describe the populations as different species and can be confident that few biologists will take exception. He faces a problem only when the implied or even demonstrated genetic discontinuity is not associated with readily recognizable phenotypic differences. For most systematists this does not become a problem because it cannot arise until there are chromosome counts for at least two morphologically comparable populations. The problem is a familiar one to investigators who have made numerous chromosome counts within a given group of organisms, particularly among herbaceous plants and invertebrates. Faced with a difference in chromosome number between populations that appear to be alike in all other respects, the taxonomist may decide that a strong barrier to gene exchange probably exists and that the populations are sibling species; whether he describes them formally depends on his concern with the practical aspects of taxonomy, in other words, on what he conceives to be the function of formal taxonomy. Alternatively, he may decide that despite the chromosomal difference there is genetic continuity between the populations and therefore they are conspecific.

Although a difference in chromosome number between populations generally signifies genetic discontinuity as well as a reduction in rate of gene exchange, there are two notable exceptions, both of which involve populations that are likely to be phenotypically indistinguishable or at least differ to no greater extent than interfertile populations having the same chromosome number.

One exception includes those cases in which fertility and gene recombination are significantly affected by the difference in chromosome number. This is frequently true when the difference in number results from simple dissociation of chromosome arms at the centromere or from "centric fusion" of two acrocentric chromosomes to form one metacentric chromosome. The latter probably always involves translocation and loss of a small centric region. Both, however, imply genetic discontinuity in that portion of the genotype lying between the centromeres of the chromosomes involved and the closest possible point of crossing-over. By inference, this area consists largely if not entirely of genetically nonspecific heterochromatin. Were this not true, discarding even a small centric region would be expected to have a phenotypic effect. Genetic discontinuity, therefore, does not necessarily imply a genetic effect, or, if so, the effect may be comparable to that resulting from short inversions or other structural differences within populations that have no effect on fertility. The point is that chromosome number *per se* has no special taxonomic significance.

The other exception to the generalization that a difference in chromosome number implies genetic discontinuity of taxonomic significance is that of autopolyploidy, which involves the simple duplication of homologous sets of chromosomes. The systematist—at least the plant systematist—has been concerned about autopolyploids because he knows that hybrids between diploids and their autopolyploid derivatives generally have low fertility. This means that the rate of gene exchange between diploids and polyploids will be correspondingly low, but since the genomes are structurally the same, chromosomes or any parts of the chromosomes from the diploids and polyploids are able to recombine with one another to the same extent that they are able to recombine among themselves. In other words, any allele or gene combination that arises in a diploid population, when transferred to a polyploid population, or vice versa, is able to recombine in that population as if it had originated there. Consequently, the difference in chromosome number affects only the rate of gene exchange between the populations.

Evaluation of the significance of autopolyploidy in systematics depends on our evaluation of the taxonomic significance of the rate of gene exchange. It is my argument that rate of gene exchange, although unquestionably of evolutionary significance, has no taxonomic significance whatever (Lewis, 1967). I will return to this question in relation to the taxonomic significance of chromosome morphology and differences in chromosome arrangement.

Chromosome morphology, as in the case of chromosome number, ordinarily has special significance in systematics only to the extent that it is indicative of chromosome rearrangement or other structural differences that affect genetic continuity. Chromosome morphology changes, of course, with the division cycle and, understandably, it is studied most often at mitotic metaphase when the chromosomes are fully contracted. Pachytene chromosomes show greater morphological detail than is shown at metaphase, but for most organisms, analyzable pachytene preparations are very difficult to obtain, and even with favorable preparations a detailed study is tedious. So, it is not surprising that such studies are few—too few, in fact, to be of concern to the systematist.

A special situation exists with respect to the polytene chromosomes of *Drosophila* and other Diptera where pachytene-like patterns of chromosomal differentiation can be studied with relative ease. For this reason, *Drosophila* provides the only example I know of in which chromosome morphology has proved useful as an indication of species differentiation independent of the implied effect of the chromosomal difference itself. I refer to Carson's conclusion (1954), based entirely on association of chromosome markers, that two apparently morphologically indistinguishable sympatric populations of *Drosophila*—*D. bocainensis* and what he has called *D. parabocainensis*—do not interbreed.

Unfortunately, not all organisms have polytene chromosomes, and most systematists are fortunate if they have information concerning the relative size of the chromosomes at mitotic metaphase, the relative position of the centromere in each chromosome, and the location of the nucleolar organizer. For a great many organisms even these simple characteristics of the chromosomes are not easily determined. Even when this information is known it may not be useful to the systematist because metaphase karyotypes that appear identical may or may not be structurally homologous. Frequently, the net effect of multiple chromosomal rearrangements is to leave the gross morphology of the chromosomes unaltered. Whether chromosomes that appear to be alike actually differ in arrangement often can be determined by studying meiosis in hybrids. Gross differences are usually evident at some stage; for example, translocations may show up as rings or chains of chromosomes, paracentric inversions as anaphase bridges and fragments, and assorted rearrangements as a decrease in chiasma frequency, which is detected most readily by the presence of univalents. Although a study of meiosis in hybrids is the most powerful technique in comparative cytology, it does not necessarily reveal all structural differences because many small rearrangements have no evident effect on meiosis, a phenomenon that Stebbins (1945) has called cryptic structural hybridity. Furthermore, genes are known that prevent or reduce pairing between structural homologues.

When hybridization is used to determine chromosome homology, one usually has an opportunity at the same time to measure directly the fertility of the hybrid, in which case cytology becomes superfluous as an indicator of this aspect of genetic interaction. Cytology may provide an explanation for the observed level of fertility and may reveal structural heterozygosity indicative of genetic discontinuity, but also it may lead the systematist astray if he has great faith in the significance of cytological evidence. I will explain by giving an example from our studies of *Clarkia.*

The clarkias to which I refer are annual plants with a gametic number of nine chromosomes and karyotypes that are morphologically indistinguishable. They occur in discrete but numerous colonies in the foothills to the east of the San Joaquin Valley of California and disjunctly in the South Coast Ranges to the west of the valley. Morphologically, one can recognize six distinct modes that are expressed geographically; four replace one another in the South Coast Ranges, and the other two occur in adjacent areas on the east side of the valley. They differ from one another conspicuously in flower color, color pattern, growth habit, and (in some instances) in soils on which they grow (Lewis, 1959; Mosquin and Lewis, 1959; Lewis and Mosquin, unpublished data).

Because of the striking morphological differences, hybrids in all combinations were obtained. We found that the chromosomes are structurally comparable and the hybrids fully fertile, with the exception of the more northern entity on the east side of the valley. This exceptional group gave hybrids with each of the others that showed very large rings or chains of chromosomes at meiosis, indicating a difference in their genomes of six or seven translocations. As might be expected, these hybrids had very low fertility, which could be attributed primarily if not entirely to irregularities in the formation and segregation of the rings and chains. With this evidence available, we confidently described the exceptional entity as *Clarkia nitens;* the remainder we designated as subspecies of *Clarkia speciosa* (Lewis and Lewis, 1955). The taxonomic and genetic relationship could not have been clearer, and we had cytological data to prove it.

Then, in a study of the comparative cytology of all the species of section *Godetia,* to which *Clarkia nitens* and *C. speciosa* belong, the cross between them was repeated, using a different population of *C. speciosa polyantha,* the subspecies adjacent to *C. nitens* on the east side of the San Joaquin Valley. To my surprise, the hybrids showed no large catenations of chromosomes and were fully fertile. Clearly this population of *polyantha* was conspecific with *C. nitens.* Furthermore, morphologically indistinguishable populations of *polyantha* from the northern and southern parts of its range were found to give hybrids of very low fertility that showed the very large rings of chromosomes earlier found in the hybrids of *C. nitens.* When a larger number of populations were intercrossed by Dr. Mosquin, the chromosomal discontinuity was found to be located near the middle of the geographical range of *polyantha,* far removed from any of the conspicuous morphological discontinuities. Here, then, was a chromosomal difference having profound effect on fertility; and when this difference was associated with phenotypic difference, it became the deciding factor in the recognition of *C. nitens* as a species.

Now that we find that the chromosomal barrier is not associated with phenotypic differentiation, does it still have the same taxonomic weight it had before? Conceptually, do we have two biological species that have adjacent morphologically indistinguishable populations? The biological species concept as ordinarily interpreted would lead one to this conclusion, but only, I suggest, because in our systematic evaluations all genetic barriers are deemed equivalent. Many systematists seemingly have reached the conclusion—to paraphrase Gertrude Stein—that a genetic barrier is a barrier is a barrier is an isolating mechanism. With this in mind, let us re-examine the *polyantha* situation.

Unquestionably, the chromosomal barrier to gene exchange between northern and southern populations of *polyantha* is formidable. Not only does it reduce fertility to a very low level and thereby greatly restrict the rate of gene exchange, but also it is recognized that translocations prevent recombination in the vicinity of the exchange. The combined effect of six or seven translocations surely represents a major genetic discontinuity. On the other hand, the chromosomal difference is not recent, to judge from the morphological differentiation within both chromosomal groups. The morphological identity of populations on each side of the chromosomal barrier strongly suggests there is genetic continuity between them despite the barrier. Is this possible? I have no doubt that it is, and a study of the chromosomes provides, I believe, the probable answer.

Clarkia chromosomes, like those of a great many other organisms, are heterochromatic near the centromere; consequently, if the breaks that resulted in translocation occurred in the heterochromatic region the genetic discontinuity may involve only heterochromatin. If, as evidence indicates, the genetic effect of heterochromatin is nonspecific, the effect of the discontinuity may be nil as long as the quantity of heterochromatin remains essentially the same. Low fertility of the hybrids, therefore, may be the only effect of the chromosomal reorganization. Although the rate of gene exchange is undoubtedly greatly reduced, a low rate of gene exchange, as I have argued in the case of autopolyploidy, has no taxonomic significance. Gene exchange between the chromosomally differentiated populations of *polyantha* may be very infrequent—just as it is between conspecific populations separated by distance—but not so infrequent as to prevent genetic innovation in one from reaching the other.

Genetic continuity between populations can be maintained by extremely low rates of gene exchange, and the populations will become genetically comparable provided that immigrant alleles once introduced into a population have a selective advantage or at least are not selected against. In systematics, therefore, it is reasonable on genetic grounds to disregard rate of gene exchange, even an extremely low rate, particularly since we do not insist on any actual gene exchange between conspecific populations. Populations that we suspect or know to be fully interfertile we unhesitatingly place in the same species even if they occur on different continents where they have not exchanged a gene for millenia and may never exchange one again. Does it make any difference in systematics, therefore, whether a low rate of gene exchange is due to infrequent hybridization, as in the case of distance, or to low fertility of the hybrid? If not, and I would so argue, there is no reason to interpret the chromosomally differentiated populations of *polyantha* as sibling, biological, or any other kind of species. Nor is there any reason to conclude that they are on the way to becoming species. By all criteria, *Clarkia nitens* is equivalent taxonomically to the other geographically expressed modes that we have called subspecies.

In conclusion, the special significance of comparative cytology in systematics lies in the usefulness of chromosomal differences as indicators of otherwise unsuspected or unproved genetic barriers between populations; but a chromosomal barrier to gene exchange, with all that it implies, has no significance in systematics unless it functions, at least by inference, to maintain genetic discontinuity between genetically differentiated populations.

REFERENCES

Carson, H. L. 1954. Interfertile sibling species in the *willistoni* group of *Drosophila.* Evolution 8:148–165.
Lewis, H. 1959. The nature of plant species. J. Arizona Acad. Sci. 1:3–7.
Lewis, H. 1967. The taxonomic significance of autopolyploidy. Taxon 16:267–271.
Lewis, H., and M. E. Lewis. 1955. The genus *Clarkia.* Univ. California Pub. Bot. 20:241–392.
Mosquin, T., and H. Lewis. 1959. [Abstract.] Variation in relation to reciprocal translocations in a diploid species of *Clarkia* (Onagraceae). Proc. IX Int. Bot. Congr. 2:272.
Stebbins, G. L. 1945. The cytological analysis of species hybrids. Bot. Rev. 11:463–486.

Discussion

R. C. Jackson

Although by design Dr. Lewis has considered only chromosomes in his discussion, we should recognize that ultrastructure studies of other cellular components are very useful to taxonomists working on so-called lower groups of plants and animals. Electron microscopy has been utilized to resolve structure at or below the power of the optical research microscope and has allowed truly comparative studies of cilia and flagella, cell-wall development and microanatomy, and various cytoplasmic organelles.

In regard to cytoplasmic organelles, it is important to note the presence of DNA in plastids, mitochondria, and such other structures as kinetosomes. In plants, especially, the interaction and possible complementarity of plastid and mitochondrial DNA with nuclear DNA may help to explain differences in fertility of reciprocal F_1 hybrids.

Dr. Lewis has discussed the application of cytological traits to systematics, but such traits are of little use to systematists if they are not used properly. In a conference such as this, I believe it is necessary that we recognize our shortcomings in the utilization of various disciplines and techniques in systematic studies.

Cytology, and more specifically cytogenetics, is now one of the older, and I believe more important, tools of the newer systematics. One would expect, therefore, a high degree of sophistication in the utilization and knowledge of this discipline. Unfortunately, this is not generally the case. For example, one reads in many cytotaxonomic papers only that the chromosome number of various taxa is such and such and that meiosis apparently was normal. The more venturesome worker may go so far as to draw elaborate phylogenetic relationships based on a series of different meiotic chromosome counts. Others may report the chromosome number in parental species and natural or artificial hybrids and comment that *pairing* at diakinesis or metaphase I of meiosis was normal, as was anaphase I. In doing so they apparently forget, or do not know, that pericentric inversion, deletion or duplication, and small reciprocal translocation configurations may not be detectable at these later stages and that pairing occurred only through pachytene. Such data as chiasma frequencies or even the number of cells studied are rarely given.

One commonly sees the statement that earlier meiotic stages could not be analyzed, but I contend that very often some information, and possibly a great deal, may be obtained from so-called nonanalyzable stages. Even when pachytene stages look like a mass of spaghetti, one can observe translocation, inversion, and duplication or deletion configurations. Many of these cytological aberrations, which are not detected by late meiotic prophase, metaphase I, or anaphase I, are thrown into the cryptic structural hybridity category of Stebbins, but their cryptic nature is due largely to an incomplete analysis.

Many cytotaxonomic studies of polyploids and their putative ancestors have not considered chiasma frequency, preferential pairing, or the possible dominance for some morphological characters by one of the parents of the original F_1 hybrid before designating the kind of polyploid involved. Taxonomic hierarchies are still used to define different kinds of polyploids, despite evidence that this can be misleading. Frequently, changes in the phenotypes of diverging taxa go hand in hand with changes in differential chromosome affinity, but this is not always the situation. Some studies have demonstrated that differential affinity can develop independently of observable phenotypic changes; and the converse is true, of course.

The increasing use of karyotype data from animals and from some plants has brought forth statements that are, at the very least, questionable. For example, it is asserted that if a certain species of one subgenus has a karyotype more like some species of a second subgenus (or genus), there is need for reassessment of the classification. I would hope that even the most elementary cytological knowledge would make clear the fact that chromosome structure can vary independently of external phenotype. Even where there is some question as to the placement of a taxon in the current system, I see no compelling reason why karyotype *per se* (or a meiotic chromosome count, as has been suggested by some botanists) should result in a change of the classification scheme employed. Certainly, more information than just chromosome number or karyotype usually is needed.

Ideally, one can best use cytogenetic analyses in controlled experiments where the attributes of particular parental types can be studied and compared in detail with F_1 and succeeding generations. However, as Dr. Lewis has pointed out, highly significant results can be obtained from studies of natural hybrids and parental populations, and these data, as with those from controlled experiments, can be used in determining lineage relationships.

A cytotaxonomist recently commented that cytotaxonomy is best left to taxonomists trained in cytology. I would agree with this statement if the taxonomist has been trained in cytogenetics, but too frequently the training is largely taxonomic, with a little training in chromosome counting. Some cytological data are better than none, but the investigator should realize that after he has gone to the trouble of making a good preparation it takes only a little more effort and training to derive maximum information from it.

Discussion

Walter H. Lewis

I shall not attempt to discuss the excellent paper by Dr. Lewis in its entirety. Rather, in these few pages I will try to elaborate on an aspect in which I am in only partial agreement with him.

For my examples I shall use two species. One of these—already noted by Dr. Lewis as one that does not take its chromosome number seriously—is *Claytonia virginica* L. From published accounts, the abnormality referred to by Dr. Lewis appears to be true. In fact, however, the only populational example of bizarre chromosomal abnormality is in the New York City area where numbers vary from $2n = 85$ to about 191. Whatever the stimulus might be for this binge I do not know, but some have suggested that getting the New York smog count from Dr. Cronquist would at least provide something for the chromosome count to correlate with!

Elsewhere, however, the situation is more orderly. Of the diploid cytotypes, the one having $n = 6$ is restricted to the geologically old and well-known relict and refugial area in the southern Applachian Mountains. Here, occurring in mixed and separate populations, are plants with $n = 7$. This race is also found in the geologically similar Ozarks, and it occurs as a common weed south of these mountains almost to the Gulf of Mexico. The third major diploid race, with $n = 8$, dominates the northern distribution of *C. virginica* and has by far the greatest continuous range of any diploid.

The primary tetraploid cytotypes of each of the diploid races ($n = 12, 14, 16$) are very common and have widespread overlapping distributions. Secondary tetraploids and higher polyploids are less frequent (W. H. Lewis, R. L. Oliver, and Y. Suda, "Cytogeography of *Claytonia virginica* and Its Allies," Annals of the Missouri Botanical Garden, 54:153–171, 1967).

Illustrated on a frequency basis with suggested evolutionary lines, in Figure 1, we find: an increase from the relict $n = 6$ race to the widespread cytotype with $n = 8$; a high frequency of the three primary autotetraploid races; a significant number of secondary autotetraploids; and, finally, a dominance of the $x = 6$ line among higher autopolyploids. So far, in no instance has a triploid—a so-called cytotypic bridge—been found, even among mixed $2x$–$4x$ populations.

Looking quickly at this species' only ally in eastern North America, we find that *C. caroliniana* Michx. has but two dominant cytotypes distinct by four pairs of chromosomes—namely $n = 8$ and $n = 12$. Heretofore these dominant races failed to have meaning in a cytological sense, but if the fact of their existence is superimposed on the results from *C. virginica,* perhaps they do. First eliminate the two diploid races of $n = 6$ and $n = 7$, both of which are of restricted

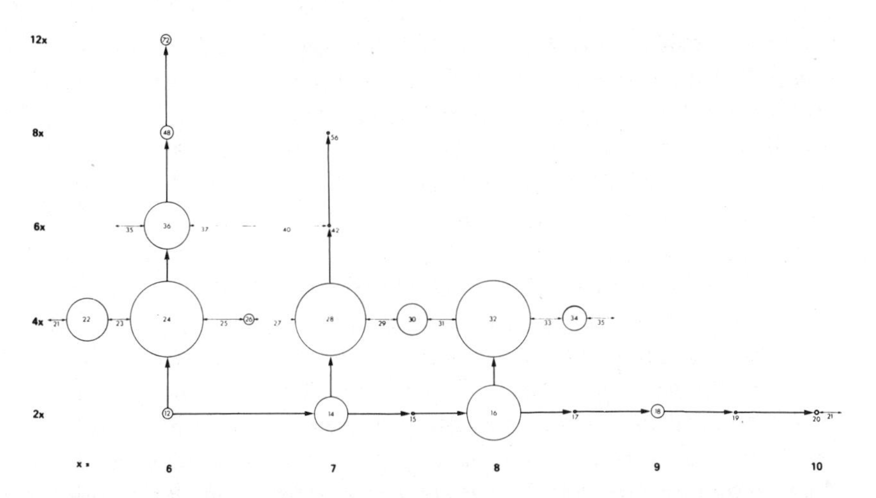

FIGURE 1 Comparative frequency of cytotypes (as $2n$) in *Claytonia virginica* and suggested evolutionary direction. The smallest circle represents the occurrence of a race in one population; other circles are to scale.

frequency in *C. virginica,* but before their extinction evolve the $n = 8$ aneudiploid race by chromosomal gain. Then by chromosomal doubling form an autotetraploid from $n = 6$ giving rise to an $n = 12$ race which is clearly a dominant one in *C. virginica.* The same infraspecific phylogeny applies to the related *C. lanceolata* Pursh from the Rocky Mountains and several other species in the West.

I think the implication here is clear—that *C. caroliniana* has advanced more rapidly than *C. virginica* in its chromosomal evolution. Its redundant chromosomes apparently have been selected for and largely stabilized at $n = 8$ and $n = 12$. Moreover, the races are geographically separate, though possibly not disjunct (data are meager for the mid-Applachian area): $n = 8$ is northern; $n = 12$ is southern. Additionally, the races can usually be separated morphologically, the narrow-leafed form being common at higher elevations of the southern Applachians and the broad-leafed form widespread to the north.

I would agree with Dr. Lewis that the taxonomist concerned solely with categories should maintain the many cytologically diverse populations of *C. virginica* under one species—they look essentially alike and they do not look like anything else. But I suspect the taxonomist who is also interested in its evolution will appreciate the significance of the low (or even nonexistent) gene exchange between, for example, the three groups of $2x$ and $4x$ races. The final outcome of such cellular diversity and isolation is unknown, of course, and a taxonomic treatment hardly could attempt to forecast it, but nevertheless a situation important for speciation exists. (More current data appear in the previously cited work by Lewis, Oliver, and Suda).

The case of *C. caroliniana* is, I believe, more acute. Here I would disagree with the conclusion of Dr. Lewis that "the rate of gene exchange [between populations] has no taxonomic significance." There is little doubt that gene exchange between the two cytotypes of *C. caroliniana* is very low, if not absent. This near or complete genetic discontinuity is correlated with both geographical and morphological differences; consequently, I consider the species of immediate concern to systematists interested in naming and describing taxa as well as to those interested in evolution. In other words, *C. caroliniana* has arrived at a stage of differentiation that is of interest and concern to everyone in systematics.

Infraspecific chromosomal changes in *C. virginica* and *C. caroliniana* unquestionably are excessive compared with most species, but they do serve to emphasize the need for a re-evaluation of autoploidy and its significance in evolution. As Dr. Ornduff noted, our thinking on autoploidy may have become stereotyped by an early introduction to the phenomenon. We learned that autoploid organisms usually are meiotically abnormal, that they are less fertile, and often more ephemeral than their diploids, and that essentially they are unimportant in speciation. There is some evidence accumulating to show that such characteristics are by no means universally true. Certainly they do not characterize *C. virginica, C. caroliniana,* and ten or so other species of *Claytonia* with known chromosomal diversity. Clearly, our box-like approach to certain problems (such as autoploidy) in comparative cytology in relation to systematics is changing. This conference is a good example of how the box may be opened to admit air.

Informal Discussion

GOTTLIEB: Dr. Lewis stressed the importance of very low rates of gene exchange between populations. In the populations of *Clarkia speciosa* about which he spoke, the gene exchange was very low, and the morphological discontinuity was very slight. It would seem that a fairly large amount of gene exchange occurred in this case. Would you comment further on the evolutionary consequences of such low rates of gene exchange?

LEWIS: Your question involves two matters–the rate of gene exchange and the amount of gene exchange. One can easily show that if a low rate of gene exchange continues for a sufficiently long time, with nothing interfering with it, the amount of exchange will be as great as a high rate of exchange over a shorter time. Comparable genotypes on each side of a barrier may indicate that the genes have gone across very fast; or it may mean that the situation has existed for a great many generations during which time, since genes in one population are equally well adapted in populations on opposite sides of the barrier, the populations have become genetically comparable.

As for the evolutionary consequences, gene exchange increases the variability of the populations that are exchanging genes, and most of us would agree that the availability of variability is of evolutionary significance. The incorporation of genes from other populations–introgression–may permit adjustment to the environment that would not be possible without this variability. Shutting off all gene exchange can be considered detrimental because a population must then generate all variability within itself. Rate of gene exchange has relevance to amount only if it is too low to provide the variability needed by a population to adjust to change before it becomes extinct.

BESCHEL: I ask Dr. Lewis whether he is serious in saying that, in a way, it does not matter if you cannot distinguish the species morphologically, and on the other hand, that it does not matter that taxonomic studies go into so much detail. As a morphological taxonomist who has to make determinations in the field, I wonder whether the cytologist could provide bottles of Navaschin's fixing fluid, or something like that, for use by field botanists; or perhaps organize a center that would make root squashes and provide us with determinations for critical morphological specimens. In the field one is not aware of just what kind of morphological difficulty he will meet with. I think the cytologists also would profit from this kind of cooperation, providing a service something like that done by Isotopes, Inc., in dating. Why not provide a counting system for us?

LEWIS: I certainly have no objection to anyone counting all the chromosomes he wants to count; and I would be very happy to supply him with the material to do so. Before you embark upon this particular sort of labor or ask for this service, you ought to consider what a chromosome count is going to do for you as a taxonomist interested in classifying organisms. There should be a clear distinction made between (1) intensively studying the chromosomes and other aspects of an organism—as some do in terms of its populations, and perhaps spend a lifetime working within a single species and learning a tremendous amount about it—and (2) using that information to construct a formal taxonomy. The taxonomic designation *"Clarkia speciosa"* conveys a certain amount of information, but it does not tell one what is known about variation in that taxon or the amount and kind of data on which the classification is based.

HELTNE: I would like to ask Dr. Lewis to explain in greater detail what he means by "genetically differentiated."

LEWIS: This, of course, extends from differentiation with respect to a single gene to having no two genes in common; there is a continuous spectrum. Therefore, when one uses genetic differentiation in relation to classification he must do so subjectively.

RAVEN: I was greatly impressed by the scope of the preceding paper and its associated discussions, which demonstrated so clearly some of the diverse situations with which plant systematists must deal. I would like, however, to offer one technical comment on the discussion by Dr. Walter Lewis. The mere absence of triploids in natural populations containing a mixture of diploid and tetraploid individuals should not be taken as a demonstration of the lack of hybridization in such situations, for the progeny of diploid × tetraploid crosses are often tetraploid (e.g., Avers, 1957). Furthermore, as Dr. Ornduff pointed out during yesterday's session, hybridization and the establishment of hybrids are very different; and as suggested by the examples he cited as well as by the work of Jones (1958), the balance between them may be extremely critical and responsive to subtle control by variation in environmental parameters.

REFERENCES

Avers, Charlotte J. 1957. Fertile hybrids derived from a wide species cross in *Aster.* Evolution 11:482–486.

Jones, K. 1958. Cytotaxonomic studies in *Holcus.* I. The chromosome complex in *Holcus mollis* L. New Phytol. 57:191–210.

R. A. REYMENT

Biometrical Techniques in Systematics

The task I have been given at this conference concerns biometrical techniques in systematics. In order to keep the presentation within reasonable limits, it will be necessary to assume that the listener has a certain acquaintance with statistical principles and jargon. Biometry may be defined as the application of the results of mathematical statistics to biological problems. As a branch of applied statistics, biometry may be considered as having a relatively long history, although its birth as a unified scheme of approach would appear to have been some 80 to 90 years ago in England.

Owing perhaps to its English-language origins, biometry's main strides in development have been taking place in the areas of English expression. To a large extent I think it is now safe to concur with Simpson *et al.* (1960), Bartlett (1965) and Sokal (1965) with respect to the observation, in the words of Bartlett, that "that there should be no need to argue a case for the essential role of statistics in quantitative biology," at least as far as the "anglophone" areas are concerned. There is still a sad lag in many parts of Europe in recognizing this fact, but lately there have been many encouraging signs that this condition is undergoing a substantial change.

The aim of this paper is to give a brief review of biometric methods that have been applied to problems in systematics and to discuss newer results that either have been based on biologic considerations or seem to offer promise of potential usefulness. For an orientation in the background of statistical procedures in systematics,

I cannot do better than to refer to the excellent account by Sokal (1965).

For this paper, the subject of systematics is regarded in a broad sense, notably, the grouping of organisms into taxa, the motivation of these groupings, and the relationships among the taxa (Simpson, 1961). For the purposes of discussion, the techniques are presented in the form of "models," even though "groups of models" might be a better term for some of the techniques. Moreover, the models are not to be regarded as statistically homogeneous concepts; rather, biological considerations have been used in deciding what constitutes a model in the current connection.

BIOMETRICAL ANALYSIS AND SYSTEMATICS

Traditionally, descriptive biometry comprises two main sections–univariate statistics and multivariate statistics. The very fact that almost all data obtained by systematists are based on several variables means that most techniques employed will, of necessity, be multivariate. It is clear that the univariate analysis of the variables often is a logical and useful first step in the treatment of data and should by no means be ignored. Some biologists tend to regard the multivariate examination of their data as supplementary (Rao, 1960, 1961); but now there is sufficient evidence to show that certain multivariate methods are vital techniques in the routine analysis and interpretation of biologic problems. Other multivariate procedures are more specifically applicable to exploratory work. Another point to be borne in mind is that whereas the immediate aim of a biologic project may be to answer a particular problem by means of a simple univariate analysis, which is quite adequate, a multivariate treatment of the data may disclose unsuspected properties that may be useful for continued research. Problems arising in systematic work that are amenable to biometric analysis are numerous. Fields of application occur in the *analysis of infraspecific variation* (Rensch, 1954), which embraces the dynamics of evolutionary processes. It is now well known that many of the basic tenets of genetics such as natural selection, gene flow, genetic drift, and polymorphism rest largely on a statistical foundation. The analysis of fossil associations is a virtually untouched field of research which may be expected to yield much information on evolutionary processes. Studies made *between populations** analyze statistical differences arising from geographic, and/or ecologic, chronologic, or other causes.

Characters suitable for biometric analysis may be of any measurable kind—morphometric, physiologic, ethologic and, where the information is available, gene frequencies. An important question to which attention ought to be paid in these investigations concerns the filtering out of environmental effects on the phenotype from genetically determined variation (e.g., Reyment and Naidin, 1962). In paleontology, for example, it is possible to approach this problem only by means of suitable statistical models. In neontology, one may attempt a combined experimental-biometrical approach.

A major task of systematics concerns the delineation of species. Very few neontologists of today, be they quantitatively oriented or not, adhere starkly to the typologic concept of days past, although paleontologists generally lag grievously in this respect.

As Sokal (1965) has pointed out, differences between species often are so obvious that statistical tests in support of their validity would be ludicrous. Biometric analysis first plays a role when it is required to examine the variation within a given species.

Statistical inference is in the nature of inductive logic and, as is to be expected, is subject to controversy. A systematist using statistical procedures should be aware of this as well as of modern trends in statistical inference.

MODEL I: ANALYSIS OF A SINGLE SAMPLE

The only type of sample considered here will be multivariate normal. A question frequently posed by the biologist concerns how many and which variables should be selected for a particular study. This question cannot be answered satisfactorily solely by a statistician because it involves a combination of biologic and statistical principles. From a statistical point of view, it is not particularly useful to base a multivariate analysis on a set of variables that are highly correlated with each other. This point becomes clearer if we consider a morphometric study involving, for example, p variables. If one adds a $(p + 1)$th variable, which is highly correlated with the original vari-

*The term "population" is used here in the biological sense; statistical populations are referred to as "universes."

ables, the amount of additional information introduced is slight, and therefore statistically uneconomical. In spite of this, however, there may be some overriding biologic reason not apparent to a statistician that necessitates the inclusion of this variable. Because of their relative availability, morphometric variables have been most used in neontology and paleontology; nevertheless, publications using physiologic, biochemical, and ethologic variables are becoming more frequent. By the very nature of fossils, paleontologists have to use more ingenuity in finding variables other than morphologic ones. However, this is not an impossible task, and information other than morphometric may be extracted from the shells of many fossils. For example, electron-microscopic and biochemical studies of organic material preserved in fossil shell substance may provide a source of useful data for statistical analysis; and it is also possible, in some groups of fossils, to make use of paleoethologic variables (Reyment, 1963a, 1966 a and b).

The analysis of a multivariate sample may be regarded as the study of the ellipsoid of scatter of the characters chosen. Such an analysis is approached most readily by way of the eigenvalues and eigenvectors of the covariance matrix of the variates (the so-called principal components).*

*In the ensuing discussions, the following conventions will be observed: Vectors will be denoted by lower case, Roman letters (except for the random observation vector, X) and matrices by Roman capital letters. As an example of a frequently occurring vector, we have the mean values of the characters $x_1, x_2, \ldots, x_p$ written as $\bar{x}' = (\bar{x}_1, \bar{x}_2, \ldots, \bar{x}_p)$. Although it may not be obvious, a set of measurements is equivalent, mathematically, to the vectors of, for example, physics. It sometimes is convenient to interpret a vector as a $(1 \times p)$ array or matrix. A $(p \times p)$ matrix comprises p rows and p columns. For example, the matrix of variances and covariances, hereinafter referred to as the covariance matrix, of a Universe is written:

$$\Sigma = \left\{ \begin{matrix} \sigma_{11}\ \sigma_{12} \ldots \sigma_{1\ell} \\ \sigma_{21}\ \sigma_{22} \ldots \sigma_{2\ell} \\ \vdots \\ \sigma_{\ell 1}\ \sigma_{\ell 2} \ldots \sigma_{\ell\ell} \end{matrix} \right.$$

The σ_{ii} are the variances of the Universe for the $i = 1, \ell$ variables, and the σ_{ij} are the covariances of these variables. Finally, following a convention introduced some 40 years ago by R. A. Fisher, Greek letters are employed to denote Universe quantities and Roman letters for the sample counterparts.

The use of principal components analysis for the description of growth has gained some vogue of late (Jolicoeur, 1963), but the idea was used by Teissier more than 30 years ago. There is a fair body of empirical evidence to support this interpretation, but also there seems to be some difference of opinion with respect to details. It is possible to identify artificially produced growth patterns by means of the first eigenvector of the logarithmic covariance matrix, which has been done (e.g., by Reyment, 1966c) for a negative coefficient of allometry. Among the objections leveled against the PCA interpretation of growth we observe that Rao (1964) has pointed out that *size* and *shape* are not well-defined concepts, and I think most biologists will concur. In a well-known paper, Penrose (1947) gave a definition of size as the linear function:

$$\frac{X_1}{\sigma_1} + \cdots + \frac{c_p X_p}{\sigma_p},$$

where σ_i is the standard deviation of variable X_i and p is the number of variables. As a definition of shape, Penrose suggested a function:

$$\frac{c_1 X_1}{\sigma_1} + \cdots + \frac{c_p X_p}{\sigma_p},$$

with $c_1 + \ldots + c_p = 0$.

The principal components interpretation of size and shape have properties similar to the functions of Penrose. If we regard the elements of the first eigenvector, say, $ba^{(1)}$, considered as an equation:

$$y_1 = b_1^{(1)} x_1 + b_2^{(1)} x_2 + \ldots + b_p^{(1)} x_p,$$

where $b^{(1)}$ is the eigenvector and p is the number of variables. If all the elements of this eigenvector are positive, a unit increase in y_1 increases the value of each X_i and, therefore, one could think of the expression in terms of *size variation.* If, as is often the case for morphometric variables, some of the elements of the second, and subsequent, eigenvectors are positive and some are negative, a unit increase in, say, y_2 increases the value of some of the X's and decreases the value of those with negative signs. Such eigenvectors might be thought of as shape factors. Rao (1964) has approached the biometical analysis of *shape* and *size* with respect to a given set of measurements $X_1, \ldots, X_p$ in terms of instrumental variables, $Z_1, \ldots, Z_m$, where the latter may include some or all of the former. For example, it may be desired to find a *size factor* of the head as characterized by head length (X_2) and head breadth (X_2) using $Z_1 = X_1$, $Z_2 = X_2$, and, in addition thereto, stature (Z_3) and chest girth (Z_4).

Let Σ be the covariance matrix of variables X_1 and X_2, Ω the covariance matrix between variables X_1, X_2, Z_1, Z_2, Z_3, Z_4, and Γ the covariance matrix for variables Z_1, Z_2, Z_3, Z_4. As input information, one requires a vector $\mathrm{r} = (r_1, r_2)$, which represents the ratios in which X_1 and X_2 change for a unit increase in the shape or size factor. This introduces a certain element of arbitrariness, but this element may not be unpleasant to the biologist, who thereby is able to exercise some control over the investigation and may be able to supply useful selections with respect to the vector elements, based on particular biologic knowledge or experience. If there are no special assumptions on which to base the choice, useful selections for the size factor are: $r_1 = 1; r_2 = 1$, or, $r_1 = \sigma_1, r_2 = -\sigma_2$, where σ_1 and σ_2 are the standard deviations of X_1 and X_2. Similarly for the shape factor, $r_1 = 1$, $r_2 = -1$, or, $r_1 = \sigma_1$, $r_2 = -\sigma_2$. The idea behind the extra variables, chosen on the grounds of expert biologic knowledge, is that they should give a better estimate of the shape of the head. It may be suggested, therefore, that the linear function to be determined

$$b_2 Z_1 + b_2 Z_2 + b_3 Z_3 + b_4 Z_4,$$

is a better size-shape estimator than just $b_1 Z_1 + b_2 Z_2$. For the estimation procedures, I refer to Rao (1964:345).

The approach by means of *instrumental variables* of the kind discussed in the foregoing model has been reviewed in a biological connection by Carlson *et al.* (1966), who have investigated the so-called Model II Regression, in which predictor and predicted variables are subject to error. The procedure advocated by these authors is one in common use in certain econometric models. These instrumental variables are selected so as to be uncorrelated with the errors in, say, the two variables being studied in a bivariate connection, and they may be used to predict one of these variables.

Another way of approaching the study of size and shape of organisms, with particular emphasis on trees of economic importance, has been tried by Fries and Matern (1966). While their model may hardly be claimed to be biological, it does not appear to be without taxonomic possibilities. They view the problem from the point of view of estimating yield from economically useful trees, in connection with which the forester requires a model that will express "taper" (= shape) and growth. The variables considered useful by foresters are measurements on the bark thickness at selected distances apart along the trunk, the multidimensionality of the model thus being decided by the density of sampling location. An expression such as $A[f_1(x) + Bf_2(x)]$ may be used to give a simple representation of the situation, where A is a *size* expression and B is a *growth* expression. Polynomials were used to give a two-parameter family of functions. The principal components of a set of regressions provide the basis for the analysis. If the polynomial selected gives an adequate representation of the growth–size interrelationship, the first two principal components should be sufficient for an adequate model. In a study of birch, Fries and Matérn interpreted the first principal component to reflect size variation. The second component could not be given a precise determination, but it was thought to be connected with "butt swell"; the third component was considered to be a shape factor. In view of the remarks that have been made concerning the rationale of rotating principal components (Imbrie, 1963; Seal, 1964), it may be noted that Fries and Matérn determine two orthogonal expressions by a process which, in effect, is equivalent to the rotation to "simple structure" as practiced in factor analysis. This was done in the hope of clarifying the results of the PCA.

DISCUSSION OF ALLOMETRY

Figure 1 gives an idea of how one might relate growth and shape of an organism by means of the major axes of the ellipsoid of scatter. To relate this to a multivariate concept of allometry, the covari-

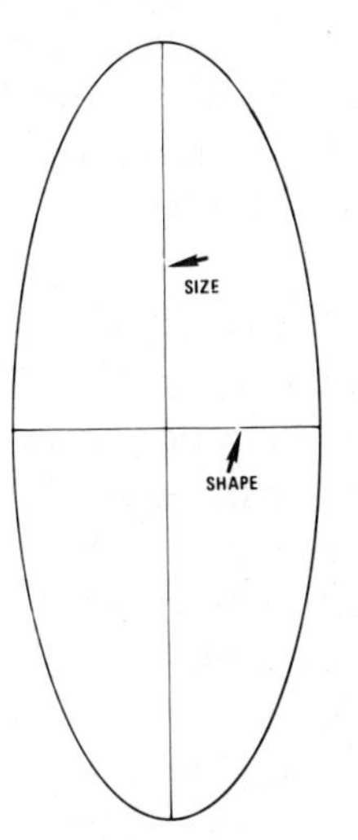

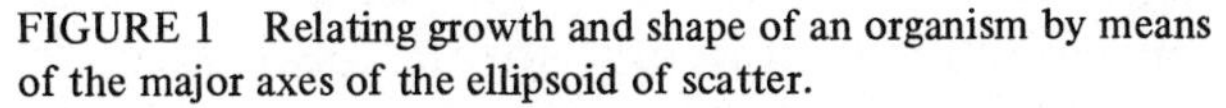
FIGURE 1 Relating growth and shape of an organism by means of the major axes of the ellipsoid of scatter.

ance matrix is based on the logarithmically transformed variables. While it may be justly claimed that the use of "unstandardized" measurements may be an aid to interpretation, at least in some studies, it seems advisable to standardize the variables. Gould (1966) has recently reviewed the terminology of allometry. The most readily appreciable allometric category is that of *ontogenetic allometry,* which may be considered in two lights: first, where one has access to data on each individual, and second, where the data comprise observations on a sample of individuals at different growth stages. Where the second kind of material is used in paleontology, the sample will, in general, suffer from the bias caused by the fact that the young individuals met a natural death, unless the sample represents a catastrophe. One also may think in terms of *evolutionary allometry,* in connection with which the samples will consist mostly of adults. These categories are a result of a genetic continuity of relationships. Allometry among members of a single population also may be studied; here, the adult usually will be the single growth stage requisite for analysis, but the adults would be of different size. This category often is referred to as *intraspecific allometry* or *individual allomorphosis.* Allometry among races or subspecies at the same growth stage (usually adult) but of different size sometimes is called *race allomorphosis.* It is also possible to consider a type of allometry with respect to species of a single genus, etc., at the same growth stage, but of different sizes. Gould has suggested a wider definition of allometry so as to have it cover changes in proportion, correlated with size variation of either the whole organism or some part of it (morphologic, physiologic, chemical). (See also Cock, 1966.)

In examining some of the principles underlying the concept of multivariate allometry, Hopkins (1967) has presented a more persuasive case for the greater generality of a factor-analytic model for multivariate allometry than the PCA model. The basic model used by Hopkins is that the Universe multivariate covariance matrix is of the form $\Sigma = \Psi + \Delta$, with Ψ deriving from systematic covariance and Δ from independent random variance of the measurements of the variables of the organism. For isometry or allometry, Ψ must be of Rank 1 for the logarithmically transformed observations. In this case, the elements of the first eigenvector of Ψ will be proportional to the "structural parameters" of the allometric growth pattern. Where Ψ was of Rank 1 but the variables displayed unequal random discrepancy variance, the first eigenvectors of Σ and Ψ were found to differ, and this most strongly where few variables were considered. A single general factor model appears to be the most useful approach for this kind of situation. If the random variance is proportional to the systematic variance, this means the diagonal elements of a matrix Σ will be proportional to the squares of the structural parameters. If all logarithmically transformed variables have the same random variance, the first eigenvectors of Σ and Ψ will be the same. The latter case is the one pertaining in Jolicoeur's (1963) model.

A clearly necessary prerequisite in an investigation of allometry is that the logarithmically transformed variates are free of size-dependent indications, as disclosed by the absence of significant nonlinearity.

Studies based on the model considered in this section must be formulated in terms of population concepts, as opposed to typologic thinking; and for this reason, it is hoped that this approach will be more widely adopted in paleontologic systematics, where typology still has a stronghold.

Further refinements in the interpretations of the multivariate statistical analysis of a population may be expected to lead to a better understanding of variation in the phenotype (nongenetic variation: cf. Mayr, 1963b:139; and Amtmann, 1966).

MODEL II: COMPARISON OF THE PROPERTIES OF TWO MULTIVARIATE SAMPLES

This model may be useful for supplying information on the agreement of growth directions and on comparative variability. Basically, the model may be regarded in the light of the geometric properties of two ellipsoids—in this case, ellipsoids of scatter. For the application of the statistical procedures to be correct, it is necessary that the variables be normally distributed. In the discussion of Model I, we have seen how the ellipsoid of scatter provides a representation of the multivariate variability of a population that is directly analogous to that of the well-known variance of univariate statistics. Also, in univariate statistics one will wish to make sure that the variances of the variable being analyzed are statistically equal for both populations and that they are normally distributed. The same reasoning applies in multivariate statistics. However, while it is not difficult to test the homogeneity of two variances, the test of homogeneity of covariance matrices is associated with certain drawbacks.

Referring back to the ellipsoid interpretation of the "scatter clouds" of the "variability" of the biological variables, it will readily be appreciated that if the variables are distributed in accordance with the multivariate normal distribution, the shape of a three-dimensional plot of many points will approximate a football equally flattened on two opposite sides. For a two-sample statistical comparison to be valid, one would require the footballs to be of the same size and to be oriented exactly in the same direction. It is possible to employ a large-sample test for ascertaining whether each principal axis of the ellipsoid of one sample is collinear with the corresponding principal axis of the other ellipsoid. It will be appreciated that in addition to the difference in orientation in the bivariate case (a simple example is shown in Figure 2), three-dimensional and higher-dimensional ellipsoids will also include the possibility of rotation. In the discussion of Model I, reference was made to the approximate growth interpretations possible in relation to the principal axes of the ellipsoids of the covariance matrix (eigenvectors). From the point of view of comparing "growth patterns" of two taxonomic entities, one might, therefore, approach the problem by comparing the orientations of the principal axes of the ellipsoids. In the foregoing section it was

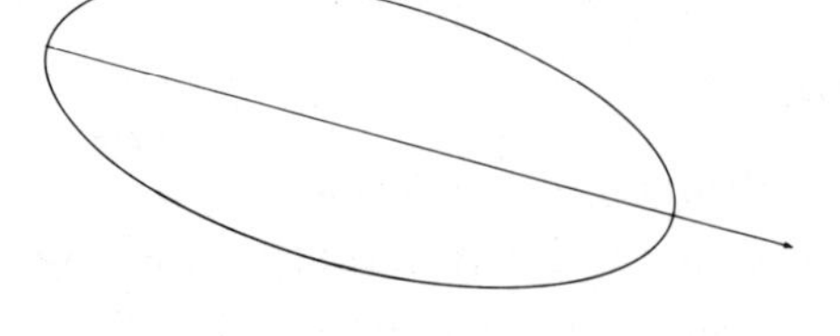

FIGURE 2 A simple example of difference in orientation in the bivariate case.

indicated in the discussion of allometry that if the logarithmically transformed variables have the same random variance, the first eigenvector of the covariance matrix will be proportional to the multivariate allometric coefficients. Where this situation prevails, it is possible to test the vectors of allometric coefficients for collinearity.

How serious a matter is it when the covariance matrices are not equal? One of the systematically interesting tests available for testing the difference between two populations on the grounds of a set of multivariate observations is the analogue of the *t*-test, the T^2-test of Hotelling. The effects of heterogeneity in covariance matrices in relation to this test have been studied by Ito and Schull (1964), who have made a preliminary large-sample analysis of the problem for two and more Universes. They have obtained the following results: where the covariance matrices are unequal but the samples are large and of equal size, the $T_0{}^2$-test is well-behaved; where two samples are almost equal in size, or for more than two samples of equal size, the test is not seriously affected by moderate inequality of covariance matrices if the samples are large; if some or all of the more than two samples are of unequal size, even moderate variations in the covariance matrices have an important effect on the level of significance and the power of the test. The univariate treatment of this problem may be followed, for example, in Scheffé (1959:334–338.) Other deviations of pertinence are violation of the assumption of multivariate normal distributions and violation of the assumption of serially uncorrelated observations.

In the univariate case, the measure of kurtosis enters into the form of the distribution as an appreciable factor if the distribution does not conform with the normal, whereas for normally distributed variables it is zero. If the measure of kurtosis differs appreciably from zero, an error may be introduced into any confidence coefficient, significance level, or power calculated under normal theory. Box (1953:318) has pointed out that comparative tests on means are insensitive to general nonnormality of the parent Universe and that this robust property is not shared by tests for equality of variances. The reason for the differential behavior of the mean in relation to the variance is that inferences about the mean are based on the distribution of a deviation measured against an internal estimate of error, calculated from the observations and valid without assumptions about normality, while inferences concerning the variance are based on the extent of the observed deviation measured against the percentage points of a theoretical distribution derived under the assumption that the effects characterized by the variances are normal.

As a practical illustration of the foregoing we may consider some calculations made on local populations of European *Rana temporaria* and *R. esculenta.* The analysis is based on the usual squared generalized distance, D^2, and the Anderson-Bahadur calculation of D^2 when the covariance matrices are not equal. The well-known Hotelling T^2 is calculated from the formula:

$$T^2 = (\bar{x}_1' - \bar{x}_2')S^{-1}(\bar{x}_1 - \bar{x}_2)\frac{N_1 N_2}{N_1 + N_2}, \qquad (1)$$

where the $\bar{x}_i$ are the sample mean vectors and S is the matrix of pooled variances and covariances; the N_i are the sample sizes. The quadratic form in the above equation is the Mahanalobis D^2.

Anderson and Bahadur (1962) considered a distance for the case of unequal covariance matrices as follows:

$$\frac{2\,b'd}{(b'S_1 b)^{1/2} + (b'S_2 b)^{1/2}}. \qquad (2)$$

Here, d is the vector of differences in the sample means, b is an analog of the vector of coefficients of the discriminant function, and S_1 and S_2 are the respective sample covariance matrices. When the covariance matrices are equal, this formula reduces to the Mahanalobis generalized distance times a constant. Although the Anderson-Bahadur distance is attractive to work with, it has not yet been connected with a test of significance. In order to obtain a significance test based on a T^2, one may proceed by means of a distance method suggested by the writer (Reyment, 1962). This method (as was pointed out at the time it was introduced) is not statistically economical because (1) it involves the loss of the degrees of freedom, and (2) it requires an average value of T^2 to be obtained, as it varies considerably under randomization. As a subroutine in a computer program, these objections are not serious for large samples. A program for tests of homogeneity of covariance matrices, the Mahanalobis' distance, Hotelling T^2, Anderson-Bahadur distance, and tests of significance will be issued shortly.*

As shown in Table 1, differences between the Anderson-Bahadur distance and the usual generalized distance may occur and be of greater magnitude than divergencies occurring where the covariance matrices are not equal. Where the differences in covariance matrices are large (and regardless of their origin), one can expect sizable unlikenesses between the two values of D^2. Generally, one might claim that for moderate inequality in covariance matrices the ordinary generalized distance is exceptionally robust; hence, in most systematic work involving living organisms, heterogeneity in covariance matrices hardly presents a problem. The situation in geology is more extreme; and owing to the interaction of various geologic factors, one may expect to encounter differences of a kind likely to influence the interpretation of generalized distance results. (See also Dempster, 1964.)

The generalized statistical distance is probably the best known and most widely used of the statistical techniques with respect to systematic work. It is intuitively attractive to the taxonomist to be able to obtain a graphical representation of his multivariate measurements in a way made possible by the topological repre-

*R. A. Reyment and W. J. Wahlstedt, "FORTRAN IV Program for Discriminant Functions and Generalized Statistical Distances for Homogeneous and Heterogeneous Covariance Matrices," *Computer Contributions,* State Geological Survey of Kansas.

TABLE 1 Squared Anderson-Bahadur Distances and Squared Mahanalobis' Distances for Seven Samples from Subpopulations of European *Rana* (*R. temporaria* and *R. esculenta*)

Sample		Mahanalobis D^2	Anderson-Bahadur D^2	Test for Heterogeneity of Covariance Matrices
R. temporaria:	N. Sweden, 40 males; S. Sweden, 33 males	3.10	3.90	Negative
R. temporaria:	N. Sweden, 30 females; S. Sweden, 33 females	0.07	0.07	Positive
R. temporaria: *R. esculenta:*	Vienna, 19 males; Vienna, 14 males	9.00	8.77	Negative
R. temporaria: *R. esculenta:*	Vienna, 28 females; Vienna, 35 females	3.37	4.02	Negative
R. esculenta:	Balkans, 29 females; Asia Minor, 28 females	1.40	1.49	Negative
R. esculenta:	N. Africa, 17 males; Spain, 8 males	0.69	0.63	Negative
R. esculenta:	N. Africa, 9 females; Spain, 12 females	5.82	7.51	Positive

sentation of a set of D^2 values. The extension allowed by the calculation of the Hotelling T^2, which permits one to obtain an opinion of the significance of taxonomic differences, is also a valuable asset. The philosophy behind the analysis of morphometric data based on multivariate measurements is due largely to the Indian school of statisticians, who first introduced the technique in conjunction with anthropomorphic studies of ethnic groups in India. The step from human beings to other organisms is not great, and the method soon appeared in taxonomic studies in zoology and botany. D^2 studies have been made of several tribes in East and West Africa and, in the sense of systematics, on various groups of vertebrates and invertebrates, fossil and living. Perhaps the most intensively studied group in this connection is that of the insects. The once time-consuming computations have been cut to a minimum (as regards human effort) by the availability of computers.

Many centers for computing have standard programs readily available for this work.

MODEL III: THE SIMULTANEOUS COMPARISON OF SEVERAL MULTIVARIATE SAMPLES

Cacoullos (1965) has investigated a problem of considerable potential used in systematics. As we have seen in the discussion of Model II, the usual form of the Mahanalobis generalized distance squared (for equal Universe covariance matrices) is

$$(\mu_1 - \mu_2)' \Sigma^{-1} (\mu_1 - \mu_2), \tag{3}$$

where μ_1 and μ_2 are the respective Universe mean vectors, and Σ is the pooled covariance matrix. Cacoullos considered the task of comparing squared generalized distances. The first problem he analyzed may be expressed in the following terms: Let Π_i be multivariate normal Universes with means μ_i ($i = 0, 1, \ldots, k; k \geq 2$), with the same known covariance matrix Σ. It is desired to select the nearest Π_j ($j = 1, \ldots, k$) to Π_0 when only μ_0 is unknown and the distance between Π_0 and Π_j is the Mahanalobis distance. The concept of the problem is shown in Figure 3. The task is then one of estimating to which of two Universes an individual is nearest, after having tested that the individual does not come from either of them. Although the problem may not appear to be useful, the following observations may indicate its systematic significance.

Consider the case of a species that could have arisen from two or more geologically older species. It is of interest to the systematist to find out to which of the older forms the younger species is most similar. Another situation is provided by a case in which a number of measurements are made on a specimen from a certain Universe. A set of other Universes is also available for consideration, each of which forms some kind of taxonomic entity. The question to be investigated is: In which of the entities does the individual fit best? Unfortunately, the chi-squared approximation for this test is not good, and caution is advised when interpreting the results.

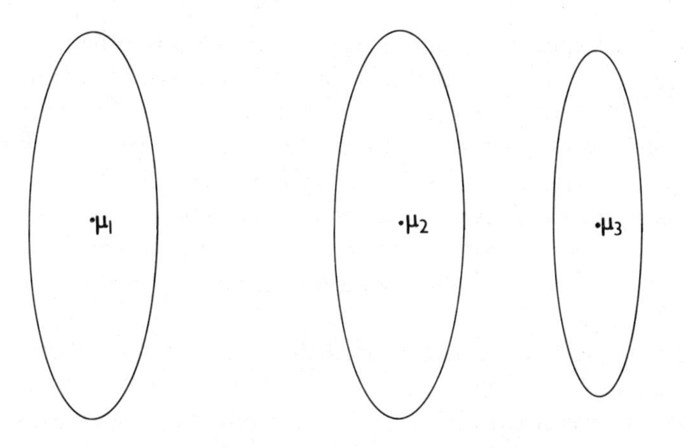

FIGURE 3 Concept of the task of comparing generalized distances by estimating to which of two Universes an individual is nearest.

It will be appreciated that the foregoing concept grades into that discussed under Model IV.

Regarding the model from the point of view of the covariance matrices, rejection of the hypothesis of equality of the Universes would normally lead to a series of analyses of the Model II category.

MODEL IV: IDENTIFICATION

In this connection, with identification we shall review the classical concept of "classification" statistics. The actual systematic problem considered by the discriminant function of Fisher is not really one of central biologic importance. Among the statisticians, Rao (1965, p. 487) has been one to realize the biological distinction between identification and classification. Cochran and Hopkins (1961) have discussed the problem of identification with multivariate qualitative data in which each measurement takes a small number of states. An interesting point stemming from their study was the suggestion that where material consists of mixed qualitative and quantitative data (the latter in the minority), the quantitative variables may, with advantage, be transformed into qualitative variables.

Basically, the identification concept may be viewed in the following terms: There are two multivariate normal Universes, Π_1 and Π_2

(Figure 4). A specimen, X, actually known to come from one of the Universes, is to be identified in regard to its correct location, on the basis of multivariate measurements. The systematic implications of this model will be discerned clearly, but it will be realized that the model is more likely to find use in paleontology than in neontology. The model may readily be extended to more than two Universes to encompass the situation where an individual is known to come from one of *p* populations. This situation is depicted schematically in Figure 5.

Burnaby (1966) has investigated the problem of identifying an individual as belonging to one of two sets of Universes. Each set consists of several Universes, mixed in unknown proportions; such a situation occurs, for example, in organisms with continuous growth. It may, therefore, be important in a purely taxonomic study to be able to produce a generalized distance and a discriminant function, invariant to the effects of growth as well as environmentally governed shape variation. In order for Burnaby's solution of the problem to be usable, satisfactory estimates of the "growth and environment" vectors are necessary. Up to now, no really satis-

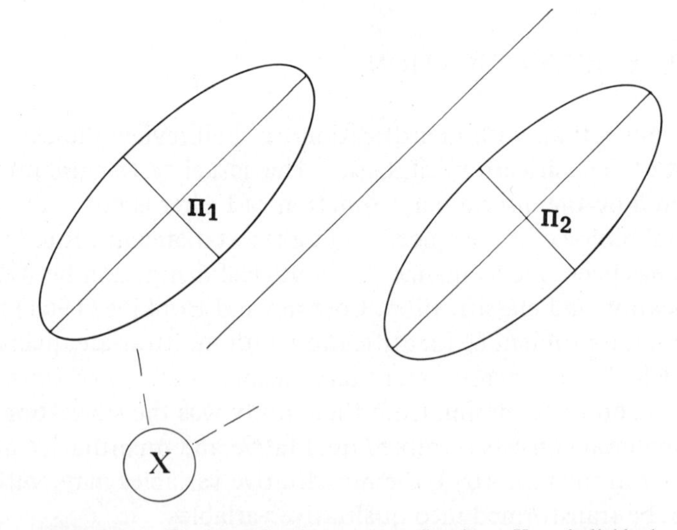

FIGURE 4 The identification concept. Specimen X, an individual known to come from one of the Universes, is to be identified in regard to its correct location on the basis of multivariate measurements.

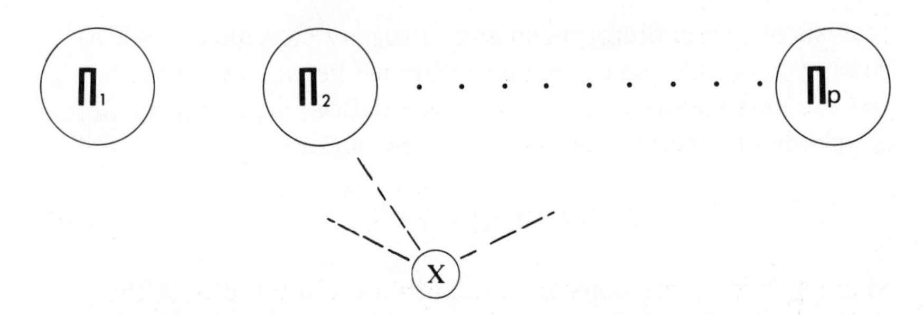

FIGURE 5 The identification model extended to encompass a situation where an individual (X) is known to come from one of the p populations.

factory means of doing this has been suggested (Burnaby, 1966: 108). Rao (1966) has explored the problem further.

A problem frequently encountered by the systematist in using discriminant functions concerns testing the significance of a particular discriminant coefficient and eliminating coefficients that do little toward aiding the discriminating process. Rao (1965), for one, indicates that standard errors of discriminant coefficients for judging the significance of a particular coefficient suffer from the disadvantage that the coefficients are not estimates of definite Universe parameters. Any satisfactory test must be based on the ratio between two coefficients. The rather widely practiced method of estimating the significance of a discriminator coefficient by using the analogy with multiple regression is, therefore, not really a useful technique. Weiner and Dunn (1966) have made a practical study of other methods of approaching the problem. One such method involves making a series of t-tests between sample means. Another method is by the stepwise calculation of the discriminant function, introducing the variates one at a time. Their computer program adds, at each step, the variate that gives the greatest reduction in the residual sum of squares. This approach was found by Weiner and Dunn to lead to a lower proportion of misclassified individuals.

Cooper (1963, 1965) has demonstrated that the use of the generalized distance as a discriminant function has several advantages over the linear discriminant function of Fisher. The distance interpretation of the quadratic form is important in systematic work, for example, in evolutionary studies (Lerman, 1965) and in the analysis of sexual dimorphism and ontogeny (Reyment, 1963b). Writing $Q_k(x)$ for the generalized distance between a vector X and the mean point μ_k of the kth population, a general quadratic discriminant function may be expressed in the form

$$G_k(x) = a_k Q_k(x) + b_k, \quad (4)$$

where a_k and b_k are constants, such that for any vector X the probability of its identification with a specified Universe is a minimum for that value of k for which the value of $G_k(x)$ is minimized, given that the *a priori* probabilities of the Universes are equal. The results obtained by Cooper show the important fact that the quadratic discriminant function is optimal for many distributions, provided the determinants of the covariance matrices are equal. An attractive feature of the quadratic discriminant is its applicability to data with nonnormal distributions.

In the light of the foregoing statement, it is of interest to compare some actual examples of linear discriminant functions calculated first under the assumption of equal covariance matrices when the covariance matrices actually are not equal, and then calculated under the assumption of nonequality of the covariance matrices. For this, two examples from the data on frogs given in Table 1 have been analyzed. The results are shown in Table 2. It is clear from these results that where the differences in covariance matrices are slight there is little effect on the discriminator coefficients. Where the difference is more serious, the discriminator coefficients are noticeably different.

TABLE 2 Comparison of Linear Discriminant Function Coefficients Data on *Rana esculenta* and *R. temporaria* [Dimensions: $x_{.1}$, body; $x_{.2}$, tibia; $x_{.3}$, heel]

Sample	Assumption $\Sigma_1 = \Sigma_2$	Assumption $\Sigma_1 \neq \Sigma_2$
R. temporaria		
N. Sweden/S. Sweden	$-5.99x_{-1} + 1.97x_{-2} + 3.81x_{-3}$	$-5.96x_{-1} + 2.01x_{-2} + 3.79x_{-3}$
R. esculenta		
N. Africa/Spain	$39.60x_{-1} - 64.51x_{-2} - 41.00x_{-3}$	$15.49x_{-1} - 20.25x_{-2} - 32.28x_{-3}$

MODEL V: THE CLASSIFICATION MODEL

Classification in taxonomy is concerned with the formation or definition of classes on the grounds of some principle. This is not the meaning given to the word in the statistical literature, where it is employed in the sense of the "identification" concept of taxonomy. Over the last ten years, interest in the theoretical background of taxonomy has been increasing steadily, particularly within the sphere known as numerical taxonomy. The bibliography is already extensive; for an analysis thereof, reference is made to Sokal and Sneath (1963) and Rohlf (1965). In the present connection, we shall confine ourselves to reviewing some important works recently published. There has been a certain amount of reservation among many biostatisticians well acquainted with multivariate statistical theory with respect to the acceptance of some of the concepts and practices of *numerical taxonomy.* Bartlett (1965:218) has remarked on the arbitrariness of some of the techniques employed, particularly in relation to the "clustering" idea as carried out by numerical taxonomists by means of inverted factor analysis (factor analysis of individuals on a sample of test scores).

For the most part, the development of numerical taxonomy has been in the hands of biologists, having had little attraction for statisticians. Gower (1966) has investigated the statistical validity of one of the techniques of numerical taxonomy—the so-called Q-technique—with respect to the concept of distance in relation to the clustering idea. The procedure requires some form of similarity or *association matrix* A. There are many problems associated with the concept of association in this connection; for example, the difficulty of justifying Adansonian equal weighting in all situations and the satisfactory treatment of mixed continuous and discontinuous data. To be fully acceptable, a similarity coefficient should provide some form of expression of the amount of information contained in the variables occurring in the analysis. It is not proposed to enter into a general discussion, here, of the pros and cons of numerical taxonomy (the interested reader is referred to Sokal and Sneath, 1963). This discussion will be confined to some aspects of the reconciliation of statistical theory and numerical taxonomy.

The model for the classification concept of numerical taxonomy may be illustrated by Figure 6. One begins with a sample of individuals of mixed origin (probably) and desires to effect a separation of this composite sample into its component elements; that is, one hopes that the mixture of individuals can be subdivided accurately into clusters, each cluster being a homogeneous entity.

It will be assumed that it has been possible to produce a satisfactory $n \times n$ association matrix A by using a good similarity coefficient based on a sample of n individuals, on each of which p variables have been measured in some unit or other (not necessarily of the same kind and not necessarily unmixed). The (i, j)th element of the association matrix is a coefficient between the ith and jth individuals. A useful approach to the analysis of the n vectors of observations is to compute the eigenvalues and eigenvectors of A, and to use the elements of the eigenvectors, in corresponding locations, as the coordinates of a new set of points, Q_i (see Table 3). Gower refers to this procedure as *principal coordinate analysis* to avoid confusion with principal component analysis. Thus, the coordinates of Q_1 are $(b_1{}^{(1)}; b_1{}^{(2)}, \ldots, b_1{}^{(n)})$, where each of the b's is the first element of the n eigenvectors. It is not unusual to find that the first two eigenvalues are large in relation to the sum of the $n - 2$ smaller eigenvalues, thus allowing the possibility of an approximate two-dimensional representation of the classification task.

The classification problem is perhaps one of the most central in systematics, and certainly it is the main one in taxonomic studies. A useful quantitative technique that also allows for differentiation with respect to the amount of information conveyed by a particular variate is indeed an important tool.

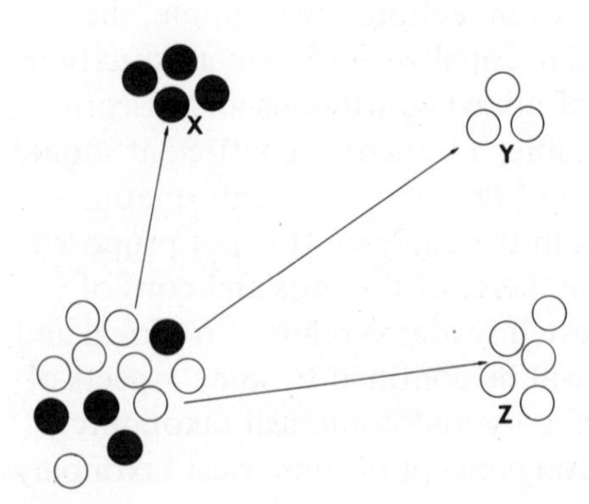

FIGURE 6 Model for the classification concept of numerical taxonomy. A sample of individuals of mixed origin is subdivided into clusters—each a homogeneous entity.

TABLE 3 Eigenvalues and Eigenvectors of the Symmetric Association Matrix A ($\bar{b}_r$ is the mean value of the elements of the rth vector)

New Coordinates	Eigenvalues $\lambda_1 \quad \lambda_2 \ldots \lambda_n$
	Eigenvectors Columnwise
Q_1	$b_1^{(1)} \; b_1^{(2)} \ldots b_1^{(n)}$
Q_2	$b_2^{(1)} \; b_2^{(2)} \ldots b_2^{(n)}$
.	. . . .
.	. . . .
.	. . . .
Q_n	$b_n^{(1)} \; b_n^{(2)} \ldots b_n^{(n)}$
Average $\bar{Q}$	$\bar{b}^{(1)} \; \bar{b}^{(2)} \ldots \bar{b}^{(n)}$

MODEL VI: THE POPULATION AFFINITY MODEL

This model is based on the well-known statistical procedure of *canonical variates.* In biological terms the idea underlying the model is that it is desired to arrange a number of Universes so that the two that are most akin will lie nearest to each other and the two that are most unlike will lie furthest from each other. It will be appreciated that this is a sort of generalization of the squared Mahanalobis' distance already discussed. In fact, a similar type of distance representation may be obtained by making a topological model of all possible squared generalized distances between samples from the Universes; such models have been used on many occasions. There are, however, certain theoretical reasons for selecting the approach by canonical variates for this type of analysis. As a matter of fact, for two samples, the method of canonical variates is identical with the squared generalized distance. A proof of this can be found in Kullback (1959). A comprehensive, elementary account of the theory of canonical variates has recently been given by Bartlett (1965), and there is a longer discussion in Seal (1964). The method of canonical variates, like so many other important multivariate statistical techniques, was introduced by Hotelling.

Figure 7 gives a schematic representation of the type of result one might hope to achieve by the use of canonical variates. We have five Universes (with equal covariance matrices), each made up of a taxonomic category that one wishes to compare. The example represented in Figure 7 is an actual plot of values for five subpopulations of European *Rana.* The first and third groups lie clearly close together on the basis of the measured variables—body length, length of tibia, and length of the heel—whereas the second, fourth, and fifth groups lie at some distance from the first and third groups, and the fourth and fifth groups are near each other.

Canonical variate analysis clearly is a very useful technique in systematic work and may be employed in studying the distance between chronologic subpopulations (e.g., Reyment, 1966a) and rates of change of a set of characters with respect to both distance and time. The writer has used it for analyzing evolutionary trends in

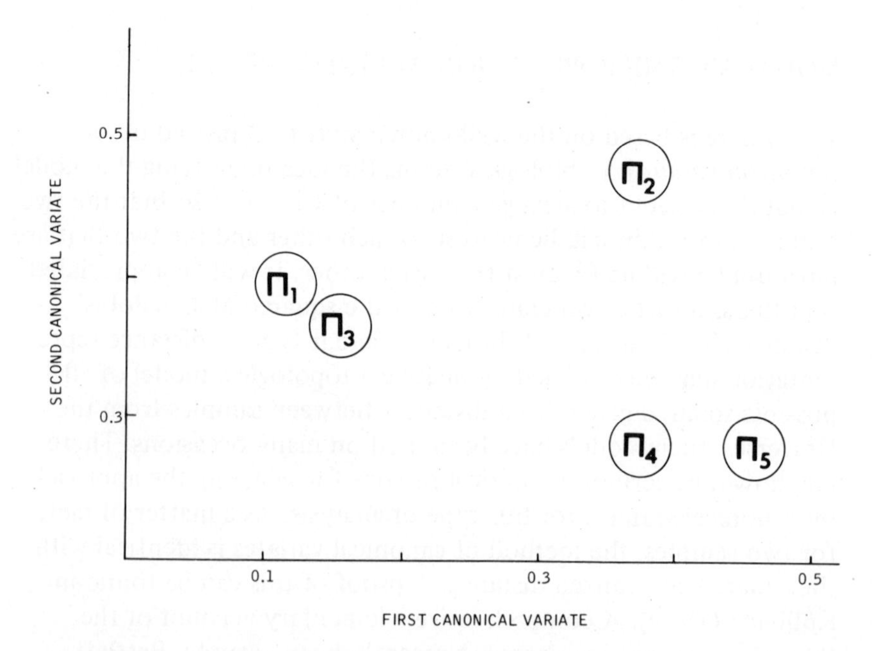

FIGURE 7 The use of canonical variates. An actual plot of values for five subpopulations of European *Rana* based on length of body, tibia, and heel.

ostracod morphology and for studying geographic variation in frogs. There are several applications in the biological literature, particularly in regard to the study of insects and mammals. In view of its usefulness, it is strange that greater application of the method has not been made.

Referring again to Figure 7, it will be seen that there are two axes–labeled as the first canonical axis and the second canonical axis. These derive from the eigenvectors of the generalized determinatal equation forming the basis of the computations. Just as in principal components, one extracts the eigenvalues and eigenvectors, but this time one is dealing with samples from several Universes, whereas in principal components the calculations are made on a covariance matrix from a single Universe. The plots in Figure 7 derive from transformed means obtained by substituting the original mean values in the first two eigenvectorial equations. Usually, the first two eigenvectors are associated with a very large part of the total variability as represented in the corresponding first two eigenvalues, as is true of the present study.

MODEL VII: THE POPULATION-OVERLAP MODEL

One of the problems that one finds rather frequently in the quantitative biologic literature concerns the question of the overlap of two or more populations on the basis of some measured character. [Overlap is not used in the sense of, for example, Mayr (1963b:502), but in its statistical sense.] For univariate studies, a simple histogram will indicate the presence of overlap. For multivariate situations, a univariate representation may be obtained by the use of the discriminant function. Statistically, this application should be located with the model dealing with identification procedures; however, from the biologic point of view, it is useful to look at it on its own, as it is a useful, practical way of approaching this type of problem. The linear discriminant function is of the form

$$z = a_1 x_1 + a_2 x_2 + \ldots + a_k x_k, \quad (5)$$

where a_i represents the discriminator coefficients and x_i represents the variables. Substitution of the measurements in Equation 5 yields two sets of "univariate" transformed observations which then may be studied by graphical methods. Many programs available at computation centers do this as a part of the regular calculations, and some programs even make the histograms.

MODEL VIII: CORRELATIONS BETWEEN SETS OF VARIABLES

This model analyzes the significance of the degree of correlation between two sets of variables—for example, the correlation between a set of morphologic variables and a set of ecologic variables. The statistical method employed is known as *canonical correlation,* another of the multivariate techniques originally introduced by Hotelling. Figure 8 provides a schematic representation of the concept. Symbols V and W could represent two ecologic factors with which the correlation of a set of measurements, X, Y, and Z, on some organism is to be estimated. In a way, the concepts behind canonical correlation and related statistical theory may be regarded as a generalization of the regression model. It will be seen that the method is particularly suitable for ecologic studies, although it was originally devised for a psychometric problem. The present writer has used canonical correlation in studying the interrelationships between organic constituents and electrochemical variates in a deltaic environment.

MODEL IX: A PREDICTION MODEL

In paleontologic systematics, one may sometimes have a good set of measurements on material of a fossil organism and it may be desired to make use of such information for predicting some missing measurement on a damaged specimen. The technique employed in this connection is multiple regression. Numerous applications of multiple regression analysis are being made by geologists and petroleum

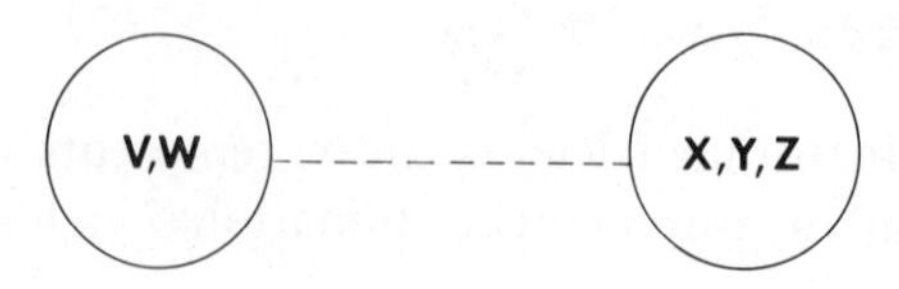

FIGURE 8 Example representing the canonical correlation method. Correlation of ecological factors (V and W) with measurements of organisms (X, Y, and Z) is to be estimated.

engineers to a variety of problems under the title of "trend surface analysis." The basic concept here is one of surface-fitting by means of polynomial regression or by using trigonometric functions in the regression equation. It seems that the computer programs already available for treating this kind of problem suitably could be applied to some analyses of geographic variation in a particular character, especially in relation to topologically correlated ecologic factors. The concept of trend surface analysis may be generalized to include a vector variable of measurements on an organism.

SOME OTHER TECHNIQUES

Although the techniques to be briefly mentioned here could have been included under the foregoing sections, it was felt that in many points they differ so much from the biologic-oriented models used in this paper that their inclusion might cloud the issue. In the discussion of Model III we covered the problem of what to do when there are more variables than measurements, as may well occur in a classification study in numerical taxonomy. Dempster (1960, 1964) has been concerned with developing a test of significance for the difference of mean vectors of two highly multivariate small samples. Every quantitative biologist will recognize the nature of the problem, as it may readily come to the fore, particularly where a large number of expensive analyses are involved in a study. Dempster's procedure is directed toward testing the same kind of situation as arises for the univariate *t*-test. The two groups to be investigated are Universes, the means of which are two points in *p*-space. The test requires the assumption of homogeneity of covariance matrices and normality of the multivariate distributions, just as does the T^2 of Hotelling. However, T^2 is undefined for $p > N_1 + N_2 - 2$, where N_1 and N_2 are the sizes of the two samples and p is the number of variates. Dempster's procedure is, therefore, a substitute for the T^2, but it lacks the desirable affinity possessed by the ordinary T^2, which means that the same value of T^2 results from any p linear combinations of the variables involved. At first, the second procedure may not appear to have much application in systematic biology. Dempster (1963b) presented a model that is a type of generalization of the test of the null hypothesis of the equality of

k-group means. Wilks' Λ-criterion is the best known of the various test criteria that have been proposed for the multivariate analog of the univariate analysis of variance. As Dempster (1963b) points out, there is no particular reason why a single test criterion should have optimum sensitivity against all failures of the null hypothesis due to differences in group mean vectors. His method replaces the single criterion with a sequence of criteria, each of which is tested separately. The criteria are the eigenvalues and eigenvectors of the correlation matrix of the p variables, which are used to obtain independent criteria $P_1, P_2, \ldots, P_p$. These are related to the variance ratio (F) and also to Wilks' lambda, as, $\Lambda = P_1 . P_2 . \cdots . P_p$. Biologists familiar with principal-components analysis and its applications in biology will appreciate the intuitive appeal of this approach.

CONCLUDING REMARKS

This exposition has presented several biometric techniques useful in systematics. In doing so, the writer has attempted to present such techniques in the form of "models" suitable for a particular biologic problem or class of problems. It should be understood by statisticians that the models are not meant to be interpreted in the sense of pure statistical models, which they are not. The time available, of course, did not permit anything like a complete review of the subject; moreover, the writer is fully aware of the considerable "bias" in what has been taken up, due to his own research interests. A discussion of biometric techniques in relation to genetics was considered to be out of place in this connection, as these constitute a theme in their own right.

It may be helpful to summarize the techniques mentioned in this paper and their purposes. They deal broadly with:

1. The analysis of the variability of a homogeneous population (from a multivariate statistical Universe) with respect to the study of patterns of growth.
2. The comparison of the variances and covariances of two populations.
3. Analysis of the differences of means of two or more samples

and the statistical distance between samples (in some form or another). This is one of the central working areas of systematics, involving, as it does, geographic, ecologic, and chronologic considerations.

4. The classic discrimination problem (identification) of assigning a specimen to one of two or more known Universes.

5. Classification by the identification of clusters "hidden" in a mixed sample but unveiled by a suitable eigen-technique.

6. Correlation between sets of variables employed for obtaining an idea of relationships between, for example, a set of measurements on a population and the ecologic variables in the environment it inhabits.

Many biometric techniques in biology have been slow to get under way (hence, systematics) because of the often time-consuming calculations and the difficulty attaching to their understanding and suitable application. The development of the electronic computer is doing much toward reducing the labor of calculation, but in doing so, it may be introducing a new problem inasmuch as all that the biologist need do (where programs are available) is to make out the control cards correctly without having to know what is going to happen to the data. Clearly, this could lead to catastrophes.

Appendix

WORKED EXAMPLES OF A FEW IMPORTANT BIOMETRIC TECHNIQUES MENTIONED IN THE TEXT

EXAMPLE 1: THE TECHNIQUE OF PRINCIPAL-COMPONENTS ANALYSIS

The multivariate statistical technique of principal-components analysis was covered in the discussion of Model I. The example considered here consisted of a sample comprising 200 individuals–adults and near-adults–of *Rana esculenta* L. collected from 10 localities in various parts of Sweden. For simplicity of presentation, only three variables will be analyzed: over-all body length, length of tibia, and length of heel protuberance. The measurements have been logarithmically transformed. The principal components were computed for the correlation matrix, although in some studies more interest would attach to the principal components of the covariance matrix.

The method of principal components is based on the mathematical procedure of determining the eigenvalues and eigenvectors of a matrix. If the correlation matrix is R, the eigenvalues are yielded by the roots of the determinantal equations

$$|R - \lambda I| = 0,$$

where I is the so-called identity matrix (with 1's along its principal diagonal and 0's in all other positions).

The eigenvectors are found by solving the set of linear equations

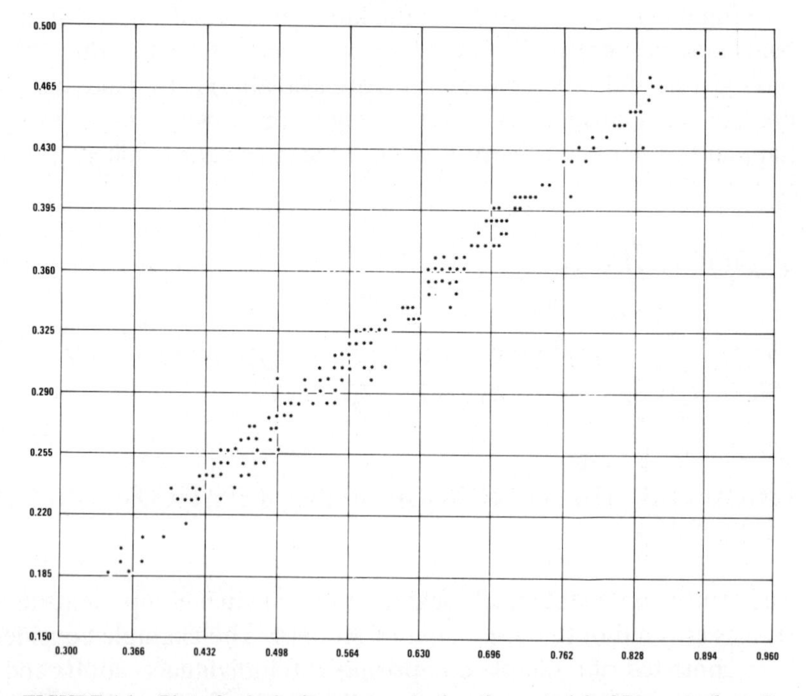

FIGURE A1 Plot of principal component values for material of *Rana esculenta* L. from Sweden.

$$(R - \lambda I)a = 0.$$

The principal components are obtained by means of the transformation

$$y = Ax,$$

where the vectors x are the original measurement vectors. Table A1 presents the salient points of the calculations for the frogs. The computations were made on the IBM 7040 at the University of Kansas, using the author's program. The transformed values, y_1 and y_2, were plotted with the aid of a subroutine attached to the main computer program for principal components. The result is shown in Figure A1.

TABLE A1 Information for the Calculation of the Principal Components of a Species of Frogs from Ten Localities in Sweden

Mean Vector (untransformed data)			
63.7257320	32.8353404		3.4060594
Correlation Matrix (of logarithmically transformed data)			
1.00000	0.94494		0.70719
0.94494	1.00000		0.68360
0.70719	0.68360		1.00000
Eigenvalues and Eigenvectors			
Eigenvalues	Eigenvectors (columns)		
2.5636	0.60104	0.34573	-0.72057
0.3820	0.59603	0.40675	0.69232
0.0544	0.53244	-0.84559	0.03841

EXAMPLE 2: THE TECHNIQUE OF T^2

This multivariate statistical procedure may be looked upon as a generalization of the well-known *t*-test of univariate statistics. Various aspects of the application and importance of T^2 were covered in the discussion of Model I. It will be illustrated with the aid of some data on cranial length, x_1, and cranial breadth, x_2, for a sample of adult male and female individuals of the frog *Rana esculenta* L. from the environs of Vienna. For the present purposes, the raw data will be used. However, there is differential growth in these variables, and in an actual investigation a more satisfactory approach would be to transform the data to their logarithms. Moreover, inasmuch as the samples consist of individuals at slightly different stages of growth, a better means of calculating the squared generalized distance for taxonomic purposes would be by the method of Burnaby (1966), providing that suitable input vectors could be found.

In order to calculate the T^2, one requires the matrix of pooled variances and covariances, which shall be called S, and the vector of differences of means, which shall be called d. The generalized statistical distance squared is then yielded by the relationship

$$D^2 = d'S^{-1} d.$$

In order to find T^2 from this, it is required only to work out the value of

$$T^2 = D^2 \frac{N_1 N_2}{N_1 + N_2},$$

where N_1 and N_2 denote the sizes of the two samples involved. In order to ascertain its significance, this result may be connected with the well-known variance ratio (F) by means of the following formula:

$$F = T^2 \frac{(N_1 + N_2 - p - 1)}{p(N_1 + N_2) - 2},$$

where p represents the number of variables.

The covariance matrices for the two samples, as well as other relevant statistics, are shown in Table A2. The pooled covariance matrix is as follows:

$$S = \begin{bmatrix} 17.903 & 19.959 \\ 19.959 & 23.397 \end{bmatrix}$$

The inverse of this matrix is

$$S^{-1} = \begin{bmatrix} 1.4049 & -0.9729 \\ -0.9729 & 0.8727 \end{bmatrix}$$

The sample size for males is 14 individuals, and for females it is 35.

This information and that in Table A2 yield, first, $D^2 = 0.197$. This is a very small value, and one would not expect it to be significant. This is also shown by the value of $T^2 = 1.969$, which converts to a value of $F = 0.964$. For 2 and 46 degrees of freedom this is far from significant, and one would conclude that male and female frogs cannot be distinguished by the measurements on cranial length and breadth. Inspection of the three covariances matrices discloses that these two variables are highly correlated. In such a situation, one might expect a rather different result from that which would be given by *t*-tests on the two variates. In this example, the multivariate method does not, however, add much, owing to the relatively slight difference in means.

TABLE A2 Information for the Calculation of T^2 for Two Samples of Frogs from Vienna

	Covariance Matrix				Mean Vector	
	Females		Males		Females	Males
Cranial length	17.683	20.290	18.479	19.095	22.860	21.821
Cranial breadth	–	24.407	–	20.755	24.397	22.843

EXAMPLE 3: COMPARING THE SHAPES OF TWO SCATTER ELLIPSOIDS

The problem of comparing the shapes of two scatter ellipsoids was dealt with in the discussion of Model I. It is given particular emphasis here because of the theoretical importance of the concepts in growth analysis.

For purposes of the present discussion, it will be taken that the N vectors of a sample, $x_1, \cdots, x_N$ (N observation vectors), with mean vector $Ex = \mu$, and with covariance matrix $E(x-\mu)(x-\mu)' = \Sigma$ are multivariate-normally distributed, and form an ellipsoid.

If one considers two *p*-variate normally distributed populations with the mean vectors μ_1 and μ_2 not necessarily different (i.e., 0_1 and 0_2 in the diagrams of Figure A2 may be coincident), and the covariance matrices Σ_1 and Σ_2, then if the test of equality of these matrices be applied (cf., Kullback, 1959) and it be concluded that $\Sigma_1 = \Sigma_2$, the following situation may prevail: Referring to diagram *a* of Figure A2, the ellipsoid Ω_1 is merely a translation of ellipsoid Ω_2; hence, AB = EF, CD = GH, and AB is parallel to EF.

If the homogeneity test for covariance matrices leads to the conclusion that $\Sigma_1 \neq \Sigma_2$, then one of the following conditions may prevail (for two dimensions): In Figure A2, diagram *b* has AB parallel to EF, CD parallel to GH, EF > AB, and GH > CD; hence, ellipsoid Ω_2 is a translation of ellipsoid Ω_1 with magnification. Diagram *c* has AB = EF, CD = GH, AB not parallel to EF, and CD not parallel to GH. Ellipsoids Ω_1 and Ω_2 have the same shape, but are rotated in relation to each other. Diagram *d* has AB $\neq$ EF. CD $\neq$ GH, AB not parallel to EF, and CD not parallel to GH; thus, ellipsoids Ω_1 and Ω_2 are differently inflated, and their axes are rotated in relation to each other.

For three or more dimensions, the situation becomes more complicated. Diagram *e* illustrates the position for three dimensions. Here, two axes of ellipsoids Ω_1 and Ω_2 are parallel to each other and AB is parallel to EF, but not the remaining axes, owing to rotation about AB and EF; hence, CD is not parallel to GH, and IJ is not parallel to LK. In this example, it has been taken that the ellipsoids have the same shape; thus, AB = EF, CD = GH, and IJ = KL. Diagram *f* indicates the positions when the second axes of Ω_1 and Ω_2 are parallel and the first and third axes are rotated about the second axes.

In order to disclose relative heterogeneity in the orientation of the axes of two ellipsoids of scatter, when the generalized test (1) indicates $\Sigma_1 \neq \Sigma_2$, it is sufficient to demonstrate that the first two axes are parallel to each other in order to localize the inequality in the covariance matrices to condition b of Figure A2; that is the case where the heterogeneity is due solely to a greater degree of scatter

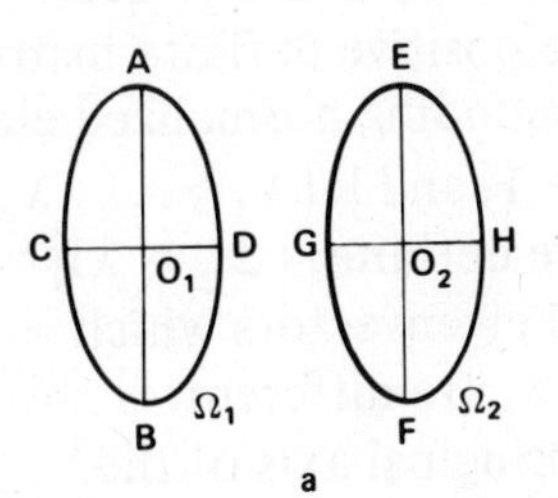

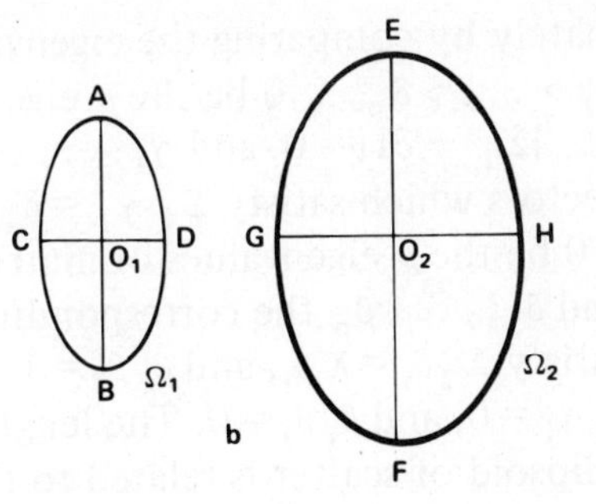

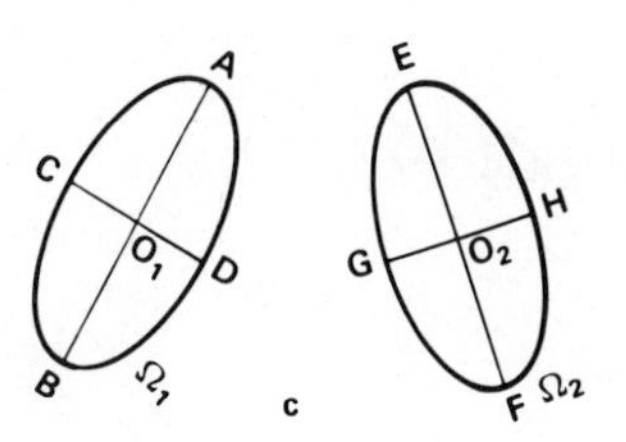

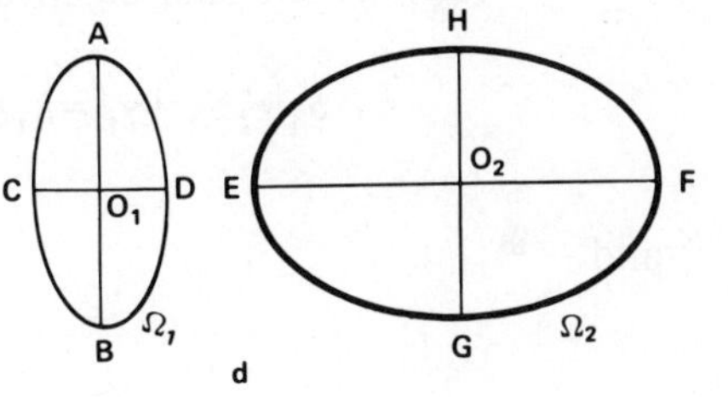

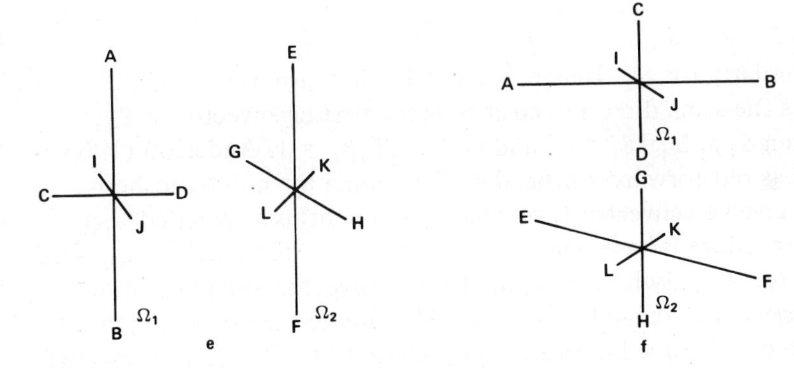

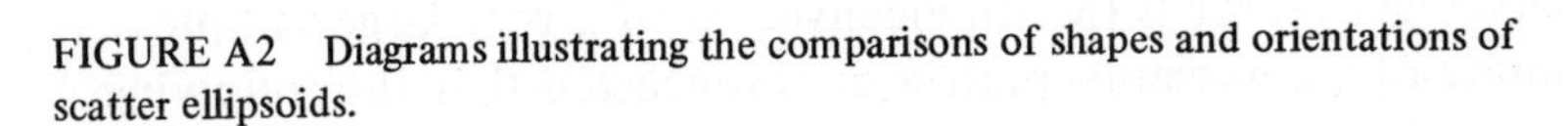
FIGURE A2 Diagrams illustrating the comparisons of shapes and orientations of scatter ellipsoids.

in the points of the points of the observational vectors forming the ellipsoids.

Some interest may attach to comparing the relative differences in the inflations of ellipsoids Ω_1 and Ω_2. This may be gauged approximately by comparing the eigenvalues of matrices Σ_1 and Σ_2. Let $\delta_1 > \ldots > \delta_p > 0$ be the p eigenvalues of the positive definite matrix Σ_1; $|\Sigma_1 - \delta I| = 0$, and $\gamma_1, \ldots, \gamma_p$ the corresponding normalized eigenvectors which satisfy $\Sigma_1 \gamma_1 = \delta_i \gamma_i$ and $\gamma_i'\gamma = 1$, and let $\lambda_1 > \ldots > \lambda_p > 0$ be the p eigenvalues of matrix Σ_2, positive definite, $|\Sigma_2 = \lambda I| = 0$ and $\beta_1, \ldots, \beta_p$ the corresponding normalized eigenvectors which satisfy $\Sigma_2\beta_i = \lambda_i\beta_i$, and $\beta_i'\beta_i = 1$. If the δ_i and λ_i are different, $\gamma_i'\gamma_j = 0$, and $\beta_i'\beta_j = 0$. The length of the ith principal axis of the ellipsoid of scatter is related to the magnitude of the corresponding eigenvalue, the variance of the ith principal component.

Referring again to the eigenvalues and eigenvectors of Σ_1 and Σ_2, one has, for the first eigenvalues and eigenvectors,

$$\delta_1\gamma_1'\Sigma_1^{-1}\gamma_1 = \delta_1\delta_1^{-1} = 1,$$

and

$$(1/\delta_1)\gamma_1'\Sigma_1\gamma_1 = (1/\delta_1)\delta_1 = 1,$$

and similarly for Σ_2. Hence, if, say, the first eigenvector of Σ_2, β_1, has the same direction cosines as the first eigenvector of Σ_1, γ_1, then $\delta_1\beta_1'\Sigma_1^{-1}\beta_1 = 1$, and $(1/\delta_1)\beta_1\Sigma_1\beta_1 = 1$. Anderson (1963: 144) has put forward a procedure for testing the null hypothesis that a given eigenvector (principal component) is a specified vector. The procedure is based on the limiting normal distribution possessed by $\sqrt{n}\,(c_1 - \gamma_1)$, where γ_1 is the first eigenvector of a population covariance matrix, and c_1 is a sample estimate thereof, based on a sample of size $(n + 1)$. As an approximate test of the hypothesis that a given eigenvector is the ith eigenvector of a very large sample estimate of a covariance matrix, it is suggested that the following version of Anderson's test might be applicable:

$$n(d_i b' S_1^{-1} b_i + (1/d_i) b_i S_1 b_i - 2). \qquad \text{(A1)}$$

Here, $(n + 1)$ is the sample size of S_1, the estimate of Σ_1, d_i is the sample estimate of δ_i, and b_i that of β_i, the latter being based on a very large sample. If $\Sigma_1 = \Sigma_2$, then $\gamma_i = \beta_i$. This criterion has, of course, more variables than the original form given by Anderson and must, therefore, be more susceptible to fluctuations.

The following example is drawn from the material on frogs of the genus *Rana* used several times in this article.

Two occurrences of females of the frog *Rana temporaria* from Vienna and southern Sweden have been used. This material comprises female individuals of varying ages, the larger sample consisting of 281 individuals. The covariance matrix, based on the Briggsian logarithms of the data (variables: body length, length of tibia, length of heel protuberance) are:

1. Swedish material (N = 19).

$$S_1 = \begin{bmatrix} 0.0017224 & 0.0016109 & 0.0011810 \\ 0.0016109 & 0.0018762 & 0.0012046 \\ 0.0011810 & 0.0012046 & 0.0021225 \end{bmatrix}.$$

2. Viennese material (N = 281).

$$S_2 = \begin{bmatrix} 0.0556612 & 0.0592309 & 0.0011810 \\ 0.0592309 & 0.0642643 & 0.0012046 \\ 0.0011810 & 0.0012046 & 0.0021225 \end{bmatrix}.$$

The generalized test for homogeneity of covariance matrices, in the form presented in Kullback (1959:317), is

$$2I\ [H_1{:}H_2(*)] = N_1 \log_e (\det S/\det S_1) + N_2 \log_e (\det S/\det S_2), \qquad (A2)$$

where $NS = N_1S_1 + N_2S_2$ and $N = N_1 + N_2$. This is approximately distributed as χ^2 with $k(k+1)/2$ degrees of freedom, where k is the number of variables. A better approximation, available for only a few dimensions, however, is given by the B-distribution (Kullback, 1959:317).

The eigenvalues of matrix S_1 for the Swedish material are, in terms of formula (3): $d_1 = 0.0045731$, $d_2 = 0.0009619$, $d_3 = 0.0001860$. The corresponding eigenvectors, g_i, are

$$G = \begin{bmatrix} 0.570590 & 0.373089 & -0.731595 \\ 0.594077 & 0.427553 & 0.681374 \\ 0.567009 & -0.823409 & 0.022314 \end{bmatrix}.$$

The eigenvalues of covariance matrix S_2 for the Austrian material are, in terms of formula (3): $\ell_1 = 0.1902537$, $\ell_2 = 0.0041737$, $\ell_3 = 0.0004964$. The corresponding eigenvectors are:

$$B = \begin{bmatrix} 0.537459 & -0.308971 & 0.784649 \\ 0.574680 & -0.546757 & -0.608933 \\ 0.617156 & 0.778199 & -0.116300 \end{bmatrix},$$

$\log_e (\det S_1) = -20.92375$, $\log_e (\det S_2) = -14.74639$, and $\log_e (\det S) = -14.89144$. $B^2 = 67.968$, which for $\beta^2 = 0.3625$, and 6 degrees of freedom is significant.

Substituting the foregoing values in (A1), the first eigenvectors yield $\chi^2 = 0.230$, which for 2 degrees of freedom is not significant. For the second eigenvectors, $\chi^2 = 1.268$, which also is not significant. Hence, there is no evidence against the collinearity of the first two eigenvector pairs in this material. Therefore, it may be concluded that the two geographically separated occurrences of *Rana* are not different with respect to growth patterns. There is a significant difference localizable to the degree of inflation of the ellipsoids of scatter, but this possibly, in part at least, is connected with the small size of the comparison sample.

EXAMPLE 4: AN APPLICATION OF THE METHOD OF CANONICAL VARIATES

The example chosen to illustrate this biometrical technique is typical of the type of problem that readily occurs in systematics studies in paleontology. The material comprises 40 samples of the Silurian brachiopod species *Craniops implicata* (Sowerby), collected by A. Martinsson from various localities throughout Gotland. (Thanks are due to Dr. Martinsson for making this interesting material available for statistical analysis.)

Three features were measured on each individual: the first variable, a measure of the surface area of the oval shell; the second variable, length of the shell; the third variable, the breadth of the shell, located at right angles to the second variable. The total number of individuals for all samples is 446. As has been pointed out in the discussion of Model VI, a necessary prerequisite for the theoretically acceptable application of the method of canonical variates is that the sample covariance matrices are homogeneous. It is hardly to be expected that a set of such a large number of geologic samples, all of rather small size, will conform with this desirable property, and such is the case here. There are several deviations from the ideal condition. An examination of the empirical properties of the distributions of the variables did not disclose any serious departures from normality, and it may be concluded that the differences in the covariance matrices may be put down to differing ranges of variability.

The information required for the calculation of the canonical variates is presented in Table A3. The results of the analysis are given in Tables A2, A3, A4 and A5 and in Figure A3.

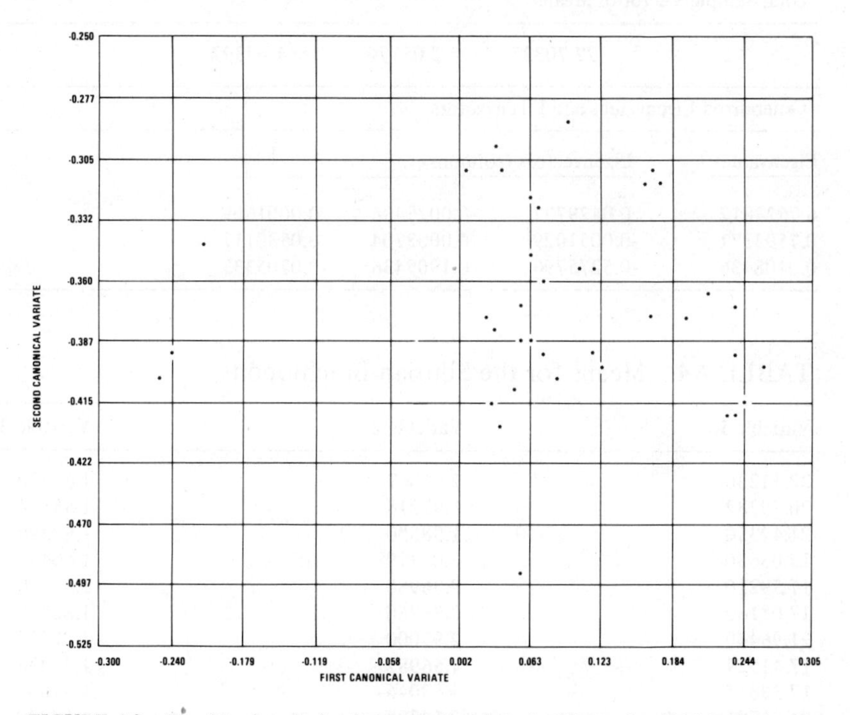

FIGURE A3 Results of analysis of canonical variates in 40 samples (446 individuals) of the Silurian brachiopod species *Cranisps implicata* (Sowerby).

TABLE A3 Information for Calculation of Canonical Variates for the Silurian Brachiopods

Sums of Squares and Cross Products for the "Among Groups"; Matrix = A:

3508.50220	345.68207	244.60942
345.68207	387.00971	25.19916
244.60942	25.19916	20.18456

Sums of Squares and Cross Products for the "Within Groups"; Matrix = W:

8561.56362	536.43011	398.55342
536.43011	428.12105	45.64975
398.55342	45.64975	35.93415

Matrix of Total Sums of Squares and Cross Products = T:

5053.06142	190.74804	153.94400
190.74804	41.11134	20.45059
153.94400	20.45059	15.74959

Total Sample Vector of Means

22.70327	2.05176	1.63392

Generalized Eigenvalues and Eigenvectors

Eigenvalues	Eigenvectors (columns)		
6.7623812	0.0429732	-0.0025496	0.0001609
0.7593371	-0.0051029	-0.0002704	0.0530117
0.0408436	-0.5275796	-0.1909436	-0.0705335

TABLE A4 Means for the Silurian Brachiopods

Variable 1	Variable 2	Variable 3
22.11230	2.64067	1.65720
20.79282	1.92218	1.55364
21.42350	1.98690	1.67390
15.03630	2.04479	1.60450
17.59210	2.36980	1.87770
17.08160	2.26260	1.82300
21.96440	2.99000	2.32360
17.41527	1.56982	1.33236
17.39815	1.63046	1.37838
24.81781	2.17788	1.59250

TABLE A4 (Continued)

Variable 1	Variable 2	Variable 3
22.01243	2.10471	1.57171
22.18975	2.14038	1.56250
18.25500	1.62086	1.39343
23.46960	2.21980	1.73700
24.19783	2.24750	1.77683
24.05043	2.18271	1.83300
19.67322	1.78367	1.45411
19.19743	1.71643	1.42586
22.91550	1.98017	1.71983
21.85871	1.99429	1.60229
23.69150	2.16017	1.84483
24.66063	2.28625	1.74575
24.40467	2.26850	1.73300
21.95825	2.02390	1.70475
25.03791	1.92991	1.64873
24.26640	1.80720	1.63380
21.77205	2.02363	1.59847
28.55183	2.67367	2.18200
20.69038	1.65962	1.36631
17.97233	1.54522	1.27000
24.58522	2.05967	1.90880
25.65053	1.91330	1.61110
21.06206	1.66576	1.36712
20.48555	1.56973	1.33682
28.17864	2.27655	1.83273
28.29190	2.26930	1.82190
22.90270	2.16430	1.72840
27.37995	2.12988	1.70875
28.13939	2.16367	1.80433
26.83725	2.34033	1.70583

TABLE A5 Canonical Variate Means for the Silurian Brachiopods

Mean 1	Mean 2	Mean 3
0.062457	-0.373524	0.026657
0.064056	-0.350192	-0.004340
0.027383	-0.374779	-0.009289
-0.210777	-0.345259	-0.002353
-0.246740	-0.404029	-0.003983
-0.239272	-0.392254	-0.005889
-0.297260	-0.500486	-0.001852
0.037452	-0.299233	-0.007955
0.012127	-0.307993	-0.007989
0.215218	-0.367942	0.007122

TABLE A5 (Continued)

Mean 1	Mean 2	Mean 3
0.106001	-0.356801	0.004258
0.118300	-0.355503	0.006827
0.041061	-0.313048	-0.009421
0.080832	-0.392108	-0.001064
0.090969	-0.401578	-0.002288
0.055333	-0.411909	-0.009708
0.069161	-0.328295	-0.004842
0.063964	-0.321668	-0.006491
0.067300	-0.387352	-0.012646
0.083830	-0.362217	-0.003777
0.033781	-0.413247	-0.011796
0.127058	-0.396833	0.002033
0.122876	-0.393741	0.001950
0.033898	-0.382043	-0.009418
0.196277	-0.379173	-0.009953
0.171624	-0.374322	-0.015530
0.081967	-0.361276	-0.001966
0.062143	-0.490158	-0.007574
0.159828	-0.314089	-0.005062
0.094418	-0.288739	-0.004770
0.038905	-0.427730	-0.021498
0.242540	-0.373546	-0.008081
0.175341	-0.315193	-0.004733
0.167042	-0.307912	-0.007780
0.232401	-0.422408	-0.004050
0.243017	-0.420627	-0.003653
0.061290	-0.389005	-0.003491
0.264235	-0.396659	-0.003210
0.246270	-0.416856	-0.008038
0.241378	-0.394775	0.008065

The method consists of solving a kind of "discriminant function,"

$$y = \alpha x ,$$

for the coefficients represented by the vector α. To make the variable y as effective a separator as possible, it is required to make the ratio

$$\eta^2 = \alpha' A\alpha / \alpha' W\alpha$$

as large as possible. Here A is the "among groups" matrix and W is the "within groups" matrix. The well-known way of doing this is to solve the set of linear equations:

$$(A - \eta^2 W)\alpha = 0 .$$

In the days before the electronic computer, this could be quite a task. However, most computer centers have a ready-made program for the type of calculations involved. The solution of the problem used here was made on the CDC 3600 computer at the University of Uppsala with the aid of a program written by the author.

The plot of the first two canonical variate means, shown in Figure A3, indicates that there is a tendency toward grouping of the data, but this is not strongly pronounced. The graphical representation does not suggest that there is a geographic or stratigraphic cause behind the locations of the points, and the nearest conclusion would seem to be that the variation represented in the variables studied is due to ecologic influences.

A test for the significance of the eigenvalues showed that the first two are significant and that the third contributes little to the comparison of the groups. The form of the test employed was that of the well-known presentation of Bartlett (cf. Seal, 1964:135).

EXAMPLE 5: APPLICATION OF THE TECHNIQUE OF CANONICAL CORRELATION

In a study of the factors determining the abundance of interstitial microanimals in the nearshore sediments of the Ivory Coast, West Africa, the author was interested in possible significant relationships between the variables pH, E_h, dissolved oxygen, calcium carbonate, and organic matter, in one set (variables $x_1, \ldots, x_5$), these being derived from the interstitial environment, and the set of variables composed of pH, E_h, and free oxygen of the superincumbent water (variables $x_6, \ldots, x_8$). The problem concerned ascertaining whether the chemical properties of the superincumbent water have a determinable effect on those of the porewater of the top layers of sediment as well as on the abundance of the organic constituents.

Briefly, the squared canonical correlations are the roots of the determinantal equation,

$$|R_{12} R_{22}^{-1} R_{12}' - \hat{\rho} R_{11}| = 0,$$

where the R_{ij} are matrices obtained by partitioning the correlation matrix, R, for all variables. In the present example, R_{11} is a (5×5) matrix, R_{22} is a (3×3) matrix and R_{12} is a (5×3) matrix. To each root of the equation there will be two vectors of coefficients—one relating to the variables of the first set, the other to the variables of the second set. The coefficients given by the vector elements may be scaled by any suitable means. Here, this has been done by scaling the largest coefficient of each set to unity. The computations shown in Table A6 were made on the IBM 7040 of the University of Kansas and checked on the CDC 3600 of the University of Uppsala, using a FORTRAN IV program. The main steps are shown in the table.

The sample size was 40 observation vectors. The results indicate that only one canonical correlation, the first, is meaningful in that it is almost significant at the 5 percent level. It is associated with the equation for the first set,

$$y_1 = -1.000x_1 - 0.806x_2 + 0.718x_3 + 0.496x_4 - 0.253x_5,$$

and the equation for the second set,

$$z_1 = 0.343x_6 - 1.000x_7 + 0.565x_8.$$

The conclusions that could be drawn from this result are that the first four variables of the first canonical variate, y_1, are important but that the first two are negatively associated with the second two. The role of the organic components clearly is not great. The correlatives of the electrochemical concomitant variates of the second set agree in behavior with those of the first set only with respect to E_h and dissolved oxygen. The major link between the subsets appears to be one involving the oxygen factor.

A canonical correlation study logically should be preceded by a test for independence of variables, which may be suitably carried out by calculating the expression $N \log_e |R|$ (Kullback, 1959), which is distributed approximately as χ^2. The value obtained in the present connection was just short of the significant level of 5 percent; therefore, the canonical correlations obtained are not unexpected.

TABLE A6 Information for the Calculation of the Canonical Correlations for the Interstitial Ecological Data. Roots of the Determinantal Equation: $\hat{\rho}_1$, 0.3461; $\hat{\rho}_2$, 0.1147; $\hat{\rho}_3$, 0.0283. Canonical Correlations Corresponding to the Roots: ζ_1, 0.588; ζ_2, 0.339; ζ_3, 0.168.

Partitioned Matrix R_{11}

1.000000	-0.077747	0.075387	-0.016047	0.406816
-0.077747	1.000000	-0.207954	0.051349	0.052337
0.075387	-0.207954	1.000000	0.035360	-0.197238
-0.016047	0.051349	0.035360	1.000000	-0.224655
0.406816	0.052337	-0.197238	-0.224655	1.000000

Partitioned Matrix R_{22}

1.000000	-0.064995	0.121925
-0.064995	1.000000	-0.404834
0.121925	-0.404834	1.000000

Partitioned Matrix R_{12}

-0.102393	0.335179	-0.221062
-0.280521	0.265663	-0.137782
0.061214	-0.184854	0.362570
-0.108068	-0.192632	0.192287
-0.012260	0.300143	-0.283166

REFERENCES

Amtmann, E. 1966. Zur Systematik afrikanischer Streifenhörnchen der Gattung *Funisciurus.* Ein Beitrag zur Problematik klimaparalleler Variation und Phänetik. Bonn. Zool. Beitr. 17:1–44.

Anderson, T. W. 1963. Asymptotic theory for principal component analysis. Ann. Math. Statist. 34:122–148.

Anderson, T. W., and R. R. Bahadur. 1962. Classification into two multivariate normal distributions with different covariance matrices. Ann. Math. Statist. 33:420–431.

Bartlett, M. S. 1965. Multivariate statistics. Theoret. Math. Biol. Blaisdell USA 1965:210–224.

Box, G. E. P. 1953. Non-normality and tests on variances. Biometrika 40:318–335.

Burnaby, T. W. 1966. Growth-invariant discriminant functions and generalized distances. Biometrics 22:96–110.

Cacoullos, T. 1965. Comparing Mahanalobis distances. I: Comparing distances between k known normal populations and another unknown. Bayes procedures when the mean vectors are unknown. Sankhyā 27(A):1–22, 23–32.

Carlson, F. E., E. Sobel, and G. S. Watson. 1966. Linear relationships between variables affected by errors. Biometrics 22:252–267.

Cochran, W. G., and C. E. Hopkins. 1961. Some classification problems with multivariate qualitative data. Biometrics 17:10–32.

Cock, A. G. 1966. Genetical aspects of metrical growth and form in animals. Quart. Rev. Biol. 41:131–190.

Cooper, P. W. 1963. Statistical classification with quadratic forms. Biometrika 50:439–448.

Cooper, P. W. 1965. Quadratic discriminant functions in pattern recognition. IEEE Trans. Information Theory 11:313–315.

Dempster, A. P. 1960. A significance test for the separation of two highly multivariate samples. Biometrics 16:41–50.

Dempster, A. P. 1963a. Multivariate theory for general stepwise methods. Ann. Math. Statist. 34:873–883.

Dempster, A. P. 1963b. Stepwise multivariate analysis of variance based on principal variables. Biometrics 19:478–490.

Dempster, A. P. 1964. Tests for the equality of two covariance matrices in relation to a best linear discriminant analysis. Ann. Math. Statist. 35:190–199.

Fries, J., and B. Matérn. 1966. On the use of multivariate methods for the construction of tree-taper curves. Res. Notes Dept. Forestry Biometry (Skogshögskolan, Stockholm) 9:85–117.

Gould, S. J. 1966. Allometry and size in ontogeny and phylogeny. Biol. Rev. 41:687–640.

Gower, J. C. 1966. A Q-technique for the calculation of canonical variates. Biometrika 53:588–589.

Hopkins, J. W. 1967. Some considerations in multivariate allometry. Biometrics 22:747–760.

Imbrie, J. 1963. Factor and vector analysis programs for analyzing geologic data. Office Naval Research Tech. Rept. 6. 135 p.

Ito, K., and W. J. Schull. 1964. On the robustness of the T_0^2 test in multivariate analysis of variance when the variance–covariance matrices are not equal. Biometrika 51:71–82.

Jolicoeur, P. 1963. The multivariate generalization of the allometry equation. Biometrics 19:497–499.

Kullback, S. 1959. Information theory and statistics. John Wiley & Sons, New York and London. 395 p.

Lerman, A. 1965. On rates of evolution of unit characters and character complexes. Evolution 19:16–25.

Mayr, E. 1963. Animal species and evolution. The Belknap Press of Harvard University Press, Cambridge, Massachusetts. 797 p.

Penrose, L. S. 1947. Some notes on discrimination. Ann. Eugen. (London)

13:228–237.
Rao, C. R. 1960. Multivariate analysis: An indispensable statistical aid in applied research. Sankhyā 22:317–338.
Rao, C. R. 1961. Some observations on multivariate statistical methods in anthropological research. Bull. Int. Statist. Inst. 38:99–109.
Rao, C. R. 1964. The use and interpretation of principal component analysis in applied research. Sankhyā 26(A):329–358.
Rao, C. R. 1965. Linear statistical inference and its applications. John Wiley & Sons, New York and London.
Rao, C. R. 1966. Discriminant functions between composite hypotheses and related problems. Biometrika 53:339–345.
Rensch, B. 1954. Neuere Probleme der Abstammungslehre. Enke, Stuttgart. 436 p.
Reyment, R. A. 1962. Observations on homogeneity of covariance matrices in paleontologic biometry. Biometrics 18:1–11.
Reyment, R. A. 1963a. Bohrlöcher bei Ostrakoden. Palöont. Z. 37:283–291.
Reyment, R. A. 1963b. Studies on Nigerian upper Cretaceous and lower Tertiary ostracoda. II Danian, Paleocene and Eocene Ostracoda. Stockholm Contr. Geol. 10. 286 p.
Reyment, R. A. 1966a. Studies on Nigerian upper Cretaceous and lower Tertiary ostracoda. III. Stratigraphical, paleoecological and biometrical conclusions. Stockholm Contr. Geol. 14. 151 p.
Reyment, R. A. 1966b. Preliminary observations on gastropod predation in the Western Niger Delta. Palaeogeography, Palaeoclimatology, Paleoecology 2:81–102.
Reyment, R. A. 1966c. *Afrobolivina africana* (Graham, de Klasz, Rérat): Quantitative Untersuchung der Variabilität einer paleozänen Foraminifere. Ecl. Geol. Helvetiae. 59:319–337.
Reyment, R. A., and D. P. Naidin. 1962. Biometric study of *Actinocamax versus* s.l. from the Upper Cretaceous of the Russian Platform. Stockholm Contr. Geol. 9:147–206.
Rohlf, F. J. 1965. Multivariate methods in taxonomy. Proc. IBM Sci. Comp. Symp. Statistics. IBM, White Plains, New York. 323 p.
Scheffé, H. S. 1959. The analysis of variance. John Wiley & Sons, New York and London. 477 p.
Seal, H. 1964. Multivariate statistical analysis for biologists. Methuen, London. 207 p.
Simpson. G. G. 1961. Principles of animal taxonomy. Columbia University Press, New York.
Simpson, G. G., A. Roe, and R. C. Lewontin. 1960. Quantitative zoology. Harcourt-Brace, New York and Burlingame. 440 p.
Sokal, R. S. 1965. Statistical methods in systematics. Biol. Rev. 40:337–391.
Sokal, R. S., and P. H. A. Sneath. 1963. Principles of numerical taxonomy. Freeman, San Francisco and London. 359 p.
Weiner, J. M., and O. J. Dunn. 1966. Elimination of variates in linear discrimination problems. Biometrics 22:268–275.

Discussion

Everett C. Olson

My remarks are concerned principally with the paleontological aspects of the paper by Dr. Reyment. Basically, the aims of systematics that deal with neontological and paleontological materials are the same, with similar ends of classification; however, the nature of the materials of the former, both in their incompleteness and in their distribution in time, requires special approaches. Some of these approaches were indicated in the several models presented in Dr. Reyment's paper.

A special problem is that death, burial, diagenesis, and exposure to erosion during the formation of what we see as the fossil record tend strongly to bias the samples as regards size, age, and distribution.

Most of the proposed models demand that there be normal distributions of the variates, and, as appropriate, identity of statistical variances and homogeneity in the covariance and correlation matrices. Serious problems plague the neozoologist with respect to distributions, but these manifestly are much more difficult for the paleozoologist. Few dependable means of arriving at sound assumptions concerning the nature of distributions exist. Exceptional cases are those in which the materials themselves, by virtue of some biological property, provide the requisite information.

The problems are least serious when tests are concerned directly with comparisons of means, but they assume considerable importance when variances are involved. In treating average fossil materials, it appears best to stay with rather simple tests whenever possible. It is equally important to be able to back-check procedures at each step.

The problems of paleontology relate in particular to (1) limitation of characters and kinds of characters available; (2) the various sources of sampling errors as related to sampling living populations; (3) lack of valid bases for assumption of normality; (4) the small size of samples in some fields; and (5) difficulties in establishing the operational taxonomic units. These problems comprise one of the factors impeding extensive work in the application of biometry to systematics of fossil materials. Some work has been done along these lines, particularly by Dr. Reyment, but the total has been very small compared with application of other methods of systematic analysis.

Dr. Reyment's statement that "typology still reigns supreme" seems to me to be considerably overdrawn. This probably stems, in part, from the fact that he deals largely with invertebrates, especially microfossils, whereas I deal largely with vertebrates.

The failure, common among paleontologists, to apply biometric techniques is not, in itself, an indication that thinking is typological. Many vertebrate paleontologists do hold population concepts in mind in the course of their assessment of taxonomies, even though they do not apply methods of comparison by biometric means. Frequently, the materials are such that this is out of the question. I believe that the gulf in basic concepts between the paleontologists and the neozoologists is not as great as Dr. Reyment's statement on typology might seem to suggest.

Dr. Reyment, working with an abundance of material and with excellent stratigraphic control, has shown how much can be done with some kinds of fossil materials. In such cases the multivariate models he has proposed can be of great value. An area of particular importance, which he mentioned but did not stress, is the role of biometrics in exploratory studies not only of taxonomy but of ecological relationships, morphology and function, and trends in time series. In my opinion, it is in these areas that the greatest advances are to be made in application of biometry to fossil organisms.

Discussion

Robert R. Sokal

It should be obvious from Dr. Reyment's comprehensive account that multivariate analysis is the technique of choice in future biometric work in systematics, although it is not yet sufficiently well appreciated by systematists. Since I concur with essentially all that Dr. Reyment has presented, there is little point in my commenting extensively on his remarks. I might ask whether he feels that Models VI and VII—which are the converse of each other—need to be distinguished, since they do use the same techniques? I add also that multiple comparison tests are necessary in multivariate analysis of variance and that simultaneous test procedures recently developed by K. R. Gabriel (Gabriel and Sokal, in manuscript) will be of great value in this connection.

A variety of applications of statistical methods to systematics might be discussed, but I have chosen to speak on numerical taxonomy—although this is not a statistical technique, in the strictest sense—because I feel that it should be discussed in the present context. Otherwise, a topic on which much research has been done and published in the last ten years (and which certainly has been on the minds of taxonomists during this time) would not be represented at all at this meeting.

Research in numerical taxonomy is under way in various laboratories in this country and abroad. Significant advances have been made in character recognition and coding, tests of the hypotheses of numerical taxonomy, methods of clustering, and methods of numerical cladistics. Dr. Rohlf will tell you something about novel ways of representing taxonomic structure. In our own laboratory there are new and (to us) exciting findings on the degree of redundancy in suites of characters, on the ability of automata to record and process taxonomic information (Rohlf and Sokal, 1967), and on the ability of biologically untrained personnel to establish meaningful classifications by means of numerical taxonomy. Evidence for an uncertainty principle in taxonomy, relating to an inherent error in constructing classifications by conventional or numerical techniques, is emerging. One of my students (Fisher, 1968) has applied numerical taxonomy in a novel way to a zoogeographic problem. At the moment an experiment is under way analyzing the judgment of taxonomists in order to gain insight into the taxonomic process.

I shall single out only three problem areas that currently are under intensive investigation. The first concerns coefficients of similarity. Different types of coefficients from the same study, regrettably, give different results. These coefficients are not jointly monotonic as one might wish them to be. However, mathematical statisticians are becoming interested in this problem, and it is quite likely that in a relatively short time we shall have better and more robust coefficients.

The second problem concerns difficulties in the systems of scaling characters. There is as yet no really satisfactory way of mixing two-state and ordered multistate characters. The coding of unordered multistate characters is especially troublesome. Colless (1967), who has discussed this issue in some detail, suggests a coefficient of association S_g for use with mixed qualitative and quantitative characters. Undoubtedly it would be profitable to study the efforts of psychologists and social scientists working with nondimensional methods of scaling and with nonmetric methods of clustering (Coombs, 1964; Guttman, 1966).

It is becoming clear that the procedures for clustering OTU's will need considerable scrutiny and improvement if stability in classifications is to be realized. Each of the methods of clustering designed so far tends to bias the resulting clusters in certain ways. For example, the weighted pair-group method with arithmetic averages (the method most frequently used to date) assumes that OTU's occur in nested, dendritic clusters. It will best cluster OTU's from a similarity matrix that does, in fact, have such phenetic relationships, and it will tend to *impose* dendritic relationships upon data that are not markedly dendritic. The degree to which the phenogram reflects the similarity matrix must indicate the degree to which the clustering method represents the underlying structure among the OTU's. It therefore is important to investigate this structure by a variety of techniques and to ascertain the nature of the phenetic constellations of OTU's in different taxonomic groups. Given an understanding of the phenetic structure of a taxonomic group, it should be possible to recommend an appropriate clustering method for it. Identical clustering methods are unlikely to serve well in every instance. To give an extreme example, members of a continuous cline would not be appropriately clustered by any of the average linkage methods. In trying various methods of clustering proposed by numerical taxonomists, we have already begun experimenting with three-dimensional models and with graph theoretical representation.

Not only will we require clustering methods that will provide us with a judicious choice, but we will also require a definition of the "goodness" of a classification. If a generally acceptable criterion for a good classification can be found, in principle it should be easy to prepare an algorithm that would move a collection of OTU's into such a position of optimum classification, if only on a trial-and-error basis. This has been the approach followed by Rubin in a recent study (1966), and Rohlf and I have established analogous criteria with our coefficient of cophenetic correlation (Rohlf and Sokal, 1967).

It is my hope that the study of these clustering methods will lead to a study of comparative phenetics of organisms. The nature of the phenetic relationship among taxonomic units should be quite different in different groups of organisms. This may be partly a function of the evolutionary history and of their genetic structure. It is quite likely, but not necessarily so, that parthenogenetic organisms will have different phenetic relations to each other than sexually reproducing organisms. Certainly the population structure of different species will be reflected in the population phenetics. As we develop a comparative insight into these relationships, we may be able to show that quite widely divergent organisms or groups of organisms may be alike in their phenetic relationships and, hence, presumably alike in their modes of evolutionary change.

REFERENCES

Colless, D. H. 1967. An examination of certain concepts in phenetic taxonomy. Syst. Zool. 16:6–27.

Coombs, C. H. 1964. A theory of data. John Wiley & Sons, New York.

Fisher, D. R. 1968. A study of faunal resemblance using numerical taxonomy and factor analysis. Syst. Zool. 17:48–63.

Guttman, L. 1966. The nonmetric breakthrough for the behavioral sciences. Proc. 2nd Nat. Conf. Data Proc., Rehoveth, Israel. 16 p.

Rohlf, F. J., and R. R. Sokal. 1967. Taxonomic structure from randomly and systematically scanned biological images. Syst. Zool. 16:246–260.

Rubin, J. 1966. An approach to organizing data into homogeneous groups. Syst. Zool. 15:169–183.

Informal Discussion

ESTABROOK: Dr. Reyment's comments are very relevant and appropriate, but I would like to share some further considerations with you. I do not feel that biology is a branch of statistics. Statistical analysis is not the only mathematical technique that might be useful in systematics. To assume that it is is to eliminate, *a priori,* from consideration many of the advances of modern mathematics that might not only serve to analyze biological information but also to make more precise the basic principles of systematics. I would urge that an open mind be kept towards such branches of mathematics as combinatorial analysis, logic, and information theory.

I would like to emphasize Dr. Reyment's admonition that care be taken before employing a given statistical technique. We must be very careful that we do not make biology fit the statistics, but make sure that statistics fit biology. Dr. Reyment pointed out that certain statistical techniques tend to frown on redundancy. One of the effects of a principal component analysis, for example, is to summarize variation more efficiently by eliminating redundancy, i.e., correlations between the descriptors. However, many practicing taxonomists accept the idea that taxa are established with correlated characters. It is the redundancy in the descriptors that enables us to delimit, and later describe, taxa.

As biologists, our primary concern should be with the advancement of biology. Toward this end, mathematics may be used to help us to a firmer understanding of the principles of biology, as well as to help us process data. Thus, before any mathematical technique is used to analyze data, it is essential that the biologist know and accept what biological principles the mathematical technique assumes to be in force. Care should be taken that the mathematics is appropriate to its biological application, rather than making mathematics a "bed of Procrustes" for the biology it is designed to serve.

CROVELLO: For our present purposes, let us recognize two stages in systematics: (1) the description of the pattern of variation in nature (taxonomy) and (2) the explanation of how this pattern arose (biosystematics). Because much numerical taxonomy has resulted in phenograms, biosystematists who are really interested in explanation of such patterns have chosen to ignore numerical taxonomy. But they should not ignore it. Numerical taxonomy can serve biosystematists as an efficient context in which to generate hypotheses of evolutionary interest without much extra effort. For instance, I may carry out a phenetic study on a certain set of characters and get one result, and then go back and pick a subset of characters and get another phenetic result. I can use this as a context for generating evolutionary hypotheses that then should be either proved or disproved later on. For example, in one phenogram based only on male characters, species A and B may cluster together, but in another phenogram based on all available characters, they may be far apart. This might suggest something about similar pollination systems to the biosystematist. The same thing can be done inversely by a character analysis, such as factor analysis.

Turning to another topic, the use of the generalized distance may not yet be preferred by taxonomists, but it certainly is preferred by statisticians. I am not quite sure that the taxonomist should weight characters by their correlation when he is trying to express phenetic relationships. This, of course, begs the question that we, as systematists, have to decide what we want to do and what we want the statisticians to help us to do.

WILLIAM BOSSERT

Computer Techniques in Systematics

It almost seems, from some of the exaggeration in the public press, that if one should trip over a power cord while walking by a computer it would be stimulated to spew forth a revision of the Carabidae. Somewhat less extreme misunderstandings of the role of automatic computers in science persist among many scientists. These misunderstandings extend even to those responsible for the funding of scientific investigation. In view of these misconceptions of the role of computers, I must make several very basic denials. First, automatic computers are not taxonomists. There is a comment popular in computer circles about physicians—and sometimes applied to business executives—that is applicable here: "Any taxonomist who is afraid of being replaced by an automatic computer probably can be." Second, computers do not even constitute new systematic techniques. "Putting it on the computer" is in no way comparable to carrying out an immunological study, for example. The computer itself is only a tool. A very powerful tool and one without which many activities would be meaningless, but still, merely a tool. In this context the techniques are computer programs, or even machine-independent algorithms.

This somewhat ungraceful word "algorithm," which has been used previously in this meeting, will become more common in systematics, and it deserves a definition. Perhaps the closest English synonym for algorithm is procedure. It is a sequential set of rules or actions selected from some repertoire of commonly understood rules or actions. These basic units may either transform data or alter the sequence of the algorithm itself. An algorithm is evaluated by carrying out the actions in the specified order.

The word has a number of formal connotations for the mathematician, only one of which is of great concern to us here. It is that an algorithm guarantees to produce some advertised result, no less and no more. This result is usually given by the last step of the evaluation. A taxonomic key is a very good example of an algorithm. Its basic repertoire includes directions for continuing the sequence of evaluation on the basis of directed observations on a specimen. The result, identification of the specimen, is given by the end point of the path taken through the key. Many algorithms, such as one to sort names alphabetically, are easy to state but difficult to evaluate; the data to be sorted may be the telephone subscribers of New York City, for example. Automatic computers, then, are machines intended for the evaluation, but not the generation, of algorithms or computer programs.

The greatest impact of automatic computing in systematics has certainly been in the application of multivariate statistical methods to problems of classification and identification. A number of packages of statistical and taxonomic computer programs have been widely distributed. Most of these require little knowledge of automatic computers, and this often leads to a false sense of security. They do require considerable statistical sophistication for successful operation, particularly in the selection of method and the interpretation of the result. I feel that these two points are essential to the continuing controversy over statistical taxonomy. Both proponents and opponents have at times ignored the variety of methods available, none of them appropriate for every problem; and they also have been unwilling to admit that the solution was not always completed in the computer printout. I was happy to hear Dr. Sokal's clear reaffirmation of his view on this when he stated, in effect, that even the restricted area of numerical phenetics is made up of a number of possible approaches. For any particular question and its associated set of data, some methods might produce results that lead to an answer; and others might not. Even among the former there would usually be a considerable range of efficiencies. Very often the use of a multivariate statistical package in taxonomy has produced results that created more questions than answers, and this at great cost. The cost is measured not only in machine time but in frustration, embarrassment, and loss of research time on the part of the investigator.

My principal concern in this situation is that too often computer taxonomy is identified with statistical taxonomy, and the computer rises or falls in favor according to the success or failure of particular statistical applications. Again, Dr. Sokal's statement was welcome. In outlining the nomenclatural status of his work he never once suggested the label of computer taxonomy for what was finally resolved to be numerical phenetics. There is a very good reason. On one hand, his methods can conceivably be applied and can certainly be criticized quite independently of any computer; and on the other hand, the variety of possible approaches he has suggested indicates that the computer cannot be identified with any one of them.

Automatic computers can, in fact, do a great deal more than evaluate statistical formulas. I would like to seize upon a recent statement by Blackwelder (1967): "Of course computers can also be used as data recovery devices to store taxonomic information, assuming that there is a taxonomist anywhere with sufficient access to a computer to use it in day to day work." It leads to the consideration of two important developments in automatic computing. The first is the development of multiple-access, time-shared computing systems. The second involves techniques for manipulating nonnumeric—that is, alphabetic or graphical—information. Before discussing these in detail I would like to give a combined illustration of them.

The following are excerpts from an interaction I had recently with a time-shared computer located in the Harvard Computing Center. It is reproduced exactly as it appeared on the printout of a teletypewriter, except that my responses have been set here in italic to distinguish them from the line typed by the computer, and editorial comments have been interspersed parenthetically. I was seated at the teletype console in the Biological Laboratories several blocks away from the Computing Center. At this time the computer was carrying perhaps 20 other quite independent conversations. In my case the computer program was directing me through a key to the Polynesian ants. Notice that the dialogue is carried on completely in English with no trace of inappropriate, detailed computer operations.

/(GO)
THIS PROGRAM SHOULD HELP YOU IDENTIFY A POLYNESIAN ANT.
THE SOURCE IS WILSON AND TAYLOR 1967.
THE KEY IS BASED ON THE WORKERS. DO YOU HAVE A SPECIMEN BEFORE YOU?
NO
TYPE YES WHEN YOU ARE READY.
NO
TYPE YES WHEN YOU ARE READY.
YES
IS THE GASTER ATTACHED TO THE MESOSOMA BY A WAIST CONSISTING OF TWO MORE OR LESS REDUCED AND NODIFORM SEGMENTS?
YES
IS THE PYGIDIUM FLATTENED AT APEX, WITH THE FLATTENED PART BORDERED WITH DENTICLES ARRANGED IN ROWS ON EACH SIDE; AND IS THERE A STRONG CARINA ON EACH SIDE OF THE UNDERSIDE OF THE HEAD RUNNING FORWARD FROM THE POSTERIOR CORNER?
NO
THE SPECIMEN IS OF THE SUBFAMILY MYRMICINAE.
I AM SORRY THE PROGRAM IS NOT COMPLETED FOR THIS SUBFAMILY.

(The program might never be completed in this part, yet the finished portion can be used easily.)

TYPE YES WHEN YOU ARE READY WITH ANOTHER SPECIMEN.
YES
IS THE GASTER ATTACHED TO THE MESOSOMA BY A WAIST CONSISTING OF TWO MORE OR LESS REDUCED AND NODIFORM SEGMENTS?
NO
IS THE STING WELL DEVELOPED AND FUNCTIONAL?
NO
IS THE SEVENTH STERNITE ROLLED INTO A SHORT VENTRO-APICAL CONE WITH A ROUND ORIFICE (WITH OR WITHOUT A CORONULA OF TINY HAIRS) THAT SERVES AS A NOZZLE FOR A DEFENSIVE SPRAY? DO NOT CONFUSE IT WITH THE CLOACAL ORIFICE, WHICH IS MORE DORSAL AND NORMALLY HIDDEN.
YES
THE SUBFAMILY IS FORMICINAE.
IS THE PETIOLE ARMED WITH TWO LARGE, LATERALLY DIRECTED HORN-LIKE SPINES?
NO
HOW MANY SEGMENTS ARE THERE TO THE ANTENNA?
12
IS THE JUNCTURE OF THE DORSAL AND BASAL FACES OF THE PROPODEUM

OF THE WORKERS (MINOR WORKERS IF POLYMORPHIC) DRAWN INTO AN ACUTE TOOTH-LIKE PROTUBERANCE?
YES
IS THE PETIOLAR NODE ARMED WITH A POSTERIOR MEDIAN TOOTH-LIKE PROTUBERANCE?
NO
THE SPECIES IS CAMPONOTUS FLAVOLIMBATUS.
WHERE WAS THE SPECIMEN COLLECTED?
SAMOA
GOOD, THE SPECIES SEEMS TO BE ENDEMIC TO SAMOA.

(A small recognition of the fact that supporting consistent information is important in the identification, or that identification alone may not be the only goal of the user.)

TYPE YES WHEN YOU ARE READY WITH ANOTHER SPECIMEN.

.
.
.

IS THE PETIOLE ARMED WITH TWO LARGE, LATERALLY DIRECTED HORN-LIKE SPINES?
NO
HOW MANY SEGMENTS ARE THERE TO THE ANTENNA?
12
IS THE JUNCTURE OF THE DORSAL AND BASAL FACES OF THE PROPODEUM OF THE WORKERS (MINOR WORKERS IF POLYMORPHIC) DRAWN INTO AN ACUTE TOOTH-LIKE PROTUBERANCE?
TES
TYPE YES OR NO PLEASE.

(Here a simple error has been detected, and suggestions are given for correcting it. In this case it would have been possible to correct the typographical error automatically.)

YES
IS THE PETIOLAR NODE ARMED WITH A POSTERIOR MEDIAN TOOTH-LIKE PROTUBERANCE?
NO
THE SPECIES IS CAMPONOTUS FLAVOLIMBATUS.
WHERE WAS THE SPECIMEN COLLECTED?
TONGA
THAT IS INTERESTING. TO DATE IT HAS BEEN FOUND ONLY ON SAMOA.

(Here for the first time new information has gone into the machine. It was false in this case and could have caused difficulties if it had been blindly added to the list of islands on which the species is found.)

TYPE YES WHEN YOU ARE READY WITH ANOTHER SPECIMEN.

.
.
.

IS THE PETIOLE ARMED WITH TWO LARGE, LATERALLY DIRECTED HORN-LIKE SPINES?
NO
HOW MANY SEGMENTS ARE THERE TO THE ANTENNA?
14
THAT IS A STRANGE ONE. YOU SHOULD CONTACT E. O. WILSON.

(In this case the new information was inconsistent with the key and evaluation could not continue.)

TYPE YES WHEN YOU ARE READY WITH ANOTHER SPECIMEN.

Let us go a bit below the surface of this interaction. My first step was to dial the computer on my teletype. The two were connected over standard telephone lines through a switchboard on the Harvard campus. Any characters I then typed on the teletype keyboard were transferred to the computer to be operated on by an active program. The program can in turn communicate by causing characters to be typed on the remote unit. Initially a basic control and accounting program, an operating monitor, was automatically activated. It asked me to supply a password, which was used by the monitor to direct billing and to specify the portion of the computer's memory to which I might have access. I selected a file by name from this memory, which contained a set of basic operational units for manipulating textual material. In this case it was the SNOBOL language (Farber *et al.*, 1964). In addition to this I selected the program that I had previously prepared to evaluate a taxonomic key. The key is (specifically, in this case) a set of labeled questions or statements and a set of answers associated with each. Each answer in turn is associated with another question label that will continue the dialogue when the user supplies that particular answer. It is possible to include in this structure a variety of error-detecting and information-gathering functions as well as the basic key. There are several simple demonstrations of this in the illustrations. This program, a sequence of SNOBOL instructions, is less than a page long and required only about an hour to prepare. Finally, the taxonomic key itself was selected from the memory. I want to stress the independence of the taxonomic key and the program that directs its evaluation, since this latter program could be used with any key. The insertion of the key itself into the computer's memory is a matter of typing only and requires no extra programming effort.

Let us now consider time-sharing and the processing of non-numeric information in more detail. There is a great economy of scale in nearly every aspect of automatic computing. This has exerted the pressure for the development of larger and larger computers, apparently taking us further and further from the sufficient access taxonomists call for in the statement mentioned earlier. A $3 million computer in the field is an absurdity; even small universities and research stations cannot consider the support of such a beast. Multiple-access, time-shared computing has been the answer of the computer scientists to this dilemma. The central concept here is that the computer can do enough in a short while to keep a researcher busy for several minutes. This is based principally on the great disparity in input–output speeds between the computer and a researcher reading and typing textual material. A large computer might transmit as many as a million characters per second while the investigator seated at a teletypewriter can use or produce at speeds of less than 100 characters per second. Considering only the communications aspect, a large computer, therefore, could service hundreds of teletypes going full speed. This input–output disparity is furthered by the fact that the user is not continually making active demands on the computer. He may be observing or making measurements to be used in the computations, running to the library to check on necessary reference data, or merely scratching his head and planning the next computation on the basis of current results. In my session with the taxonomic key, for example, I was connected by telephone line to the computer for about 20 minutes, while the central computer with its memory was serving me for less than 20 seconds. With this ratio one can see that I was virtually invisible to the 20 or so other users of the computer's time, as they were to me. Although each of the independent users has an apparent freedom of use of the large computer over this time, the operation costs could be divided among all of us. The resulting fractional charge made the access as financially reasonable as did the connection by dialing a telephone make it physically simple.

The second development in computer science I want to discuss in more detail concerns techniques for manipulating nonnumeric information. The basic computer language used in the taxonomic key illustration and the program in this language that operated on the key and the user's responses are both good examples of this, but in no way do they convey the extent of the developments. Significant techniques are available for abstracting, cataloging, editing, typesetting, and, in limited areas, retrieving information from textual material. Nonnumeric information is not limited to alphabetics. Some of the fundamental problems involved in inputting and storing pictorial or graphical information in automatic computers have been solved. The computer processing of the pictures of Mars from the space vehicle is probably familiar to you. Automatic karyotyping of cells and the use of a computer in visualizing protein configurations are examples closer to the subject of this conference. A great deal of work is still required in this area. While a picture is often worth a thousand words, it is, unfortunately, by most current coding schemes, *more* than a thousand words in the computer memory. The importance to taxonomy is obvious, however, and I believe Dr. Rohlf will comment further on this.

Research in automatic computing seems directed largely to furthering these developments until large central computer utilities are available to which users can gain access freely and remotely through terminals ranging in complexity from a touch-tone telephone to entire separate computers, and in which the user interacts with the computer in a manner and language suited to the problem rather than to the computer. Several large information transfer and storage projects are under way in expectation of exploiting this freedom of access. Automation of the Library of Congress (Council on Library Resources, 1963) is being attempted, and this should indicate the scale possible for such systems. An even more ambitious project, in my opinion, is Project Intrex, a coordinated program of information transfer experiments at the Massachusetts Institute of Technology (Overhage and Harman, 1965). These experiments involve the application and organization of scientific information as well as its retrieval from a central store.

I feel we should consider the possibility of taking advantage of these developments in the establishment of one or more central computer taxonomic information stores. The initial work in the projects I have mentioned indicates that this would be technically and economically feasible by the early or middle 1970's, and plans in this direction could be made now. The system would consist of a central moderate-size computer for handling communication between remote consoles and a very large central memory file. This memory would contain, as in the illustration, basic operating programs and program language interpreters, specific programs to act on both internal and incoming information, and, finally, the body of taxonomic information itself. The details of the design of the system would depend on the exact nature and form of this latter body. It would be inappropriate to specify these now. I want merely to state that neither the volume nor the variety of sources and applications of this material is a relevant block to its automatic use.

The cost of such a system would not be small. A computer with a multibillion-character storage capacity will cost $4 million or $5 million, exclusive of remote terminals; and the development of programs and preparation of data would amount to a comparable sum. In addition, continued maintenance and updating of the system could require a budget on the order of $1 million each year. I would say that over all we must consider an expenditure equivalent to an endowment of about $20 million. It is possible that cooperation with similar projects could reduce this somewhat. There certainly would be some overlap in program requirements between a project such as this and, for example, the automation of the Library of Congress; and the physical system would be similar to that planned by Intrex. In a recent conversation, Dr. D. J. Rogers told me that 90 percent of the world's taxonomists would be shocked by such an expense. This cost is certainly great enough that, if the system is viewed solely as a taxonomic archive to be used by specialists for identification and classification purposes, other methods might be preferable. One can print a lot of monographs for $20 million, of course, and an organized card file such as that proposed by Brown (1961) could certainly meet all needs of this sort. To make sense, the system must be recognized as a clearinghouse and store for information of biogeographical, ecological, and behavioral importance; and there should be a regular flow of such information into the system from the users.

The computer–user dialogue given above is a simple example of this, where a new observation of the species was reported and would thereafter be included in the regular response of the key to an identification. There must, of course, be some control over the inclusion of information in the file; either automatic, as at the end of the illustration, or through some system of authoritative review. Given some simple control, however, this dynamic taxonomic record in the computer could be the basis for developing theoretical structures in all areas of population biology. Certainly not the least potential of the system is in the area of education in systematics. With the use of an on-line, remote terminal in the classroom it would be possible to reconstruct taxonomic studies from original data to classification, dynamically involving the class in a fashion impossible with a standard lecture presentation.

A major problem in the justification of a project such as this is that its true value cannot be extrapolated from current experience. One can imagine certain introductory studies of this type that might yield some valuable experience. For example, one might limit the body of information in the file to that concerning distributions and densities of rare species. That is, the *Red Data Book* of the International Union for Conservation of Nature and Natural Resources could be automated (e.g., Simon, 1966). While requiring only a fairly limited physical system, this introductory study could prove expensive because virtually the entire variety of operating programs would still be required. I want to stress this point. The basic programs needed to manipulate the information file are to a great extent independent of the size of the file. An alternative first step would be a catalog of molecular information of the type we have been discussing here. It was mentioned earlier in the conference that this information is becoming available more rapidly than the journals can report it. A time-shared computer system would be ideal for keeping track of it. Either of these first studies would have a logical (although not trivial) extension to a complete system.

Because the technical problems are being overcome and the potential of the product is so great for the advancement of population biology, it is difficult for me to be deterred by the many drawbacks to a project of this sort. Quite obvious ones are the conflicts between the exchange of information through the computer store and the traditional concepts of publication. This problem, as it relates to the copyright laws is being considered by the United States Congress. I am more deeply worried about the many blocks that exist or might arise to hinder the essential communication between computer scientists and biologists in the course of the project. Neither group alone could produce a viable system.

REFERENCES

Blackwelder, R. E. 1967. A critique of numerical taxonomy. Syst. Zool. 16:64–72.

Brown, W. L. 1961. An international taxonomic register of preliminary proposals. Syst. Zool. 10:80–85.

Council on Library Resources, Inc. 1963. Automation and the Library of Congress. U. S. Government Printing Office, Washington, D.C. 88 p.

Farber, D. J., R. E. Griswold, and I. P. Polonsky. 1964. *SNOBOL,* a string manipulation language. J. Ass. for Comp. Mach. 11:21–30.

Overhage, Carl F. J., and Joyce R. Harman [ed], 1965 Intrex. M.I.T. Press, Cambridge, Massachusetts, and London, England. 276 p.

Simon, N. 1966. The red data book, Mammalia, Vol. 1. International Union for Conservation of Nature and Natural Resources, Morges, Switzerland. 225 p.

Discussion

David J. Rogers

Perhaps the most significant implications in Dr. Bossert's presentation were intellectual ones. The computer system does not rise or fall, is not successful or unsuccessful, on the basis of how it is used. There has been a sufficient number of papers denouncing the computer in taxonomy to indicate a widespread misunderstanding about the computer as an instrument. The stored program of the computer is the set of instructions provided to the device by the operator. If the operator provides inadequate instructions, or if his data are not properly prepared for the particular program, then the device carries out a poor set of operations. The opposite is equally true; if the stored program is a good one and the data are properly structured, one may anticipate good results.

But the computer does force us to be more logical, more scientific, in our methodology, than we were required to be in the pre-computer days. It is essential that we know beforehand precisely what is needed in order for us to achieve the desired results. The various ways in which the computer can be used must be understood, otherwise there will be only some more of the results that we have already seen—poor reflections of our ideas about what the computer ought to have given us. If statistical taxonomic methods prove not to be the most appropriate procedures for doing taxonomic work on the computer, it behooves us to seek the difficulty with the author of the program, not the wiring or circuitry of the machine. From this it should be evident that the computer is a tool, a very complex tool, different in most respects from any other, and an outgrowth of our needs for ever faster computational capabilities. The primary limitation to the use of the computer is our own ingenuity.

Programming for computers is a very recent profession. In biological circles, it has been thought that anyone who wished to use the computer could take a few courses in programming languages and then proceed with his work. For some purposes and in some areas this is true, but for the more complex tasks, such as classification, the aid of a mathematician and programmer are essential, and the biologist will be well-served to enlist the aid of people who are professionally trained in these areas. It is unlikely that the biologist will have sufficient time to cope with the very large body of skills being developed in either the programming or the hardware of computers. To get the maximum benefit from any one machine (or at least one of the larger and later generation), much time, effort, and energy must be expended to keep abreast. Eventually we may be able to instruct a computer to use colloquial English, but this is not possible at the moment.

Dr. Bossert has indicated that the computer may be used for keys. He demonstrated one key that had been made up to aid in the identification of Polynesian ants. Perhaps eventually it will be a practical matter to keep such programs in the memory of a computer, available for instant service, but there is not much likelihood that this will be a compelling sales pitch to those who must provide the financial support for the work. Would it not be better to have the computer go to work with the description of the unknown, and, without the man–machine interaction demonstrated by Dr. Bossert, give the best possible set of determinations for the unknown ant? I think there are more immediate needs for computers than that example demonstrated. If the demonstration had been intended only to show the potential flexibility of computer systems, that would be different, but I hope no one got the impression that we will make this our primary use of the hardware.

The potentiality of one, or a few, large central computers for biological-information retrieval was mentioned. The need for a large information system for biology can hardly be overstressed. Much practical information about biological subjects is demanded daily, and the present method of providing answers either to the lay public or for more strictly scientific endeavors is not necessarily the most satisfactory. The design and operation of such a system, however, will require much strenuous effort by numbers of biologists and allied librarians, computer designers, and programmers. For it to be worth much, we, as taxonomists, must be centrally located in the operation and must contribute to its development. The central question, therefore, is one of whether we are willing to give up some of our own research to achieve such goals.

There is no reason to believe that the computer cannot serve the biological community in much the same way that the computers are used in business operations, that is, performing chores such as accounting for specimens, making inventories of collections, and doing clerical work involving repetitive drudgery.

Two large projects indicate the potential use of computers as aids to more efficient operations. These are the taxonomic work to be done in Hawaii under the auspices of the International Biological Program and the proposed project on the Flora of North America. Both of these operations would be well advised to establish a set of procedures for automatic data processing to aid them in accomplishing their goals within a reasonable time. In these cases, a number of options are open to the workers, in terms of programs available to store, sort, and keep abreast of incoming raw data, and to take the raw data through various correlations necessary for proper interpretation. These types of programs can be adapted to the projects, provided there is a little lead time.

We are just entering the age of computer-aided taxonomy. Our own fully computerized classification was recently published [H. S. Irwin and D. J. Rogers. 1967. Monographic Studies in *Cassia* (Leguminosae–Caesalpinoideae). II. A Taximetric Study of Section Apoucouita. Memoirs of the New York Botanical Garden. 16:71–120]. To our knowledge, this is the first case of a group of plants being subjected to computer analysis, and this followed by actual taxonomic reporting. Other more sophisticated cases certainly will be appearing. We look forward to the valuable aid we can derive from computers.

Discussion

F. James Rohlf

The area of information retrieval mentioned by Dr. Bossert is certainly an important one. Such systems have obvious practical applications and great potential for the future. Assuming a "clean file" of taxonomic information, there are many questions that could be asked about presently known information that is difficult to get at now.

My comments will relate to some other areas in which the use of computers can be applied to taxonomy.

1. A very important application is that of automatic or semiautomatic data-recording devices that present their results in a computer-compatible format (or perhaps directly to a computer). For example, optical scanners are being used to scan (at a variety of wavelengths) and quantify two-dimensional images of simple biological structures. The major problem at present is not that of engineering hardware but rather that of logical analysis of information. Detailed morphometric studies of selected structures (such as an insect wing) for tens of thousands of specimens should be practical rather soon. This should relieve much of the drudgery of recording characters required in morphometric studies.

2. Given a matrix of data (n characters measured over t OTU's), the next step is that of its analysis. The advantage of a computer here is its high speed and accuracy. At present there are many pro-

grams (some involving systems of programs) to aid in the display of data structures. This is not as simple as was once thought. It turns out that it is difficult to fully comprehend multivariate relationships. Various methods of summary—for example, phenograms, principal-components analysis, factor analysis, and so forth—are needed. At present, no single method is ideal. The most appropriate method depends upon the structure or the patterns of similarity in the given study. It is quite clear now that a phenogram is not necessarily the optimal way to summarize phenetic relationships. Remote graphic computer consoles should facilitate the manipulation and display of the data from several points of view—possibly points of view specified on the basis of some hypotheses—to see which produces the best fit to the data. Now, man-machine interaction is also possible, and this is of interest in numerical taxonomy because several of the newer approaches involve the defining of a criterion describing the "goodness" of a given classification but do not specify an analytic method for finding this optimum classification. Thus, the computer must proceed by trial-and-error. Since there are far more combinations than can be practically computed and tested, it is reasonable to consider allowing a taxonomist to specify reasonable classifications for the computer to check.

3. A third level then, is reached where one wishes to save the results of the above analyses (and the data upon which they are based) in a form to which others can have convenient access. This is the general area of information storage and retrieval that has been discussed.

I would ask Dr. Bossert two specific questions in regard to his example of a taxonomic key. In response to a query by the computer, is it possible to type a question mark (indicating that you do not know the answer to the question) as a response? And, is it possible to give the computer (at any stage in the identification process) information other than that for which it specifically asked? For example, if the taxonomist notices that the specimen at hand has a rather unusual structure, it would be desirable for the computer to be able to take this quickly into consideration. Without these types of abilities, I see little point in placing a taxonomic key on a computer. It is just as well having it available in printed form, either as done conventionally or perhaps in the form of some of the newer programmed texts. It is possible to conceive of a type of key that would take advantage of the capabilities of a digital computer and that probably would be sufficiently more efficient to justify the increased cost. This would be a program that would have the ability to restructure the key so that questions could be asked in any order the user desires. If at any point the user has no preference, then the program would decide on the optimal question to be asked. These capabilities are required if the system is to be used by taxonomists who already have some degree of experience with a given group.

BOSSERT: Wasn't that in one of the slides? As I was typing, one of my responses was "TES." The computer's reply to this was "TYPE YES OR NO." As a matter of fact, in this very simple illustration I had not allowed for this, although corrections certainly would be included in any realistic application of this technique to taxonomy.

Discussion

James A. Peters

The development of time-shared, multiaccess computing systems utilizing standard teletype machines and the availability of extremely simple programming languages are recent events that provide an opportunity for some major changes in the work of systematists. Time-sharing has practically eliminated the problems of computer access that previously precluded computer use for the day-to-day solution of systematic problems. Computer languages such as Dartmouth's "BASIC" have eliminated a major stumbling block in computer utilization–machine programming. As a consequence, none of the many problems that plagued me in computer utilization after I began using the IBM facilities here at the University of Michigan almost 20 years ago exist today. The explosive development of commercial multiaccess systems, still less than two years old, has made possible direct connection to a time-shared computer in most major cities of the United States. For example, the Smithsonian Institution now has available–in the length of time it takes to dial a telephone number–a full computer layout that can run almost every statistical analysis that my colleagues and I find useful in our systematic work. The language, designed for conversational exchange with the computer, is so simple that one can learn it after a few hours of instruction, and we now compose our own programs as necessary. I can run an analysis of the data for a sample—from a snake population, for instance—including standard deviations, standard errors, regressions, correlation coefficients, and even a plot of the data on a graph with an x- and y-axis, all within a few minutes. If, the next day, I receive additional specimens from another museum, I can add them in with no more effort than that required to punch the new data on paper tape and rerun the whole set of variables, with no scheduling, no additional programming, and no waiting.

This, however, is only one of the new doors for systematics that have been opened by time-shared, multiaccess computer use. A second advantage is the possibility of storing identification keys in the computer memory. More as a test of my understanding of programming in BASIC than because of its potential use, I recently wrote a program for a key to the genera of snakes occurring in Ecuador, translating directly from the key in my paper published in 1960. The necessary data were grouped into 14 units, and the computer selected alternatives within these groups. A short time after completing this exercise, I began preparing a similar key to the genera of snakes of the entire Neotropical Region. It proved to be very easy to incorporate additional genera into the Ecuadorian key by running the same 14 pieces of data for a non-Ecuadorian genus through the computer, which resulted in a printout of the Ecuadorian genus with the most similar constellation of characters. The second genus was then added by programming an alternative for the group in which a character contrasted with one of the Ecuadorian genus. The final step was greatly simplified by comparing directly the 14 encoded characters for both genera from direct printouts. In the preparation of the Catalog of Neotropical Squamata, this program for identification of the genera will be translated back into the dichotomies of a key for publication.

Still another potentiality, at present totally unexploited, is the utilization of the teletype used in time-sharing for rapid communication between institutions engaged in systematic researches. The availability to museums of a means of rapid, long-distance exchange of information could mean major changes in their everyday operations. Quick information on particular specimens, lists of available material, verification of questioned data, and other such day-to-day museum functions could be completed in minutes rather than involving weeks through the mails. Also, if it is feasible for me to prepare and store a key to the Neotropical snake genera in my local computer's memory, it is equally feasible for a herpetologist at the American Museum of Natural History to do the same for New Guinea frogs, or for a herpetologist at the California Academy of Sciences to do it for Asiatic lizards. When I am faced, in the not too distant future, with the identification of a collection from an area beyond my immediate familiarity, I might call New York on my teletype, feed my data into the computer there, and have it print back generic or even specific identifications on my machine. Since a computer key can be programmed to include new taxa in a matter of minutes, one could be assured of identifications based on the most recent information rather than having to use out-of-date published keys. This aspect of time-shared computing could lead rapidly to some revolutionary changes in systematic activities, since the publication patterns of the past would be recognized as superfluous and obsolete. Part of our systematic responsibilities would be maintaining and making available such storage banks of information.

Perhaps the most significant advantage of this new tool, however, is the simplicity of using it. If the program is properly constructed, all the novice need do is feed the data in as instructed *by the program itself,* tell the machine "RUN," and watch the answers being typed out. This eliminates the necessity of having to become familiar with the formulae for calculation of standard statistical measures. At institutions where time-shared computer service is available, courses in quantitative or statistical biology could be taught in such a way that the student could focus his attention on understanding the concepts and applications of statistics, and the mechanical steps involved in getting to the results could be de-emphasized, just as the gear ratios involved need not be understood in order to cut sections with a microtome. Numerical taxonomy can take its proper place in systematics as an invaluable tool that can never replace the sound judgment based on knowledge and experience that is the hallmark of a good systematist, but it can make it much easier for him to arrive at the point of making those judgments.

Informal Discussion

GILMARTIN: We have been hearing a lot about the urgency of getting at the tropical species, but I ask the plant systematists how long they are going to leave the tropical flora in the hands of the alpha-taxonomists. Unless one agrees with Ehrlich's suggestion that we are spreading ourselves too thin and should instead concentrate on a very few organisms, it seems that now is the time to approach the botany of the tropics from a systematic viewpoint as well as from the alpha-taxonomic viewpoint. It is undeniable that taxonomy or plant systematics is not being approached very much in the tropical forest—the tropical flora where specimens of individual species are few and far between.

CRONQUIST: There are more than enough problems to keep all of us busy for a long time, and people work on the things in which they are interested. Although my own work is not tropically directed, there are several people at the institution where I work whose work essentially is tropically directed. We could argue about what proportion of study ought to be directed to this or to that, but I do not think the problem you mention is being totally overlooked.

CUTLER: As someone who has spent several hours in museums going through yellowing log books and checking through file cards trying to get information related to specimens, I feel it would be a major convenience to have this information stored in a computer. Is this feasible?

PETERS: I think that, at present, there are two things that are not practical to store in computers: one is catalog data and the other is bibliographic data. I say this primarily because of the expense that is involved in putting such data in and taking it out as compared with the utility of the material. However, I think there are a great number of things important to systematics that are being retrieved and constantly used, and those are the things I think we ought to be talking about in the storage system proposed by Dr. Bossert.

CUTLER: If a person could request a printout pertaining to a particular species or genus that would have on it certain ecological information–such as locality, depth, temperature, and similar information–that would save him a trip to Washington or New York to glean it on his own, I think it would greatly increase the usefulness or value of such data.

ROGERS: I sympathize with you, and I disagree with Dr. Peters. Instead of doing clerical work, I would rather use an easy technique or methodology for putting away dusty, rusty old figures that are not particularly interesting to anyone but me. There are techniques now being generated whereby one can feed his data into a system and have the information sorted into various facets in which he is interested and have it screened by the Smithsonian Institution or some other such national storehouse or warehouse.

EDWARD O. WILSON

Summary of the Conference

It is singularly hard to judge the goals of systematics or to describe the methods systematists use to approach them. Let me add at once that this feeling of disorientation, which practicing systematists themselves as a rule share, does not stem from any lack of intellectual content in the subject matter. It comes from a simpler, more human cause, namely the circumstance that most systematists do not approach their work as problem solvers. It has occasionally been said that the perfect experimental biologist selects a problem first and then seeks the organism ideally suited to its solution. In contrast, the typical systematist selects the organism first—for the love of it. Now this is a great strength, for the systematist devotes his career to the organism and thereby often comes upon problems of general significance that would not be discovered otherwise; but these problems are found incidentally. Perhaps the ideal program for a systematist would be to continue selecting the organism first, for whatever personal reasons move him, as a kind of totem animal (or plant), then to seek actively the problem for the solution of which the organism is ideally suited.

Yet even this ideal strategy of research will do little for the pure science of systematics, because of the way we have come to define this field. What is a *pure* systematist? He might be defined as a biologist who works on such a large number of species that he has only enough time to consider classification and phylogeny. If he narrows his focus, his unique knowledge provides him with a good chance to make discoveries in genetics, ecology, behavior, and physiology, as well as in taxonomy. But then we come to know him as a geneticist, or an ecologist, or a behaviorist, or a physiologist. It clearly will not do to define systematics as classification plus all these other fields, because that would be robbing the discipline of its true meaning. I think it would be appropriate just to acknowledge everything that systematists do for the rest of biology (and that is a great deal indeed), then, for the moment, to subordinate the service aspect and to concentrate on those problems of intellectual merit peculiar to systematics.

These problems exist in abundance. This International Conference on Systematic Biology has gone far to restate the proprietary goals of systematics as a set of concrete problems and thus to provide the discipline with a new sense of identity.

LANGUAGE AND LOGIC

The procedures of systematics are still very diffuse and hard to formalize, but systematics is not just an art, and systematists work with much more than intuition. There is, as M. T. Ghiselin and W. H. Wagner, Jr., pointed out, a strong element of the hypothetico-deductive method of modern science in systematics. The difficulty has been that until recently not much trouble has been taken to make the operating principles explicit, and a great deal of confused and confusing controversy has developed which is, in the final analysis, semantic. A lot of the argumentation over the species and subspecies concepts, the uncertainties of homology versus non-homology, and the confrontation between the "numerical" and "classical" taxonomies have been of this kind.

The way out has been indicated by the recent formal analyses of such authors as Hennig (1966), Gregg (1954), Hull (1964), Ghiselin (1966 a and b) and Gisin (1967), who in some cases have begun to go down to the roots of formal logic and even epistemology.

Ghiselin, for example, following Wittgenstein, has argued that so-called natural classifications that are supposed to be based on "over-all similarity" cannot have this basis in actuality, because there is no objectively finite number of characters to which a measure of similarity can refer. Only when the sample of characters used is explicitly listed can a classification be freed of the metaphysical taint. To be sure, the greater the number of characters used, the more information the classification contains. But the goal of measuring a quality of over-all similarity remains meaningless.

Probably the greatest and most important confusion in systematics has surrounded the interpretation of the use of phylogenetic trees. Instead of a single tree indicating phyletic distances (the amounts of change that led to two or more taxa) in some ill-defined and subjective way, an attempt is now being made to measure and relate three quantities: *phenetic distance,* the difference in phenotype between any two points in the tree, in whatever characters have been selected; *patristic distance,* the genetically based change that occurred in the characters between two points; and *cladistic distance,* the number of branching points between two points in the tree. A good deal of attention to this problem has been paid by Hennig (1966), Cain and Harrison (1960), Camin and Sokal (1965), Farris (1967), Gisin (1967), and Wagner (this volume, page 67), to mention a few. Although the abstract structure of a phylogeny has now been clarified to some extent by these authors, immense practical difficulties remain. For example, the most appropriate measure of the three distances just mentioned, especially in groups where fossil evidence is scanty; the method of relating the distances to each other and their employment to form a classification in some standard form; and the use of the new information to throw light on evolution–all remain to be worked out. These methodological problems are, in my opinion, among the most difficult in modern science, and they stand as a challenge to both biologists and mathematicians.

THE SEARCH FOR NEW CHARACTERS

During the past few years, the development of many clever and sophisticated new approaches by biologists of various specialties has resulted in the accelerated growth of data of relevance to both taxonomy and phylogeny. Biochemists are now contributing to the search in several very significant ways.

1. The vast store of information accumulated on secondary plant products has been related to systematics by Hegnauer (1962, 1963), Alston and Turner (1963), Swain (1963), and Leone (1964). Of

course, natural-products chemistry of plants has been greatly advanced over that in animals, although the gap is now being narrowed somewhat by the new interest in animal defensive secretions and pheromones.

2. Comparative electrophoretic studies of proteins have been pushed to a relatively advanced state, as illustrated by the work of H. C. Dessauer and his associates, of J. L. Hubby and L. H. Throckmorton, and of C. G. Sibley. Comparative serology is also undergoing a revival (*e.g.*, Leone, 1964; Butler and Leone, 1967), although it is a relatively coarse technique and seems destined to play a role secondary to the newer methods.

3. Progress is being made on the complete analysis of primary structure of a few proteins, such as hemoglobin, insulin, the dehydrogenases, and cytochrome *c,* with some illuminating results in phylogeny that will be discussed briefly below.

4. DNA composition has been used extensively and effectively in bacterial studies, as described by De Ley (this volume, page 248).

Different classes of compounds vary drastically in their usefulness as taxonomic characters. The informational macromolecules (proteins and nucleic acids) contain far more information about evolutionary change and are hence intrinsically more valuable for phylogenetic studies than smaller molecules such as the secondary plant substances.

5. Several promising new techniques are being employed to measure differences among species in protein and nucleic acid structure. Among these are the fingerprinting technique of rapid, partial protein mapping, and the measurement, developed by Marshall *et al.* (1967), of the degree of recognition of the RNA codons of one species by transfer RNA of another species.

There is a pleasing absence of molecular triumphalism in most of this biochemical work:

> It should be emphasized that the use of the new biochemical procedures will not supercede the classical phylogenetic and taxonomic studies but will add quantitative parameters for use together with the classical approach. Specific problems that the classical methods cannot resolve may be solved by the comparative enzyme techniques. . . . Perhaps, in years to come, investigators utilizing both classical and molecular biology approaches will be able to clarify the intricate mechanisms involved in evolutionary change and in the origin of new species. (Kaplan, 1965).

Biochemists have quickly learned on their own the basic and ancient law of systematics, which has been so well expressed by Cronquist (1957) as follows:

Every taxonomic character is potentially important, and no character has an inherent, fixed importance; each character is only as important as it proves to be in any particular instance in defining a group which has been perceived on the basis of all the available evidence.

And, indeed, no single biochemical character has provided the magic yardstick. Each class of molecules has proven faulty to some degree when tested against the known fossil record. Thus, according to insulin structure, we find that the pig is closer to the whale than it is to the cow, horse, and sheep. Yet, as E. Margoliash and C. G. Sibley stressed, protein structure offers the most information of any immediately available set of taxonomic characters. It is "the most delicate expression possible of the phenotype of an organism," to use Francis Crick's phrase, because the primary structure is a direct, colinear translation of DNA itself. It is even more accurate and relevant to say that protein structure as a whole provides a set of characters of great range in resolving power. G. Gorman and H. C. Dessauer, for example, have found that in the Lesser Antillean species of the lizard genus *Anolis,* lactic dehydrogenases are useful only in distinguishing species groups or higher taxa; hemoglobins, on the other hand, differ among but not within species; while transferrins vary among populations of the same species. So, like morphological traits, different kinds of proteins evolve at different rates. Those that evolve slowest provide what we call the conservative characters and are useful at the familial level or above. Those that evolve the fastest are useful at the population level. One of the things that makes protein structure quite special is that, since all genetic change has to be translated to the phenotypes by enzymes, some proteins *ipso facto* must evolve as fast as or faster than all other characters. In other words, some proteins display the greatest possible resolving power for taxonomic studies.

The usefulness of this great searching power has been illustrated in the hybridization studies by H. C. Dessauer and his associates on lizards and anurans and by J. Hunziker on grasses. In some cases, the parental proteins exist side by side and in equal quantities in

F_1 hybrids, providing the most definitive evidence of hybrid origin. The potential of protein studies has also been demonstrated in groups where other characters have relatively poor resolving power, for example, birds and bacteria. Molecular studies in such groups have been moving at a faster pace than most of us outside the field have realized. I am impressed by the fact that C. G. Sibley has analyzed the egg-white proteins of over 2,000 species of birds belonging to all 27 orders and 146 of the 170 living families; and even a nonornithologist can follow with interest the new information produced on the relationships of such famous groups as the rattites and Drepaniidae. I have also been impressed by the accomplishment of E. Margoliash and his coworkers in defining the primary structure of cytochrome *c* in 20 species of organisms and by J. De Ley's report of the current wealth of DNA data in bacteria: the DNA base composition now worked out in 2,000 species belonging to 127 bacterial genera. I feel we have to go along with certain persuasive arguments by the biochemists. The data from nucleic acids and proteins are bound to yield more information in the end, and for a quite simple reason: even if a given phenotypic character converges in two taxa, the codon and amino acid sequences underlying the character are probably going to continue to diverge to permit this evolutionary change to occur. So, to reverse the familiar French epigram, the more things become the same, the more different they really are.

Hopefully the biochemists will now draw close to phylogenetic problems of greater consequence than have occupied them in the past. How many biochemists, and biologists for that matter, know that the great substantive questions of animal phylogeny are still mostly unsettled? Let me list several of these questions, and here I will borrow in part from an earlier list given for the same purpose by Ernst Mayr (1965):

1. What protozoans gave rise to the metazoans? And how many times?
2. In early metazoan evolution, did the Coelenterata give rise to the Platyhelminthes, or was it the other way around?
3. What group gave rise to both the deuterostomians and the protostomians? In this regard, what are the relationships of the little-known lophophorate phyla?
4. Where, really, did the vertebrates come from?

A good deal of morphological and physiological evidence has, of course, already been directed at these problems, but because much of it is contradictory or equivocal, new data at the molecular level are much to be desired.

While we are cultivating our new biochemical associates, however, we must not forget that new characters of power and precision are by no means limited to molecules. R. D. Alexander, M. J. Littlejohn, and D. W. Tinkle demonstrated by theory and exemplification that behavioral characters are extremely sensitive at the species level. As Alexander has put it, behavior is "that aspect of the animal phenotype which is simultaneously most directly selected and most complexly and indirectly related to the genotype." Behavioral characters are pivotal in the development of prezygotic isolating mechanisms. They are among the first to develop in population differentiation, and they are reinforced, in many instances probably within the space of only a few generations, by contact among newly formed cognate species. R. D. Alexander, T. E. Moore, and T. J. Walker have already taken the first steps toward using courtship song as the initial character at the alpha-level of much of the classification of the Orthoptera, supplementing or even replacing the traditional morphological characters. It is to be admitted that in spite of a large body of anecdotal accounts and conjecture on the subject, really definitive analyses of the speciation process, such as the experimental studies of W. F. Blair, M. J. Littlejohn, and N. G. Smith, are still few and incomplete (see, for example, Smith, 1966). Although the study of speciation is central to the theory of systematics, it is still in a primitive stage of development. And if that is true, then the broader type of behavioral study of the sort being conducted by Tinkle, in which behavior is related to demography and population structure, can be said to be just beginning. Tinkle has shown that in populations of the lizard *Uta stansburiana,* such elementary traits as polygamy (versus monogamy) and territoriality (versus nonterritorial clustering) are intimately and probably causally connected to the properties of the survivorship curve.

The species as a category is crucial to all reasoning in systematics. R. Ornduff once again brought the curse of botany to the biological species concept. Like so many of his colleagues before him, he vexed the zoologists by citing the great problems created by apomixis, autogamy, irregular hybridization, and so on; and he went farther to point out that these well-known states are not necessarily dead ends but can be interchanged by plant populations in a kaleidoscopic fashion. Ornduff and others argued correctly that the species concept has to be re-examined critically in each group in which it is used. Most zoologists are willing to agree that many groups of plants do differ from most animal groups in ways that are important to taxonomic theory.

A. R. Kruckeberg and R. K. Selander demonstrated that certain ecological characters are also maximally sensitive at the species (or population) level, partly because isolated populations evolve most rapidly as they penetrate new niches. The process is graphically illustrated in the serpentine and other edaphic plant endemics (e.g., Kruckeberg, 1957). In order to become sympatric, related bird species must acquire minimal ecological differences. This is the fundamental basis for adaptive radiation, and it can also occur to a limited degree within single species in the form of increased sexual dimorphism.

Harlan Lewis (1966; this volume, page 523) described chromosomal changes involved in the creation of genetic barriers in plants and therefore of unusual value in population-level classification. He showed how, given a respectable amount of chromosome variation, it is possible in many cases to draw probable phylogenies based exclusively on living species. But Lewis cautioned that chromosomal characters are intrinsically no better than other taxonomic characters, and in the true botanical tradition, he disavowed the use of reproductive incompatibility as the universal species criterion.

What the speakers in speciation theory and ecology (Alexander, Kruckeberg, Lewis, Littlejohn, Ornduff, Selander, and Tinkle) expressed in common was the idea that a knowledge of behavior and population biology leads to the characters of maximum value in separating and evaluating biological species or equivalent basic units at the population level. Such characters have to be ferreted out with the same degree of skill and insight that goes into the analysis of primary structure of proteins. And, conversely, studies of population biology must start with species-level taxonomy.

Comparative morphology is often considered to be the least systematic and predictive contributor to modern systematics, but

W. Bock and his discussants argued otherwise. Where different phyletic lines have evolved the same structure in different ways, the outcome may look the same but the basic construction will often differ strikingly. The differences, referred to as "paradaptive" by Bock, are important as taxonomic characters since one construction cannot be replaced by another; therefore, they provide clues of maximum usefulness in drawing phylogenies. Examples that have been added by Bock to the already long list in classical comparative morphology include the variety of foot modifications in climbing and perching birds.

Finally, R. Reyment described the way new characters can be formed from combinations of old characters. The technique of principal-component (of variation) analysis produces the linear combination of single variables that contains the greatest variance in one or more populations. The related linear discriminant function provides the best means of separating two populations on the basis of many variables. The usefulness of the technique lies in its combination of multiple variables with a correction for correlation. As a consequence, it is possible to deal in a statistically valid and reproducible way with such complex and otherwise ill-defined characters as shape, and even "wolfness," "dogness," "fishness," or whatever.

THE MEASUREMENT OF EVOLUTIONARY AND TAXONOMIC DISTANCE

In the course of their evolutionary studies, the protein chemists have hit upon a phenomenon of great potential importance in systematics. That is, some of the more conservative enzymes and other biologically active proteins tend to evolve at a roughly constant rate. This means that amino acid substitutions occur at about the same rate over long periods of time. For example, the horse and man differ both in cytochrome *c* and hemoglobin (α-chain) by exactly 12 amino acids per residue. N. O. Kaplan, E. Margoliash, G. Matsuda and their coworkers have provided evidence to suggest that the effect is widespread and may thus provide us with an evolutionary clock for the measurement of phylogeny. The relatively detailed data on cytochrome *c* provided by

Margoliash suggest that amino acids are being substituted on the average of about one every 23,000,000 years. However, when the phylogenetic tree recently drawn by Fitch and Margoliash (1967) is examined, one finds that the method is reliable only at the level of the order or class and above. So we may ask, if protein variation is to be used as an evolutionary clock, how accurate is this protein clock? To the nearest 10 million years? To the nearest 100 million years? Further protein data are, of course, greatly to be desired, and the calibration of the various protein clocks, hopefully running at different speeds, would surely be one of the most exciting developments in future systematics.

Meanwhile, further progress in evolutionary measurements is going on at the species level. Hubby and Throckmorton (1965) have analyzed electropherograms of over 360 proteins in nine species of the *Drosophila virilis* group. By projecting the differences found in banding patterns onto the cladogram worked out earlier by Stone *et al.* (1960) on the basis of karyotypes, Hubby and Throckmorton estimate that 60 percent of the genome is held in common among the nine species, 25 percent in common by species in a given clade (phyletic branch), and 15 percent is unique to a given species. After reconstructing the "ancestral" genome on the basis of the proteins, Hubby and Throckmorton then further inferred that 20–30 percent of the gene pool was involved in the process of speciation. The implications of this new approach to studies of speciation are vast.

I find it very difficult to evaluate the usefulness of numerical phenetics as a measurement technique. The matter is still a subject for heated debate in the pages of *Systematic Zoology* and other journals, and this conference did not go into it deeply. The essential idea, as given by Sokal and Sneath in their now famous 1963 book, can be summarized as follows: A large sample of randomly chosen phenotypic characters will represent a large sample of the genome; if each character is given an equal weight, the total (or average) difference obtained between taxa might serve as the best possible measure of patristic distance as well as phenetic distance. This very simple hypothesis and the persuasive style in which it was presented have had a galvanizing effect on systematics, and it has come to the rescue of bacteriology and some other underdeveloped areas. But insofar as it consists of a specific set of biological propositions, it does not seem to be holding up very well in the early stages of testing. Several authors, including Olson (1964), Minkoff (1965), Eades (1965), and Sokal and Michener (1967) have found that slight alterations in technique cause considerable alteration in the final "phenogram," on which further conclusions must be based. Perhaps the use of Mahalanobis' distance, which takes character correlation into account, together with a standard clustering technique, could solve that problem. But there still remains the disturbing fact that different life stages and even different body parts of the same life stage can give rise to different phenograms, as in the work of Rohlf (1963) on mosquitoes and that of Michener and Sokal (1966) on bees. Perhaps more importantly, many authors have produced arguments against the doctrine of equal weighting of characters, including Bock, Ghiselin, and, it seems, Sokal himself in his work with Camin on the construction of phylogenies. W. H. Bossert argued that no matter how good numerical phenetics or any other particular package of mensuration techniques proves to be in the end, its success or failure should not affect the general use of applied mathematics in systematics. Reyment then performed the particularly valuable service of cataloging, in the form of general models, the many methods of multivariate statistics that can be brought to bear. I think it is most important at this time in the development of quantitative systematics for those of us who are not statisticians not to confuse "numerical taxonomy" (or, more precisely, numerical phenetics) with the field of quantitative taxonomy as a whole.

At this point, perhaps the least one can say about the specific proposition of numerical phenetics is that it has crisply defined the issues, provoked equally crisp responses from the phylogenists, and set in motion the new analytic phase so well displayed in the papers presented in this volume.

THE PROCESSING OF INFORMATION

At the close of the conference Bossert presented an intriguing vision of greatly increased rates of transmission of information–

and instant access from any part of the country to large central computer facilities that hold the sum of our taxonomic knowledge. What was exciting about this presentation was the estimate that the system can be achieved at a reasonable cost sometime in the 1970's. Ecologists, biogeographers, and others who are compelled to search for information on unfamiliar groups or on collections from unfamiliar parts of the world will find the prospect even more attractive than the professional taxonomists.

Systematics, *pure* systematics, the substantive part of day-to-day taxonomy and the theory that makes up the bulk of these proceedings, is an extraordinarily polyglot yet viable science at the present time. Its proprietary goals, which I have tried to identify as the theme of this summary, are among the most interesting and difficult in modern science, and they should occupy us, the best minds we can attract to join us, and our successors for many years to come.

REFERENCES

Alston, R. C., and B. L. Turner. 1963. Biochemical systematics. Prentice-Hall, Englewood Cliffs, N.J.

Butler, J. E., and C. A. Leone. 1967. Immunotaxonomic investigations of the Coleoptera. Syst. Zool. 16:56–63.

Cain, A. J., and G. A. Harrison. 1960. Phyletic weighting. Proc. Zool. Soc. London 135:1–31.

Camin, J. H., and R. R. Sokal. 1965. A method for deducing branching sequences in phylogeny. Evolution 19:311–326.

Cronquist, A. 1957. Outline of a new system of families and orders of dicotyledons. Bull. Jard. Bot. Bruxelles, 27:13–40.

Eades, D. C. 1965. The inappropriateness of the correlation coefficient as a measure of taxonomic resemblance. Syst. Zool. 14:98–100.

Farris, J. S. 1967. The meaning of relationship and taxonomic procedure. Syst. Zool. 16:44–51.

Fitch, W. M., and E. Margoliash. 1967. Construction of phylogenetic trees. Science 155:279–284.

Ghiselin, M. T. 1966a. An application of the theory of definitions to systematic principles. Syst. Zool. 15:127–130.

Ghiselin, M. T. 1966b. On psychologism in the logic of taxonomic controversies. Syst. Zool. 15:207–215.

Gisin, H. 1967. La systématique idéale. Z. Zool. Syst. Evolutionsforsch. 5:111–128.

Gregg, J. R. 1954. The language of taxonomy. Columbia University Press, New York.

Hegnauer, R. 1962. Chemotaxonomie der Pflanzen, eine übersicht über die Verbreitung und die systematische Bedeutung der Pflanzenstoffe. Band I. Thallophyten, Bryophyten, Pteridophyten und Gymnospermen. Birkhäuser Verlag, Basel/Stuttgart.

Hegnauer, R. 1963. Ibid. Band II. Monocotyledonae.

Hennig, W. 1966. Phylogenetic systematics. University of Illinois Press. (Translated from the German by D. D. Davis and R. Zanger.)

Hubby, J. L., and L. H. Throckmorton. 1965. Protein differences in *Drosophila.* II. Comparative species genetics and evolutionary problems. Genetics 52:203–215.

Hull, D. L. 1964. Consistency and monophyly. Syst. Zool. 13:1–11.

Kaplan, N. O. 1965. Evolution of dyhydrogenases, *in* H. J. Vogel [ed] Evolving genes and proteins. Academic Press, New York.

Kruckeberg, A. R. 1957. Variation in fertility of hybrids between isolated populations of the serpentine species, *Streptanthus glandulosus* Hook. Evolution 9:185–211.

Leone, C. A. [ed]. 1964. Taxonomic biochemistry and serology. Ronald Press, New York.

Lewis, H. 1966. Speciation in flowering plants. Science 152:167–172.

Marshall, R. E., C. T. Caskey, and M. Nirenberg. 1967. Fine structure of RNA codewords recognized by bacterial, amphibian, and mammalian transfer RNA. Science 155:820–826.

Mayr, E. 1965. Classification and phylogeny. Am. Zool. 5:165–174.

Michener, C. D., and R. R. Sokal. 1966. Two tests of the Hypothesis of Nonspecificity in the *Hoplitis* complex. Ann. Entomol. Soc. Am. 59:1211–1217.

Minkoff, E. 1965. The effects on classification of slight alterations in numerical technique. Syst. Zool. 14:196–213.

Olson, E. C. 1964. Morphological integration and the meaning of characters in classification systems, *in* V. H. Heywood and J. McNeill [ed] Phenetic and phylogenetic classification. Systematics Association, Pub. No. 6. p. 123–156.

Rohlf, F. J. 1963. Congruence of larval and adult classification in *Aedes* (Diptera: Culicidae). Syst. Zool. 12:97–117.

Smith, N. G. 1966. Evolution of some arctic gulls (Larus): An experimental study of isolating mechanisms. Ornithol. Monogr., Am. Ornithol. Union 4:1–99.

Sokal, R. R., and C. D. Michener. 1967. The effects of different numerical techniques on the phenetic classification of bees of the *Hoplitis* complex (Megachilidae). Proc. Linn. Soc. London 178:59–74.

Sokal, R. R., and P. H. A. Sneath. 1963. Principles of numerical taxonomy. Freeman, San Francisco and London.

Stone, W. S., W. C. Guest, and F. D. Wilson. 1960. The evolutionary implications of the cytological polymorphism and phylogeny of the virilis group of *Drosophila.* Proc. Nat. Acad. Sci. U.S. 46:350–361.

Swain, T. [ed]. 1963. Chemical plant taxonomy. Academic Press, London and New York.

Participants

SPEAKERS AND DISCUSSANTS

RICHARD D. ALEXANDER, Museum of Zoology, The University of Michigan, Ann Arbor, Michigan 48104

W. FRANK BLAIR, Department of Zoology, University of Texas, Austin, Texas 78712

WALTER J. BOCK, Department of Biological Sciences, Columbia University, New York, New York 10027

WILLIAM BOSSERT, Department of Biology, Division of Engineering and Applied Physics, Harvard University, Cambridge, Massachusetts 02138

BERT G. BREHM, Department of Biology, Reed College, Portland, Oregon 97202

LINCOLN P. BROWER, Department of Biology, Amherst College, Amherst, Massachusetts 01002

KENTON L. CHAMBERS, Herbarium, Department of Botany, Oregon State University, Corvallis, Oregon 97331

BRYAN C. CLARKE, Department of Zoology, University of Edinburgh, West Mains Road, Edinburgh 9, Scotland

JOZEF DE LEY, Laboratorium voor Microbiologie, Rijksuniversiteit - Ghent, Belgium

HERBERT C. DESSAUER, Department of Biochemistry, Louisiana State University Medical Center, New Orleans, Louisiana 70112

W. M. FITCH, Department of Physiological Chemistry, The University of Wisconsin

MICHAEL T. GHISELIN, Department of Zoology, University of California at Berkeley, Berkeley, California 94720

HERMAN GISIN,* Musèum d'Histoire Naturelle, Ville de Gèneve, Genève, Switzerland

MORRIS GOODMAN, Department of Anatomy, Wayne State University, Detroit, Michigan 48207

HELEN HEISE, Department of Philosophy, University of California at Santa Barbara, Santa Barbara, California 93106

DAVID L. HULL, Philosophy Department, University of Wisconsin–Milwaukee, Milwaukee, Wisconsin 53201

JUAN H. HUNZIKER, Facultad de Ciencias Exactas y Naturales, Universidad de Buenos Aires, Moreno 963, Buenos Aires, Argentina

ROBERT F. INGER, Field Museum of Natural History, Chicago, Illinois 60605

R. C. JACKSON, Department of Botany, University of Kansas, Lawrence, Kansas 66044

PAUL A. JOHNSGARD, Department of Zoology, University of Nebraska, Lincoln, Nebraska 68508

ALLEN KEAST, Department of Biology, Queen's University, Kingston, Ontario, Canada

A. R. KRUCKEBERG, Department of Botany, University of Washington, Seattle, Washington 98105

HARLAN LEWIS, Department of Botanical Sciences, University of California at Los Angeles, Los Angeles, California 90024

WALTER H. LEWIS, Missouri Botanical Garden, 2315 Tower Grove Avenue, St. Louis, Missouri 63110

MURRAY J. LITTLEJOHN, Department of Zoology, University of Melbourne, Parkville, N. 2, Victoria, Australia

MANLEY MANDEL, Department of Biology, University of Texas M. D. Anderson Hospital and Tumor Institute, Houston, Texas 77025

EMANUEL MARGOLIASH, Department of Molecular Biology, Abbott Laboratories, North Chicago, Illinois 60064

ERNST MAYR, Museum of Comparative Zoology, Harvard University, Cambridge, Massachusetts 02138

*Deceased August 16, 1967.

CALVIN McMILLAN, Department of Botany, University of Texas, Austin, Texas 78712

EVIATAR NEVO, The Hebrew University of Jerusalem, Jerusalem, Israel

A. GEOFFREY NORMAN, Vice President for Research, The University of Michigan, Ann Arbor, Michigan 48104

EVERETT C. OLSON, Walker Museum, University of Chicago, Chicago, Illinois 60637

ROBERT ORNDUFF, Department of Botany, University of California at Berkeley, Berkeley, California 94720

JAMES A. PETTERS, Division of Reptiles and Amphibians, U. S. National Museum, Smithsonian Institution, Washington, D. C. 20560

PETER H. RAVEN, Division of Systematic Biology, Stanford University, Stanford, California 94305

ARNOLD W. RAVIN, Department of Biology, University of Chicago, Chicago, Illinois 60637

R. A. REYMENT, Department of Historical Geology and Paleontology, University of Uppsala, Box 558 S-751 22, Uppsala 1, Sweden

DAVID J. ROGERS, Taximetrics Laboratory, University of Colorado, Boulder, Colorado 80302

F. JAMES ROHLF, Department of Entomology, University of Kansas, Lawrence, Kansas 66045

HERBERT H. ROSS, Section of Faunistic Surveys and Insect Identification, Illinois Natural History Survey, Urbana, Illinois 61801

ROBERT K. SELANDER, Department of Zoology, University of Texas, Austin, Texas 78712

CHARLES G. SIBLEY, Peabody Museum of Natural History, Yale University, New Haven, Connecticut 06520

ROBERT R. SOKAL, Department of Entomology, University of Kansas, Lawrence, Kansas 66044

OTTO T. SOLBRIG, Department of Botany, University of Michigan, Ann Arbor, Michigan 48104

FRANS A. STAFLEU, Botanical Museum, 106 Lange Nieuwstraat, Utrecht, Netherlands

MORTIMER P. STARR, Department of Bacteriology, University of California at Davis, Davis, California 95616

WILLIAM L. STERN, Department of Botany, University of Maryland, College Park, Maryland 20740

H. J. THOMPSON, Department of Botanical Sciences, University of California at Los Angeles, Los Angeles, California 90024

LYNN H. THROCKMORTON, Department of Biology, University of Chicago, Chicago, Illinois 60637

DONALD W. TINKLE, Museum of Zoology, The University of Michigan, Ann Arbor, Michigan 48104

WARREN H. WAGNER, JR., Botanical Gardens, The University of Michigan, Ann Arbor, Michigan 48105

DAVID B. WAKE, Department of Anatomy, University of Chicago, Chicago, Illinois 60637

PHILIP V. WELLS, Department of Botany, University of Kansas, Lawrence, Kansas 66045

EDWARD O. WILSON, Biological Laboratories, Harvard University, Cambridge, Massachusetts 02138

PARTICIPANTS IN INFORMAL DISCUSSIONS:

ROLAND E. BESCHEL, Department of Biology, Queen's University, Kingston, Ontario, Canada

ARTHUR CRONQUIST, Senior Curator, The New York Botanical Garden, Bronx, New York 10458

THEODORE J. CROVELLO, Department of Biology, University of Notre Dame, Notre Dame, Indiana 46556

EDWARD B. CUTLER, Department of Biology, Utica College, Utica, New York 13502

GEORGE F. ESTABROOK, Taximetrics Laboratory, University of Colorado, Boulder, Colorado 80302

JAMES S. FARRIS, Museum of Zoology, The University of Michigan, Ann Arbor, Michigan 48104

AMY JEAN GILMARTIN, Museum of Vertebrate Zoology, University of California at Berkeley, Berkeley, California 93924

LESLIE D. GOTTLIEB, Department of Botany, The University of Michigan, Ann Arbor, Michigan 48104

WILLIAM F. GRANT, Department of Genetics, McGill University, Montreal, Canada

PAUL G. HELTNE, Department of Anatomy, University of Chicago, Chicago, Illinois 60637

LESTER L. SHORT, JR., Department of Ornithology, American Museum of Natural History, New York, New York 10024

HENRY TOWNES, American Entomological Institute, Ann Arbor, Michigan 48105